1993
Yearbook
of Science
and the
Future

1993

Yearbook
of Science
and the
Future

Encyclopædia

Britannica, Inc.

Chicago
Auckland
Geneva
London
Madrid
Manila
Paris
Rome
Seoul
Sydney
Tokyo
Toronto

1993

Yearbook
of Science
and the
Future

Editor
David Calhoun

Associate Editor
Charles Cegielski

Editorial Staff
Daphne Daume, Karen Sparks,
Arthur Latham, Melinda Shepherd

Creative Director, Art
Cynthia Peterson

Operations Manager, Art
Marsha Mackenzie

Senior Picture Editor
Kathy Nakamura

Picture Editors
Harriett Hiland, Karen Wollins

Layout Artists and Illustrators
Kathryn Diffley, John L. Draves,
Steven N. Kapusta, James I. Montes

Art Production Supervisor
Stephanie Motz

Art Staff
Patricia A. Henle, Sandra M. Kieffer,
Diana M. Pitstick

Manager, Cartography
Barbra A. Vogel

Cartography Staff
Laurie Anderson, Kathryn Piffl

Manager, Copy Department
Anita Wolff

Copy Supervisors
Julian Ronning, Barbara Whitney

Copy Staff
Elizabeth A. Blowers, Ellen Finkelstein,
John Mathews, Deirdre McAllister,
Letricia Riley

Manager, Production Control
Mary C. Srodon

Production Control Staff
Marilyn L. Barton, Stephanie A. Green, Lee Anne Wiggins

Encyclopædia Britannica, Inc.

Contents

Feature Articles

Encyclopædia Britannica Science Update

The Science Year in Review

A Science Classic

Institutions of Science

In Search of the First Americans

by Vaughn M. Bryant, Jr.

As much of the world celebrates the 500th anniversary of the European "discovery" of the Americas, archaeologists strive to determine—and to agree on—when the first humans to upstage Columbus actually arrived.

A few years ago, while driving through a fierce snowstorm toward Raton, New Mexico, I caught sight of a turnoff marked "Folsom—8 miles." The implications took me by surprise. Why, just a few minutes away was. . . . Yielding to a sudden urge, I slithered onto the icy side road and soon reached a few abandoned stores, some weather-beaten frame houses, an old hotel, and a tiny grocery store with a post office and gas pump. Ahead, through the blowing snow, loomed a frame building with a battered sign hanging by a single nail: "Museum."

In a large, dim, unheated room I saw dusty relics ranging in age from the pioneer farmers to World War II—tools, broken toys, military uniforms, old machine guns, photos. Open on a counter, next to an empty pickle jar labeled "Donations," lay a guest register with curling pages, its last entry more than a year old. Slowly my eyes adjusted to the poor light. In a far corner the skull of an extinct bison hung on the wall. Next to it stood a small, hand-lettered display of badly faded photos of the momentous excavation that had been carried out nearby in the 1920s. Shivering in the cold, reading the labels, and listening to a distant window shutter banging in the wind, I was overcome by wonder. I was really here! Folsom—called by many the most important breakthrough in the archaeology of North America. And perhaps it was.

For it was here that a black cowboy named George McJunkin found what was to become the first indisputable evidence of the earliest Americans, hunters who had roamed the vast grasslands of North America when mammoths, mastodons, and now-extinct forms of giant bison were common. But, despite its revelations, Folsom begged the question: Were they *really* the earliest Americans? Searching for the answer has fueled a controversy that continues unabated today.

From Columbus through Darwin . . .

When Columbus opened the New World to exploration by Europeans, archaeology was more speculation and myth than science. Columbus called the natives "Indios" because he believed that San Salvador in The Bahamas was an island off the coast of Asia, then collectively known as the Indies.

During the next three centuries Europeans subjugated all of the Americas. Cannons and guns proved better than stone knives, arrows, and spears, while strange European diseases spread quickly and killed millions. This ease of conquest convinced Europeans that the Indians were inferior, simplistic, and unintelligent—even though reports of the Aztec, Maya, and Inca civilizations suggested otherwise. Although some curiosity was expressed about the origins of these people, most Europeans accepted the explanations of Pope Alexander VI and other clergymen of the early 1500s that the Indians were descendants of one of the Lost Tribes of Israel exiled from Assyria during the 1st millennium BC. Alternate theories proposed that their ancestors had come from the fabled lost continent of Atlantis or had been survivors of the biblical flood.

In the late 1500s the Jesuit priest José de Acosta proposed that the New World's native peoples were descended from small groups of Asians

VAUGHN M. BRYANT, JR., is Professor and Department Head, Department of Anthropology, Texas A&M University, College Station.

(Overleaf) Illustration by Ron Villani

10

Subjugation of Native Americans by the Europeans who traveled to the New World after Columbus is vividly depicted in the 20th-century Mexican artist Diego Rivera's mural of the Spanish Conquest. Although some curiosity was expressed about the origins of the Indians, the ease with which they were conquered suggested to Europeans an inferior and unintelligent people who might easily be explained as being degenerate descendants of one of the Lost Tribes of Israel or perhaps of the survivors of the biblical flood.

who, like the many strange animals in the New World, somehow had wandered overland into the Americas. As an alternate theory he suggested that the first Americans were Asians who had arrived by sea when their ships were blown off course. Yet his ideas were ignored, as no one could imagine how such feats would have been possible.

Thomas Jefferson, one of the first to see the Indians as a rapidly disappearing part of American culture, urged that their customs and languages be studied and recorded. In the late 1700s he carefully excavated a large Indian mound near his Virginia estate and then wrote the first North American archaeological report, a three-page paper explaining how such mounds were used for burial purposes.

Not until the mid-1800s did events in Central America and Europe raise new questions about the arrival time of the first Americans and force scholars to acknowledge the possibility of much older settlements. In the 1840s the American archaeologist John Stephens and the English illustrator and archaeologist Frederick Catherwood conducted the first comprehensive study of the ancient Maya areas of southern Mexico and Guatemala. Their beautiful and accurate drawings of temples and their accompanying text convinced readers that the large Maya ceremonial centers had been built by a people many centuries before. Their work did much to dispel a growing myth that the Maya civilization had been founded by lost Egyptians. Also in the 1840s, American historian William Prescott's widely read books *History of the Conquest of Mexico* and *History of the Conquest of Peru* offered convincing evidence that the conquered Aztec and Inca civilizations had been highly complex and had grown out of much earlier cultures. Finally, serious scholars began to wonder if New World cultures possibly could be as old as, or even older than, those of Europe, Africa, or Asia.

11

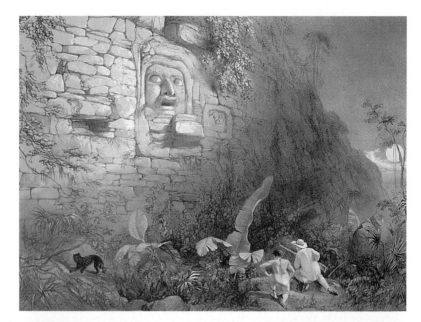

In the mid-1800s the Frenchman Jacques Boucher de Perthes found hundreds of large stone tools and the bones of long-extinct animals in the gravel beds of the Somme River in northern France. Then, in 1856, workers at a quarry site near Düsseldorf, Germany, uncovered the fossil skull of a Neanderthal. These events helped shatter the long-held Christian belief, originally proposed in 1650 by Archbishop James Ussher of Ireland, that God created the world and humanity in six days in the year 4004 BC.

British naturalists Charles Darwin and Alfred Russel Wallace added to the upheaval in 1859 by jointly proposing new concepts and ideas about evolutionary processes and the tremendous, almost unimaginable antiquity of animals and humankind. Darwin suggested that humanity first evolved in Africa. Others, including German evolutionist Ernst Haeckel, ridiculed an African genesis and proposed Asia as the cradle of humanity,

12

a claim that seemed correct after the Dutch anatomist Eugène Dubois discovered the bones of a pre-Neanderthal group, *Homo erectus,* in deposits of the Solo River in Java during the late 1800s.

Suddenly the race was on! Which continent contained the earliest records of humans, Asia or Africa? Also in question was the age of the many stone tools being found in buried deposits throughout Europe. These tools were assigned to the Paleolithic Period, a term introduced by British geologist John Lubbock to cover the vast span of human prehistory. It was not long before North American scientists began looking for stone tools in support of what they believed was a similar New World Paleolithic.

The first big news broke in the fall of 1876 when Frederic Putnam of Harvard University's Peabody Museum and Charles Abbott, an amateur naturalist, found what they thought to be the first reliable European-type Paleolithic stone tools in gravel beds of the Delaware River near Trenton, New Jersey. Soon, an excited press and public began following scientists and amateurs as they looked for additional evidence of the North American Paleolithic Period. As each new find was reported, everyone wanted to call it the oldest site and make claims that it was thousands of years older than anything else yet found. More so than museums, the leading newspapers funded the search, hoping to get an exclusive story on the next sensational discovery.

. . . to Folsom and Clovis
By the end of the 1880s a belief in the existence of a North American Paleolithic was almost universally accepted by the leading archaeologists and geologists of the era. An exception was John Wesley Powell, director of the Smithsonian Institution's Bureau of Ethnology. In 1887 he appointed geologist William Holmes to prepare a detailed report on each new claim of discovery of ancient peoples in the Americas. Powell

Excavation of an Indian mound in Louisiana around 1850 (top left) is depicted in a detail of a painting by American artist John J. Egan. By the end of the 1880s, the flood of claims for evidence of ever more ancient peoples in the Americas led the Smithsonian Institution's John Wesley Powell (top right, with an Indian guide) to appoint geologist William Holmes (above) to investigate the reports. As hundreds of claims were examined, however, each seemed to lack sufficient proof of authenticity.

(Top left) The Saint Louis Art Museum, Eliza McMillan Fund Purchase; (top right) Earthquake Information Bulletin no. 295, U.S. Geological Survey; (bottom) Smithsonian Institution, Washington, D.C.; photo, Marianne Gurley

13

wanted to counteract the flood of unsubstantiated press reports of new discoveries allegedly dating back tens of thousands of years.

Requests for news of new finds brought nearly a thousand responses to the Smithsonian. In time, however, as the evidence was examined by experts, it came to seem that each discovery was flawed. Each lacked one or more of three essential elements needed for indisputable proof of authenticity. First, a site had to contain tools, weapons, or other artifacts definitely made by humans or contain the remains of human skeletons. Second, the human-made materials had to be buried in a way that clearly showed they came from specific layers of undisturbed sediments. Third, the age of the site had to be determined by accurate dating methods.

Then, late in the 19th century, geologist G. Frederick Wright heated up the controversy by using much of the disputed evidence as the basis for two books about pre-ice-age cultures in North America. Well written and widely read, they helped polarize the public's view and added new pressures on scientists to accept much of the circumstantial evidence.

After the turn of the century, and certainly by the 1920s, the argument had grown so heated that few professional scholars or students dared risk

Around 1910 George McJunkin (above), a black cowboy and ranch foreman, found what was to become the first indisputable evidence for Paleo-Indian hunters who had roamed New Mexico more than 10,000 years ago, but the significance of the stone point and fossil bones he pulled from the ground near Folsom went unrecognized for a decade and a half. When scientists finally did excavate the Folsom site, it yielded a wealth of bones and stone artifacts, including a human-made stone point lodged between the fossil rib bones of an extinct giant bison (right).

their reputations by questioning the unproven, yet often accepted, belief among scientists that there was no real proof of humans in the Americas before 4,000 years ago. Into the midst of that tension, between 1925 and 1928, came the excavations of the Folsom site. Here, finally, was the big breakthrough; not only was Folsom the first American site to meet the three essential elements, but it also more than doubled the 4,000-year date. Folsom's indisputable evidence revealed that early Indians, known today as Paleo-Indians, had hunted a species of giant bison that became extinct nearly 10,000 years ago. The Folsom site contained a wealth of bones and stone artifacts—and more. In one deposit a human-made stone point was found lodged between the ribs of an extinct bison.

14

A Colorado location called Dent was the first site to confirm a clear relationship between Paleo-Indian hunters and extinct mammoths like the articulated juvenile specimen from Dent shown at left. Among the finds of the scientists who excavated the site in the early 1930s (below left) was a stone spear point positioned between the bones of a nearly complete and articulated mammoth skeleton—proof that the animal's remains and its probable cause of death had not been disturbed since their incorporation into the deposits in which they were found.

Soon work in Colorado, Texas, and New Mexico turned up other sites containing more fossil bison bones, or bones of other extinct animals like the camel, the mammoth, and a breed of horses, all of which had disappeared with the giant bison. More and more of the new sites yielded the same association, first seen at Folsom, between extinct animal bones and human-made stone tools and spear points. But as the relationship of ancient hunter and ancient prey became clear, a new mystery arose. Some tools and points matched Folsom's, but others did not. Different styles of tools and weapons implied different groups of Paleo-Indians, who may have lived at different times. So again the question arose: Which group was the older?

15

George A. Agogino, Eastern New Mexico University, Portales

Clovis-type stone points like those pictured, which come from Blackwater Draw in New Mexico, closely resemble others found at Clovis, Dent, and other sites in the U.S. Southwest. The largest spear point is more than 10 centimeters (4 inches) long. The discovery at Clovis of Clovis-type points and mammoth bones in deposits lying directly below other deposits containing Folsom points and extinct bison bones demonstrated that Clovis points were the older. It also pushed back the existence of humans in the Americas to more than 11,000 years ago.

The first site to confirm a clear relationship between extinct mammoths and Paleo-Indian hunters was a Colorado location called Dent, excavated in the early 1930s. There scientists found a type of large stone spear point that differed from the Folsom points. One specimen lay directly under a mammoth pelvis, and another between the bones of a second mammoth. The position of the second mammoth skeleton was especially important because it was nearly complete and articulated—*i.e.*, the bones were positioned as in life—proving that the deposits in which it was found had remained undisturbed since the animal's death and that the stone point probably caused death.

The age of the Dent site, however, and its chronological relationship to the Folsom group of Paleo-Indians remained undetermined for another 15 years, until the excavations of a Paleo-Indian site near Clovis, New Mexico, in 1949–50. At Clovis a Dent-type stone spear point was found among mammoth bones in deposits lying directly below other deposits that contained extinct bison bones and Folsom spear points. The mystery was solved. The Dent-type spear points, now called Clovis points, had to be the older. Moreover, this discovery pushed back the existence of humans in the New World to more than 11,000 years ago.

The story of the hunt for the first Americans does not end with Clovis. In the 40 years since, scientists have excavated many new sites and have again become embroiled over the interpretation of them. Moreover, another issue, reinvigorated by Clovis, has entered into the hunt, for it has to do with the opportunities that early humans had to get to the New World. Thus, before the newer evidence for *when* humans arrived is considered, it will be helpful to look at that second issue—*how* they arrived.

The journey east

In the decades since the Folsom and Clovis sites were first studied, new scientific techniques and refinement of old ones have clarified many

16

ideas about the first Americans—who they were, how they arrived, the animals they hunted, and the harsh climate they had to overcome.

Physical anthropologists using skeletal, dental, genetic, and blood-grouping studies have compared living American Indians with populations of eastern Asia. Their evidence is overwhelming in confirming that the first Americans were hunters who came from Asia. But did they travel by sea or by land? Archaeologists like Knut Fladmark of Simon Fraser University, Vancouver, British Columbia, and Ruth Gruhn of the University of Alberta believe that an early crossing to North America was possible by sea and that the first Americans could have used a coastal route to reach areas as far south as California while much of the continent was buried beneath glacial ice. In spite of their argument most scientists still think that a land crossing and central migration into the continent is more likely.

Some geologists, like David Hopkins of the University of Alaska, have spent their careers studying the environmental changes in western Alaska, eastern Siberia, and the area between. Records of glaciation, rises and falls in ancient sea levels, and surface topography suggest to Hopkins that there were two main periods when the Bering Sea was low enough to expose a wide landmass, now called Beringia, connecting Asia with North America. He notes that Beringia was exposed between 75,000 and 45,000 years ago and again between 25,000 and 14,000 years ago. Until recently, no archaeological sites in eastern Siberia had proved older than 40,000 years of age, leaving only the second of Hopkins' periods for serious consideration as a time for the first crossing. However, reports of new sites being found in Siberia imply that humans may have lived in areas near Beringia as early as 70,000 years ago.

It is reasonable to ask why people would leave Asia and walk to North America over a land bridge. No one knows, but there appear to have

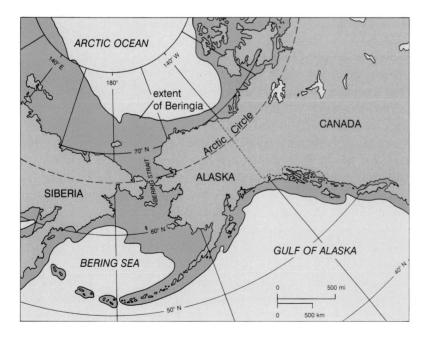

Beringia at its estimated maximum extent some 20,000 years ago is shown in relation to the outlines of Siberia and Alaska as they are today. Studies suggest two main periods, 75,000–45,000 years ago and 25,000–14,000 years ago, when the Bering Sea was low enough to expose such a land bridge between Asia and North America.

been no special reasons for doing so. Perhaps the first transcontinental travelers were small groups of Asian hunters and their families who, not even aware that the region was a land bridge, followed seasonal migrations of Arctic animals back and forth over Beringia. Eventually some peoples became trapped in Alaska when sea levels rose and the land connection flooded. Paleoecologists Paul Colinvaux of the Smithsonian Institution and Steven Young of the University of Vermont have offered their separate ideas about the Beringian environment, both of which tend to support this theory. From buried pollen records used as indicators of plants that once grew in Beringia, Colinvaux concludes that the land bridge was inhospitable, barren tundra offering limited plant resources for either grazing animals or humans. His research suggests that the Beringian climate was unpredictable and forbidding from the beginning of its last opening around 25,000 years ago until just before rising sea levels finally tempered the environment and supported grasslands and scrub vegetation. The improved conditions around 14,000 years ago, he believes, attracted herds of animals and hunters into the New World. Young, on the other hand, thinks that the fossil pollen records, combined with known distributions of modern plants in western Alaska, indicate a 10,000-year period beginning nearly 25,000 years ago during which Beringian vegetation could have supported a variety of large herd animals and the Asian hunters who followed them.

What foods these first travelers ate on their way to the Americas is one of many intriguing questions. Some scholars, like Dale Guthrie of the University of Alaska, believe that the first Americans were hunters who preyed mainly on mastodons, mammoths, giant bison, and similar large herd mammals. Others think that they ate a variety of plant foods and relied on small rabbit- and deer-sized animals that could easily be caught; killing a large game animal would have been a rare occasion for them. A correct interpretation of the food preferences of these early hunters would help scientists gain a clearer picture of their culture and life-styles.

Clovis versus pre-Clovis

Volumes of articles and books have been written on the first Americans. Over this issue, however, archaeologists remain split into two groups. For some, who can be called the Clovis-first group, Clovis-type hunters or their immediate ancestors were the first Americans, arriving in the New World no earlier than about 12,000 years ago. On the other hand, the pre-Clovis group favors a more remote occupation of the Americas, no later than 15,000 years ago and perhaps, according to a few, as early as several hundred thousand years ago. For them, Clovis is but one link in the middle of a chain of early American cultures.

Making reconciliation so difficult is the lack of specific evidence that both sides will accept as indisputable records of early Americans. Each group has its distinguished scholars, its own ideas and hypotheses, and a list of sites on which to base its convictions.

Members of the pre-Clovis group, among them Ruth Gruhn and Alan Bryan of the University of Alberta; George Carter of Texas A&M Univer-

18

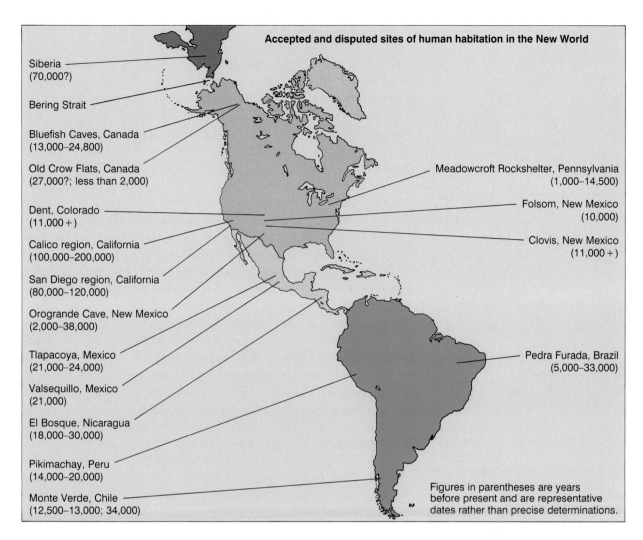

Accepted and disputed sites of human habitation in the New World

Siberia
(70,000?)

Bering Strait

Bluefish Caves, Canada
(13,000–24,800)

Old Crow Flats, Canada
(27,000?; less than 2,000)

Dent, Colorado
(11,000+)

Calico region, California
(100,000–200,000)

San Diego region, California
(80,000–120,000)

Orogrande Cave, New Mexico
(2,000–38,000)

Tlapacoya, Mexico
(21,000–24,000)

Valsequillo, Mexico
(21,000)

El Bosque, Nicaragua
(18,000–30,000)

Pikimachay, Peru
(14,000–20,000)

Monte Verde, Chile
(12,500–13,000; 34,000)

Meadowcroft Rockshelter, Pennsylvania
(1,000–14,500)

Folsom, New Mexico
(10,000)

Clovis, New Mexico
(11,000+)

Pedra Furada, Brazil
(5,000–33,000)

Figures in parentheses are years
before present and are representative
dates rather than precise determinations.

sity, College Station; Richard MacNeish of the Andover (Massachusetts) Foundation for Archaeological Research; James Adovasio of Mercyhurst College, Erie, Pennsylvania; Tom Dillehay of the University of Kentucky, Lexington; Richard Morlan of the National Museum of Man, Ottawa; and Jacques Cinq-Mars of the Canadian Museum of Civilization, Hull, Quebec, all favor slightly different time periods during which the first pre-Clovis peoples reached the Americas. As a group, however, they believe that hunters first migrated from Siberia across the Beringian land bridge more than 15,000 years ago and that their descendants then spread very slowly southward from Alaska to other areas of the Americas south of glacier-covered Canada. In their view, these early Americans took thousands of years to reach areas as distant as the southern tip of South America.

Pre-Clovis scholars believe that the technological skills of the earliest Americans were not as refined as those of the later Clovis populations. Thus, hardened wood, broken bones, antlers, and cracked river cobbles often served as their weapons and tools. Remains of pre-Clovis peoples are meager, these scholars acknowledge, but because artifacts of bone,

Map of the New World locates a selection of Clovis and pre-Clovis sites. Archaeologists who believe that Clovis-type hunters or their immediate ancestors were the first Americans envision humans moving southward out of Alaska no more than 12,000 years ago. Those who favor a more remote, pre-Clovis arrival in the Americas think that it occurred no later than 15,000 years ago and perhaps much earlier.

19

The Arctic site known as Old Crow Flats, near the Yukon-Alaskan border, yielded a caribou bone flesher, a butchering tool, that originally gave a radiocarbon date of 27,000 years. That estimate recently was called into question, however, after a redating of the bone by means of accelerator mass spectrometry gave an age of less than 2,000 years.

antler, and wood decay rapidly, the finding of even mere scraps of evidence is thought remarkable considering the age of the sites.

The Clovis-first group is led by such members as C. Vance Haynes and Paul Martin, both of the University of Arizona; Thomas Lynch of Cornell University, Ithaca, New York; Larry Agenbroad of Northern Arizona University, Flagstaff; and Michael Waters of Texas A&M University. Although each may have a slightly different point of view, their argument in essence begins 25,000–30,000 years ago in eastern Europe, where hunters learned how to attack and kill large mammoths. So successful were they that soon they concentrated on mammoth hunting. They wandered slowly eastward, following mammoth herds, until they reached the tip of eastern Siberia 15,000–20,000 years ago. In the continued pursuit of mammoths, some hunters either wandered across Beringia into Alaska just before the land bridge flooded for the last time around 14,000 years ago, or they first entered the New World during the next thousand-year period by walking across the frozen, narrow sea between the two continents.

Then, as the continental glaciers began melting, ice-free corridors opened and provided conduits into the heartland of North America. Once free to migrate, the mammoth hunters followed their prey southward out of Alaska. Along the way they developed new types of weapons unique to the Americas, like the spear points found at Dent and Clovis. Clovis-first scholars believe that the southward movement began about 12,000 years ago and was completed in about 1,000 years. In other words, Clovis-type big-game hunters spread from the top to the bottom of the Americas at essentially breakneck speed. Moreover, Martin and some others think that the skill of the Clovis hunters, combined with their rapid population growth, decimated the mammoth and caused its extinction during this period.

When asked about the possibility of much earlier populations in the New World, the Clovis-first group says that no sites with indisputable evidence exist to support the claim. They contend that the evidence associated with each purported pre-Clovis site is flawed. Either the associations of human artifacts and early dates are inconclusive or the deposits are mixed and disturbed. In other cases, they say, materials that have been dated to pre-Clovis times by means of radiocarbon, or carbon-14, dating techniques (*see* Sidebar) are contaminated with much older material; consequently, artifacts claimed to be pre-Clovis may not be that old.

Candidates for pre-Clovis occupation

Of the numerous pre-Clovis sites and pieces of evidence discovered during the past century, many have been dismissed by even the most ardent pre-Clovis scholars as being too problematic or inconclusive. There are, nevertheless, a few key sites that come up repeatedly when the issue of the earliest Americans is discussed.

Two Arctic sites are often mentioned. The older, a locale in the Yukon's Old Crow Flats, yielded one carved bone tool once thought to show that early hunters had roamed the Yukon-Alaskan borderlands about 27,000

Radiocarbon Dating

At a New York City public lecture in 1948, U.S. chemist Willard Libby announced a new technique that would revolutionize the field of archaeology and win him a Nobel Prize. He discovered that the bombardment of nitrogen atoms by free neutrons in the upper atmosphere created a radioactive isotope of carbon having a total of 14 protons and neutrons in its nucleus, rather than 12 or 13. After experimenting, he devised a way to use the unstable isotope as the basis for a method for dating once-living materials, a technique he called radiocarbon dating.

The validity of radiocarbon dating depends on the stability of a number of conditions. First, Libby observed that three different carbon isotopes occur in nature and that the concentration of each has remained constant in the atmosphere for the past 50,000 years. Two of them, carbon-12 and carbon-13 (^{12}C and ^{13}C), are stable and do not change. However, the third one, carbon-14 (^{14}C), slowly decays back to nitrogen at a fixed rate. Second, he discovered that each of the three carbon isotopes combines with oxygen in the atmosphere to form carbon dioxide (CO_2). The atmospheric concentrations of the three types of CO_2 also remain constant. During photosynthesis, plants use all three types to form cellulose and thus incorporate the three carbon isotopes, including ^{14}C, into their tissues. Plant-eating animals absorb ^{14}C from their food, and carnivores then absorb it from the animals they eat.

As long as a plant or animal is living and taking in food or air, the amount of ^{14}C that it loses through radioactive decay is continually replenished. Once dead, the organism no longer absorbs ^{14}C, and its remains begin losing the isotope at the rate of one half the total amount per each 5,700 years. This interval is called the half-life of ^{14}C. After 11,400 years (5,700 + 5,700), for example, only a fourth of the original concentration remains. It is the decay of ^{14}C in organic materials that provides archaeologists with the basis for determining the age of a site. The lower the concentration of ^{14}C remaining in a sample, the older the age. Eventually the concentration of ^{14}C becomes so low that it can no longer be detected in a sample. That point is reached when the sample is about 50,000 years old, making this age the maximum limit of radiocarbon dating.

Buried organic materials do not always produce dates that accurately represent an archaeological "event" or "occupation," because contamination occurs. For example, if buried soil contains tiny pieces of charcoal from a 10,000-year-old campfire but also tiny flecks of coal millions of years old, then a radiocarbon test of a sample may yield a date much older than 10,000 years. Coal is so old that it no longer contains any ^{14}C; thus, its presence artificially lowers the concentration of the isotope in the sample.

Misleadingly recent dates can also occur. Rootlets from plants sometimes grow into older sediments, contaminating them with organic material high in ^{14}C. Hundreds or thousands of years later such deposits will still yield dates that are too recent unless all the rootlets are first found and removed.

The examples above represent only a few of the problems associated with radiocarbon dating. They explain why most archaeologists insist on obtaining multiple ^{14}C dates to reduce the chances for error. Experience reveals that charcoal and wood generally produce the most reliable dates, while shell, bone, and soil are easily contaminated and can yield false dates.

Refinement of radiocarbon dating has added to the present controversy over the first Americans by calling into question some of the ^{14}C dates obtained during the past 40 years. In the 1970s scientists discovered that precision in the dating of samples could be improved by means of accelerator mass spectrometry (AMS), a technique that allows the different carbon isotopes in a sample to be sorted out atom by atom and their concentrations compared directly. As an additional benefit, AMS dating requires a comparatively small sample, only 10–100 milligrams (about 0.0004–0.004 ounce). Consequently, a date can be obtained from a single buried seed, a single strand of cloth, or even a nearly invisible speck of charcoal. By contrast, conventional radiocarbon dating requires a sample of about five grams (about 0.2 ounce).

Prior to the development of radiocarbon techniques, accurate and precise dating of ancient sites was difficult and often impossible. Even today, some investigators still argue for the reliability of other dating techniques such as the degree of surface weathering on stone tools, the depth of sediment accumulation, and changes in the composition of proteins and amino acids still trapped in fossil bones. Of all the dating techniques, however, only dates based on radiocarbon analyses are presently accepted as the best and most conclusive.

Organic samples to be dated are first burned and converted to CO_2 in an apparatus like the one shown. Radiation counters then measure the amount of ^{14}C in the gas.

Photos, Jacques Cinq-Mars, Archaeological Survey of Canada, Canadian Museum of Civilization

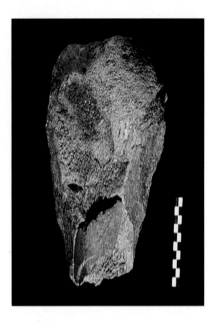

Aerial view (above right) shows one of the caves and associated excavation area of the Bluefish Caves site, located on the Yukon-Alaskan border southwest of Old Crow Flats. Among materials found at the site is a mammoth bone core (above) that yields a radiocarbon date of about 23,500 years. According to Jacques Cinq-Mars, the core bears marks of human butchering activity, including scars made by flake removal at the lower end of the core. One flake has been refitted into its scar at the bottom center.

years ago. The age estimate came from a conventional radiocarbon dating of bone material. However, recent redating of the material by means of accelerator mass spectrometry, a refinement of radiocarbon dating, indicates that what was regarded as the best evidence for pre-Clovis occupation in the Arctic is actually less than 2,000 years old.

The second Arctic site is the Bluefish Caves, located 65 kilometers (40 miles) southwest of Old Crow Flats. There Jacques Cinq-Mars found what he believes are ancient bone and stone tools associated with animal bones bearing cut marks made by stone knives during butchering. The bones include extinct horse and mammoth bones that yield radiocarbon dates of 13,000–24,800 years. Nevertheless, skeptics are not convinced that either the marked bones or the bone and stone tools date from the

(Left) San Bernardino County Museum, Redlands, Calif.; photo, Friends of Calico; (right) George F. Carter, Texas A&M University, College Station

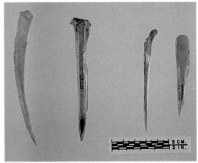

pre-Clovis time periods to which they are assigned. Also, some suspect that the sediments have been mixed as a result of repeated cycles of freezing and thawing.

Because the continental United States is the most archaeologically investigated region in the New World, it is also the area with the most sites claimed to be pre-Clovis in age. The oldest is the Calico region near Barstow, California. There, in the Mojave Desert, Ruth Simpson of the San Bernardino County (California) Museum and her colleagues found hundreds of flaked stones in deposits ranging in age from 100,000 to 200,000 years. These finds are hotly debated by Vance Haynes and others, who assert that all of the flaked stones were chipped by geologic forces, not humans. Nearby, in the San Diego region, George Carter spent decades recovering thousands of flaked stones from deposits he believes to represent human campsites and fire hearths. Geologically these deposits range in age from 80,000 to more than 120,000 years. As with the remains from the Calico region, however, there is disagreement about whether Carter's finds are really the products of human activity or are the result of natural forces. A third site, the Meadowcroft Rockshelter in southwestern Pennsylvania, is also under fire from the skeptics, who question the validity of its early radiocarbon dates that suggest ancient hunters used the site as long ago as 14,000 to 14,500 years. Instead, they argue that the material on which the dates are based and the early human remains found there are not associated.

The most recent U.S. pre-Clovis candidate is a site Richard MacNeish has been excavating in southeastern New Mexico. His Orogrande Cave contains a long and well-stratified sequence of extinct animal and plant remains extending back nearly 40,000 years. Among the remains are several human palm and hand prints preserved in fire-hardened clay, chipped stones, and a wide variety of broken animal bones. These materials and numerous radiocarbon dates have convinced MacNeish and

Scientists working at the Meadowcroft Rockshelter in Pennsylvania carefully search the site's deeply stratified deposits while tagging and recording their observations. According to James Adovasio, radiocarbon dates from various layers indicate that humans used the shelter periodically over a span ranging from about 1,000 years ago to thousands of years before the time of the Clovis hunters. The occupants left behind a variety of such objects as bone tools (above) and stone blades and points.

Photos, James M. Adovasio, Mercyhurst College, Erie, Penn.

A flaked stone interpreted by Ruth Simpson to be a notched scraper made by early humans (opposite page, bottom left) is one of hundreds found at the Calico region in California in deposits estimated geologically to be 100,000 to 200,000 years old. From the nearby San Diego site, in deposits ranging in age from 80,000 to more than 120,000 years, George Carter recovered thousands of what he classifies as scrapers, pointed tools, and other artifacts (opposite page, bottom right).

Photos, Vaughn M. Bryant, Jr.

Richard MacNeish (above, in foreground) displays some of his most recent finds from Orogrande Cave in New Mexico, which include ancient human palm prints preserved in fire-hardened clay. MacNeish's excavations of the site (above right) have allowed him to construct what he is convinced is a long record of human occupation spanning more than 30,000 years.

others of the cave's long record of human occupation spanning more than 30,000 years. Not all who have visited the site are convinced, however. Dena Dincauze of the University of Massachusetts and Vance Haynes, for example, argue that the many stone items are of natural origin because they "do not show the typical chipping marks expected during human manufacture."

Central America also has several suspected pre-Clovis locales. At the El Bosque site in Nicaragua, Alan Bryan, Ruth Gruhn, and William Irving of the University of Toronto discovered a bed of mostly whole, but scattered extinct animal bones, chipped stones, and concentrations of animal bones and rectangular-shaped areas of river pebbles that they interpreted to be human-made. Radiocarbon dates on bone place the age of the deposits between 18,000 and 30,000 years, but skeptics argue that the dates are based on contaminated materials and the chipped stones are the works of nature.

Like El Bosque, the Mexican sites of Valsequillo and Tlapacoya contain suspected human-made materials associated with early radiocarbon dates. At Valsequillo archaeologists Juan Camacho and Cynthia Irwin-Williams excavated a series of sites, one of which yielded a chipped stone tool in deposits dated 21,000 years ago. At Tlapacoya the bones of extinct animals, suspected fire hearths, and a number of obsidian stone flakes were found in deposits between 21,000 and 24,000 years old. Skeptics, however, interpret the suspected fire hearths as the remains of grass fires and the obsidian flakes to be unrelated to either the extinct animal bones or the pre-Clovis-dated materials.

In the thin strip of Chile near the tip of South America lies the site of Monte Verde. Tom Dillehay has supervised excavations there that reveal the remains of a settlement containing wooden, bone, and stone artifacts and the bones of seven mastodons. The first set of radiocarbon

24

Photos, Tom D. Dillehay,
University of Kentucky, Lexington

dates placed the site's age between 12,500 and 13,000 years. Additional dates from an even lower level suggest an age of 34,000 years. Although skeptics agree on the high quality of excavation and on the importance of the site, they raise questions about possible mixing of the geologic strata and of the materials selected for dating. Some also suspect that the dated samples might be contaminated. If so, this may explain erroneous dates that seem too old.

Two other South American sites often mentioned in Clovis-first–pre-Clovis debates are Pikimachay and Pedra Furada. In the early 1970s MacNeish supervised excavation of the Peruvian rock shelter of Piki-machay. In the bottom deposits he found extinct sloth and horse bones, charcoal, and fist-sized pieces of volcanic tuff rocks that he believed had been chipped to form sharp edges. Although radiocarbon dates from these bottom levels range from 14,000 to 20,000 years, Clovis-first scholars remain unconvinced. They question the radiocarbon dates and assert that the tuff rocks are insufficient evidence for pre-Clovis human activity.

The final South American location is in northern Brazil, where in the 1980s Niède Guidon of the École des Hautes en Sciences Sociales in

A U-shaped architectural form of sand and gravel (above), which probably supported a structure of wood and hide, is included among a rich collection of wood and plant remains, clay-lined pits, stone tools, and extinct animal bones uncovered by Tom Dillehay at the Monte Verde site in southern Chile. One tool consists of a stone attached to a wooden shaft (left). If radiocarbon dating of the site is accurate, it indicates that humans had migrated nearly to the tip of South America between 12,500 and 13,000 years ago.

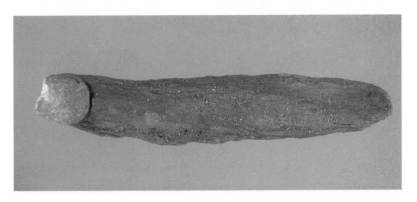

Paris excavated the site of Toca do Boqueirão da Pedra Furada. In a 70-meter (230-foot)-long rock shelter filled with the oldest known cave art in the Americas, Guidon found hundreds of chipped and broken stones and rock-lined areas that she describes as fire hearths. Over 40 radiocarbon dates now suggest that the deposits range in age from 5,000 to more than 33,000 years. Skeptics, most of whom have not yet visited the site, are already claiming the chipped and broken stones are of natural origin and that the hearths are areas that burned naturally during ancient grass fires.

The fascination of a mystery

Anthropology reveals that humans everywhere are curious. Throughout time, peoples have created elaborate ways of dealing with mysteries in their lives. Before science, they turned to myths and legends to explain the unexplainable. Later they replaced many of those fabrications with facts. Yet even today, people are captivated by an unsolved mystery, spellbound by the possibility, for example, that creatures like the Yeti roam the Himalayas or that the remains of Noah's Ark lie waiting to be

25

A view of a Peruvian valley and the distant Andes is framed by the entrance of the Pikimachay rock shelter (top), where Richard MacNeish found bones, charcoal, and other materials that he asserts indicate a human occupation between 14,000 and 20,000 years ago. Artifacts from the younger deposits include a pointed tool fashioned from a toe bone of an extinct horse (above).

found. The typical scientist might offer only a slim chance that either of these mysteries would be solved because both are based on myths, not reality. Nevertheless, the idea that either might somehow be true still feeds human curiosity, challenges the mind for answers, and supports the tabloids.

So it is with the quest to find the first Americans. The answer, which falls somewhere between myth and reality, continues to attract attention. If everyone were suddenly to accept the view that the Clovis cultures were indeed the first Americans, then the search would be over. And the romantic images conjured up by the speculations of some pre-Clovis scholars would also fade. Did Neanderthals or other ancient humans ever live in the Americas? Certain pre-Clovis supporters think so. What about even earlier groups of humans? Maybe, say some of the more liberal of the group.

The question may never be fully resolved—even though a growing number of Clovis-first experts admit that Meadowcroft and Monte Verde are the two pre-Clovis sites that stand the best chance of being vindicated as authentic. One side has already set forth its rules for sites, while the other side has offered its own reasons why those criteria seem unreasonable for the oldest of the early sites. Some observers have remarked, only half humorously, that the only find likely to satisfy both sides is a human skeleton clutching a banner that proclaims, "I am the first American."

Of the best evidence found in the Americas, most was discovered during the last 50 years—and by accident. Few systematic searches have ever been conducted in key areas where scientists actually think answers might lie. Archaeological searches are expensive and lengthy. Finding the money to support the work and capable scientists willing to

26

invest the time have always been important constraints. Furthermore, if certain speculations are true, the most important unsearched areas now lie beneath the waters of the American coastal regions. This last point was emphasized by the discovery in the 1960s of a probable campsite of a group of early Americans on the continental shelf off the shores of Chesapeake Bay at a depth of 43 meters (140 feet). Exploration of such remote locales, however, must await adequate funding, new excavation techniques, and the special skills of underwater archaeologists.

At the start of the 20th century, archaeologists could not imagine the kinds of scientific advances that would soon be applied to the search for the first Americans. Radiocarbon-dating techniques, reconstruction of ancient climates and vegetation by means of studies of fossil pollen, genetic analysis of the relatedness of cultural groups around the world, and information about the varieties and habits of long-extinct animals were all unknown less than 100 years ago. Like those earlier scientists, we cannot foresee the advances that will prove the most important to archaeology. The search for the first people to set foot in the New World may end within our lifetime, or it may not. Until it does conclude, imagination and inquisitiveness will ensure that it remains among science's most alluring mysteries.

The Dinosaur Renaissance

by Robert T. Bakker

The many discoveries of dinosaur fossils in recent years have caused scientists to change their ideas about these animals. No longer are they all considered to be dull, cold-blooded, slowly evolving reptiles.

Back in the 1950s, when many of the dinosaur hunters now active were growing up, there was a uniform set of beliefs about how dinosaurs lived, how they evolved, and how they died out. Since 1955, however, this "Dinosaur Catechism" has fallen completely apart. During the last two decades nearly everything "known" about the dinosaurian way of life has been erased, and a whole new array of challenging theories has emerged. For anyone who loves these Mesozoic monsters, these are the most exciting times since the dinosaur gold rush of the 1870s, when the first complete skeletons, dug up in the American West, astounded both academia and the general public.

At the core of the Dinosaur Catechism were the things that these animals supposedly could not do. Since dinosaurs were assumed to be mere overgrown lizards, equipped with weak hearts, flaccid lungs, and small mental powers, the list of dinosaur deficiencies was long: (1) Dinosaurs were dull parents. Like a female tortoise who lays her eggs, covers them, and then leaves, never to see them hatch, dinosaurs allegedly were uninvolved parents who did not invest much time or worry in their progeny's welfare. (2) Dinosaurs were unexciting lovers. Dinosaur courtship supposedly lacked all the bright color flaunted by birds or the energetic male contests of many big mammals. (3) Dinosaurs were evolutionary sluggards. Groups of dinosaur species supposedly lasted for immense periods of time without accumulating any notable adaptive improvements. By contrast, warm-blooded birds and mammals modernize their Darwinian equipment rapidly and produce evolutionary bursts during which dozens of new species appear. (4) Dinosaurs were warm-weather warriors—they relied on their immense bulk and a warm climate to survive and could not handle cold winters. (5) Dinosaur viscera were seriously deficient, with brains, hearts, and lungs underpowered by mammal or bird standards. (6) Dinosaurs ruled by default, enjoying success only as long as no worthy challengers appeared; when the climate changed and smart mammals evolved, the dinosaurs died out completely, leaving no modern descendants.

In the following discussion I will review these orthodox theories by using evidence from two of the best known epochs in dinosaur history, the Late Jurassic, about 160 million to 144 million years ago, and the Late Cretaceous, about 98 million to 66 million years ago. It is important to put this dinosaur history into the proper evolutionary context of warfare between the classes of animals. The class Mammalia (creatures with hair and milk glands) and the class Aves (the birds) are the only warm-blooded classes alive in today's world, while the class Reptilia (turtles, crocodilians, lizards, and snakes) is entirely cold-blooded, with metabolic heat production only a tenth as high as that of a bird or mammal of the same body size. How did these classes interact through geologic time, and which class should include dinosaurs?

Dinosaur parenthood

The "lay-them-and-leave-them" approach to eggs and offspring places hatchlings on their own right out of the egg; as a result, infant mortality

ROBERT T. BAKKER is a Research Associate of the University Museum, University of Colorado, Boulder.

(Overleaf) Seventy million years ago, on Alaska's North Slope, a family of plant-eating Pachyrhinosaurus starts its yearly migration through the September snows. The dominant bull drives away a half-grown carnivorous Albertosaurus that is threatening the calf. New discoveries portray dinosaurs as active and colorful, with brilliant courtship colors, strong social organization, and the ability to cope with cold habitats. Illustration by Ron Villani under the direction of Robert T. Bakker

30

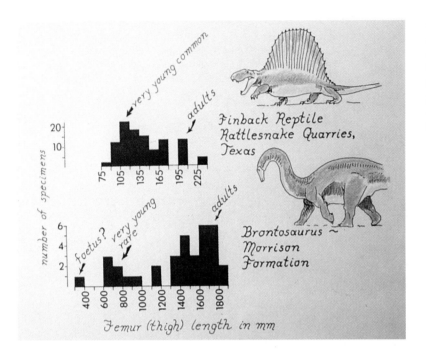

Figure labels:
very young common
adults
Finback Reptile Rattlesnake Quarries, Texas

foetus? very young rare
adults
Brontosaurus ~ Morrison Formation

number of specimens

Femur (thigh) length in mm

Brontosaur parenting kept infant mortality low, as indicated by a graph of thigh-bone length for a sample of Brontosaurus *and the primitive reptile* Dimetrodon. *Very few brontosaur specimens came from very young individuals, but in* Dimetrodon *infant mortality was high, and baby thighs are common.*

Illustration by Robert T. Bakker

is high. This high mortality shows up in fossil beds; youngsters that died in great numbers, unprotected by parents, were buried and fossilized by the score. Field work at the Como Bluff brontosaur beds in Wyoming has uncovered fossil pieces of hundreds of baby turtles scattered throughout the sediments laid down in rivers and swamps. But adult turtle specimens are rare—exactly the pattern one would expect from a long-lived reptile with the minimalist style of parenting. High mortality early in life was the rule for fossil cold-blooded Reptilia, even for the fin-backed predator *Dimetrodon,* an early ancestor of mammals that lived before the first dinosaurs.

Brontosaurus (also called *Apatosaurus*), a big vegetarian dinosaur, 30 tons adult weight, is a common fossil in the same beds that are full of baby turtles. But *Brontosaurus* babies are exceedingly rare—most specimens are adult or at least two-thirds grown. Fossil data show that brontosaurs had reduced infant mortality to as low a level as modern elephants. And the few baby brontosaurs that are found are not found alone. Every young skeleton was buried among the bones of full-sized individuals. Evidently, baby brontosaurs lived—and died—in the company of adults.

Fossil footprints tell the same story. Trackways left by *Brontosaurus* and its close kin are common in Colorado, Texas, and Africa. Most of the footprints are from adults or large young, but a few are those of small babies. And in every case the baby footprints are tightly surrounded by the enormous, meter-wide tracks of dozens of adults. In fact, the very largest footprints are usually on the extreme periphery of the brontosaur group and must represent the biggest bulls (or dominant cows). The baby brontosaurs were not alone and vulnerable but packed safely into a defensively organized herd. No living species of cold-blooded reptile protects its young this way.

31

Even though Brontosaurus *had a tiny brain by bird standards, fossil footprints and bones from 140 million years ago in Wyoming reveal that these dinosaurs were effective parents who kept infant mortality to a minimum.*

Dinosaur courtship and evolutionary rates

Not only did dinosaurs excel as protective parents but their courtship was far more colorful and energetic than what is seen among lizards and turtles today. It is traditional to portray dinosaur skin as gray and somber, the rationalization being that big animals today—rhinos, hippos, elephants—are so colored. But all of these mammals are color-blind. Bright hues cannot evolve among color-blind species. Bright colors do evolve in groups that can see colors and that evolve rapidly; among such animals many species live together, and each species needs a unique way to advertise for mates. Birds are the best example. In each tropical habitat today, dozens of closely related tropical bird species must attract desirable mates from the appropriate gene pool. Brilliant patterns on the male birds are the rule, a different color scheme for each species, even though the gaudy plumage results in higher losses to hawks and other predators.

Did dinosaurs see color? The closest living dinosaur relatives are crocodilians and birds, both of which can distinguish colors. (Crocodiles court their mates at night and so do not use color identification marks.)

32

And nearly all dinosaur skulls had large eye sockets and large optic lobes (shown by the imprint on the bones surrounding the brain). Therefore, dinosaurs almost certainly were very birdlike in being visually oriented, color-sighted animals.

The variety of courtship patterns that evolve in a group of species depends on the speed of evolution. If the dinosaur family tree evolved fast and produced many closely related species living together, it might be expected that they would use colored identification badges the way that birds do today. In fact, snout anatomy provides abundant evidence that dinosaurian faunas were very rich and that most habitats were jammed with species. At Como Bluff, in the brontosaur beds (about 140 million years old), four big predatory dinosaur species, all about the same size, were found. The four can be distinguished from one another at a glance by the distinctive crests on their skulls in front and behind the eyes and along the snouts; no doubt, that is the way the four species told each other apart. It is on these crests that bright color probably evolved in the males to make identification easy at a distance.

Species identification crests evolved in spectacular profusion in meat-eating dinosaurs of the tyrannosaur family, in the herbivores of the duckbill family, and in the horned herbivores of the *Triceratops* family. In the Judith River beds of Alberta (about 74 million years old), there are three tyrannosaur species and at least a half dozen each from the horned dinosaur and duckbill families. Every single species has an unmistak-

Four species of giant predators coexisted in the mid-Morrison age, 143 million years ago, and each had a distinctive head profile of crests and knobs. Dinosaur eyes were birdlike and probably could distinguish colors. Bright colors probably highlighted the crests, giving each species a distinctive avian-style identification system. The four species are Ceratosaurus nasicornis *(top left),* Allosaurus atrox *(top right),* Edmarka rex *(bottom left), and* Allosaurus fragilis *(bottom right).*

Illustration by Pat Ortega under the direction of Robert T. Bakker

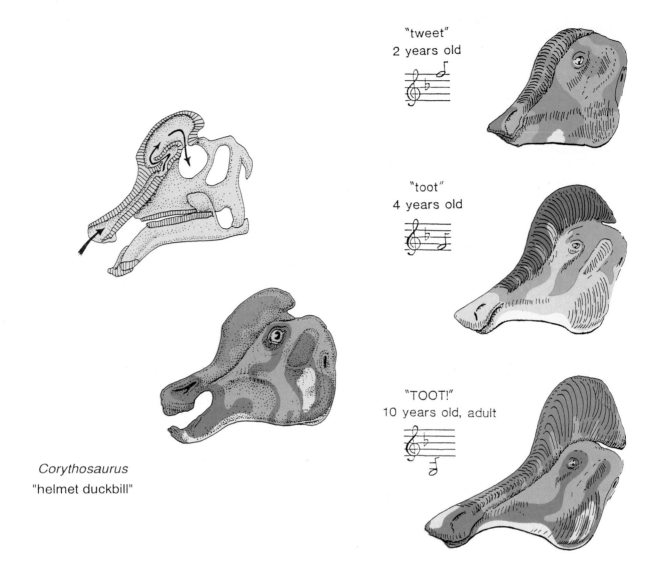

"tweet"
2 years old

"toot"
4 years old

"TOOT!"
10 years old, adult

Corythosaurus
"helmet duckbill"

able advertising mark on the head. Throughout dinosaurian history the fastest-evolving part of the body was the identification system of frills, crests, and bony warts, and this style of rapid evolution matches the pattern seen in hot-blooded birds much more closely than that of big cold-blooded reptiles such as crocodiles and turtles.

Dinosaurian courtship was not limited to bright hues on cranial message boards. Most plant-eating species had echo chambers built into the snout bones around their nostrils, and in brontosaurs, armored dinosaurs, and duckbills, these reverberation structures evolved into quite convoluted and multicompartmented devices. The echo chambers were fast-evolving components so that each species would have a distinctive call. Skull bones have the tonal qualities of hardwood, and the mating calls of the crested duck-billed dinosaurs must have resembled the deeper ranges of bassoons and oboes.

Big cold-blooded reptiles, such as tortoises and crocodilians, evolve so slowly that each family group of species survives for fifty million to a

34

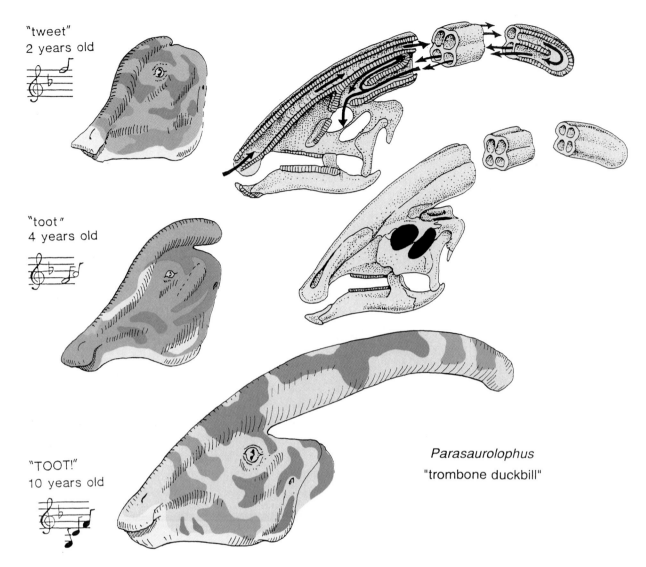

"tweet"
2 years old

"toot"
4 years old

"TOOT!"
10 years old

Parasaurolophus
"trombone duckbill"

hundred million years with little change. Only minor features distinguish present-day alligators and crocodiles from their ancestors in the Judith River fauna 74 million years ago. Even the crocodiles of the brontosaur beds, 140 million years old, if alive today would look perfectly modern to a zookeeper in a reptile house. Dinosaur evolution, in sharp contrast, took place at such a rapid pace that species would evolve and disappear in a million years and entire families of species would last only 20 million years.

A demonstration of evolutionary rates can be seen at Como Bluff, where the brontosaur beds (known technically as the Morrison Formation) are about 90 meters (300 feet) thick and were deposited from 145 million through 140 million years ago, during the last six million years of the Jurassic Period. Evolution in crocodiles was too slow to make much change in their skulls during that time, but the dinosaur fauna changed and changed again in the same interval, and no dinosaur species lasted through the entire six million years.

Dinosaur voices changed during puberty, as revealed by two closely related duckbill dinosaurs, Corythosaurus (opposite page) and Parasaurolophus (above), who lived side by side in Alberta. At hatching neither species had enlarged echo chambers, and the two would be hard to tell apart by sight or sound. But as the youngsters approached adult size, the tootling chambers suddenly began to grow, making the differences between the species obvious. Fully mature duckbills must have had startling differences in song.

Illustration by Robert T. Bakker

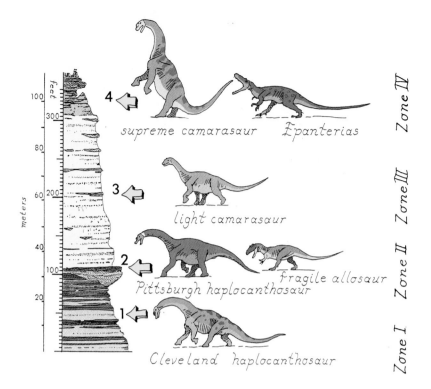

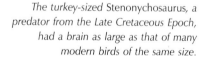

Dinosaurs in the Arctic snow

If dinosaurs functioned like oversized reptiles, no dinosaur could have lived in the long, dark, Arctic winters. Most of the well-known dinosaur beds contain fossil plants that indicate a warm, frost-free climate—both the Judith River and the Como Bluff dinosaur beds are in this category. During the Age of Dinosaurs, warm climates extended much farther north than at present, all the way to central Alberta. Recent expeditions, however, found dinosaur beds about the same age as the Judith River fauna in the North Slope of Alaska. At that high latitude there would have been four months of Arctic winter night, and the fossil plants reveal that the winter cold was about as severe as it is in Vancouver, British Columbia, today—cold enough for some snowstorms and far too frigid for big land reptiles like tortoises. If dinosaurs had only a reptilian grade of metabolism, they would not have been able to survive the four months of cold.

But dinosaurs, including large duckbills, horned dinosaurs, and tyrannosaurs, are found in the Alaskan beds. These elephant-sized species might have survived by migrating south hundreds of kilometers toward the warmer winter habitats that then existed in Alberta and Montana. However, no modern-day land reptiles migrate, for the simple reason that they do not have enough metabolic energy for long-distance walking. Only a warm-blooded dinosaur could migrate the way that caribou and elephants do in the modern world.

Tiny dinosaurs lived in the high-latitude Arctic, too; teeth of fox-sized troödont predators are found in the Alaskan beds. Even a warm-blooded dinosaur that small would not have the energy to migrate, and

36

so the troödonts must have stayed through the Arctic winter. Either the troödonts hunted small mammals in the cold—the dinosaurian equivalent of Arctic foxes—or they went into deep hibernation for four months.

Dinosaur hearts, lungs, and brains

It is undeniably true that most big, multiton dinosaurs, *Brontosaurus* included, had brains only one-tenth as big as a modern mammal of equivalent body bulk. But the old theory that smart mammals exterminated big, stupid dinosaurs does not hold up under the avalanche of new data. Some dinosaurs did have big brains. At least four different families of small dinosaur species evolved enlarged cerebral hemispheres, and these dinosaurs had brains as large for their body size as those possessed by ostriches and other big ground birds. In the Judith River fossil beds the troödonts and other big-brained carnivores are the commonest fox-sized predators, and these fast-thinking, fast-running meat eaters must have hunted the small, furry mammals of the time, including the ancestors of monkeys, apes, and humans.

If humans cling to the old idea that their ancestors were the brightest and best evolutionary products during the Age of Dinosaurs, it is a bit humiliating to realize that the brains of these mammals were inferior to the brains in the troödont dinosaurs that were chasing them. It is simply not true that greater intelligence gave mammals the Darwinian edge over dinosaurs. Just the opposite occurred—brains were evolving faster in the small dinosaurs than in mammals. Throughout the Age of

A carnivorous dinosaur, Troödon, chases a shrewlike mammal in Alberta 74 million years ago. Throughout the Age of Dinosaurs, furry, warm-blooded mammals were kept small by the threat from dinosaur predators. Troödon had a larger and more complex brain, better lungs, and a larger heart than were possessed by any mammal of the time.

Illustration by Pat Ortega under the direction of Robert T. Bakker

Dinosaurs, a total of 160 million years, quick-stepping small dinosaurs chased and harassed mammals so continuously that class Mammalia as a group could not evolve a single species larger than a woodchuck.

Even old-fashioned theories saw the troödonts as birdlike in many ways, but small-brained vegetarians like *Brontosaurus* also were constructed with an abundance of avian adaptive accessories. Brontosaur neck bones were 1.2-meter (4-foot)-wide versions of turkey necks, each bone hollowed out and full of air chambers connected to the lungs. Air chambers give modern bird lungs nearly twice the efficiency of mammal lungs in providing oxygen to the bloodstream, and brontosaurs breathed with avian-style lungs. Heart power was also prodigious in all dinosaurs. The first three ribs in the chest, where the heart and tips of the lungs are housed, are very long in small, medium-sized, and large dinosaur species, both vegetarian and carnivorous.

Success through bulk

The most persistent misconception about dinosaurs is that they did not need warm-blooded metabolism to succeed because they were bulky enough to keep their bodies warm with minimum physiological heat. In fact, though, most big dinosaur species were no larger than modern elephants, animals weighing from three to five tons. Elephants are emphatically warm-blooded; they have metabolic heat production per hour that is far higher than what a lizard or turtle would have at the same body weight. All the dominant multiton animals on land today are warm-blooded, even in the equatorial tropics where climates are mild. The high heat production is an absolute necessity for large animals, allowing them to keep their body temperature from varying even a few degrees under all circumstances. Even a drop as little as 2.8° C (5° F) in body temperature would result in a 30% decrease in muscle and nerve performance. If big dinosaurs had only a tortoise level of heat production, nothing would have stopped warm-blooded little mammals and little dinosaurs from evolving into large sizes and exterminating the cold-blooded dinosaur species. Therefore, a cold-blooded *Brontosaurus* does not make evolutionary sense.

Old theories postulated that the only active warm-blooded dinosaurs were the very small, fast-moving carnivores such as *Troödon*. The giant dinosaurs supposedly had body-heat mechanisms that were far inferior. New studies of dinosaur skull anatomy reveal that this alleged gap in physiology between small and large dinosaurs never existed. Orthodox classifications put troödonts in the coelurosaur group of small predators and segregate tyrannosaurs into the carnosaur group of giant carnivores. However, computed tomography (CT)-scan technology provides a deep look inside fossil skulls, and the results shatter the coelurosaur/carnosaur theory. Both tyrannosaur and troödont skulls are full of air chambers built into the interior spaces of bones around the snout, over the eyes, and around the cheek, ear, and brain. All these air spaces were connected to anatomic ductwork leading to the windpipe and lungs, an arrangement that is just about 100% identical to the pattern in bird skulls. Another

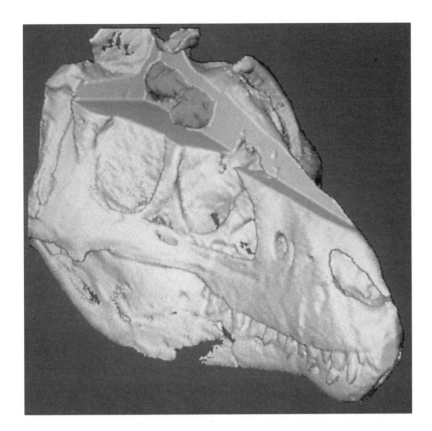

Computed tomography scan of the skull of a 6-meter (20-foot)-long predator, Nanotyrannus, reveals birdlike air chambers built into the bones around the brain (green area) and thin, curled, bony sheets in the snout. These features are designed to heat the air inhaled through the nostrils and to keep the dinosaur's large brain cool.

Andrew Leitch

avian feature in both troödonts and tyrannosaurs is the way in which the neck muscles were attached to the back of the skull; the muscles were more complex than in other dinosaurs and gave these predators great agility in head-neck movements.

The number of birdlike adaptations in the heads of tyrannosaurs and troödonts is so large that these two dinosaurian meat eaters, one tiny and one gigantic, must be very closely related. Just as a house cat and a 275-kilogram (600-pound) Siberian tiger are small and large versions of the same warm-blooded Mammalian family, the tyrannosaur and the troödont were the opposite ends of the size range in a warm-blooded dinosaur clan.

Dinosaur extinction—a warm-blooded way to die

Dinosaur extinction itself is another piece of evidence for a warm-blooded evolutionary mode. Dinosaurs did not suffer worldwide die-offs just once. There were five or more extinction events during the 160 million years of dinosaur history, and each time it was only the large, active animals on land that were targeted by the extermination agent. Small mammals, frogs, salamanders, and lizards survived untouched at each event, as did large turtles and crocodilians in lakes and rivers.

Altogether, throughout the entire history of life on land, the exterminator agent has struck a dozen or more times. The most recent big terrestrial extinction was during the last Ice Age, when mammoths, giant ground sloths, saber-toothed tigers, huge bears, scores of other

39

large-bodied mammals, and many large ground birds disappeared. Nevertheless, during this crisis there was no major die-off of chipmunks, frogs, snakes, or alligators. Extermination events hit big warm-blooded mammals four or five times before the Ice Age, and during these extinctions, too, the small animals and large species in freshwater habitats went unscathed.

Who or what is the exterminator agent? This question generates continued heated debate, but whatever the identity of the kill-off specialist turns out to be, it targets only large, active, warm-blooded species on land. There has never been a worldwide die-off of cold-blooded lizards, snakes, or turtles. The repeated extinction crisis suffered by dinosaurs is the evolutionary price paid by all warm-blooded family trees of species. It is a Darwinian rule that large animals with fast-evolving styles of change are vulnerable to sudden exterminations of most or all species. If the brontosaur family really was a swamp-bound group of cold-blooded species, the family would still be alive.

Dinosaurs alive

It is ironic that dinosaurs are, indeed, still alive today—some 8,300–8,700 species of them. The biggest weighs only 135 kilograms (300 pounds), and the average species is only a few grams in weight. These living dinosaurians are the class Aves, the birds. The evidence from skull structure is overwhelming that all birds are direct descendants of a small meat-eating dinosaur. Thus, the class Aves is the bushy evolutionary crown of the dinosaurian family tree, and to lump the dinosaurs into the class Reptilia is no longer a tenable taxonomic theory. Hummingbirds, turkeys, ostriches, *Tyrannosaurus*, and *Brontosaurus* are members of the same class, the great group of species with the grandest legacy of ecological success.

PHYLLIS JANIK, author of the sidebar, below, is a writer/photographer.

The Great Chasmosaur Dig of 1991

It is now part of the Chihuahuan Desert. But if tourists could time travel to Texas' Big Bend National Park of 80 million years ago, they might think they had taken a wrong turn. The region was swampy, bordered by a mid-continental seaway. Prehistoric developers might have named the place Cretaceous Lake, where lucky humans could catch glimpses of *Dinosuchus*, a 15-meter (50-foot)-long crocodile. Or herds of wading hadrosaurs. Or the giant *Quetzalcoatlus*, the ancestral-Texas version of a pterodactyl.

On March 26, 1991, Thomas Evans experienced the Late Cretaceous firsthand when he discovered the 80 million-year-old skull of *Chasmosaurus mariscalensis*, the only complete specimen of its kind ever found. Evans, then a graduating senior at the University of Chicago, had just completed an 11-week evolutionary biology course and accompanied his class on its optional spring-break field trip.

Sponsored by the university and led by paleontologist Paul Sereno, the group was in Big Bend to study the park's geology and to experience a day or two in the life of a typical paleontologist: a lot of hiking, a lot of searching and sifting, only rare success in finding anything. Sereno had been given permission to visit a section of the park that had proved fruitful for University of Texas paleontologists for 40 years.

After a brief orientation by Sereno, students broke up into small groups or wandered off on their own to explore. Evans, who had never worked in the field, made his discovery less than two hours after the group arrived in the designated area. Noticing a few centimeters of "what looked like bone sticking out of the sand," he called over to graduate student Bill Stevens. They assessed the fossil as other class members gathered around. Sereno's assistant, Catherine Forster, who had written her doctoral thesis on horned dinosaurs, identified the now-apparent head as that of a chasmosaur. The specimen had three horns; the two horns over the brow extended perhaps 0.6 meter (2 feet). A bony "frill" or "shield," an integral part of the skull, fanned out over the neck area. Further digging was not difficult because the burial had taken place in a sandy pocket of the shale that the Aguja Formation comprises. Most likely a former lagoon near the shore of the inland sea, the sand yielded plant debris and, fortunately, a layer of gypsum that provided a convenient shelf on which the massive head rested.

Because the University of Texas holds one of only two permits to collect vertebrate fossils within the park boundaries, Sereno notified the university. The Balcones Research Center there immediately sent two of its field experts, Bob Rainey and Earl Yarmer, to prepare the skull and retrieve it for further research. They reached Big Bend on March 27, and on March 28–30, assisted by graduate student Anne Weil, used plaster and burlap to jacket and cap the specimen. They then loaded it into their van for its ride across the state to the laboratory.

Both Sereno's group and the University of Texas preparators realized that the left side of the skull, the side first spotted by Evans, had eroded for at least several years, partially and perhaps intermittently exposed but nonetheless vulnerable to the elements. Thus weatherbeaten, the horncore and left half of the shield, or frill, had disintegrated. During the next four months Yarmer worked at removing the plaster and burlap to expose the buried, better preserved side. In July, Sereno, Forster, Evans, and Hilary Tindle, another student from the original group,

conducted research at Balcones and confirmed the dinosaur's identity: *Chasmosaurus mariscalensis*. On the basis of the size of the head, 1.2 × 1.5 meters (4 × 5 feet) the animal would have been approximately 9 meters (30 feet) long and would have weighted about five tons.

Prior to the Evans find, scientists had only minimal knowledge of this type of dinosaur. Years earlier, paleontologist Thomas M. Lehman of Texas Tech University had discovered fragments and identified the genus and then had realized that the bones indicated a new species. Lehman named it *mariscalensis* after Big Bend's Mariscal Mountains. The skull of the fully mature chasmosaur discovered by Evans provides an unparalleled opportunity to gain information concerning its own species and also to compare that information with what has been learned about the other two chasmosaur species, *Chasmosaurus belli* and *Chasmosaurus russelli*. Remains of those species have been found in the northern U.S. and Canada, and the fact that *mariscalensis* was found in west Texas indicates that chasmosaurs inhabited areas much farther south than had previously been assumed.

When Sereno, Forster, Evans, and Tindle returned to Texas in July, they conducted research on the better-preserved side of the fossil. Its unusual quality of preservation assisted them in identifying structures never before seen in a ceratopsid. By early 1992 Yarmer was preparing the skull for eventual exhibition at the Texas Memorial Museum in Austin. Visitors would then be able to view this remarkable find and experience what Sereno has called a once-in-a-lifetime phenomenon.

 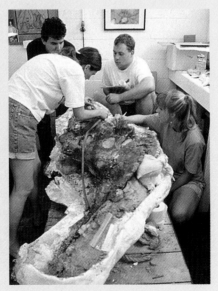

A researcher examines the site in Big Bend National Park, Texas, where in 1991 a student on his first field trip discovered an 80 million-year-old skull of Chasmosaurus mariscalensis, the first complete specimen of its kind to be found (far left). After the skull's removal to a laboratory, a team of scientists, including the discoverer, second from right, studies its better-preserved right side.

Earth
The Gulf War's Silent Victim

by Patricia J. West

Called by some the worst environmental disaster in modern times, the Persian Gulf war of 1991 defaced the natural ecology of the Middle East with an oily blot whose effects will take scientists many years to comprehend.

War exacts many costs: societies are disrupted, property is destroyed, and lives are lost. Such clashes between people have occurred for millennia; history books overflow with accounts of how humankind settles its differences. Until recent times, however, the costs of war to the Earth's environment have seldom been tallied. Earlier analyses rarely considered the ecological disruptions and losses that mark most conflicts. Even recent accounts in most cases have failed to address the full environmental impact of military actions. In fact, such costs are great; the destruction of the Earth's natural habitats means destruction of the resources that sustain life, including human lives. In all wars the environment is a victim.

The Persian Gulf war of 1991 was no exception. The use of force by the U.S. and its allies in early 1991 against Saddam Hussein, ruler of Iraq, following his invasion of neighboring Kuwait has altered the environment of the Middle East for years to come. In that region lies a fragile desert habitat contiguous with a rich marine environment. The Gulf war resulted in great damage to both ecosystems, prompting the Worldwatch Institute to declare it the greatest environmental disaster in modern history.

The Persian Gulf region comprises some of the richest oil fields in the world, a resource that has been fought over for almost a century. Indeed, the major reason for the Iraqi invasion in August 1990 was possession of Kuwait's oil fields. More than 60% of the world's oil originates from the Gulf region. During the war this same resource became a weapon when Iraqi soldiers set fire to more than half of Kuwait's 1,200 oil wells and released huge amounts of oil into the waters of the Gulf. The effects of those actions were compounded by massive air strikes conducted by the allied forces, which hit Iraq's oil refineries and oil tankers.

Allied armament churns up the desert surface and darkens the air near Kuwait City in late February 1991, adding its contribution to the disruption of the environment of the Middle East brought about by the Persian Gulf war.

PATRICIA J. WEST is an Environmental Information Specialist for Westinghouse Savannah River Co., Aiken, South Carolina, and a free-lance science writer.

(Overleaf) Photograph by Steve McCurry— Magnum

Air strikes, coupled with the buildup and movement of military forces before and during the war, also resulted in severe damage to the desert area. Disruption of the soil and vegetation is of concern particularly because of the possible effects on human life. Scientists have predicted that the bombings and damage caused by massive military construction and occupation and by off-road vehicles, such as tanks, will result in increased sandstorms for the next several years.

The detailed environmental consequences of the Gulf war, which lasted only six weeks, will not be known for many years. Part of the difficulty lies in trying to collect scientific data in a war zone. The war has made access to parts of the Middle East difficult, and in many cases equipment and trained personnel have become scarce. Furthermore, the ability of scientists in Kuwait and Iran to make studies has been impaired by damage to research institutions. Additionally, some sources claim that the governments of the U.S. and other nations have censored information about the environmental effects of the war. For example, scientists at the U.S. Department of Energy's Lawrence Livermore (California) National Laboratory allegedly were instructed not to discuss the environmental effects of the war with reporters.

A history of environmental destruction

Although major and minor wars have been fought almost uninterrupted over the course of human history, the way wars are conducted has changed significantly. New technology, including modern weapons of mass destruction, has increased humankind's ability to destroy huge tracts of land and the life they support with a single blow. In fact, environmental destruction is a popular military strategy.

Intentional destruction of ecosystems as a way of hurting or impeding the enemy is an ancient practice. History records an instance of this tactic at the end of the Peloponnesian War of 431–404 BC. Sparta's ultimate conquest of Athens was achieved in part because of the ability of the Spartans to destroy systematically the grain crops of Athens, which resulted in near starvation of the city's population.

Environmental destruction as a consequence of war, whether purposeful or not, can take various forms. Vegetation may be killed, soil surfaces altered, water supplies polluted, or air quality compromised. Harm also may come to wildlife, large and small. Occasionally animals are specifically targeted during conflicts. The U.S. government bombed and killed elephants as "vehicles of transport" during the war in Vietnam. In the 19th century American bison that once ranged across North America were systematically killed during the U.S.-Indian wars, thus undermining the livelihood of such tribes as Apache, Sioux, and Cheyenne.

Although wartime damage today is usually wrought by technology, for example, chemical weapons, high-explosive munitions, and atomic bombs, fire has a long tradition as an agent of destruction. In ancient history examples of "scorched-earth" tactics are common. One of the earliest dates to 512 BC, when the retreating Scythians practiced a self-inflicted scorched-earth policy to impede the advancing Persians. More recently, during the German advance into the Soviet Union in 1941, Soviet troops used the same strategy to effect, burning crops as they retreated deep into Russia. Union Gen. William Tecumseh Sherman's march to the sea during the American Civil War involved the burning of great tracts of land, mostly across Virginia and Georgia. The North used fire to destroy crops and starve the Confederate States into submission.

Dever—Black Star

Soviet soldiers conducted scorched-earth tactics, burning village structures and crops, in their retreat from the German advance into the U.S.S.R. in 1941. As had armies throughout history before them, the Soviets hoped that destroying the environment would impede enemy forces and deny them valuable resources.

During the 1960s and early '70s, U.S. planes sprayed the herbicide Agent Orange over large tracts of forests in Vietnam (top) to defoliate areas of possible concealment for the enemy and to destroy food crops. Like much of Vietnam, Dong Loc Valley (above) still bears scars from the extensive wartime bombing. Some of the larger craters are being put to use as fish ponds.

Chemicals also have been used effectively during wartime to destroy natural resources of the enemy's territory. The Bible mentions one of the earliest known uses, about 3,000 years ago, when Abimelech's forces spread salt as a soil poison on the conquered city of Shechem, near present-day Nabulus on the West Bank. An often-cited use of chemicals occurred during the 1960s and '70s in Vietnam. U.S. strategy included the systematic destruction of thick forests that covered South Vietnam in order to deny concealment and agricultural use to the enemy. An estimated 2¼ million hectares (5½ million acres) were affected by bombing, mechanized land clearing, napalming, and chemical defoliation. The best known of those tactics was the massive defoliation caused by aerial spraying of the herbicide Agent Orange. Twenty years after the last raids by the U.S. Air Force, vast tracts of Vietnam are still bare.

The landscape of much of Vietnam also bears scars from extensive battering by high-explosive weapons. Conventional bombs and shells were employed in unprecedented quantities during the war, according to Arthur H. Westing of Westing Associates, Putney, Vermont, an ecologist who has specialized in the environmental impact of warfare. He found that 90% of those munitions were directed at ill-defined targets; that is, rural areas. The consequence of the bombing and shelling was an estimated 25 million craters, some measuring 30 meters (100 feet) across. While the Vietnamese are still working to fill these in and to convert some of the larger craters into fish-farming ponds, the natural environment of their country may never be the same.

The tremendous destructive potential of nuclear weapons was tasted briefly at the end of World War II. The two atomic bombs dropped in August 1945 nearly eliminated the Japanese cities of Hiroshima and Nagasaki, setting everything ablaze within kilometers of the blasts. Although the loss of more than 100,000 human lives has overshadowed concern for damage done to the environment, the bombings did reveal something of the environmental effects of atomic weapons. Almost all plant and animal life was killed instantly by the energy release of the bombs; birds were seen to ignite in midair. Postwar testing of nuclear weapons also has had serious environmental consequences. Detonations of atomic and hydrogen bombs in the Marshall Islands between 1946 and 1958 so badly contaminated the atolls of Enewetak and Bikini that attempts to repatriate the islands' inhabitants have been thwarted by lingering radiation despite massive cleanup efforts. Although the environmental toll of nuclear explosions unquestionably was great in some instances, conclusive studies on their overall effects do not exist.

If for too long the environmental consequences of military conflicts had been neglected, the vivid photos and video images of blazing wells and smoke-blackened skies, of Kuwaiti children hospitalized for respiratory problems, and of oil-soaked wildlife presented by the news media in its coverage of the Gulf war seemed to signal a turning point. In early 1991, amid increased ecological awareness around the world, as both scientists and the public worried about urban pollution, the destruction of natural habitats and the consequent loss of plant and animal species, and the

46

An atomic bomb detonates over evacuated Bikini atoll in July 1946 (top). Lingering radiation from U.S. nuclear weapons testing in the Marshall Islands between 1946 and 1958 has delayed repatriation of Bikini's inhabitants for more than four decades as scientists and engineers have sought acceptable cleanup techniques. A pumpkin that was grown on Bikini in 1985 (so labeled in the photo at left) in an experimental patch in which the top 38 centimeters (15 inches) of soil had been removed shows a reduced but still unacceptable level of radioactivity. The spike on the instrument screen indicates a high level of cesium-137 present in the pumpkin.

possibility of human-induced global warming, the war's effects became the most visible and most acute environmental issue in recent memory.

The oil in the Gulf

The Gulf war was responsible for one of the greatest spills of oil in history. Beginning in January 1991 an estimated one million to six million barrels of oil were released into the Persian Gulf. (A barrel of oil equals 42 gallons or about 159 liters.) Earlier reports had placed the total at 10 million barrels. Because the spill was actually a series of releases, officials have been unsure of the quantity of oil actually discharged. For purposes of comparison, the notorious 1989 spill from the tanker *Exxon Valdez* off the Alaskan coast amounted to about 250,000 barrels. The biggest release was caused by Iraqi soldiers who dynamited a loading area

47

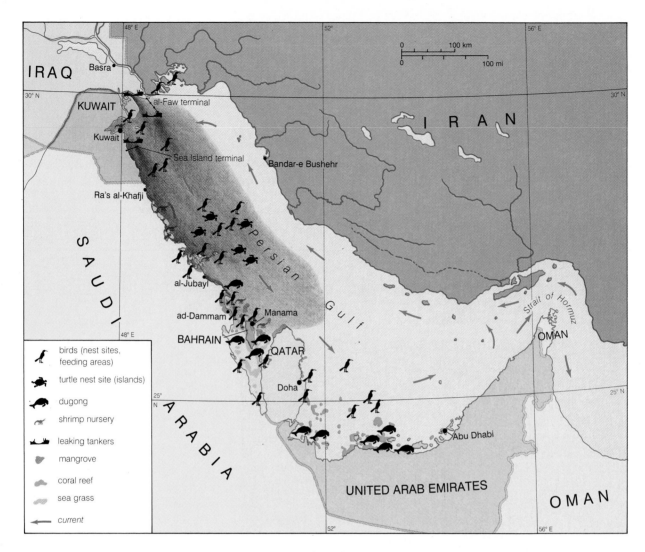

Beginning in January 1991 an estimated one million to six million barrels of oil were released into Persian Gulf waters from sources that included loaded Iraqi tankers and the Sea Island terminal off Kuwait. Under the influence of the Gulf's counterclockwise current, oil traveled down the coasts of Kuwait and Saudi Arabia, remaining for the most part north of al-Jubayl. Seabirds and wading birds inhabiting the northwestern Gulf coast were hard hit by the oil, as were mangrove swamps and salt marshes. The spill also posed threats to various marine mammals, sea turtles, fish, and corals in the polluted region, although by the end of the year it appeared that most of those animals had been spared. As much as 25% of the shrimp industry of the area was thought to have been affected.

known as Sea Island off Kuwait. Oil was also released when allied and Iraqi artillery barrages ruptured storage tanks and damaged refineries. Finally, Iraqi forces brought in loaded tankers and deliberately dumped their black cargoes into the waters of the Gulf.

The appearance of oil in Persian Gulf waters is a frequent occurrence. Extraction and transport operations in the area result in an annual release into Gulf waters of quantities of oil estimated as high as 250,000 barrels. Such is the case in all parts of the world that support the oil industry; oil trails mark the major shipping routes. Spills caused by tanker accidents are just one source of oil contamination. Routine tanker discharges, industrial runoff, and offshore drilling all contribute to the oil pollution that occurs continually around the world.

The Gulf release polluted almost 500 kilometers (300 miles) of shore-line, mostly sandy and rocky beaches interspersed with marsh and mud flats along the northern Saudi Arabian coast. Most of the oil ended up in intertidal, or shallow, habitats. Salt marshes and mangrove forests were very heavily oiled. Scientists estimated that oil affected more than 50%

48

Burning oil from a Kuwaiti offshore rig sends up clouds of smoke after having been set ablaze by allied aircraft. In late January 1991 Iraqi soldiers deliberately sent oil from the rig gushing into the sea, prompting an allied decision to burn the slick in hopes of making it more manageable.

of the mangroves, a rare habitat along the Saudi coast. These natural areas provide breeding, nursing, and feeding habitats as well as refuge for fish and invertebrates, including commercially important species such as shrimp.

Much of the early concern for the animals of the Gulf centered on the marine mammals. Several species of dolphins and porpoises are found in the Gulf, along with the dugong, a large mammal related to the manatee of the Caribbean and the southeastern U.S. coasts. According to Tony Preen of James Cook University, North Queensland, Australia, who worked in Saudi Arabia with an oil-spill response group, a large die-off of marine mammals was seen between late February and early April 1991, but it was not thought to be caused directly by the oil slick. Later study suggested that the oil was not directly affecting these species as seriously as had been feared. Part of the reason is that dugongs do not inhabit the northern Saudi coast, where most of the oil was concentrated.

Seabirds, including black-necked and crested grebes and Socotra and great cormorants, were hit hard by the oil. In spite of the effort of various rescue groups, who established centers where people could bring sick birds, at least 20,000–30,000 seabirds are believed to have died.

Wading birds such as herons, plovers, and flamingos live along the now-polluted coast. The Gulf is especially important to migratory waders; several million birds pass through the area twice yearly. Many birds became oiled during stopovers in the Gulf, and scientists believed that the animals may have been unable to complete their migration. Scientists also have expressed apprehension that the breeding of some species may be unsuccessful, presumably because of the disruption of migration. A survey begun in 1991 by the International Council for Bird Preservation, in concert with Saudi scientists, is attempting to determine how many birds use the area and how many were affected by the oil.

The coasts, islands, and waters of the Persian Gulf provide breeding and feeding habitats for many species of wildlife. The Caspian tern (above), which winters on Gulf shores and breeds on sandbanks, is one of numerous water birds that live in or migrate through the region. The familiar bottle-nosed dolphin (above right) and several other species of marine mammals are found in the Gulf, as is the green turtle (right), which digs its egg nests on islands off Saudi Arabia.

The oil's threat to coral reefs in the Gulf has been another concern. Scientists have worried that coral, a vital link in the food chain in the ocean, would be coated by the oil. Furthermore, some experts have speculated that the oil slick could block out the sunlight necessary for the life of the coral. Reef communities are sensitive to environmental change, and little is known about the vulnerability of the coral animals themselves or of the fish, sponges, and other organisms associated with them. Some evidence suggests that oil affects reproduction and feeding of coral. Since the early months following the spill, scientists have determined that the deeper parts of the Gulf that harbor the reefs will probably be spared.

The outlook for fish is more positive than for other organisms in the Gulf ecosystem. The region has long supported fisheries that provide a livelihood for millions of people. More than 850 species of fish dwell in the Persian Gulf. Five species—a dottyback, a butterfly fish, a cardinal fish, a wrasse, and a parrot fish—live nowhere else. Some ecologists predicted that these five species could be reduced or exterminated. After the first several months following the war, however, die-offs of fish were fairly small and patchily distributed. Nevertheless, many different fish species, including bottom, surface, and mid-water feeders, have been found dead in the waters and along the shoreline of the Gulf. Furthermore, as much as 25% of the shrimp industry of the area was affected by the spill.

Compounding the pollution in the Persian Gulf, as well as creating new threats of its own, has been the oil that spilled into the Kuwaiti desert during the well fires and afterward. According to Kuwaiti estimates, 35 million barrels of oil lay in shallow lakes around the oil fields in late 1991, while U.S. military engineers said that the quantity could be several times higher. Some of the oil lakes were within kilometers of the Gulf waters, prompting Saudi officials to express fears that rains could wash some of the standing oil into the sea. Kuwaiti scientists were also concerned with the possibilities that the oil, or harmful substances leached from it, could contaminate groundwater and that hydrocarbons in the air from evaporation of the oil could affect human health.

It has been estimated that water flow in the Gulf takes about six years to flush 90% of contaminants through the Strait of Hormuz, which is only 55 kilometers (35 miles) wide at its narrowest. The Gulf and the life that it supports, however, have proved to be resilient to the oil that has regularly polluted them during standard operations. Most scientists agree that the scars left by the Gulf war are massive but that the wildlife populations in the area will eventually recover.

Kuwait's burning wells

Combustion products from Kuwait's burning oil wells posed one of the war's greatest threats to the environment. Some scientists called it perhaps the worst human-made atmospheric pollution event in history. Over 600 wells were torched by retreating Iraqi troops as the war came to a close. The plume of smoke, which contained soot, carbon dioxide, and toxic gases, extended downwind more than 800 kilometers (500 miles).

The Gulf release is thought to have killed 20,000–30,000 seabirds, despite rescue efforts (bottom right) and centers that were set up to take in sick, oil-soaked animals. What will never be known are the numbers of insects (bottom left), crustaceans, mollusks, fish, plants, and other less conspicuous organisms also claimed by the slicks and the mudlike sludge washed ashore.

Adding to the disaster of the Gulf spill were the millions of barrels of oil that pooled in the Kuwaiti desert during the well fires and afterward. Some scientists expressed concerns that the standing oil or substances leached from it could contaminate groundwater or that hydrocarbons evaporating from the oil into the air could endanger human health.

Most of the wells were ignited by dynamite in late February 1991. (A small group near the Kuwait-Saudi border were set ablaze in late January and early February.) Estimates of the amount of oil involved varied considerably. Oil industry officials in Kuwait said that about six million barrels were being consumed per day, a number that exceeded Kuwait's prewar production capacity. Other estimates put the total at only 25% of this figure, which was still a significant fraction of world oil production (over 62 million barrels per day in the late 1980s). On the basis of the higher estimate, Frederick Warner of the University of Essex, Colchester, England, calculated that 100,000 tons of carbon in the form of soot and 50,000 tons of sulfur dioxide—the main constituent of acid rain—were released into the atmosphere each day.

The total cost to Kuwait of putting out the fires and getting the wells back on line has been put in the billions of dollars. At the end of the war Kuwait hired two dozen fire-fighting teams to extinguish the fires. Although early estimates of the time it would take to put out the fires had ranged from two to seven years, all of them were snuffed out by the end of 1991. The extent of the fire as well as logistical problems faced by the fire fighters, such as the presence of Iraqi land mines surrounding the wells, had led many to overestimate the difficulty of the task.

The possibility that Iraq might ignite the oil fields had been raised by atmospheric scientists and others as early as September 1990, when Saddam Hussein threatened to destroy Kuwait's wells if forced from the territory that his army had seized a month before. King Hussein of Jordan and his science adviser, Abdullah Toukan, voiced one such warning at the second World Climate Conference in November 1990. Their calculations showed that global warming would be enhanced by emissions of carbon dioxide, a major contributor to the Earth's greenhouse effect, from the

fires. By some estimates the oil fires increased worldwide emissions of carbon dioxide by as much as 5%, although many scientists believed the increase was much less.

Indeed, after the well fires became a reality, the earliest predictions about the damage the smoke and gases would cause were grim. Enhanced global warming was just one of a host of predicted climatic effects, including short-term global cooling, disrupted monsoons in India, and increased acid rain.

The idea that the fires might cool the Earth's climate was brought up immediately after the war. "Nuclear winter" scenarios—predictions similar to those drawn from studies done in the 1980s that modeled the climatic effects of a large-scale nuclear exchange—were proposed by such scientists as Paul J. Crutzen of the Max Planck Institute for Chemistry, Mainz, Germany. He and other experts speculated that large amounts of smoke would be carried into the upper atmosphere, shrouding much of the Earth from the Sun. If the smoke were thick enough, appreciable cooling or even freezing could occur. A team of U.S. scientists, however, later showed that such a prediction was not realistic owing to the nature of the smoke, which had stayed two to three kilometers (one and a quarter to two miles) above the Earth's surface. Richard Small of the Pacific-Sierra Research Corp., Los Angeles, California, found that, unlike the ash from volcanic eruptions, which is believed to be a major factor in global temperature changes, oil-fire soot is heavy and will not stay airborne long. Therefore, it cannot spread far enough to cause worldwide cooling. In fact, a group of scientists from the Meteorological Office in Great Britain calculated that most of the soot would be deposited on the ground in the region within a week of its emission.

Dismissal of the possibility of global cooling brought reassurance that the monsoon in southern Asia would not be affected. John Cox of the Campaign for Nuclear Disarmament in Great Britain had proposed that

Estimates of the amount of Kuwaiti oil being consumed by well fires (above) at the height of the conflagration ranged from 1.5 million to 6 million barrels per day. Using the high figure, one expert calculated that 100,000 tons of carbon in the form of soot and 50,000 tons of sulfur dioxide were being released into the atmosphere each day. At the end of the war, teams of fire fighters were called in to extinguish the fires (above left). Early on, it was thought that some wells would be burning as long as seven years, but in fact the last fire was put out before the end of 1991.

(Opposite page, bottom) Landsat satellite images taken over a two-month period in 1991 show the progressive destruction of Kuwait's oil fields during and after the allied campaign against Iraq, which took place from January 17 to February 28. On January 6 the wells are intact (left); by February 15 a number of them are on fire, their plumes drifting southward; and by March 3, days after the end of the war, much of Kuwait lies under a pall of smoke from more than 600 burning wells.

As the oil fires blazed, smoke covered much of Kuwait City (top). In towns located near burning oil fields, "noon looked like midnight" according to one news photographer, who snapped a picture of children given masks for protection by a local hospital (bottom). While medical interest was focused on the possibilities of immediate health problems from soot and toxic gases, some experts voiced concerns about how little was known about the long-term health risks of exposure to the smoke of burned crude oil.

smoke-induced cooling could weaken the monsoons, which bring the rain necessary for crops in India, Pakistan, and other countries. Cox speculated that such an effect would cause a drought afflicting millions of people. Later, however, scientists said that the influence on the monsoons would be negligible and, indeed, reports from Asia in the latter part of 1991 indicated that monsoon rains were within the normal range.

Acid rain is one predicted consequence of the oil fires that has proved fairly accurate. The fires loaded the local atmosphere with large amounts of sulfur dioxide, which reacted with water to form sulfuric acid, resulting in acid rain over Kuwait and Iran. Computer models had predicted that such rain could destroy all crops and natural vegetation in Kuwait within a few months, though such effects were not observed. Data gathered by Lawrence Radke of the National Center for Atmospheric Research, Boulder, Colorado, and his colleagues indicated that although

54

large amounts of sulfur dioxide were emitted, the effects were diluted considerably downwind. On the other hand, Soviet scientists announced unprecedented amounts of acid rain in southern Russia. Such conflicting reports were a reminder to atmospheric scientists about how much remained to be learned.

Acid rain was just one effect of the fires on the local environment of the Gulf region. Black rain, caused by the massive amounts of airborne soot, fell on crops and water supplies, while black snow was expected for the mountains of Iran, Iraq, and Turkey. Because the smoke blocked sunlight in the region, reported daytime temperatures were as much as 15° C (27° F) below normal. Below the smoke, air pollution was severe, with the number of soot particles at ground level hundreds of times higher than normal. As the soot fell out of the sky, large areas of the land were blackened. Some medical experts emphasized how little was known about the composition and potential long-term health hazards of the smoke from burnt Kuwaiti crude oil. Whereas much interest was focused on monitoring the immediate health problems from soot and toxic gases, the more telling effects, such as cancer, could come from particles containing heavy metals and certain organic compounds, and they might not appear for years.

Jürgen Hahn of the Fraunhofer Institute for Atmospheric Environmental Research in Garmisch-Partenkirchen, Germany, forecast additional effects in the region. The surface of plants could become coated with a thick oily layer resulting from soot; this deposit in turn could become a major environmental hazard. Another concern expressed by Hahn involved the settling of soot on the water surface in the Gulf, which could affect water quality and, ultimately, aquatic organisms.

By early 1992 it appeared that some of the more dire predictions of worldwide impact had been exaggerated, but the plants, animals, and people of the Persian Gulf indeed felt the fires' effects. Pollution on this scale had never been seen before, and in the year following the war it was difficult to draw conclusions about its full consequences. Although the environment of the Middle East suffered, scientists have added to their understanding of the effects of fire on the climate and the atmosphere.

The fragile desert ecosystem

One of the less-publicized environmental consequences of the Gulf war was the damage done to the great expanses of the eastern Arabian Desert. Off-road vehicles, military construction, and bombs have dramatically altered the geomorphology of the desert. Scientists fear that there may be repercussions on human settlements as a result.

Some idea of the extent of the disruption has been gained from satellite images, in which even the tracks of single vehicles such as trucks and tanks can be distinguished. Military sources have commented that on a day-to-day basis the tonnage of bombs dropped by the United States during the Gulf war exceeded that dropped during World War II. In addition, the desert was left littered with unexploded munitions, including mines, shells, and other ordnance.

During the oil fires the soot and black rain that fell from the sky polluted indigenous plant life (above), crops, and water supplies. So rapid at times was the rate of soot deposit that tracks made on the blackened desert by passing vehicles (above right) were recovered within hours.

The military actions of the war disturbed the natural surface of the desert, which is stabilized by a crusty layer of large pebbles that serve to keep the sand in place. The terrain, built up over thousands of years, is extremely fragile. According to Farouk El-Baz, director of the Center for Remote Sensing at Boston University, the disruption of the soil surface and its associated vegetation threatens to increase sand and dust storms in the deserts of Kuwait, southeastern Saudi Arabia, and southern Iraq. Research conducted by El-Baz revealed that massive movement of sand could engulf airports, agricultural crops, and even cities. Similar dust storms were experienced as a consequence of the Iran-Iraq war of the 1980s; airports often were forced to shut down to avoid the damage caused by sand sucked into jet engines. El-Baz warned that such effects would again be felt, and quite rapidly, owing to the nature of shifting sands.

56

Sand drifts and dunes originating from Gulf war activities encroach upon a road in northern Kuwait (top). Off-road vehicle movements, construction, and bombing and shelling have disturbed the natural surface of the desert, which is normally covered by a single layer of pea- to walnut-sized pebbles (bottom). It has been predicted that disruption of the surface and its associated vegetation will increase sand and dust storms in the deserts of Kuwait, southern Saudi Arabia, and southern Iraq.

The desert regions of the world have been disturbed by wartime activities before. Recovery in these areas, which support only 2.5% of the world's human population, is slow. In the U.S. Mojave Desert, for example, the tracks of Gen. George Patton's tanks, made while preparing for action in World War II, are still visible in the sand a half century later.

Earl W. Lathrop of Loma Linda (California) University, who studied the recovery of deserts in research on military maneuver areas, found that military actions in deserts could have long-lasting effects. He examined World War II military camps, roadways, and armored-vehicle exercises in California deserts to determine their impact on the creosote bush and other desert plant species commonly found in those regions. His work revealed that military activities affect the amount and diversity of the indigenous plants, as well as their productivity. He estimated that it would take over 200 years for the plant cover in the areas to recover fully.

Even in peacetime, desert regions have been disturbed by weapons of war. In the isolated desert of Nevada, for example, almost 700 nuclear devices have been exploded by the U.S. and Great Britain since the 1940s, of which about 100 were above ground. Such testing has caused great local environmental damage, including loss of wildlife and plants, disturbance of the soil surface, and groundwater contamination. Although the impact of the explosions has been studied and the results published openly, the full extent of the damage may never be known. It is not surprising, therefore, that even with years of careful study, a comprehensive understanding of the effects of the Persian Gulf war on the desert of the Middle East will be difficult to achieve.

What the war wrought

The six-week Gulf war polluted the natural environment as never before witnessed by a worldwide audience. Unlike its reaction to other wars, the public responded with support for the massive cleanup that was necessary at the war's end. Strong response also came from environmentalists. Carl Pope of the Sierra Club advocated ratification and enforcement of treaties that prohibited environmental warfare as a deliberate tactic and urged people to pressure the United States and other nations to honor existing treaties that protect against wartime abuse of the environment.

Protection mechanisms presently in place include a multilateral environmental modification convention, adopted in 1977, which exhorts nations to agree to avoid environmental destruction as a military strategy; the U.S. became a party to that treaty in 1980. Earlier international agreements also addressed, if only indirectly, the excessive disruption of natural environments during war. The Hague declaration of 1899 and the Geneva protocol of 1925, for example, both prohibited poisonous gases as

U.S. Air Force helicopters at the Nevada Test Site fly over a few of the hundreds of craters that have formed from surface collapse following the underground detonation of nuclear weapons. Although studies of the effects of nearly a half century of nuclear weapons tests have revealed extensive damage to the local Nevada desert environment, the full impact may never be known. A comprehensive understanding of the effects of the Persian Gulf war on the Middle East desert environment may be similarly difficult to achieve.

U.S. Department of Energy

weapons of war. Other treaties exist that are designed to protect certain components of the Earth, such as Antarctica, the Åland Islands in the north Baltic Sea, and the Svalbard archipelago in the Arctic. As a way to avoid wide-ranging environmental destruction during war, Arthur Westing has proposed prohibiting nuclear weapons and any other weapons or techniques that have the potential to devastate large areas of the Earth.

Without greater controls in place, environmental degradation during war is inevitable. Although the damage from the Persian Gulf war was not as great as first predicted, the potential for global consequences seemed perilously close. Humankind, with its dependence on a planet already under heavy environmental assault in peacetime, must take strong measures to ensure that wartime activities do not worsen the situation.

Nelson Island, one of the South Shetland Islands, is among lands covered by the Antarctic Treaty. An unprecedented landmark in diplomacy signed by 12 nations in 1959, the treaty preserves areas south of latitude 60° S for nonmilitary scientific pursuits and specifically prohibits nuclear explosions. The need for more far-reaching agreements that ban or limit environmental degradation as a consequence or a deliberate tactic of military activity was brought home to a worldwide audience by news coverage of the Gulf war, in which the potential global consequences of warfare appeared all too chillingly real.

FOR ADDITIONAL READING

J.P. Robinson, *The Effects of Weapons on Ecosystems* (Pergamon Press, 1979).

J. Seager (ed.), *The State of the Earth Atlas* (Simon & Schuster, 1990).

Stockholm International Peace Research Institute, *Ecological Consequences of the Second Indochina War* (Almquist & Wiksell International, 1976).

Stockholm International Peace Research Institute, *Warfare in a Fragile World: Military Impact on the Human Environment* (Taylor & Francis Ltd., 1980).

A.H. Westing (ed.), *Cultural Norms, War and the Environment* (Oxford University Press, 1988).

THE SALVATION ISLANDS

by Noel D. Vietmeyer

To preserve the rarest birds on Earth, New Zealand biologists have set aside special islands as sanctuaries. The strategy seems to be working.

What is to be done when a species has been reduced to a single breeding specimen? Norfolk Island faced that question in the 1980s. With just one female left, its native owl seemed to have no hope of surviving. Moreover, that island to the east of Australia was not facing this problem alone. During the last few years Australia, Papua New Guinea, Mauritius, Seychelles, New Caledonia, two Christmas Islands, Lord Howe Island, and others in the Southern Hemisphere also were experiencing the imminent extinction of a native species—usually a bird. In each case the answer was: "Call in New Zealand!"

Increasingly, when a species is verging on extinction, nations are turning in desperation to New Zealand, whose record at rescuing imminently endangered species is probably unexcelled. New Zealand biologists are now managing many of the world's rarest birds (not to mention snails, lizards, and insects). They have earned international renown as rescuers of endangered species.

The remarkable success of these pioneers has come about through the application of good science and enormous effort. However, backing up all their efforts is an important new tool: special islands set aside just to house endangered species—islands so exclusive that all rats, mice, cats, goats, and other mammals are destroyed, and people are prohibited from landing. In a sense it is as if New Zealanders are returning a small slice of the land to its status before humans arrived and then handing it back to its original occupants.

Unique bird life

In the beginning New Zealand was blessed with birds. When Capt. James Cook stumbled upon it in 1769, his scientist companion, Sir Joseph Banks, described the experience of going ashore. There was, he said, a "most extraordinary sweetness of music emanating from the land, of such loudness, moreover, that we were determined that there must be an indescribable abundance of birds."

Canterbury Museum, Christchurch, N.Z.; photo, J.N. Taylor, W.A. Taylor Collection

Homestead on the west coast of New Zealand around 1900 reveals animals imported from their former homeland by immigrants from Britain. These animals destroyed much of New Zealand's native bird and plant life.

The country was then like a giant aviary of the South Seas, a place inhabited by many birds but few other kinds of animals. For this, there was a reason. In geologic times tectonic plates moving across the Earth's mantle had isolated New Zealand from all the other landmasses in such a distant era that no mammal had had a chance to set foot on it. Consequently, there were no rats, cats, dogs, weasels, foxes, or other enemies of birds. Birds, of course, could get there by flying, and New Zealand thus became an avian paradise. The birds were so tame and trusting that the explorers had to shoo them off their musket barrels just to spot the specimens they wanted.

At that time, only slightly more than two centuries ago, New Zealand was a world of unique birds. Many could not fly at all, and some others could merely glide; some were "giants"—far bigger than their counterparts elsewhere; quite a few lived on or even under the ground; and many looked strikingly different from their overseas relatives. One ostrichlike species was 3 meters (10 feet) tall. A large green parrot had forsaken the forests to live in the snows on the mountains. Another parrot could not fly: it waddled around the forest floor and clambered, beak and claw, up and down trees. Indeed, the kiwi had rejected flying so long ago that it was the only bird lacking any obvious evidence of wings.

Then, starting in the 1840s, a tide of eager Britons began pouring into this exclusive bird land. Most were middle-class Victorians seeking a cozy spot for their new homes. Homesick and convinced of the superiority of everything British, they were soon importing the plants and animals of the "Old Country." To improve the process, they set up special organizations. These "acclimatization societies" helped them haul in rabbits, pigs, goats, deer (10 species), foxes, weasels, stoats, grouse, geese, swans, sparrows (two species), starlings, blackbirds, thrushes, trout, salmon, and many more.

The result was environmental catastrophe. Around them the rats, mice, cats, dogs, stoats, and weasels found all kinds of defenseless bird life—

NOEL D. VIETMEYER is a Senior Program Officer with the National Research Council in Washington, D.C.

(Overleaf) The kakapo is one of New Zealand's endangered birds. The largest of all parrots, it purrs like a cat and cannot fly. Photograph by Rod Morris

much of it on the ground and unable to get airborne. The deer, rabbits, possums, goats, pigs, and others found the forests full of succulent forage. Unfortunately, none of it had ever faced herbivores before; many of the plants died when grazed. And to add to all that destruction, the new settlers began felling the forests to make farms and fences and buildings.

Soon New Zealand's environment was forever changed, and the feathered populations were declining precipitously. With less than 0.2% of the world's landmass, New Zealand today has 11% of the world's endangered birds. Currently the authoritative list of endangered species, the *Red Data Book*, lists 35 New Zealand birds as rare, endangered, or vulnerable.

What to do?

Coping with the responsibility of rescuing 11% of the world's endangered birds has not been easy. New Zealand's total human population, just over three million, is smaller than that of the metropolitan areas of San Francisco or Washington, D.C., for example. Its biologists, therefore, are necessarily few. In addition, the country has suffered financial difficulties in recent years, and a shrinking national budget has severely slashed conservation activities.

However, the handful of endangered-species specialists in the government's Department of Conservation (DoC) make up in dedication what they have been denied in numbers and finances. Tackling the challenges vigorously, they developed detailed knowledge of the biology and behavior of the different endangered species and created innovative methods for

Rod Morris

Workers for New Zealand's Department of Conservation seek to trap endangered birds on South Island. When caught, the birds are transferred to specially prepared habitats on small nearby islands.

capturing, moving, and managing an amazing menagerie of rare birds. Their methods included tape-recorded calls and decoys to lure various species into the open, dogs specially trained to track a given species, boxes designed to carry rare birds, diets and incubators customized for chicks of many kinds, and methods of mass destruction for all the different mammals the Victorians had loosed on the landscape. These methods, however, could hardly have successfully rescued many endangered birds without a new and daring technique: island reserves.

New Zealand has more than 700 inshore and outlying islands. By 1991 more than 20 had been set aside as exclusive residences for endangered birds. Some are large and lush, some mere rocks. They range from Raoul Island in the subtropics to Campbell Island in the subantarctic. In several cases all the remaining specimens of a species were gathered and moved to one or more of these offshore sanctuaries, each of which had been "renovated" and custom fitted for the safety and successful breeding of its new inhabitants. Even biologists must apply for authorization to visit these islands, and most requests are routinely rejected.

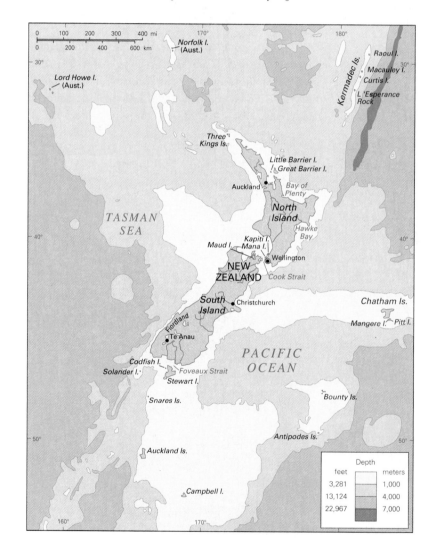

(Left) Department of Conservation; photo, D.V. Merton; (right) Rod Morris

Little Mangere Island (above left) in the early 1970s was home to the last seven black robins (above) in the world. Because it had been cleared for a helicopter pad, the island had become too windswept for the long-term survival of the robins. In 1976 the birds were transferred to a specially prepared area on nearby Mangere Island.

As might be imagined, the operation is not without its tensions. To literally hold a species in the palm of one's hand is daunting in the extreme. Indeed, intervening in the life of an endangered species is perhaps the ultimate biological challenge. To do so is also to invite some criticism: anyone can dream up disaster scenarios whereby whole populations isolated on an island or two are wiped out.

The risks are indeed high, but were it not for those islands and the biologists who dared to use them, at least four New Zealand bird species would already be gone, and a dozen or so more would have little hope of a secure future. One of those survivors is the black robin. In the 1970s it teetered on the brink of extinction. Only seven specimens remained, isolated on the dank, windswept Chatham Islands, 850 kilometers (500 miles) east of New Zealand in the Pacific Ocean. There the species had retreated to a single rock stack known as Little Mangere Island and was confined to 5 hectares (12 acres) of scrubby forest. As far as anyone knew, that had been the last remaining population for at least a century. By 1976 it had sunk to its all-time low—two pairs and three males without mates. The black robin was by then the most highly endangered bird in the world. Moreover, most of the seven were elderly, and their patch of forest was dying. There seemed to be no hope of saving them.

It was at that gloomy point that Don Merton took the species into his charge. Merton is a DoC biologist who specializes in preserving endangered birds. Literally marooning himself on nearby Mangere Island, which had a healthy patch of forest, he spent months clearing out infestations of rats, cats, and goats; providing clean, fumigated nests, screened from predatory birds; and planting native trees. Then he moved over to Little Mangere and organized a complex operation to transfer the whole black robin population to the new home he had prepared.

Aided by several DoC staff members, Merton coaxed every black robin on Earth into specially designed boxes. He gently strapped the boxes to the backs of helpers, who carried them gingerly down a crumbly cliff—

A male black robin is placed in a crate (top) for transfer from Little Mangere Island to Mangere Island, and a pair of robins is carried in a crate down a steep cliff on Little Mangere (above). Top right, Old Yellow (named for the color of its leg band), a male black robin, is held prior to its release after relocation to Mangere Island.

hand over hand down a rope affixed to the 200-meter (650-foot)-high sheer rock face. At the bottom they loaded the precious cargo onto a small dinghy, motored across to Mangere Island, landed the boxes through the surf, and hauled them over slippery rocks to Merton's refurbished forest.

During this ordeal the little creatures (which are hardly bigger than hummingbirds) might well have died of shock and made Merton the butt of worldwide condemnation, not to mention ridicule. Amazingly, however, there was no mishap. The black robin, a species that had not been off Little Mangere for more than a century, settled quickly into its new world. Within hours the birds had paired up (one female instantly switched mates and took up with one of the formerly lonely males) and were building new nests and starting life afresh.

For four years Merton left the seven to their own devices, but when he visited in 1980 only five remained. A single breeding female—Old Blue (named for the color of her leg band)—was all that was left to carry on the species. The world's rarest bird species now appeared absolutely doomed. This time, no one gave it any chance.

No one, that is, except Merton. Leaving his family in New Zealand, the dogged biologist moved to Mangere Island to live with "his" birds. Through months of observation, he came to understand Old Blue's every habit. In 1981 he stole her clutch of two eggs and, carrying them in a small aluminum container tucked inside his shirt, placed them in a warbler's nest. As anticipated, Old Blue laid a second clutch, but Merton had made a mistake: the transplanted chicks could not stand the warbler's diet. All died after about 10 days on it.

The following year, Merton purloined Old Blue's eggs again, but this time he ferried them to a tomtit's nest on South East Island, an hour away. He had to carry them on a small boat and through rough seas. Luckily, the female tomtit hatched them as if they were her own and proved to be a super mom. Her foster chicks thrived on tomtit food. And, as before, Old Blue laid another clutch to make up for her loss.

Following this success, Merton kept transferring Old Blue's eggs to tomtit nests on South East Island until by 1984 the little bird had produced enough to boost the black robin population to over 30. This rise from virtual extinction to possible safety was spectacular progress,

66

and in 1984, when Merton discovered that Old Blue was missing, New Zealanders took it as a national calamity. Her death was announced by a formal proclamation from Parliament.

Actually, though, Old Blue's end had been long overdue. In fact, her life had been a miracle of sorts: she had achieved the age of 14—more than twice the black robin's normal life span. Moreover, she had begun breeding only after age nine, a time when black robins have usually been dead for at least two years.

Through her almost incredible longevity, however, Old Blue had saved her species. Between 1979 and 1983 she was the only breeding female, but by the early 1990s the black robin's future seemed assured. In 1987 the population topped 60, and in 1988 Merton counted 53 adults and 56 chicks. So far, there has been no indication of any genetic degeneration in this highly inbred population. What was once the world's rarest bird is responding to a biologist's care and to its safe island refuge.

Preparing the way

In order to establish the black robin on Mangere Island, Merton had to remove all the alien predators. This is perhaps the major challenge in trying to save New Zealand's native species. The myriad descendants of the mammals brought by the British in the 1800s make any effort at saving birds especially forbidding. Catching every last rat, cat, goat, stoat, pig, weasel, or mouse can be an overwhelming undertaking. Ironically, New Zealand's conservationists therefore spend much of their time and effort devising special techniques and equipment for killing animals. They have also turned to the public and to private industry for help with manpower and pesticidal supplies. And the combination is bringing success. The case of Mana Island is a recent, but by no means unique, example.

Like some giant aircraft carrier projecting from the sea north of Wellington, Mana is a blocky, flat-topped monolith. Farmers and the government, which used it as a quarantine station for imported livestock, kept it covered with sheep for more than a century. The island was thus

Department of Conservation; photo, D.V. Merton

Old Blue was the only black robin breeding female from 1979 to 1983.

Don Merton, a New Zealand biologist, holds a nest of black robin eggs on a specially built tray, while their tomtit foster parent stands on the edge of the tray (below). A tomtit foster parent feeds two black robin fledglings on South East Island (below left). Merton's strategy saved the black robin from extinction.

Photos, Department of Conservation; (left) D.V. Merton; (right) Rick Thorpe

shorn of most of its native vegetation. But it had one overriding virtue: it had never become populated by stoats, weasels, or even rats. As a haven for endangered birds it would have seemed to be ideal except for one thing—Mana had mice.

Although only 200 hectares (500 acres) in area, Mana in the 1980s had more than a million mice (maybe several million during the summers). The ground sometimes crawled with the creatures. At certain seasons Trevor Jann, who was managing the island for the DoC, could hardly open his door without having a gray horde scamper into his house. One night he caught 204 in a single trap (a clever device incorporating a rotating tray that dumped mice willy-nilly into a bucket of water). But even traps of such machinelike efficiency were inadequate to clear Mana. So the DoC, with the help of a conservation group, an oil company, and thousands of citizen volunteers, launched an all-out campaign.

The attack began in July 1989 with an aerial assault: a plane bombed Mana with pellets of rodenticide, the first of a series of such bombardments. Then DoC staff and hundreds of volunteers descended on the island, laying out a vast grid of string, with north–south and east–west lines every 25 meters (80 feet). It was not easy; a quarter of Mana is tumbling cliffs. However, clambering up gullies, down rock faces, and over the hills, the volunteers laid down the kilometers of strings that eventually came to look like a giant net laid over the whole island.

Next, the volunteers set out 5,000 bait stations, one at each point where the strings intersected. In this way they were able cover every niche, nook, and corner of the island. Each bait station was composed of a piece of plastic drainage pipe containing a few pellets of poison. The pipe was yellow, and the poison was dyed blue and made bitter to deter any small birds that might happen to get near it.

Mana Island was cleared of several million mice in 1989 and 1990 by means of some 5,000 poison bait stations laid in a grid pattern across its entire surface. Shorn of its original vegetation by sheep and other livestock, Mana was replanted with trees. It was expected to become a sanctuary for many endangered birds, lizards, and insects.

G.R. Roberts

An adult male kakapo dances and raises its wings to display its plumage to a female in a courtship ritual that has not been observed in any other species of parrot.

The process worked; the million mice fell for the bait. Late in 1990 the DoC declared Mana to be "squeaky clean." Not a single mouse had been seen in almost a year. It was a triumph—the first time anywhere in the world that an island that size had been cleared of mice.

However, eradicating alien creatures is just the first step in the process of returning the land to what it was like before people dumped four-footed mammals onto it. During the course of several years, more than 4,000 people (most of them volunteers) crossed the choppy seas to help grow, tend, and transplant over 60,000 native-tree seedlings. By late 1991 many of the trees were already more than 2 meters (6.6 feet) tall, and the aura of the ancient New Zealand forest was returning—not to mention the insects, berries, and other foods that native birds need.

Soon Mana will be a haven for many highly endangered birds, including the saddleback, fernbird, pipit, kakapo, takahe, antipodes parakeet, and little spotted kiwi, as well as endangered lizards and insects. It will thus be one of the most precious places on Earth.

A rare parrot

Already, a few of the world's most critically endangered species reside on Mana. One of them, the kakapo, is the largest of all parrots. It is also the amazing bird that clambers up and down trees because it cannot fly. And that is merely the first of its weird qualities; it purrs like a cat and smells like a posy of fragrant flowers. It also looks more like a big green owl than a parrot. It is so docile and trusting that it allows itself to be picked up and handled without demur or apparent concern.

Despite having lived on the planet for tens of thousands of years, the kakapo may not be around much longer. Already rarer than the giant panda or black rhino, it is a slow and fickle breeder and is too placid for its own good—it will not, for example, defend itself against cats or other four-legged predators. As a result, it has become one of the world's

Department of Conservation; photos, D. Crouchley

A biologist places a radio transmitter on a kakapo on Stewart Island (above right). By using a receiver and aerial, a researcher can then easily locate kakapos that have been so equipped (above).

most critically endangered species. Only 43 remain, and of those a mere 15 are females.

With such a small number, the species is at a crisis point. Ornithologists conclude that they have only about five years in which to save it. Thus, the DoC, in conjunction with the Royal Forest and Bird Protection Society, launched an all-out five-year kakapo recovery plan. One advantage of this species is that a kakapo can live for up to 70 years; if the present ones can be protected, therefore, there should be time to find ways to rebuild the population.

Before Europeans arrived, the kakapo occurred throughout New Zealand. It is, however, now gone from the two main islands and was long considered extinct everywhere else as well. Nonetheless, in 1977 a few breeding kakapos were miraculously rediscovered; they had survived in a far corner of Stewart Island, a damp, remote area that people seldom visit. The discovery was made possible by the innovative technique of training dogs to track these strange birds by their sweet scent. It was

This kakapo on Stewart Island is one of many that have been killed by cats. Because the feral cat population on Stewart Island cannot be controlled, the kakapos that remain there are being captured and transferred to other islands.

Department of Conservation; photo, A. Munn

Little Barrier Island (left) is the new home of a 26-day-old kakapo chick (above). Kakapos were also taken to Mana, Kapiti, Maud, and Codfish islands.

also made just in time. Biologists put transmitters on several, but in just 18 months most of those kakapos were eaten by cats that had gone wild on Stewart Island. The scientists then realized that the species had no future—indeed, it already was living on borrowed time.

Stewart Island is too big to be freed of feral cats, and so the whole kakapo population was tracked down by dogs, gathered up, and flown to sanctuary islands. Some were taken to Mana; others to Little Barrier, Kapiti, Maud, and Codfish. There they are being studied to learn more about their habits, foods, growth rates, health care, and other features that may eventually boost their chances of survival.

Merton now coordinates the five-year kakapo recovery program for the DoC. So far there have been no breakthroughs comparable to the one when he found that tomtits could be foster mothers for black robin chicks. Nonetheless, a hint that the project may succeed has come from the kakapos on Little Barrier Island.

One of the most valued of the bird havens, Little Barrier is close to New Zealand's largest city, Auckland. It is also 2,000 kilometers (1,200 miles) north of the kakapo's former home on Stewart Island, and its sub-tropical climate is very different. However, the big parrots appear to like it; they have made nests, mated, and laid eggs. By late 1991, however, there had been no practical success; all the chicks had died.

Nevertheless, there is now hope. The kakapo at least has a series of safe homes and many eager human helpers. The Auckland Zoo is learning how to rear kakapo chicks, and although it has not yet succeeded in raising any to adulthood, its bird specialists are confident that they soon will do so. The parrot that once had no possibility of survival today seems at last to have a chance.

Lost and found

The Chatham Island black robin and the kakapo parrot are just 2 of more than 30 species that New Zealand biologists are dragging back from the

71

The takahe, a flightless blue-green rail, was believed to be extinct for about 50 years until rediscovered on New Zealand's South Island in 1948.

edge of extinction. A third is the takahe. With it, too, the immense value of islands as havens has been demonstrated.

A blue-green flightless rail, a bit larger than a chicken, the takahe (pronounced TAH-ka-hee) is one of the most famous of all ornithological organisms. Once it almost ranked in the public mind with the dodo. Individual specimens were found (and killed) in 1849, 1851, 1879, and 1898; then nothing more was heard of this bird. Everyone believed, and without question, that it was gone. The skin of the 1849 bird was stuffed and displayed near the dodo at the British Museum.

Then, in the 1940s a New Zealand country doctor, Geoffrey Orbell, began following his hunch that the takahe may have survived in a valley hidden away in the southeastern corner of South Island. That region, known as Fiordland, is so rugged and remote that much of it was then unexplored wilderness. On Nov. 20, 1948, Orbell was deep in the heart of the valley when two takahe calmly strode out of a nearby clump of tussock grass and stared at him. It was one of the most dramatic moments in ornithological history.

The discovery made headlines worldwide. The birds are big and brilliant, with cobalt blue breasts and heads, green toned backs, and massive scarlet and pink beaks. Unlike the tiny black robins or the unprepossessing kakapo, these shiny bright birds have the looks to muster instant public interest.

Orbell went on to discover a colony of perhaps 500 takahe in that hidden valley. In the four decades since the discovery, though, all has not gone well for the flock. By 1988 it had been reduced to only about 120. A ground dweller too ponderous to fly, it is extremely vulnerable to stoats and other predators. Moreover, like most New Zealand native birds, it lays only a few eggs at a time. (With no highly efficient predators around, there was no need for more; the breeding success was already high). Now even its food supply is threatened. Over the years deer herds have built up in Orbell's valley and have consumed so many of the plants the takahe eat that malnutrition seems to be a prime contributor to the bird's decline.

By 1992, however, many specimens had been moved to sanctuary islands. Eleven were taken to Mana, for instance. So that they would not be disturbed by the massive mouse-eradication project in 1989, they were shipped to nearby Kapiti Island for safekeeping. Today seven have been moved back to Mana. All this manipulation has helped ensure the future of the unique bird; six chicks were produced on Mana and Kapiti during that period.

Nevertheless, sanctuary islands are not the only tool used in this case. The main takahe population, still in its remote Fiordland valley, is being helped as well. Most of the deer have been hauled off to deer farms; the plants have been fertilized from the air to provide the birds with more food; and each year some of the eggs are removed for hatching in a special facility built for the purpose near the town of Te Anau.

This egg heist is a little different from Merton's black-robin example. Takahe usually lay two eggs but rear only one chick, and so each season

Photos, Department of Conservation; (top left) P. Morrison; (top right) R. Lavers; (bottom right) C. Smuts-Kennedy

DoC biologists pick up the extra egg from as many nests as they can find. Each egg is placed in a portable incubator and whisked by helicopter to the special takahe facility. There it is hatched, and the chick is reared until it can fend for itself, at which time it is returned to the wild. The whole process is accomplished without the chicks' ever seeing people. The facility is fitted with one-way mirrors, and the biologists use hand puppets shaped like heads of takahe mothers and wired to emit the right sounds. Takahe are so friendly that were this not done, the chicks might delude themselves into thinking they were humans and thus reject their own kin.

The takahe's future seems increasingly secure with every passing year. There are believed to be about 200 in Orbell's valley now. Others are in safekeeping on the sanctuary islands. The population that less than a decade ago was down to 120 now tops 260. Merton notes that after 25 years of intensive efforts to breed the birds, there seems to be no stopping them now.

About 500 takahe were found in 1948 in a valley in Fiordland, a rugged area of South Island (above left). By 1988 the population had been reduced to some 120 because the flightless bird had fallen victim to stoats and other predators. Some takahe were removed to other islands, but some were left in the valley. Of the latter, some were equipped with radio transmitters (top) so that they could be monitored, and one egg was removed from each two-egg nest that was found because takahe rear only one chick at a time. These eggs were measured to determine when they would hatch (above) and then placed in portable incubators for removal to a hatching facility.

Other nations

New Zealand's skills are increasingly being called upon by other nations, especially those in the Southern Hemisphere. Hundreds of unique species live in the island states of the South Pacific and Indian oceans, and many are verging on extinction. Indeed, given the smallness of its landmass, the region is said to have the greatest concentration of rare and endangered birds in the world.

The birds of that area live largely on scattered, often barren or inhospitable sites, and their rescue has been hampered by their isolation. Many occur at a single location—sometimes a mere rock in the ocean— and they can become extinct as a result of the slightest environmental disturbance. Consequently, many need urgent help. Rats, cats, goats, stoats, mongooses, and tree snakes are loose on various islands. In addition, hunters, diseases, and the loss of habitats to logging, mining,

73

The last hurricane palm (right, in the top center of the photograph) stands on Round Island off the coast of Mauritius. The palm, as well as many species of birds and reptiles on the island, had been driven to near extinction by hordes of rabbits. By spreading poison bait throughout the island (below), Don Merton and his colleagues eliminated the rabbits.

farming, or severe storms have upset the precarious ecological balance. All these hazards have put the future of dozens of birds in jeopardy.

Introduced mammals (especially those as small, prolific, and secretive as mice) are so difficult to control that everyone had assumed there was no possible way they could be eradicated or even significantly reduced in numbers. But the New Zealanders have opened people's eyes to new possibilities. Increasingly, their services are being requested. In the early 1980s, for example, Merton was called to Mauritius, the former home of the dodo. His task there was to rehabilitate Round Island.

A domelike rock lying off the coast of Mauritius, Round Island is believed to have more endangered species per unit area than any other single spot on Earth. Its birds include the echo parakeet and the Trinidade petrel, both of them verging on extinction. Its endemic animals include four lizards and two snakes—all of them extremely rare. And its plants

74

include the bottle palm, of which only eight adult specimens remain, and the hurricane palm, which has only one standing specimen.

Specifically, Merton's task was to rid Round Island of rabbits. The place was so overrun with these animals that its soil and vegetation had all but disappeared. Most observers considered it an ecological disaster beyond reclaim. Previous efforts at protecting its birds and plants had proved impossible because of the rabbits. Merton was given two months to succeed where all others had failed.

Along with two colleagues from the DoC, Merton flew to Mauritius. On Round Island the three set up camp and settled in for a couple of months of rabbit reduction. Using an anticoagulant bait and a baiting strategy customized for the terrain and the pest, they succeeded in removing every one—and with time to spare. At 375 hectares (925 acres), Round Island is thought to be the largest island ever to have been cleared of rabbits.

Nonetheless, Merton and his colleagues were not satisfied. Without being asked, they tackled nearby Egret Island. It, too, had great potential as a sanctuary for endangered species but was infested by rats. They cleared it as well—all 25 hectares (63 acres)—and set another world record: the largest island to be cleared of rats.

On both islands the results have been heartening. The endangered plants and birds are returning with vigor. A dense growth of herbs, grasses, and creepers is colonizing even the most eroded slopes. In addition, native plants whose existence was unsuspected have appeared—to the surprise of the world's botanists. Furthermore, the insects and berries have returned, and the lizards and rare snakes are flourishing.

Hope for the future

Round Island and Egret Island are just two Southern Hemisphere trouble spots that New Zealand bird experts have tackled. They have also helped, among others, Norfolk Island (boobook owl and white-eye), New Caledonia (kagu), West Australia (noisy scrub bird), South Australia (bettong), and Fiji (silktail). In most cases sanctuary islands have been established in those places.

And back in New Zealand the program is progressing. Already there are more than 30 rare and endangered bird species on the various island reserves. Most are thriving and building robust populations, some of which will be used as "seed sources" to "replant" the species back on the mainland.

This is naturalistic conservation. Instead of being in zoos, the birds are where they can rebuild themselves naturally and with their ancient instincts intact. Such work is also done at little cost in either manpower or money; on most of the islands the birds are left entirely to themselves. Yet various types of management can be applied if they are needed.

As a result of all these activities, New Zealanders lead in what potentially could be a melancholy field of endeavor. They have instead made it uplifting. All in all, it can be said that New Zealand biologists like Merton are holding the future of 11% of the world's most endangered birds firmly in their capable hands.

Knot Theory and Space-Time

by Carlo Rovelli

The classification of knots is connected in a profound way with many problems in mathematics and the physical sciences. Recent research indicates that knots are related to the submicroscopic structure of physical space.

Knots are objects of our everyday lives. We use one knot to tie our shoes, another to tie a necktie. For mountain climbers correct knots on their ropes have vital importance, and for the sailor the ability to tie many different knots is a prerequisite of the profession. But how many ways can a rope be knotted? Can a complete catalog of all the knots be written? This does not seem to be a particularly difficult question, but it is. Indeed, nobody knows the solution. The problem has been studied for a long time. A branch of mathematics, denoted "knot theory" and devoted to cataloging all the knots, has developed. However, the problem remains open.

In recent years knot theory has undergone an impressive development. A variety of techniques for labeling and distinguishing knots have been found. What is more surprising is that mathematicians have discovered that the problem of the classification of the knots is deeply connected with many problems in mathematics and other sciences. For instance, knots are related to various sectors of algebra, to statistical mechanics, to quantum field theory in three dimensions, to the classification of particles in two dimensions, and to the study of DNA (deoxyribonucleic acid) configurations in biology.

During the last few years a striking utilization of knot theory has appeared: knots seem to be related to the submicroscopic structure of physical space. There are indications that the very texture of space can be seen as a knotty tangle of threads. Thus, in learning how to classify knots one would also learn how space is made. This article presents an overview of this extraordinary and fascinating cluster of problems and ideas. It describes how the mathematical theory of knots originated, its achievements, and its relation to certain problems in physics. In particular, it describes the application of knot theory to the physics of space so as to provide the reader with at least an idea of how a relation between knots and the intimate microstructure of physical space may emerge.

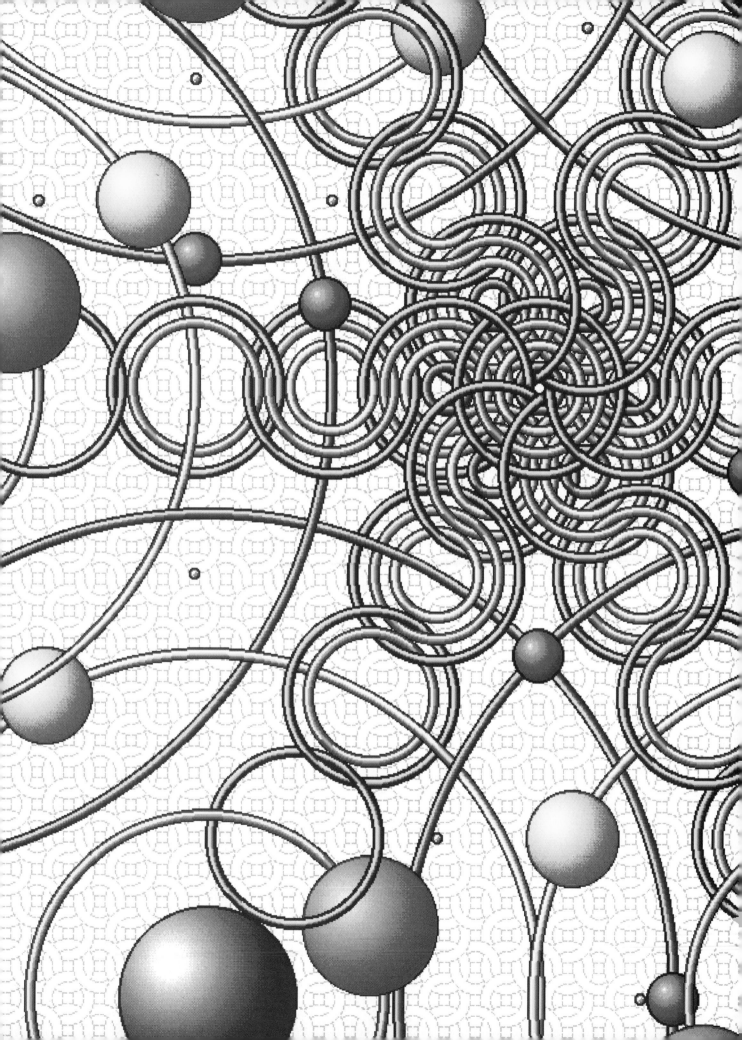

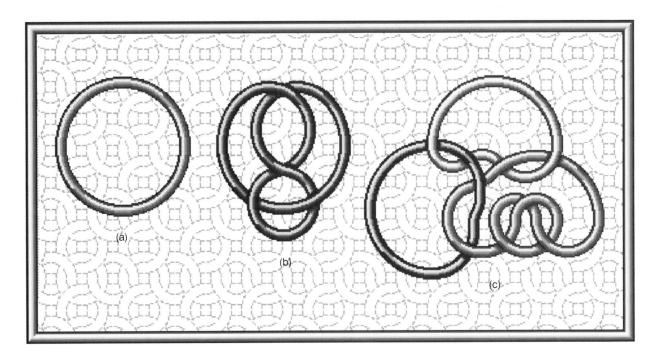

Figure 1. (a) The simplest knot, denoted the unknot; (b) a knot with four crossings; (c) a link.

CARLO ROVELLI is a Professor of Physics at the University of Pittsburgh, Pennsylvania, and a Researcher in Physics at the University of Trento, Italy.

Illustrations by John Craig

Origin of the theory

The story of the way in which mathematicians became interested in the classification of knots is one of the many examples of cross-fertilization between physics and mathematics. During the 19th century a major problem in physics consisted in understanding whether atoms (a concept borrowed from chemistry) really exist, how they are made, and what distinguishes atoms of different chemical elements from one another (say, a gold atom from an oxygen atom). Lord Kelvin, one of the fathers of thermodynamics, suggested that atoms are small, looplike "vortices" in the ether; atoms of different chemical elements would be distinguished by the different way in which the little looplike vortex was knotted. The more complex the knotting, the heavier and bigger the atom.

To investigate the validity of this conjecture, it was important to understand something about the different ways in which a loop could be knotted. A Scottish collaborator of Lord Kelvin, Peter Guthrie Tait, published the first paper on the classification of knots in 1876. Lord Kelvin's idea was simple and wonderful because it reduced light, electricity, and matter—in a word, everything—to a common substance, the ether. However, like many wonderful ideas, it turned out to be wrong. Atoms do exist, but they are made in a completely different fashion; they are not knotted vortices. Nonetheless, the problem of the enumeration of the knots had been posed. Mathematicians had discovered that this was a valid pursuit, and so knot theory was born.

From the point of view of mathematics, *knot* can be defined as follows. One starts with a loop—a closed smooth curve—in space. The loop must never intersect itself. Then two closed loops represent the same knot if one of them can be deformed continuously into the other without ever introducing self-intersections. Equivalently, one may think of space as superstretchable rubber; two closed loops represent the same knot if one can stretch, bend, and shrink the space until one curve takes the position of the other. A moment of reflection will convince one that these two definitions are equivalent and correspond to the intuitive idea of a knot. Often one is also interested in the concept of *link*: a link is formed by several loops, knotted and linked one with the other. A knot is a link formed by a single loop. Sometimes the term *knot* is also used to denote links.

After Tait's paper, many works appeared on the subject of enumerating knots and links. By 1900 there were tables with hundreds of drawings of different knots. A drawing of a knot has a certain number of crossings, or overlaps, as in Figure 1. It makes sense to begin by drawing those knots that have few crossings. The tables existing in 1900 included all knots with up to 10 crossings.

For drawing all the knots with up to a certain number of crossings, the problem is a combinatorial one, and it is easy to verify that all have been drawn. Then drawings must be eliminated any time that there are two drawings of the same knot. Though this may seem easy, one can never be quite sure that every repetition has been eliminated; drawings may look very different and still represent the same knot. For instance, it is clear that the two drawings in Figure 2 represent the same knot; one can readily imagine how to deform the first into the second. But it is not so easy to judge the two drawings shown in Figure 3; do they represent the same knot? (They do, but they were listed as distinct on the tables, and only in 1970 was it recognized that one could be deformed into the other.)

This is precisely the problem of knot theory: how can one know for certain whether two complicated drawings are depicting the same knot? For a classification of knots with any number of crossings, some ingenious idea was needed for testing whether two drawings represent, in fact, the same knot.

Figure 2. Two drawings of the same knot.

Figure 3. Two drawings of the same knot, not recognized as the same until 1970.

Alexander and Jones polynomials

Toward the end of the 1920s, such an ingenious idea was found. The discovery was independently made by two mathematicians: James Waddell Alexander and Kurt Reidemeister. Their idea was to invent a rule to associate a set of integers $(a_0, a_1, \ldots a_n)$ to each drawing. The rule must be such that if two drawings have different $(a_0, a_1, \ldots a_n)$-numbers, they must represent different knots. It is customary to think of these numbers as the coefficients of a polynomial: $P(t) = a_0 + a_1 t + a_2 t^2 + \ldots + a_n t^n$; this polynomial is now denoted as the Alexander polynomial of the knot. If one has a drawing of a knot, the Alexander polynomial can be computed via a certain simple set of rules that involve exchanging the upper and lower lines at the crossings and disentangling the knot step by step. For example, the polynomial associated to the knot of Figure 4 (a Buddhist symbol representing the illusory character of time) turns out to be $P(t) = 4 - 7t + 4t^2$. A theorem provides the assurance that if different polynomials are computed from two drawings, the two drawings represent different knots. By using the Alexander polynomial, mathematicians were able to compute the polynomials of all the drawings with up to nine crossings in the 1900 tables; all the drawings turned out to be different from one another. Thus, the complete classification of the knots with up to nine crossings was accomplished. However, the Alexander polynomial is not sufficient for a full classification; in fact, it was soon realized that there are different knots with the same Alexander polynomial. Thus, the Alexander polynomial distinguishes many knots from one another but not all of them. This was more or less the situation for half a century, until 1984.

In 1984 Vaughan Jones, a mathematician of the University of California at Berkeley, invented a new polynomial—a new rule for assigning a group of integers to each drawing. (The Jones polynomial of the Buddhist knot of Figure 4 is $P(t) = 1 - 2t + 3t^2 - 2t^3 + 3t^4 - 2t^5 + t^6 - t^7$.) The Jones polynomial does not distinguish all the knots either, but it does distinguish between knots that are not distinguished by the Alexander polynomial. Thus, in a sense it is just an additional instrument. But what is more interesting about the Jones polynomial is that it establishes a relation with statistical mechanics. This relation was suggested by Jones himself, but it was Lou Kauffman, a mathematician from Chicago, who first began to understand this connection in a direct way. He demonstrated that the calculation of the polynomial for a given knot is the same calculation as that for computing the statistical properties of certain statistical mechanical systems called Potts-models.

The discovery of the Jones polynomial and the relation between knot theory and statistical mechanics opened a new era of rapid evolution in knot theory. Using the relation to statistical mechanics, mathematicians found that it was possible to invent many new polynomials; essentially they developed techniques in which one starts from certain statistical models and then constructs a new polynomial from each one of them. According to Michael Atiyah, a mathematician at the University of Oxford, it is likely that the set of all the knot polynomials already discovered is large enough to distinguish between any two different knots. This conclusion, however, has not yet been proved. Thus, a solution seems close, but for the moment the problem of classifying the knots remains open.

Knot theory and general covariance

While mathematicians use physical models to obtain instruments for dealing with knots, physicists are beginning to use knot theory as an instrument for understanding nature. Before the application of knot theory to the exploration of the microstructure of space is described, two curious applications of knot theory, one referring to physics in one space dimension and one to physics in two space dimensions, will be briefly discussed.

Figure 4. A knot based on the Buddhist symbol representing the illusory character of time; the Alexander polynomial assigned to this knot is $P(t) = 4 - 7t + 4t^2$.

The first application of knot theory refers to the classification of elementary particles. Elementary particles belong to two general types: fermions (an example is the electron) and bosons (an example is the photon), characterized by different statistical properties. (Fermions have a tendency to stay away from each other, and they tend to behave as particles when observed at macroscopic scales. Bosons tend to arrange themselves one on top of the other, and at macroscopic scales they are better described as waves.) Starting from general assumptions, it is possible to prove that every particle is either a fermion or a boson. Some physicists, however, are interested in studying what the world would look like if space had only one dimension rather than three. A curious result is that in one-dimensional space there may exist not only fermions and bosons but also many other types of particles. The Swiss physicist Jurg Frölich developed a general theory for particles that could exist in one-dimensional space. The principal equations he uses (denoted the Yang-Baxter equations) are the same equations that Jones used to find his knot polynomial. Thus, the classification of types of particles in one dimension is related to the classification of the knots. Consequently, Lord Kelvin's idea that atoms could be labeled by different knots would have been somehow correct if space had been one-dimensional.

A second application of knot theory was discovered by Edward Witten, a physicist and mathematician working at the Institute for Advanced Study in Princeton, New Jersey. Witten studied physics in two space dimensions (flatland). In his theoretical picture he includes a peculiar ingredient: general covariance. General covariance is a property of certain physical theories. The most famous theory with this property is Einstein's theory of gravitation, the theory known as general relativity. For a better understanding of the rest of this article, an idea of what general covariance is will be useful. A general covariant theory is a theory in which one postulates that it has no meaning to say "where" the objects are with respect to space (or space-time). The only statement with meaning is one that says where objects are with respect to one another. Thus, in such a theory if one imagines taking all the dynamical objects described by the theory (such as particles, planets, electromagnetic field, gravitational field) and moving all these objects by stretching, shrinking, and bending the space, one does not produce any physically different configuration because there is no way to say "where something is" with respect to absolute space. If everything is moved together, the displacement is not observable.

According to what is known about nature, at the fundamental level the world is described by a theory with the property of general covariance, provided gravity is not neglected. Therefore, in nature, space points are not distinguishable by themselves, and one can never say "where" things are but only "where" they are with respect to other things; for instance, with respect to the soil of the Earth or to the electromagnetic field or to the gravitational field.

The fact that nature is described by a theory with the property of general covariance is probably the most profound discovery of Albert

Einstein. The full implications of this discovery are perhaps not entirely understood even now, 75 years after the publication of Einstein's theory. The careful reader has probably noticed that the concept of "stretching, shrinking, and bending" the space, an essential aspect of general covariance, is the same concept as the "stretching, shrinking, and bending" employed above in defining the knots. This connection between knot theory and general covariance is the profound reason for the possible relevance of knot theory to the description of nature.

Thus, Witten studied a general covariant physical theory in two space dimensions or, as one usually says, in three space-time dimensions. He considered closed curves in the three-dimensional space-time and studied the value of a certain quantity Z computed along those curves. Since the theory is generally covariant, by stretching, shrinking, and bending space-time, the quantity Z does not change. But by stretching, shrinking, and bending space-time, the curve along which Z is computed can be deformed into any other curve knotted in the same way. Therefore, the quantity Z does not depend on the specific curve on which it is computed but only on the way this curve is knotted. In 1989 Witten was able to compute Z in his theory. He obtained the surprising result that the value of Z on a given knot is precisely the Jones polynomial of the knot. Thus, Witten's result relates the mathematical theory of the Jones polynomial to a specific physical theory. Witten's motivation was precisely to search for such a relationship, following an indication by Michael Atiyah, who was the first to suggest that a relationship of this kind should exist.

In August 1990 at the International Congress of Mathematicians held in Kyoto, Japan, the most prestigious prize for a mathematician, the Fields Medal, was awarded to Vaughan Jones, for the discovery of the Jones polynomial, and to Witten, "for his work connecting theoretical physics to modern mathematics." To signify the honor that the world credits to high mathematics, the two scientists were received and congratulated by the emperor and empress of Japan at the Imperial Palace in Tokyo.

In using advanced mathematical tools in theoretical physics, and at the same time applying physical ideas to mathematical problems, Witten's work is a modern realization of the traditionally fruitful exchange between mathematics and physics. At the same time, Witten's influential work is representative of a peculiar trend in contemporary theoretical physics: the study of physical theories more for their abstract or mathematical interest than for their direct application to reality. Witten's result on the Jones polynomial, however, has a direct significance for fundamental physics because it evidences the connection between knot theory and general covariance. This connection is also at the core of the application of knot theory to the microstructure of true physical space, as discussed below.

Microstructure of physical space

The last application of knot theory to be described refers directly to the actual description of reality (after all, the space we inhabit is not one- or two-dimensional but three-dimensional). The subject is the still-unsolved problem of the quantum description of the gravitational field, or "quantum gravity." First, a brief discussion of the problem of quantum gravity is necessary.

At the beginning of this century, theoretical physics achieved two major breakthroughs: quantum theory and general relativity. Quantum theory is a general theory of motion that replaces 19th-century classical mechanics. Every physical object in the universe, scientists believe, behaves according to some general rules summarized in the quantum theory. A characteristic feature of quantum theory is that continuous physical variables are replaced by variables taking discrete values; that is, they vary step by step. For example, according to old classical mechanics, the radius of the orbit of the electron in the atom could take any possible value; according to the quantum theory, the radius can take only certain precise ("quantized") values: the electron may "jump" from one allowed orbit to another.

The predictions of quantum theory differ from the predictions of classical mechanics only when small scales are involved. Thus, classical mechanics are used at large scales, such as building bridges, and quantum theory is employed only in dealing with microphysics.

General relativity is the dynamical theory of one particular physical "object": gravity. General relativity, too, has a kind of fundamental character, precisely because it is a general covariant theory. Everything in the universe is affected by the gravitational force, and when gravity is taken into account, every physical theory becomes generally covariant. Thus, the consequences of the general covariance of general relativity are universal, and the theory implies general consequences about space-time itself. Indeed, general relativity can be seen as the theory of space and time: according to general relativity the gravitational field, the carrier of gravity, is the same entity as the geometry, namely the "shape," of space-time. To use a metaphor that Einstein himself suggested, the gravitational field can be seen as an immense and all-filling jellyfish in which everything is immersed. Because of general covariance the concept of "position" of any object makes sense only if it is understood with respect to the jellyfish. Thus, if one stretches, shrinks, or bends the jellyfish together with any object contained in it, the result of the deformation is unobservable.

General relativity has been confirmed by spectacular experiments, and some physicists consider it the most elegant theory in physics. However, the theory has a serious difficulty. Nobody has been able to apply the rules of quantum theory to general relativity. By applying these rules in a straightforward way, one obtains evident inconsistencies. In real experiments and predictions this is not a problem, because all the experiments where gravity is involved fall well within the "large-scale" range, in which classical mechanics works very well and quantum theory is superfluous. However, the situation is profoundly disappointing; the two best theories about reality seem incompatible. In addition, since general relativity is the theory of space-time and quantum mechanics is the theory of small scales, it is not possible to study the properties of space-time at very short scales, because these properties must be described by the quantum regime of general relativity.

The problems in reconciling general relativity with quantum theory were noticed as early as the 1930s. Since then, a great deal of ingenuity has been devoted to "quantizing gravity"; namely, to combining general relativity and quantum theory. Ingenious alternative ways of applying the quantum rules to general relativity were proposed, but none succeeded. Recently, however, a new approach to the problem has raised new excitement and hopes. This approach, denoted as the loop-representation, was developed by Lee Smolin, a theoretical physicist at Syracuse (New York) University, and by the author of this article. Nobody knows if this is really the right direction to take, but for the moment this approach seems to work. The most characteristic feature of this approach is the fact that one of its essential ingredients is knot theory.

The first step on the path to this approach was the work of another physicist, Abhay Ashtekar, also working at Syracuse University. In 1986 Ashtekar was able to translate general relativity into a new mathematical language in which the equations are simpler than those originally written by Einstein. In this new formulation general relativity seems to accept quantum theory more easily. In fact, it was soon realized that the equations that combine quantum theory and general relativity could be solved if they were rewritten in Ashtekar's new language. (This was recognized in two steps, first by Ted Jacobson and Smolin in 1987 and then by Smolin and the author in 1988.) What is surprising is that the solutions of these equations turned out to be labeled by knot theory; that is, there exists one solution for each different knot (more precisely, for each link).

The description of the quantum properties of gravity in terms of these knot-solutions is the "loop representation" of quantum gravity. Each of these knot-solutions represents a possible configuration of the gravitational field when quantum theory is taken into account, and a configuration of the gravitational field means a configuration of space-time. Therefore, the problem of knot classification turns out to be virtually the problem of the classification of the possible quantum configurations of space-time.

This result is very nonintuitive at first sight. Thinking of physical space conjures up an image of a three-dimensional continuum. Those who have studied general relativity can imagine this continuum as more or less curved (the jellyfish). But what is the relationship between this continuum picture and the knots of knot theory? A relationship does exist, and the following discussion will attempt to elucidate it. The best way to understand this relationship is to examine the "knot-solution" that describes the physical space as it is around us. This solution was discovered in 1991 by Ashtekar, Smolin, and the author. It corresponds to the knot (more precisely the link) that can be described as follows. Imagine filling physical space with innumerable small circular loops; the loops are intertwined, like an expanded version of medieval chain mail. The set of all these loops fills the entire space. The knot defined by all the linked loops has been called the Weave, a term chosen because the linked loops

Figure 5. A rough scale model of the Weave, the knot that describes physical space as it is seen around us.

form a large structure similar to the entangled knots of macramé. Figure 5 is a photograph of a very rough scale model of the Weave.

The Weave is the knot that describes the space as it is seen around one. The important point to keep in mind in visualizing the relationship between the Weave and the physical space is that the radius of the loops is extraordinarily small: about 10^{-33} centimeters (the so-called Planck-length). There are one million billion billion billion (one followed by 33 zeros) tiny circles in one centimeter. Thus, it is not surprising that space looks so smooth, just as a T-shirt seen from a distance looks smooth though at close range the pattern of interwoven threads is revealed. There are one thousand billion billion little circles within the radius of an atomic nucleus. Thus, one is dealing with scales that are extremely small, so small that no technology has been devised that can provide a view of the submicroscopic texture of the Weave.

Can this picture of the Weave be justified on physical grounds? First, one should consider the quantum theory. The characteristic feature of quantum theory is the replacement of continuous variables with discrete variables. This feature is clearly at work in the Weave: continuous physical space has been replaced with a discrete "texture." Distance is not a continuous variable anymore; it exists only in discrete steps as the number of steps (loop by loop) on the Weave. Thus, the replacement of the jellyfish with the immense lattice of little loops is comprehensible in terms of basic quantum ideas.

But why should physical space be described just by the knot formed by all the little loops rather than by the loops themselves? If the Weave is taken and stretched, folded, and shrunk at will, it still defines the same knot. Does it represent the same space? Yes, because this is precisely general covariance. There is nothing that distinguishes the regular Weave from a deformed Weave; it is the Weave itself that defines what space is and what "position" is. The "position" of any physical object is defined only with respect to the Weave; the "position" of the Weave itself has no meaning at all. The discreteness at the core of quantum theory and the general covariance at the core of general relativity conspire to bring knot theory into the game: discreteness implies that space has a latticelike structure, so that the jellyfish is replaced by the tangle of loops; general covariance requires that it is only the way these loops are knotted that matters.

Future prospects

The conclusion is that the intimate structure of space can be imagined as a knotty tangle, and knot theory classifies the possible configurations of space. It should be emphasized that this theory is still at the level of a hypothesis. For the moment, one can only say, as did Viola in *Twelfth Night*: "O Time! thou must untangle this, not I; / It is too hard a knot for me to untie." Nonetheless, there is a consistent picture of space that emerges from this loop-representation approach to quantum gravity. Maybe we are just beginning to obtain the first theoretical indications about the structure of space at extremely small distances.

Nature is a tangled web of mysteries. The struggle to disentangle some of these mysteries is fascinating and enchanting. It is important to continue to explore the possible ways of thinking about the world and the devising of the conceptual instruments needed for this endeavor. The apparently simple problem of writing a catalog of the different ways in which a rope may be knotted not only is a very difficult problem but may also even result in being one of those instruments—a key tool for the comprehension of the nature of physical space.

The Search for the KT Crater

by Walter Alvarez

Evidence in the geologic record points to a collision between the Earth and a large asteroid or comet as the cause of the mass extinction that killed the dinosaurs and many other animals and plants. Scientists are now trying to find the crater made by the collision.

WALTER ALVAREZ is a Professor of Geology at the University of California at Berkeley.

(Overleaf) The collision of a large asteroid or comet with Earth approximately 65 million years ago, an event that many scientists believe caused the extinction of the dinosaurs and many other animals and plants, would have produced a crater as large as 180 kilometers (120 miles) in diameter. In this view, about 30 seconds after impact, the maximum depth and diameter of the crater have been reached. An expanding shock wave spreads from the point of impact. Inside the rim a giant vortex of incandescent vapor and debris rolls skyward, and above the crater a cloud of incandescent vapor and molten droplets of the impactor expands rapidly into the vacuum blown into the upper atmosphere by the passage of the impactor and its shock wave.
Illustration by Don Davis

The history of life on Earth, as revealed in stratified sedimentary rocks, is a tale of gradual evolution, occasionally punctuated by sudden mass extinctions in which many species of plants and animals perish. The most recent of the mass extinctions occurred 65 million years ago. It marked the demise of the dinosaurs and many invertebrate marine animals, as well as serious, though incomplete, extinctions among many other groups, such as the single-celled marine animals called foraminifera. Sixty-five million years ago is the distant past by human standards, but it is fairly recent in the long sweep of Earth history, in which the largest mass extinction occurred about 250 million years ago, life began at least 3 billion years ago, and the Earth itself originated 4.6 billion years ago. The extinction event 65 million years ago has long been used as a milestone in Earth history, separating the preceding Cretaceous Period from the subsequent Tertiary Period, and so is called the Cretaceous-Tertiary, or KT, boundary.

In 1978 a group at the University of California at Berkeley (physicist Luis Alvarez, chemists Frank Asaro and Helen Michel, and I—a geologist) found abnormal amounts of the element iridium in a one-centimeter (0.4-inch)-thick clay bed that marks the KT boundary in Italy. Iridium is very rare throughout the solar system and is even more depleted in the Earth's crust because it alloys with iron; consequently, most of the Earth's original allotment of iridium is probably stored in the Earth's iron core. After several years of additional measurements and debate, the research team concluded that the anomalous iridium had reached the Earth as a small fraction of a large asteroid or comet that struck the planet 65 million years ago. The team suggested that this impact would have lofted so much dust into the atmosphere around the planet that the surface would have become very dark for some months, stopping photosynthesis and producing mass extinction among the animals by starvation.

During the 1980s researchers discovered many lines of evidence that supported the impact theory for the KT mass extinction. Paleontologists studying the fossil record showed that the extinction in many groups of animals and plants was extremely abrupt. Tiny rock spherules were found in the KT boundary layer around the world and were shown to have originated as droplets of rock melted by the heat of the impact, ejected through the atmosphere in a giant impact fireball, and scattered in ballistic trajectories outside the atmosphere. Grains of quartz sand from the KT boundary were shown to have features produced only by great shock pressures, which occur in nature only during impact events. Finally, these features—iridium anomalies, impact-melt spherules, and shocked-quartz grains—were found worldwide in the KT boundary but were absent elsewhere in the record of the Earth's history except as markers for a handful of other impact events.

Acceptance of the impact theory for the KT boundary grew, although some geologists and paleontologists, maintaining the traditional distaste for sudden events, continued to attribute the KT extinction to such normal Earthbound causes as sea-level changes, climate variations, or volcanism. Nonetheless, as the impact theory grew ever stronger, one

A Cretaceous-Tertiary (KT) boundary layer in the western United States reveals a white claystone band about 65 million years old sandwiched between black coal beds. The claystone contains an iridium anomaly, shock-metamorphosed quartz grains, and impact spherules, all of which are produced during large-scale asteroid or comet impacts with the Earth.

continuing disappointment remained: no one could say where the impact had occurred. The impact should have produced a crater perhaps 150 kilometers (one kilometer = 0.62 miles) in diameter—larger than any impact crater surviving on our geologically active planet (although much larger ones are preserved on the dead surface of the Moon). Researchers pointed out that 20% of the surface of the Earth existing 65 million years ago was ocean crust that has subsequently disappeared back into the deep Earth through the process of subduction of oceanic plates (the edge of one plate sinking below the edge of another); as a result, there was one chance in five that the crater no longer existed. Nevertheless, it was a major disappointment to have so much evidence for impact but no smoking-gun crater.

However, this is changing at last. Beginning about the middle of 1990 many different scientists interested in the KT boundary homed in on the Gulf of Mexico and Caribbean as a likely site for the KT impact, and they discovered a very large, buried circular structure on the Yucatán Peninsula of Mexico that appears to be an excellent candidate for the crater. The case is not yet closed, but the atmosphere is now charged with excitement.

Pointers to the Gulf of Mexico-Caribbean region

How does one search for the crater that would have resulted from a giant impact at the KT boundary? First, researchers looked at all the known craters on Earth and found none large enough or of the right age. Another possibility was that the amount of anomalous iridium or the size and abundance of impact spherules or shocked quartz might increase toward the impact site, but the data available through the 1980s did not reveal any such trend.

91

Yet another approach would be to look in marine sedimentary rocks for the deposits of the tsunami (tidal wave) that would have resulted from an impact in the ocean. The impacting object was estimated to have been 10 kilometers in diameter. If it fell in an ocean five kilometers deep, the height of the resulting wave might have been as great as the depth of the ocean. By the late 1980s many marine KT boundary sites had been discovered throughout the world. Generally, however, there was no indication at these sites of any physical disturbance of the sediments at KT boundary time. Only in one place was there a slightly abnormal sedimentary deposit at the boundary; this was along the Brazos River in Texas. This site was on the continental shelf at KT time, below sea level at a depth where mostly fine sediment was deposited and where there were rarely storms or waves capable of moving coarser sediment. At the KT boundary, marked by extinction and an iridium anomaly, however, there were a few beds of sandstone, indicating a brief episode of stronger water movement.

The Brazos KT sediments were slightly unusual but not strange enough to attract immediate attention. In 1985 Dutch geologists Jan Smit of the Free University, Amsterdam, and A.J.T. Romein of the State University of Utrecht, The Netherlands, remarked that the Brazos River sediments might be the result of water disturbance near the impact site. Then in 1988 sedimentologist Joanne Bourgeois of the University of Washington led a team that reported that the Brazos sandstone was not a normal marine sandstone but was, instead, something very unusual, probably the result of a tsunami. The Brazos KT bed caught the attention of Alan Hildebrand, a graduate student at the University of Arizona, and his thesis adviser, William Boynton, and they started thinking about the possibility of an impact in the Gulf of Mexico-Caribbean area.

One other site showed some indications of coarse deposits at the KT boundary. This was near the town of Beloc, on the southern peninsula of Haiti. Discovered and studied by Florida International University geologist Florentin Maurrasse, the Beloc site also pointed to the Gulf of Mexico-Caribbean area and was destined to provide some of the most crucial evidence.

For some reason the Brazos and Beloc information did not impress me as much as it should have, and I eventually came to an interest in this area by another route. Early in 1990 I realized that not only would a tsunami leave unusual sedimentary deposits but it could also erode the seafloor, even in the deep ocean. It seemed that in marine sections near a giant KT tsunami, quite a lot of the Upper Cretaceous should be missing because of tsunami erosion; consequently, the earliest Tertiary strata should rest on some level arbitrarily far down in the Cretaceous. This absence of sediment might be easier to recognize than the peculiar sedimentary deposit of the tsunami. Much information on ages of marine sediments had been collected by the Deep Sea Drilling Project and its successor, the Ocean Drilling Program, which had drilled more than 600 scientific wells in the ocean since 1968. I searched through the data from these wells and quickly realized that this erosional "signature"

of a KT tsunami occurred in several wells in the Gulf of Mexico and almost nowhere else. At that point I too began to take the Gulf-Caribbean seriously as the KT impact site and became interested in the candidate craters that scientists were suggesting in the area.

Candidate craters

With the Brazos section suggesting impact in the Gulf or Caribbean, researchers began looking for possible impact structures in those places. The structure should be a circular crater perhaps 150 kilometers in diameter. Virtually all impact craters are circular, which seems surprising because most impacts are oblique and one would, therefore, expect an oblique impact to scoop out an oblong crater. The Moon is covered with circular craters, and the lack of elongated ones formerly had led most scientists to conclude that the craters were due to volcanism. But the Apollo explorations on the Moon made it clear that the lunar craters were the result of impacts, and the reason for their circular shape is now well understood. A comet or asteroid hitting the Earth, the Moon, or another planet or satellite is traveling at a very high velocity (between 11 and 80 kilometers per second in the case of the Earth). At this velocity it has enormous kinetic energy. On hitting the Earth, it penetrates many kilometers below the surface as it is slowing down, and in the process of slowing down much of its kinetic energy is converted to heat. This heat causes a gigantic explosion. In the case of the KT impactor, the explosion probably released 10,000 times as much energy as is contained in all the present nuclear arsenals (though it must be remembered that in the case of an impact, this is not nuclear energy but just the energy of motion of a big rock moving fast). The result is an enormous explosion centered perhaps 10 or 20 kilometers below the Earth's surface, the depth to which the impactor has penetrated. Such an explosion produces a circular crater regardless of whether the impact is oblique—circular because it is blown out rather than scooped out.

The estimate of a crater 150 kilometers in diameter is derived partly from calculations of the energy of the impact explosion and partly from observations of the known craters on the Earth. Craters on the Earth that are up to 100 kilometers in diameter do not seem to have produced mass extinctions, and so something bigger would be needed to explain the KT extinction.

At least four places in the Gulf-Caribbean area have been suggested as possible KT impact craters. Hildebrand and Boynton were first to locate a feature on the floor of the Caribbean Sea, off the coast of Colombia, that seemed to be roughly circular and about the right size. Not much information about this feature was available, as it is seen mainly on a few seismic exploration lines. Bruce Bohor of the U.S. Geological Survey in Denver, Colorado, and Russell Seitz of Cambridge, Massachusetts, followed another lead. Western geologists have not had access to Cuba for many years, but a publication by the Polish geologist Andrzej Pszczol-kowski described features that sounded like possible indicators of impact on or very near Cuba. However, subsequent work by Bohor, Seitz, and other U.S., Cuban, and Canadian geologists downgraded this possibility. Maurrasse was one of the few geologists with access both to Cuba and to Haiti (on the island of Hispaniola), and his observations on KT deposits there suggested to him that the impact site may be in the sea between the two islands. No specific structure has yet been identified, and this possibility awaits further studies. The most exciting candidate structure at this time is in Mexico, straddling the north coast of the Yucatán Peninsula and centered on the town of Chicxulub.

The Chicxulub structure

Yucatán is a flat, low-lying peninsula underlain by limestones that extend northward as the shallow-water Campeche Platform before dropping off into the deep Gulf of Mexico. During the 1950s and 1960s Petróleos Mexicanos (Pemex; Mexico's national oil company) explored the Yucatán Peninsula with geophysical tools in a search for possible oil or gas resources. At that time it identified a feature centered on Chicxulub and drilled it; it was later determined to be circular and 180 kilometers in diameter. The structure did not produce hydrocarbons, but it was strangely anomalous. Instead of the usual thick limestone sequence of Yucatán, three wells near Chicxulub revealed only a thin limestone section and then rock that had clearly once been molten. Coming to the logical conclusion that these were igneous rocks, the Pemex geologists mapped this as a small, anomalous volcanic province and concluded that there was no reason to explore it further for oil.

In 1981 the U.S. geophysicist Glen Penfield and his Mexican colleague Antonio Camargo made the startling suggestion that the Chicxulub structure was not volcanic at all but was instead an impact crater. The melt rock, they suggested, was not volcanic but was melted by impact. This happened just as the Berkeley researchers published the paper suggesting that the KT extinction was the result of impact. One would have thought that these two hypotheses would have immediately been linked, with Chicxulub as a prime candidate for the KT crater, but that did not happen for 10 years. Perhaps the delay was due to lack of communication between commercial and academic geologists, but it was not until 1990, when Hildebrand and Penfield began a collaboration, that Chicxulub became a key target for KT research.

Is Chicxulub really a giant KT impact crater? If samples from those Pemex wells were available, the answer would probably be quickly apparent. Unfortunately, the cores were destroyed when the warehouse in which they were stored burned down. Penfield and his Mexican colleagues tried to find the ruined warehouse and the burned cores but to no avail. However, Penfield and Hildebrand did manage to recover a few small pieces that had been taken from the cores and sent to interested geologists many years ago, and those samples are being studied.

At present, the interpretation of the Chicxulub structure must be based on information about the Pemex wells that was published by Ernesto López Ramos in his book *Geología de México*. Figure 1 shows a cross section based on the three wells inside the circular structure and four wells

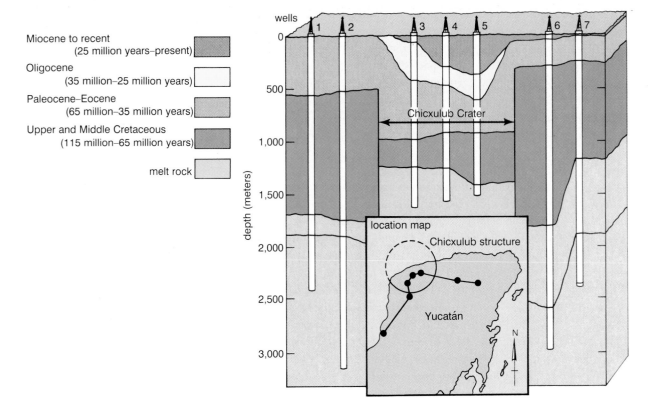

Miocene to recent
(25 million years–present)

Oligocene
(35 million–25 million years)

Paleocene–Eocene
(65 million–35 million years)

Upper and Middle Cretaceous
(115 million–65 million years)

melt rock

Figure 1. The Chicxulub crater, a candidate for the KT impact, is shown in cross section. The information for this drawing was obtained by Mexico's national oil company when it drilled seven wells in the area in a search for petroleum. Three of the wells were found to be within the crater, and four were outside of it (see location map). For additional information, see text.

outside it. In this schematic drawing the horizontal scale is greatly compressed, which distorts the geometry but shows the relationships more clearly. The well data show that the boundary between the Cretaceous and the overlying Paleocene Epoch of the Tertiary Period is at a depth of about 300 to 500 meters outside the structure but at about 1,000 meters inside it (one meter = 3.28 feet). It is this depressed center that marks the structure as a crater. If it were a volcano, the central part would be elevated. This suggests that the melt rock in the center is impact melt, not a volcanic product, and this interpretation is being tested with the few small samples available.

The figure shows Cretaceous rock above the melt rock in the three wells inside the crater. If this is correct and the Cretaceous is sediment in place, then the melt rock is clearly too old to have resulted from a KT event. However, the interpretation in the figure may be wrong—either the sediment may be misdated (all the ages shown in the figure are based on fossils) or, if the date is correct, the Cretaceous material in the crater could be preimpact debris that fell back, or was washed back, into the crater after an impact at KT boundary time.

Another interesting feature is the presence of Oligocene strata only within the limits of the crater. The Oligocene Epoch of the Tertiary Period was a time of abnormally low sea level, and this feature suggests that during the Oligocene the Chicxulub crater still formed a deep marine embayment in the north margin of Yucatán, while the rest of Yucatán was above sea level.

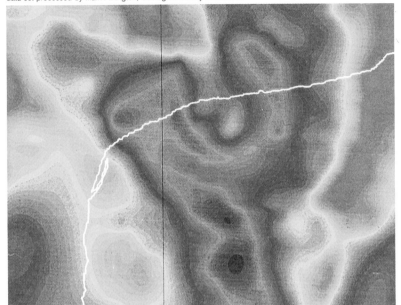

Gravity data from the Decade of North American Geology
data set processed by Mark Pilkington, Geological Survey of Canada

Gravity map of the Yucatán Peninsula outlines the Chicxulub crater. The blues and purples reveal a nearly complete circular "floor," and the yellows and oranges show a central uplift and irregular outer ring. The coastline is shown in white.

The Chicxulub crater is the best candidate yet found for the KT boundary crater, but it remains tantalizingly out of reach under a kilometer of younger deposits. Until Chicxulub can be redrilled, researchers must look elsewhere for evidence to decide whether it really is the KT crater. Their best strategy is to search as closely as possible to Yucatán for places where the KT boundary is exposed at the surface or is penetrated by drill holes. The Brazos River is one such place, and Beloc is another. In addition, my colleagues and I have reinterpreted two old Deep Sea Drilling Project holes in the Gulf of Mexico and discovered a fascinating outcrop exposure in northeastern Mexico.

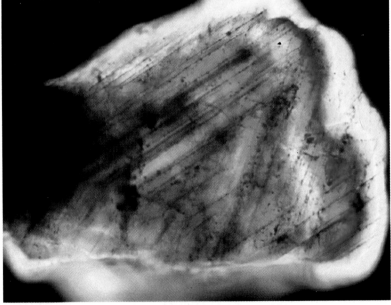

Alan R. Hildebrand

Shocked-quartz grain, indicative of a large-scale impact, was discovered in the Chicxulub crater. Parallel dark lines are microscopic fracture planes formed from the shock waves of an impact.

KT boundary stratigraphic sections

The Brazos River localities were critical in first focusing attention on the Gulf-Caribbean region. More recently, Maurrasse's Beloc section has been particularly important. In a set of apparently independent discoveries, several groups of scientists have found glass in the Beloc KT boundary. This is of great importance, first, because the glass from Haiti is characteristic of tektites (melt-rock droplets produced in impact explosions and well known from younger impacts) and, second, because the fresh glass preserves the chemical signature of the target rock. Elsewhere around the world, spherules that originated as impact-melt droplets are abundant in the KT boundary, but the original glass has long since been altered to clay and other secondary minerals, so the chemical fingerprint of the original glass has been destroyed.

Greenish-brown layer of clay at a KT boundary site near the town of Beloc, Haiti, contains the largest shocked-quartz grains yet discovered and tektites, evidence of a major impact. The clay is termed an "ejecta layer" because it contains material ejected by the impact. Its thickness is 0.45–1.2 meters (1.5–4 feet); ejecta layers this thick only occur close to the Yucatán.

David Kring

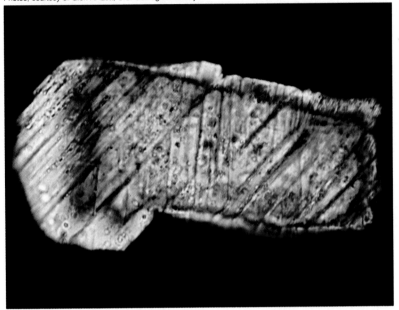

The discovery of the Beloc tektite glass by various scientists thus caused great excitement. Hildebrand recognized tektites in Maurrasse's collection. Haraldur Sigurdsson of the University of Rhode Island found glass in new samples from Beloc; Maurrasse and Robin Bates of television station WGBH/Boston revisited the outcrop, and Glen Izett of the U.S. Geological Survey led a team that extracted and studied glass from Maurrasse's samples. Robert Rocchia from the National Center for Scientific Research at Saclay, France, led another team that collected and studied glass-bearing samples from Beloc. Studies completed and still in progress on the Beloc glass are providing a wealth of information on the KT event. One important discovery is that some of the Beloc glass is far richer in calcium than any normal volcanic rock. This supports impact as opposed to the alternative volcanic hypothesis and points toward Yucatán, where the limestone bedrock is composed of calcium carbonate.

As discussed above, Deep Sea Drilling Project holes with signs of KT tsunami erosion are prominent in the Gulf of Mexico. Among the most notable are DSDP sites 536 and 540 in the deep-water passage between Yucatán and Florida. These scientific research holes were drilled in 1980–81, just as the impact theory for the KT extinction was being proposed, and it appears that their significance was not appreciated at the time. The holes were incompletely cored, and Smit and I fit the two holes together into a composite stratigraphic section (Figure 2) that tells the story of the KT event in this location, which is only about 400 kilometers from the Chicxulub crater.

In the Middle Cretaceous this area was a carbonate platform; consequently, the Middle Cretaceous is represented at the sites by shallow-water limestones. The area must have subsided to greater depth in the Late Cretaceous, but deep-water deposits are missing, perhaps because of tsunami erosion. At site 540 there is a 45-meter-thick sequence

Shocked-quartz grain (above left) was found at the KT boundary site near Beloc, Haiti. Its characteristics indicate that a large impact occurred nearby about 65 million years ago. Also found at Beloc and providing further evidence for an impact were tektites, 10 of which are shown above.

99

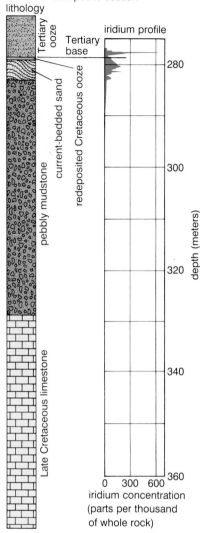

Stratigraphy of DSDP sites 536 and 540 composite section

lithology

Tertiary ooze

Tertiary base

iridium profile

current-bedded sand

redeposited Cretaceous ooze

pebbly mudstone

Late Cretaceous limestone

depth (meters)

280

300

320

340

360

0   300   600

iridium concentration
(parts per thousand
of whole rock)

Figure 2. Composite stratigraphic section from the Deep Sea Drilling Project (DSDP) sites 536 and 540 in the deep-water passage between Yucatán and Florida shows the abundance of iridium at the KT boundary that signifies a nearby impact. For additional information, see text.

of deformed mud that contains white limestone pebbles. This represents a submarine landslide, and it may have been triggered by the KT impact, perhaps by seismic waves traveling in the bedrock floor of the Gulf of Mexico. Paleomagnetic studies by William Lowrie at the Swiss Federal Institute of Technology, Zürich, suggest that the submarine landslide could be of KT age, although this part of the story is not yet certain.

Above the deformed mud is a five-meter layer of current-bedded sand, which also is seen at site 536. Current bedding reveals that the normally very quiet water conditions that characterized these deep sites in the Late Cretaceous and Early Tertiary were briefly interrupted by an abnormal episode of strong currents. Microfossils demonstrate that this episode occurred precisely at the KT boundary and, if it was indeed the result of an impact at nearby Chicxulub, this would date the crater better than any information presently available from the crater itself. The current-bedded sand in the two Deep Sea Drilling Project holes is also remarkable in that it is made of a clay that is the result of alteration of glass, and Miriam Kastner of the University of California at San Diego recently discovered preserved glass in the current-bedded sand from both holes. Her discovery further ties this deposit to Beloc and Chicxulub.

Above the current-bedded glass sand in site 536, there is a 30-centimeter-thick layer of very-fine-grained sediment containing tiny Cretaceous microfossils. It appears to be the fine silt, stirred up and suspended by the KT impact wave, that settled out after the Gulf of Mexico quieted down. Above that is the earliest fossil zone of the Tertiary.

Asaro measured the iridium in sites 536 and 540. He found virtually no iridium in the disturbed mud, and so if the mud really was a submarine landslide triggered by the KT impact, it must have slid immediately before the material ejected by the impact, with its component of iridium from the impactor, reached this site. The current-bedded glass sand has a moderate level of iridium, confirming the impact origin of the glass. But the iridium peak is in the fine sediment that settled out immediately after the KT event; this iridium probably came from vaporized impactor material that was carried above the atmosphere in the fireball and only gradually settled out.

After finding so much valuable information in the cores from sites 536 and 540, Smit and I and our Berkeley colleagues, Alessandro Montanari and Nicola Swinburne, decided to hunt for surface exposures of the KT boundary in northeastern Mexico, a dry area with good outcrop and as close to Yucatán as we thought we could find the KT boundary at the surface. In February 1991, after a series of misadventures and disappointments, we finally located a wonderful KT boundary outcrop in the Arroyo el Mimbral between Ciudad Victoria and Tampico.

At KT boundary time this area was in the Gulf of Mexico, under water probably more than half a kilometer deep, where only very fine-grained sediments slowly settled to the bottom. Precisely at the KT boundary, as defined by abundant microfossils, the fine-grained sediment is interrupted by a strange, coarse-grained bed as much as three meters thick.

Alan R. Hildebrand

The lowest part of this bed is full of spherules, like those of Beloc. We were not successful in finding preserved glass in these spherules, but Hildebrand and two researchers from the University of California at Davis, Stanley Margolis and Philippe Claeys, soon found glass in samples that we gave them. Thus, by early 1992 four KT glass sites near Yucatán had been discovered. The Mimbral glasses have the character of impact melt and bear the chemical fingerprint of the impact site. The texture of the spherule bed suggests that the spherules, after arriving on the fly from the impact site, were thrown about by a violent current or wave, capable of disturbing water at surprising depth.

The next layer in the Mimbral KT bed contains abundant fragments of wood, which would not be expected in such a deep-water setting. They suggest that the impact wave devastated the coastal forests and then carried the debris back into the deep Gulf. The top of the Mimbral KT bed has several thin layers of current-bedded sand separated by fine-grained, quiet-water mud, which may indicate that the impact wave sloshed back and forth in the Gulf several times before finally quieting down.

In January 1992 a Mexican-Dutch-U.S. team returned to northeastern Mexico for further study of the KT boundary. José Manuel Grajales of the Mexican Petroleum Institute and Pemex geologists Mauricio Guzman, Ricardo Martínez, Pedro Romero, Eduardo Ruiz, and Manuel Zambrano, working with Smit, Swinburne, and me, found nine more KT boundary sites, marked by spherules and tsunami deposits. The case for impact nearby, probably on Yucatán, thus appeared even stronger.

Glass from the KT boundary site at Mimbral in northeastern Mexico has the character of impact melt (above). Also in northeastern Mexico, at El Mulato, is a recently discovered exposed KT boundary (below).

Courtesy of Walter Alvarez

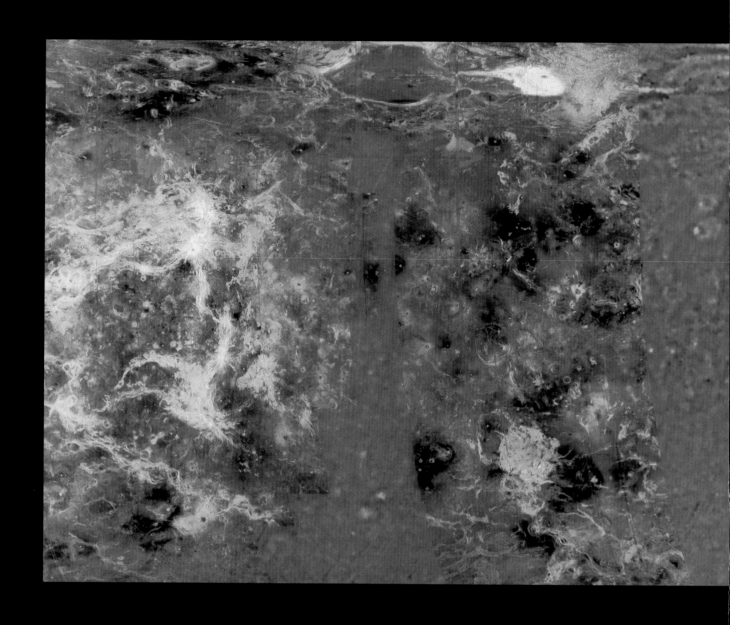

DEMYSTIFYING
THE MISTY PLANET

by Joseph Veverka

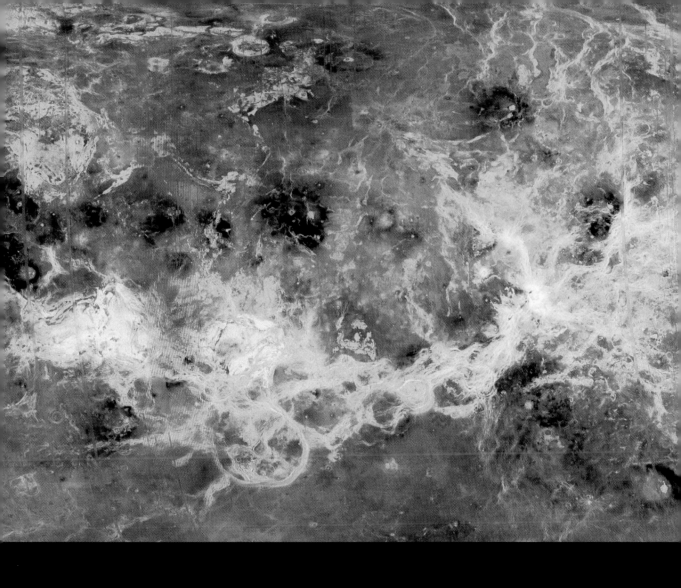

Past space missions and telescopic observations have shown that Venus, once thought to be Earth's "sister planet," more closely resembles the classical picture of hell. Now, detailed surface images from the spacecraft Magellan are uncovering vast differences in the geologic processes that have shaped the two worlds.

Scientific knowledge of Venus has taken a powerful leap forward since late 1990 thanks to the ongoing, systematic radar mapping of the planet by the U.S. spacecraft Magellan. Perpetually shrouded by thick clouds, the Venusian surface can be imaged only by means of radar techniques. By early 1992 Magellan had charted more than 95% of Venus, much of it at a resolution fine enough to show features the size of a football stadium on Earth. Analysis of the images is beginning to answer some of the most important questions about the current state of the planet's surface and about its past history. But Venus remains a planet of mystery, and there are still many things about it that are not understood.

It may seem surprising that Venus should be such an enigma. In certain superficial ways, of all the planets in the solar system Venus is most like Earth. In size and mass it is almost a duplicate. Further, as Earth's closest planetary neighbor it is easily accessible to both telescopes and spacecraft. Indeed, more spacecraft have investigated Venus than any other planet. Since the first flyby visit by the U.S. probe Mariner 2 in 1962, almost two dozen spacecraft have studied Venus in different ways. Most have physically penetrated the planet's thick cloud layer to investigate details of the atmosphere, while a few have made successful landings and reported important findings about the surface. In June 1985 two instrumented balloons, dropped by Soviet Vega space probes, studied the middle levels of the atmosphere.

Magellan does not represent the first attempt to peer beneath Venus' veil with radar. For more than two decades images of its surface have been obtained from radio waves sent from ground stations on Earth. These signals, in the radar range of the electromagnetic spectrum, penetrate the clouds and are reflected back to Earth by the Venusian surface. In 1978 the U.S. Pioneer Venus orbiter made the first low-resolution global surface maps, and in 1983 two Soviet orbiters carried out the first partial detailed radar mapping of the planet. But Magellan has provided an unprecedentedly clear view of what Venus is like, both because of its improved ability to see detail and, in particular, because of the near completeness of its mapping. Mapping the surface of Venus is no small task: the planet is about the size of Earth, but it is all land and not three-quarters covered by oceans.

From the wealth of new information obtained from Magellan, it is becoming clear that the traditional habit of thinking of Venus as a slightly different kind of Earth must be abandoned. In spite of gross similarities, Earth and Venus are very different planets, both atmospherically and geologically.

Venus by eye and telescope

Venus is difficult to ignore. Besides the Moon it is often the most conspicuous object in the night sky. Little wonder that early cultures such as the Maya attached great significance to its cyclic celestial displays. At times Venus is so bright that it is mistaken for an artificial light, an aircraft, or a UFO, depending on the observer's imagination. And in spite of what Napoleon Bonaparte appears to have been told by his sycophan-

JOSEPH VEVERKA is Professor of Astronomy at Cornell University, Ithaca, New York.

(Overleaf) Nearly the entire surface of Venus is shown in a cylindrical projection map made from Magellan radar data, with gaps filled in with lower-resolution Pioneer Venus data. The positions of various surface features coincide roughly with those on the Mercator projection map from Pioneer Venus on page 116. Features that are more radar-reflective appear brighter; added color is based on color images of the surface of Venus made from Soviet Venera landers. Photograph courtesy of the Jet Propulsion Laboratory

From its orbit above Venus the Magellan spacecraft peers beneath the planet's clouds in an artist's conception. Magellan's large, high-gain dish antenna maps one 20-kilometer (12-mile)-wide strip of the Venusian surface with radar signals during each orbit; it also doubles as a communications antenna for transmitting data and maintaining contact with the Earth. The spacecraft's altimeter antenna, the rectangular horn at the edge of the dish, times the radar echoes returning from the surface, thereby providing information on elevations.

tic attendants about an auspicious connection between a "rare" daytime sighting of Venus in 1794 and the general's recent military achievements, it is not uncommon to see Venus in broad daylight if one knows where to look. In part, the planet is so brilliant because of its thick cover of highly reflective clouds. It is now known that this cover extends in an unbroken veil from about 30 to some 70 kilometers above the surface. (One kilometer is about 0.62 mile.) The clouds vexed astronomers for years. What are they made of? And can one peer through them to study the surface below?

By the end of the 18th century, Venus' atmosphere was evident to astronomers. One remarkable contribution was made by the Russian polymath Mikhail Vasilyevich Lomonosov on the basis of observations of a passage of Venus across the Sun's disk. Such events, called transits, are rare, occurring in pairs about eight years apart at intervals of just over a century. Lomonosov was struck by the fact that during the transit of 1761 Venus did not always look like a small dark disk. Rather, when seen against the edge of the Sun, the planet appeared for an instant surrounded by a brilliant ring of light. Lomonosov correctly interpreted the ring as sunlight being refracted by a substantial atmosphere around the

105

An illustration from G.W. Pope's fictional Wonderful Adventures on Venus *(1895) reflects the popular conception of the planet at the turn of the century—a watery world filled with hot, steamy swamps that might even harbor creatures resembling those from Earth's prehistoric past. During the 1960s and '70s scientists determined that water was scarce or absent on Venus and that its yellowish clouds were made of sulfuric acid.*

planet. Some two centuries were to elapse before definitive information on the makeup of this atmosphere and its clouds would be obtained.

Lacking conclusive data, astronomers of the 19th and early 20th centuries assumed that the bright clouds, like those of Earth, were water clouds. From this era date concepts of Venus as a hot, steamy swamp. As spectroscopic techniques gradually improved, it became evident that such a view was flawed. If the clouds were water, it was reasonable to expect at least small amounts of water vapor near their tops. Yet by the mid-1960s it was realized that, far from being common, water vapor was scarce or absent near the cloud tops. Instead of finding water vapor, these increasingly detailed spectral studies were turning up seemingly strange minor constituents: traces of acid vapors such as hydrofluoric acid and hydrochloric acid.

An important clue, missed by most planetary scientists, was the planet's tinge of color. The clouds of Venus, although very bright, were not white like terrestrial clouds but yellowish.

Probing the atmosphere and clouds

By the dawn of the space age in the late 1950s, detailed spectroscopic studies of Venus from telescopes on Earth had shown that the planet's atmosphere is 96% carbon dioxide, while concurrent measurements of its thermal radiation at microwave and radio wavelengths suggested strongly that the surface is extremely hot. Any remaining doubts about the latter possibility were eliminated by the very first space missions. The Soviet Union's early Venera probes, which descended on parachutes into the Venusian atmosphere in the late 1960s, proved conclusively that Venus has a hot, massive atmosphere exerting a surface pressure 90 times that of Earth and having a temperature of about 750 K (480° C, or 890° F). The pressure corresponds to that encountered in Earth's oceans at a depth of 900 meters (one meter is about 3.3 feet), whereas

106

the temperature is considerably hotter than a broiling oven. Such a massive atmosphere stores heat so efficiently that variations of temperature over the planet's surface are small. Variations that do occur are related primarily to elevation differences. On average, temperatures in the lower atmosphere of Venus, near the surface, fall about 8 K for each kilometer increase in altitude. Typical elevation differences on Venus are a few kilometers or less.

Early Venus probes were not instrumented to determine the composition of the clouds, and it was the ingenuity of astronomers using telescopes on Earth that first solved the mystery in the 1970s. The essential clue came from the way that the clouds polarize sunlight. Light from the Sun is essentially unpolarized; a pair of polarized sunglasses, for example, will not filter direct sunlight any more than will ordinary sunglasses. Once sunlight is scattered by a solid surface or a cloud top, however, it can acquire different amounts of polarization. It is this effect that allows polarized sunglasses to cut down glare from water, roadways, and other light-scattering surfaces. In the case of clouds, the degree to which scattered light is polarized depends on several factors. One is what might be called texture; that is, the size and shape of the cloud particles. Another is the makeup of the cloud material, which determines its index of refraction, a measure of the degree that light is bent in passing through the material.

Analysis of how Venus' clouds polarize sunlight led to two important conclusions, both of which were confirmed later by probe measurements. First, the clouds consist of very tiny round particles. The round shape indicates that the particles are liquid droplets and not solid crystals. Second, the observed index of refraction from the clouds is significantly higher than that of water; in fact, it is exactly that of very concentrated

Temperature profiles, compositions, and surface pressures are compared for the atmospheres of Venus and Earth. In the lower Venusian atmosphere, within and below the clouds, the temperature increases with decreasing altitude until it reaches about 750 K (480° C, or 890° F) at the surface, compared with an average surface temperature on Earth of about 290 K (roughly 15° C, or 60° F). Venus' surface pressure of 90 Earth atmospheres corresponds to that found in the Earth's oceans at a depth of 900 meters (2,970 feet).

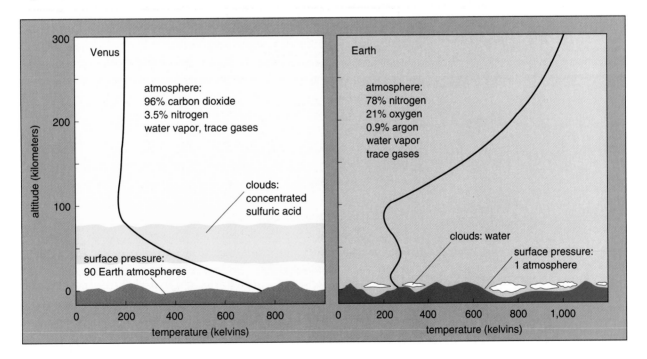

solutions of sulfuric acid. Such a composition is also consistent with the yellowish tint of the cloud tops. All at once, the scarcity of water vapor in the upper atmosphere made sense: sulfuric acid is a very hygroscopic, or water-hungry, compound, and all of the available water is tied up in the cloud droplets.

Almost certainly the sulfuric acid is derived from reactions between water molecules and sulfur dioxide gas, both minor constituents of Venus' atmosphere. Volcanic eruptions are probably the main source of the sulfur dioxide, as they are for Earth's atmosphere. Does acid rain ever fall on Venus? Very likely it does in the higher atmosphere, but the lower atmosphere is so hot that any falling droplets would evaporate before reaching the surface. Measurements show that below 30 kilometers the atmosphere is free of clouds.

As thick as the clouds are, some diffuse sunlight does reach the surface—a few percent of that striking the planet, according to measurements taken by landers. This small fraction, which must produce a dim twilightlike illumination, is sufficient to maintain the planet's torrid temperature by a process popularly called the greenhouse effect. It is the same process that is receiving increasing attention on Earth as human activities continue to pollute the atmosphere.

The tiny fraction of sunlight that filters down to the Venusian surface would normally heat it to a point at which most of the emitted heat, or infrared, radiation had an average wavelength of some 10 micrometers. But the atmosphere and clouds of Venus are opaque to radiation of that wavelength. As a result, the radiation, rather than escaping to space, is trapped and further warms the surface. Fortunately, such a vicious circle does not continue forever. It is known that as a body becomes hotter, it radiates the peak of its energy at progressively shorter wavelengths. Thus, as the surface of Venus heats up, its emitted infrared radiation peaks at shorter and shorter wavelengths until a point is reached at which the atmosphere is sufficiently transparent for some heat to escape. Then an energy balance, or equilibrium, is achieved: energy that escapes equals the amount absorbed from sunlight. For Venus this balance is reached near a temperature of 750 K. Although the name greenhouse effect for the process seems entrenched, it is actually more figurative than literal in meaning. Experiments have shown that a garden greenhouse works more like a covered cooking pot; it keeps warm primarily not by trapping radiation but by providing a lid in the form of its roof, which prevents warm air from "boiling" away.

How Earth escaped the fate of Venus

Venus has a hot, dense, carbon dioxide atmosphere; Earth, a relatively cool, much thinner one made mostly of nitrogen. In the early 1970s scientists began to realize that, in spite of their vast differences, the two atmospheres are fundamentally linked. The origins of both can be explained by the idea that, far from being primordial, they are the result of outgassing by volcanic processes since the formation of the two planets. Furthermore, strong evidence exists that the types of gases released and

their relative amounts were similar: predominantly carbon dioxide, water vapor, and nitrogen. These are the very gases that volcanoes continue to spew out on Earth and probably on Venus, though perhaps not as vigorously as in the past.

According to this scenario, the profound differences between Venus and Earth today are directly attributable to the respective distances of the two planets from the Sun and hence to their surface temperatures in the distant past, before either evolved its present atmosphere. Temperature is the critical factor because it determines the physical state of water: solid, liquid, or vapor. When outgassing began, it is likely that surface temperatures on Earth were close to present ones. As atmospheric pressure built up with continued outgassing, water vapor became compressed to a liquid, and the liquid water then began dissolving the carbon dioxide. With both water and carbon dioxide eliminated from the atmosphere, nitrogen remained as the major constituent. (The oxygen in Earth's atmosphere is a latter addition, attributable to biological activity.) Water vapor and carbon dioxide turn out to be good atmospheric "greenhouse gases"; that is, they efficiently trap heat radiated from the surface. Nitrogen, on the other hand, is not. Consequently, as Earth's atmosphere built up, not only did it remain comparatively thin but it also gave Earth much less of the greenhouse warming that made Venus a broiler.

Since Venus is closer to the Sun, its early surface temperature was too high to allow water vapor to turn to liquid. As a result all of the outgassed water vapor remained in the atmosphere along with carbon dioxide and nitrogen. As outgassing progressed, the atmosphere grew more dense. As the greenhouse effect of the water vapor and carbon dioxide became

Artist's conception of present-day volcanism on Venus may resemble the kind of outgassing activity that took place, though perhaps more vigorously, on the planet in the past. Despite the vast differences between the present atmospheres of Venus and Earth, the origins of both can be explained by the idea that they are the result of volcanic outgassing since the formation of the two planets. Evidence also exists that the types of gases released and their relative amounts were similar—mostly carbon dioxide, water vapor, and nitrogen, the same gases that volcanoes on Earth continue to emit today.

more efficient, surface temperatures rose higher. The important point is that conditions near the surface of Venus never got cool enough to allow water to condense and thus to remove itself and the carbon dioxide. The fact that Earth was at the right distance from the Sun for liquid water and oceans to form saved the planet from becoming an inferno.

Are there clues that this dramatic scenario really took place? First, one can examine the story of carbon dioxide on Earth. According to the model, Earth should have outgassed an amount of carbon dioxide equivalent to that in the atmosphere of Venus today. On Earth the gas supposedly dissolved in the oceans and eventually was turned into sedimentary rocks by shell-building organisms and other processes. While it is difficult to estimate accurately the amount of carbon dioxide locked up in Earth's sedimentary rocks, by all accounts it is close to that required by the model—the equivalent of about 100 Earth atmospheres.

Second, if the model is correct, Venus, like Earth, should have outgassed about one atmosphere of nitrogen. Being chemically inert, the nitrogen should still be in Venus' atmosphere. Indeed, probe measurements show that Venus retains the expected amount.

One implication of the scenario is that Venus should have outgassed the equivalent of an Earth ocean of water, only a negligible fraction of which is accounted for by the acid droplets that make up the clouds. Turned into gas, one ocean of water is equivalent to 257 Earth atmospheres. Calculations have shown that in Venus' warm atmosphere water vapor would be transported efficiently to high levels where water molecules can be broken apart quickly by the Sun's ultraviolet radiation. The expected result is the production of gaseous hydrogen and oxygen and the rapid escape of the former into space owing to its low mass.

Some clues that Venus lost the equivalent of an ocean of water may be preserved in the details of the current isotopic composition of the atmosphere. The great majority of water molecules contain hydrogen in the form of its ordinary light isotope (hydrogen-1), but in a small proportion of them one of the hydrogen atoms is a heavy isotope known as deuterium (hydrogen-2). If a substantial amount of Venus' water vapor was dissociated, one might expect the atmosphere to be enriched in deuterium relative to the ordinary isotope because under certain circumstances the lighter isotope will escape more readily than the heavier one. The first evidence that such an enrichment is present came from measurements made by one of the Pioneer Venus entry probes. More recently the enrichment was confirmed by measurements made from Earth. For various technical reasons it is difficult to convert the observed enrichment into a definite amount of outgassed water, but its discovery supports the scenario of how Venus' atmosphere evolved.

The other part of the story is to explain what happened to the large amount of water-derived oxygen, a gas that is too heavy to have escaped readily from the planet. On a volcanically active planet on which new surface rocks continue to be supplied in profusion, it would be easy to dispose of large amounts of oxygen by chemical combination with fresh rocks. As is discussed below, Venus is indeed a volcanically active planet, and there is direct evidence that oxidation of the surface is an efficient, ongoing process. One of the remarkable discoveries made by the Soviet landers is that the surface of Venus has a reddish tinge, presumably because it is oxidized.

Venus below the clouds

The earliest radar studies of Venus in the 1960s, though barely capable of distinguishing the planet's principal surface features, revealed the unexpected and astounding fact that the planet is spinning slowly backward. Whereas Venus takes 225 days to go around the Sun, it takes 243 days to spin once around its pole. By comparison, Earth and Mars both rotate relatively fast (in about 24 hours) and in the same direction that they orbit the Sun. If Venus started out with a spin similar to that of Earth or Mars, something dramatic must have happened. One suggestion is that Venus "swallowed up" a retrograde moon, one that had been orbiting the planet in a direction opposite to the planet's spin at the time. Tidal forces would pull such a moon slowly toward the planet, leading to its ultimate demise. Such a catastrophic collision with an oppositely revolving moon could reverse the planet's spin and also explain why Venus, unlike most of the other planets, does not have a satellite. What really happened to Venus, however, remains unknown.

The spin of Venus is remarkable in another way, for which there is also no generally accepted explanation. The spin is so coupled to the orbital motion that whenever Earth and Venus are closest (every 584 days on average), the same face of Venus points toward Earth. Is this a mere coincidence, or has Earth somehow influenced Venus? The issue remains unresolved, no convincing mechanism having been found by which Earth could affect its neighbor in this way. The situation nevertheless has an important implication since the best radar studies of Venus from Earth can be carried out when the planets are nearest. Thus, from Earth the most detailed radar views always have shown the same face of Venus.

While the bulk of Venus' massive atmosphere moves along at the same pace as the planet's spin, near the cloud tops the atmosphere has a remarkably different motion. Imaged at violet and ultraviolet wavelengths, Venus displays a diffuse but distinct semiperiodic pattern of markings. They show that the topmost levels of the clouds, at some 70 to 80 kilometers' altitude, whiz around the planet on average every four or five days in the same direction as the surface. The physical cause of this "superrotation," though dynamically complicated, is understood by meteorologists and is related to the fact that most of the Sun's heat input is deposited within the cloud layers high above the surface. The markings owe their visibility to the production of sulfur (presumably from sulfur dioxide gas, the sulfuric acid in the cloud droplets, or both) by chemical processes powered by ultraviolet energy from the Sun.

Early views of the surface

Even though the first radar images of Venus were limited in resolution, they enabled scientists to reach important conclusions. Almost imme-

An image made in ultraviolet light by the Pioneer Venus orbiter spacecraft in 1980 shows the diffuse pattern of markings present in Venus' cloud tops. Followed in a series of images over time, the markings reveal that the uppermost cloud layers, at an altitude of 70 to 80 kilometers (40 to 50 miles), "superrotate" around the planet on average every four to five days in the same direction as the planet's 243-day spin. The markings owe their visibility to the production of sulfur by Sun-powered chemical processes in the cloud droplets.

111

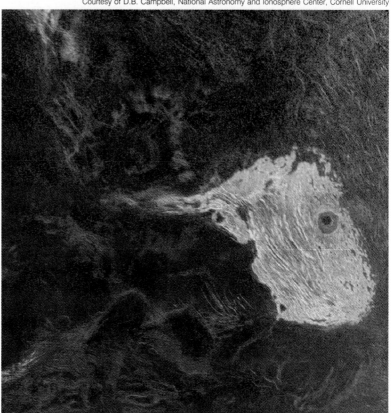

Image of Maxwell Montes and the surrounding region in Ishtar Terra, made in the 1980s with the Arecibo radio telescope in Puerto Rico, is among the better radar views of Venus from Earth and serves to demonstrate the resolution limits of ground-based radar mapping. (For comparison, the right-hand photo on page 118 shows essentially the same region in an image made from data gathered by the Soviet Venera 15 and 16 orbiters.)
Early Earth-based radar maps of Venus identified several areas, such as Beta Regio, as probably volcanic in origin. Their lack of detail, however, did not allow scientists to identify enough impact craters to date the surface accurately or to answer whether plate tectonics operates on Venus as it does on Earth.

diately several areas were identified as probably volcanic in origin. For example, a region near the equator known as Beta Regio was seen to have at least two structures similar in shape and elevation profile to large basaltic shield volcanoes on Earth; these are shallow-sloped lava domes that have been built up from comparatively quiet eruptions. (Radar has one important advantage over "ordinary" imaging by reflected light: in addition to revealing the shape, or morphology, of the surface, from the timing of the echoes it can provide information on elevations, or topography, as well.) The finding that basaltic volcanism is common on Venus has been confirmed by all subsequent studies, most importantly by a series of chemical analyses performed on surface rocks by some half dozen Soviet landers in different areas of the planet, including Beta Regio.

What was not clear from the earliest studies was the age of the Venusian surface. How old are the prominent volcanic features? Is volcanism an important ongoing process on the planet now? Is Venus geologically as active a planet as Earth? Since geologic activity is driven by a planet's interior heat, the close similarity of the bulk properties of Earth and Venus argued for broadly similar thermal histories and, hence, similar degrees of geologic activity.

The best way to judge the age of a planetary surface via remote observation is from impact scars—in particular, from the number of craters preserved on its surface. Because of limited resolution, the early radar results were inconclusive. No huge craters or basins, such as those that

112

make up the maria of the Moon, were detected, implying that the surface of Venus dates to a time more recent than some four million years, when large objects were still commonly colliding with the planets and their satellites. That much seemed clear, but identifying enough smaller impact craters to date the surface accurately proved difficult.

The early radar images were also searched for evidence that Venus, like Earth, might display plate tectonics. Such evidence might include a global pattern of tectonic effects—*i.e.,* features created by crustal deformations, for example, folded mountain belts, rift valleys, and faults—that mark the boundaries of large plates of crust. Again, the images lacked enough detail to provide an answer.

Does Venus work like Earth?

Plate tectonics, the unifying paradigm in terms of which geologists attempt to understand how the planet Earth works, successfully integrated such older ideas as continental drift and ocean spreading into a complete worldview. What are the main features of this idea, and can they apply to Venus?

When planets like Venus and Earth formed, their interiors were very hot. Much of the early heat came from the release of gravitational energy as the planets were built up from smaller bodies. To this was added the heat from the gradual decay of naturally occurring radioactive materials like uranium. For the past three billion to four billion years, the planets have been cooling off. Even today Earth is still hot on the inside, and there is no reason to suppose that Venus is different in this respect. A planet with a hot interior and cooler surroundings must lose heat. The big question is how it does so.

A simple model of the solid Earth offers a reasonable basis for assumptions about Venus. Accordingly, both planets can be pictured as having metallic cores covered by rocky mantles. The core-mantle boundary is placed at about half the distance from the surface to the core. On Earth the core-mantle boundary is known to be located some 2,900 kilometers below the surface, or about 45% of the way to the center. From seismic data it is suspected that the innermost part of Earth's core is solid but that the outer portions are fluid. Earth's rocky mantle behaves in a complicated fashion, responding as a solid to stresses on short time scales but demonstrating fluid behavior over the long time intervals relevant to many geologic processes. The outer layers of Earth's mantle are called the asthenosphere. Above the asthenosphere lie the planet's rigid outermost layers, technically called the lithosphere.

For low rates of heat transport, conduction through the solid lithosphere may suffice to remove heat escaping from the deep interior. For larger amounts to escape, some convection—actual movement of material—must take place. Of the many possibilities, at least two occur on Earth. Such areas as Hawaii and parts of Africa show volcanic activity marked by localized outpouring of lavas. These so-called hot spots are presumably associated with areas in the mantle called mantle plumes, in which molten mantle rock "boils up" to the surface.

A more important way that Earth loses heat is through plate tectonics, beginning with the eruption of basaltic lavas along raised cracks on the seafloor that make up the ocean ridges. As the lava flows cool, they become enormous plates of solid rock that move away from the ridges at rates measured typically in centimeters per year. The plates make up the lithosphere, while the underlying, deformable asthenosphere acts as a conveyor belt on which the plates are carried. As the plates cool, they become less buoyant and begin to sink, or subduct. It is believed that partway down into the asthenosphere, increasing pressure transforms the lithospheric rock into a denser form, which sinks more readily into the asthenosphere, pulling the rest of the plate with it. Plate tectonics is thought to be Earth's major way of cooling down.

Today the Earth's lithosphere is divided into about a dozen major plates. Although most of the present ocean floor is only 200 million years old or less, plate tectonics on Earth is a much older process. Seafloor that formed earlier than 200 million years ago has been recycled via subduction back into the mantle. The continents, on the other hand, seem to tell a different story. Made mostly of rocks like granite, which are lighter than basalt, the continents are quite buoyant and resist sinking

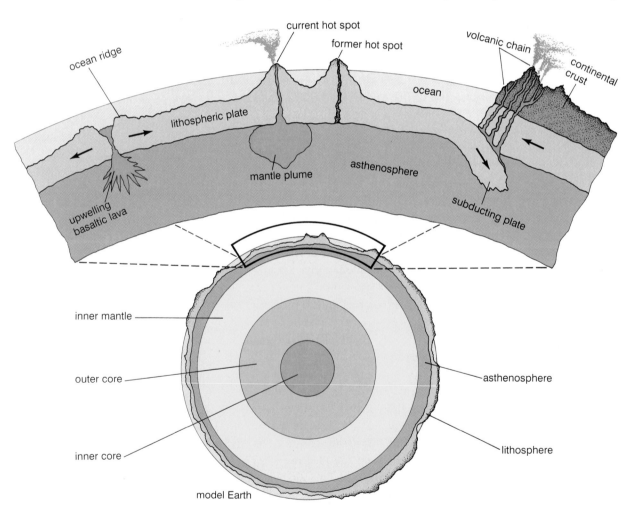

into the asthenosphere. Their origin is a hotly debated issue. The central portions of the continents appear to be remnants of the Earth's ancient crust, in some cases dating back billions of years, before plate tectonics became fully developed. Along the continental margins more recent materials have been added from incompletely subducted plates.

A popular idea is that plate tectonics developed on Earth only after the lithosphere cooled enough to permit such transitions to higher density rocks as described above. Earlier than about two billion years ago, the crust may have been too buoyant to sink, but this conclusion is far from certain. Some geologists believe there is evidence of plate tectonics on Earth almost as far back as four billion years ago, shortly after the crust began to cool following the period of early heavy bombardment.

Clues from Pioneer Venus

Asking whether plate tectonics may be occurring on Venus comes down to asking by what means Venus is losing its internal heat today. Some pertinent information came in 1978 from Pioneer Venus, a complex double-spacecraft mission that included both a multiprobe study of the planet's atmosphere and an orbiter that mapped the planet's topography and gravity field. Resolution was low, but coverage was almost global. The mission provided two important clues that lithospheric processes on Venus are different from those on Earth.

First, the distribution of elevations on Venus turned out to be very different from that on Earth. Elevations on Earth cluster strongly around one of two values; one is the mean level of the continents, the other

(Opposite page) Attempts to explain how Venus loses its interior heat begin with an assumption that the planet shares the features of a simple model of the solid Earth, in which a metallic core is covered by a rocky mantle, which in turn is overlaid with a rigid outer lithosphere. On Earth large amounts of heat are transported to the surface by volcanic activity at the sites of localized hot spots, where underlying mantle plumes break through the lithosphere with outpouring of lava. A more important heat-loss mechanism is plate tectonics, beginning at the mid-ocean ridges with the upwelling of hot basaltic lava, which cools to form the plates that constitute the lithosphere, and ending with the downward plunge, or subduction, of the cold plates into the upper mantle, the asthenosphere. In their search for whether Venus also loses heat through plate tectonics, scientists have looked for global patterns of such characteristic features as rift valleys, volcanic chains, folded mountain belts, and faults that mark the plate boundaries on Earth.

One clue about the lithospheric processes operating on Venus came in 1978 from topographical data collected by the Pioneer Venus orbiter. When the distributions of elevations on Venus were plotted, they were found to cluster around one value, the planet's mean radius. By contrast, elevations on Earth show two peaks; one is the mean level of the continents, and the other is that of the ocean floor. Venus' failure to show the continent-seafloor elevation split that characterizes plate tectonic activity on Earth was a strong hint that the two planets do not work the same way.

that of the ocean floor. By contrast, Venus displays only one mean value. Pioneer Venus found that more than two-thirds of the planet's surface is a rolling plain having an elevation within one kilometer of the planet's mean radius of 6,051 kilometers. The lack of a continent-seafloor elevation split, a hallmark of plate tectonic activity on Earth, was a strong hint that Venus and Earth are not behaving the same way.

A second clue supporting the same conclusion was that elevation differences on Venus are accompanied by increased local gravity. A remarkable property of Earth is that gravitational attraction does not increase over mountains and other topographic highs as much as one might expect from the excess lithospheric mass that seems to be involved. This behavior is understood as an effect of the buoyant nature of the continents, whose mountains tend to be made of lighter rocks. On Venus elevations appear to represent actual extra lithospheric mass, which must be supported in some way other than by "floating" on an asthenosphere. One way to support such excess mass is by having a thick, rigid lithosphere. To provide the needed support, however, some of the topographic highs of Venus appear to require a rigid crust 100 kilometers thick or more. Is it likely that such a thick rigid lithosphere can exist on a planet whose outer layers are as warm as those of Venus? Another means of achieving the needed support is dynamic; the elevated areas are maintained by the upwelling of hot mantle plumes. In either case the situation is not Earthlike.

A topographical Mercator projection map produced from Pioneer Venus orbiter data covers about 83% of the Venusian surface. Elevations are color coded from blue (lowest) to red (highest). Before Pioneer Venus' radar mapping, less than 1% of the planet's elevations had been measured by Earth-based radar. The mapping revealed two continent-like elevated regions, Aphrodite Terra near the equator and Ishtar Terra in the northern hemisphere, that seem to have been rifted and folded by some kind of tectonic activity. Aphrodite Terra is the larger of the two regions; it appears smaller because Mercator projection maps exaggerate sizes near the poles.

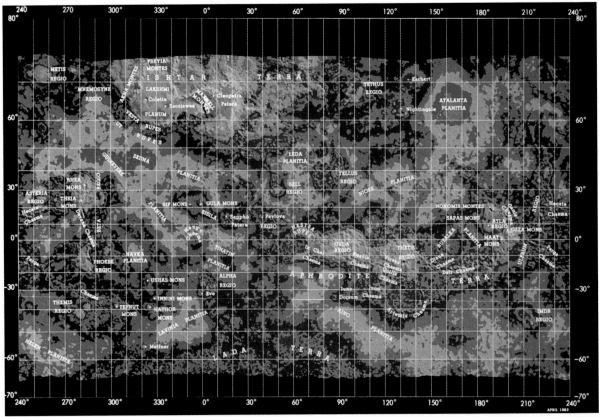

The topographical map produced by Pioneer Venus also revealed two continent-like elevated regions of terrain that seem to have been rifted and folded in a complex way by tectonic activity of some kind. Aphrodite Terra, about the size of Africa, rises some two to four kilometers above the mean level of the plains. Australia-sized Ishtar Terra rises to a similar mean level except where the elevation peaks at 11 kilometers at Maxwell Montes, revealed by later radar mapping to be one of the solar system's largest volcanoes. Although the limited-resolution maps of Pioneer Venus did not allow scientists to determine conclusively how Aphrodite and Ishtar formed, they produced no firm evidence for plate tectonics on Venus.

Contributions by Venera 15 and 16

In 1983 two Soviet orbiters, Venera 15 and 16, began mapping the northern hemisphere of Venus at a resolution adequate to reveal, for the first time, the full complexity of Venusian geology. That geology was shown to be dominated by basaltic volcanism and very active processes of crustal deformation. Clear evidence was found of mountains that had been built up through folding, but a generally accepted resolution of the issue of plate tectonics on Venus was not forthcoming.

A most important discovery made by the Veneras was that novel types of basaltic volcanism occur on Venus. Scientists identified large circular areas hundreds of kilometers across, clearly the centers of volcanic eruptions. These so-called coronas, unique to Venus, are believed to be a manifestation of hot-spot volcanism and provide another vivid reminder of the considerable differences between Venus and Earth.

Because of better resolution, Venera data made the identification of impact craters more reliable and finally resolved the question of the age of the Venusian surface. No ancient areas were found. Most of the surface dates to the last billion years or less, with some areas perhaps undergoing renewal at present. This conclusion has been confirmed and amplified by the more extensive Magellan data.

Magellan: many answers, new questions

Since August 1990 the Magellan spacecraft has mapped nearly all of the surface of Venus at resolutions high enough to distinguish features less than 300 meters apart. How has that accomplishment improved understanding of the planet?

As discussed above, a fundamental goal has been to identify the dominant form of heat loss on Venus, be it plate tectonics, hot-spot volcanism, or perhaps some other process not occurring on Earth. Another has been to refine the age estimates of various parts of the planet's surface.

What a geologist finds so striking about the appearance of Venus from the Magellan images is the crispness of the surface. Under the high temperature and pressure on Venus, chemical reactions—and hence a "weathering" of sharp features—would be expected to proceed at an accelerated pace. Yet the lack of moisture, and especially the absence of liquid water, counteracts this tendency dramatically and leads to a

Photos, Russian Academy of Sciences; courtesy of the U.S. Geological Survey, Flagstaff, Ariz.

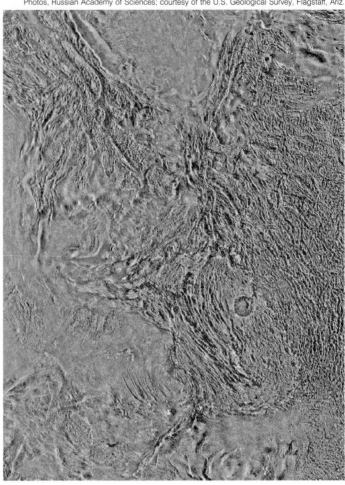

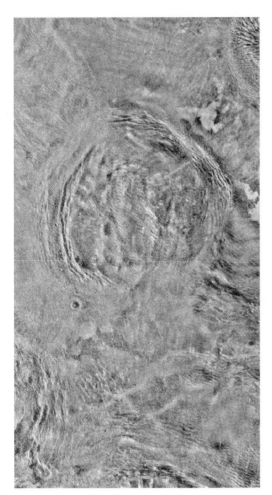

Radar image of rugged mountain belts in the Maxwell Montes area (above right) is an example of the high resolution achieved by the Soviet Venera 15 and 16 orbiters. The Venera maps allowed scientists to see, for the first time, the full range of Venusian geology—one dominated by complex processes of crustal deformation and volcanism. A novel type of basaltic volcanism was identified in the form of coronas, large circular areas—like Anahit corona shown above—that are clearly the centers of volcanic eruptions.

dearth of erosion. Whereas on Earth the sequence of geologic events that produced a particular surface feature can be reconstructed only with painstaking effort, on Venus the clues remain sharply preserved.

This increased ability to see what happened offers many benefits, not only in working out geologic processes on Venus but also in gaining insights into geologic processes on other terrestrial planets. One example involves several of the volcanic areas on Venus that are scarred by long channels, truly colossal features several kilometers wide and hundreds of kilometers long. From the circumstances on Venus it is evident that such features were produced by flows of basaltic lava. Such a conclusion raises the possibility that some generally similar channels on Mars may owe at least part of their origin to lava flows rather than entirely to running water, as has often been argued.

Magellan has shown that vast outpourings of very fluid lavas, akin to some of the basaltic flows occurring in such places as Hawaii, have been and continue to be common. Although basaltic volcanism is dominant, there is evidence of other types of volcanic activity as well. Some locales show signs of the eruption of more viscous lavas and the consequent production of topographic features resembling very flat inverted cupcakes

118

Part of a channel less than 2 kilometers (1.2 miles) wide but 6,800 kilometers (4,200 miles) long, presumably carved out by flowing lava, appears in crisp detail in a radar image from the Magellan spacecraft. Strikingly apparent in the Magellan images is the lack of erosion on Venus, where the clues to the geologic processes that produced particular surface features remain sharply preserved for scientists to study.

and similar to so-called rhyolite domes on Earth. Some of these features, which have been dubbed pancake domes, are much larger than their analogues on Earth, one particular example being about 26 kilometers wide and 600 meters high (although a few features of this type as large as about 100 kilometers across have been seen).

Images from Magellan show features that look very much like cinder cones on Earth, evidence that explosive eruptions also occur. Because of the much higher atmospheric pressure at the surface of Venus, explosive volcanism should be a rarer phenomenon than it is on Earth.

By far the most dramatic and characteristic volcanic features on Venus are the coronas, several hundred of which have been identified. They appear as concentric rings in some cases hundreds of kilometers across, with associated signs of volcanic activity in the form of lava flows and of tectonic activity appearing most often as downdropping along concentric faults. Thought to be surface manifestations of upwelling over mantle hot spots, coronas may account for a major fraction of the heat transport from the planet's interior.

A closely related new feature seen in Magellan images is called a nova. Typically novae consist of a starlike pattern, some 200 kilometers across,

A low-angle view of the Venusian shield volcano Gula Mons is simulated by computer from Magellan radar-mapping and altimetry data. The viewpoint is located southwest of the peak and at the same elevation as its summit, about three kilometers (two miles).

Magellan found numerous examples of structures resembling very flat inverted cupcakes, including a grouping in the Eistla region of Venus (right) and another on the east edge of Alpha Regio (below, in a computer-simulated low-angle view). Dubbed pancake domes, the features appear to be the product of a unique type of volcanic activity characterized by the eruption of lavas that are more viscous than typical basaltic flows.

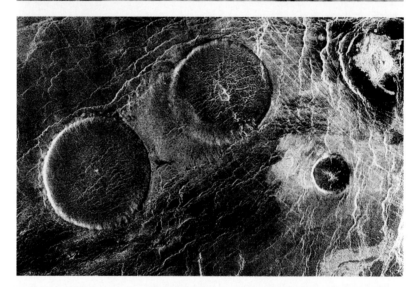

of radiating linear fractures. Novae may be surface expressions of magma injection into near-surface fractures.

In many areas of Venus the colossal volcanic features that have been built up and the successive overlaying of newer lava flows on older ones make it clear that the crust has not moved relative to the deep centers of eruptive activity. There is thus little evidence for the type of lithospheric plate movement over hot spots that is producing such volcanic island chains as the Hawaiian Islands on Earth. The apparent absence of lateral lithospheric motion, while consistent with the overall lack of obvious plate tectonics, is puzzling because features much like folded mountain belts are seen in some areas of Venus. Such tectonic features suggest that some lateral lithospheric movement and associated recycling of the surface must be occurring, though evidently not in an Earthly style or on

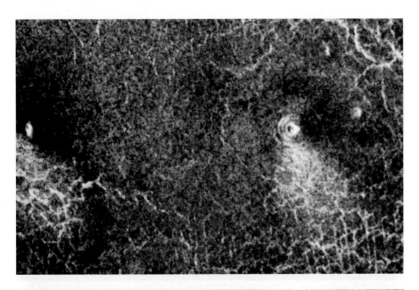

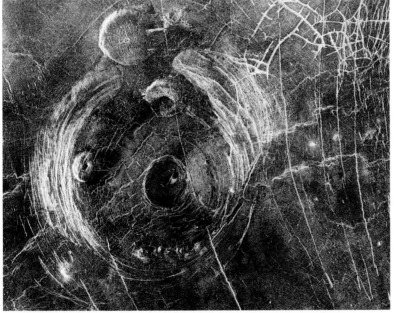

(Top) NASA, (bottom) JPL

Evidence from Magellan for explosive volcanism on Venus includes an image of a crater resembling a cinder cone on Earth (top, right-hand portion of image). The bright surface deposit that radiates away from the crater toward the bottom of the image appears to be pyroclastic fallout from a volcanic explosion plume. The most dramatic and characteristic volcanic features on Venus are the coronas, several hundred of which have been identified in Magellan images. One impressive example is 200-kilometer (120-mile)-wide Aine Corona (bottom), located on a plain to the south of Aphrodite Terra. Also visible are two pancake domes, one of which lies within the corona's ring of fractures, and a set of small domes near the bottom of the ring.

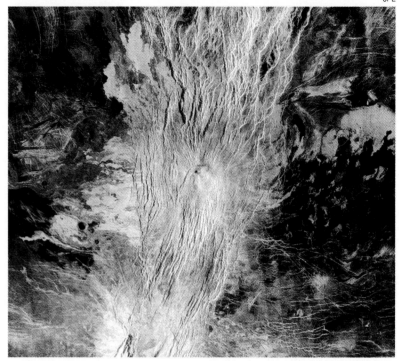

Devana Chasma on Venus' equator shows complex deformation including rifting and deep fractures in an image from Magellan. Although Magellan found no evidence for plate tectonics in the Earthly sense, its detailing of features resembling rift zones, folded and faulted mountain belts, and other signs of tectonic activity suggest some kind of lateral lithospheric movement.

an Earthly scale. Analysis of the Magellan data, while still far from making Venus "fully understood," has nonetheless revealed that the building and recycling of plates is not a major way of cooling Venus. Rather, something very Venusian appears to be going on. The planet seems to be losing its internal heat by means of stationary hot-spot–mantle-plume activity manifested by localized features such as the coronas.

The continent-like features remain a puzzle. Perhaps, like the continents of Earth, they will turn out to have a lower density than that of the underlying lithosphere, but so far detailed compositional measurements are lacking. Perhaps also, like some of Earth's continents, at least part of them may be remnants of Venus' early crust.

Magellan's images show clearly the effect of Venus' present-day thick atmosphere on incoming objects. Craters smaller than about three kilometers across are totally absent, indicating that objects capable of producing craters up to this size break apart and burn up before reaching the surface. Craters up to about 15 kilometers across appear in clusters and show other evidence that they resulted from bodies that broke up in the atmosphere. Ejecta blankets, the layers of material tossed up around craters from the impacts, possess many peculiarities, including flow features that may be the result of cushioning of the ejecta by the hot planetary atmosphere. Studies of the pristinely detailed ejecta patterns will lead scientists to a better understanding of the cratering process not only on Venus but on other planets as well. One of the peculiar and not well-explained features of Venusian ejecta patterns is their common marked asymmetry, a characteristic seen to be unusual on other bodies in the solar system.

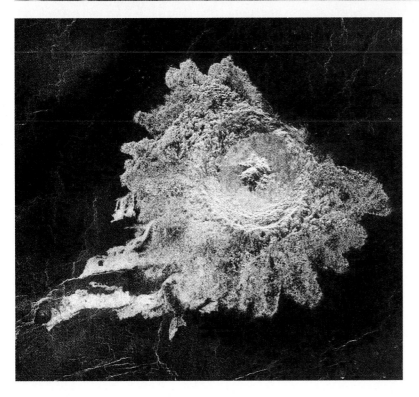

A trio of large craters (above), each roughly 40 to 60 kilometers (25 to 40 miles) wide, in Lavinia Planitia west of Alpha Regio were created by incoming objects large enough to survive the descent through the thick atmosphere of Venus. Magellan's images show no craters smaller than 3 kilometers (2 miles) across and contain evidence that craters up to about 15 kilometers (10 miles) across resulted from bodies that broke up before impact. The ejecta blankets of some craters, like 32-kilometer (20-mile)-wide Aurelia (left), have a pronounced asymmetry, a feature believed to be an effect of the thick atmosphere but one that is not yet well explained.

Perhaps the most peculiar surface features linked with cratering on Venus are large dark markings, several hundred kilometers in size, that accompany some of the fresher, larger craters. Parabolic in shape and always found downwind of their craters, they have been interpreted as deposits of ejecta plumes wafted downstream by upper-atmosphere winds. Their preservation on the surface may again be due to a relative lack of weathering. Since they appear darker in the radar images, they must be slightly rougher than surrounding areas. On Mars and Earth comparable features have never been noticed, possibly because they are destroyed rapidly by weathering even if they form.

Wind-formed surface features can be expected on any planet having surface winds strong enough to move loose materials, if such materials are present. Even in the absence of water, chemical weathering on Venus must produce some wind-movable material. Given the high density of the atmosphere, only low wind speeds are needed to move surface materials. Models of atmospheric circulation predict winds of a few meters per second near the surface, estimates that have been confirmed by the few direct measurements made by landers so far. Not surprisingly, wind-formed features such as dune fields and streaks of wind-deposited materials in the lees of topographic obstacles are beginning to be identified in the Magellan images.

The next step: an inside look

Studies of Venus over the past 30 years, culminating with the Magellan mission, have led to greatly improved knowledge of the planet's surface, atmosphere, and cloud layers. By contrast, scientists still know almost nothing about the planet's interior. This gap in knowledge is not surprising. Most of the information about Earth's interior has come from measuring how seismic waves from earthquakes travel through the interior. Comparable measurements for Venus have not been made. Scientists need information about near-surface (lithospheric and upper-mantle) structure to explain the volcanic and tectonic processes revealed by Magellan. In addition, they need firm data on the deep interior structure to explain one of the planet's major puzzles, the absence of a magnetic field.

Even on Earth the process by which the magnetic field is generated is not satisfactorily understood. A key ingredient seems to be some sort of churning motion within a conductor. On Earth this critical region is located in the outer portions of the metallic core. But details are uncertain: What is it that keeps the core churning? Is the churning caused by friction and slipping at the core-mantle boundary? Is it possibly caused by tidal forces from the Moon? Might it possibly be due to the freezing out of small volumes of outer-core melt onto the inner core? Is the Earth's comparatively rapid spin important in keeping the churning going?

The spin of Venus is indeed very slow, and perhaps the planet's interior is also somewhat different. The two planets show a slight difference in density, which—according to one interpretation—may mean that Venus is richer in sulfur than is Earth. Sulfur could modify melting points in

124

JPL

A global view synthesized from eight months of Magellan mapping data reveals a "demisted" Venus—a panorama of volcanic sculpture and tectonic deformation that contrasts sharply with the cloudy-ball picture of the planet of a few decades earlier. Nevertheless, the process of demystifying Venus remains to be completed. For the next step scientists hope to probe the near surface and deep interior of the planet with seismic measurements by means of a network of instruments deployed on the surface.

the interior and alter its temperature profile. It may be that Venus does not have a solid inner core.

Despite superficial similarities, Earth and Venus could turn out to have very different interior structures. On the other hand, their interiors may be pretty much alike except for differences in churning activity. In either case, the payoff for resolving the issue will be a better understanding of the geochemistry and geophysics of all the Earthlike planets.

The best way of getting at the interior structure of Venus is by means of a series of seismic measurements. The abundant signs of volcanic activity and the pervasive evidence of crustal deformation of all types suggest that Venus must be seismically active. Thus, an important goal for future exploration is the emplacement of a network of seismic sensors to elucidate the planet's internal structure. Because of Venus' severe surface environment—broiling heat and crushing pressure—the technological challenge is formidable. So far, no instruments have survived more than a short time on the planet's surface. Nevertheless, a successful mission of this type would accomplish the next great step in understanding Venus and inevitably would provide important insights into how Earth works as well.

Gene Therapy
A New Frontier in Medicine

by Kenneth W. Culver, R. Michael Blaese,
and W. French Anderson

For decades physicians, scientists, and families have dreamed of a genetic cure for the more than 5,000 known genetic illnesses. Now there is a light at the end of the tunnel.

The dream of genetic cures began nearly 100 years ago when the concept of a gene as hereditary material was first suggested. Only 40 years ago the structure of DNA (deoxyribonucleic acid), the building blocks of genes, was confirmed. Since that time more than 2,500 out of an estimated 50,000–100,000 genes in human chromosomes have been identified. As we advance into the final decade of the 20th century, we are now witnessing the beginning of the era of genetic healing. The long-awaited first use of gene therapy on a human patient began on Sept. 14, 1990, with an attempt to correct genetically a rare genetic immunodeficiency disease called adenosine deaminase (ADA) deficiency.

Adenosine deaminase deficiency

Each human has two adenosine deaminase genes, one on each chromosome 20, that produce an enzyme that is essential for the complete development and normal functioning of the immune system. Therefore, the ADA gene is found in all cells of the body and under normal circumstances continuously produces the ADA enzyme inside every cell. Children develop ADA deficiency, or ADA(−), when they inherit two defective ADA genes, one from each parent. If the child inherits one normal gene and one defective gene, the immune system is capable of normal function and development, but this individual is now a carrier of one defective gene and has the potential for passing that defective gene on to his or her offspring. The risk of having a child with ADA deficiency is 25% with each pregnancy if both mother and father carry a defective ADA gene. ADA deficiency is a rare disease, with an incidence of less than one in 100,000 births.

Children afflicted with ADA(−) have a significant deficiency in immune function. They are unable to produce specific antibodies following immunization with vaccines such as tetanus and diphtheria. In addition,

KENNETH W. CULVER *is a Senior Clinical Investigator at the National Institutes of Health.*
R. MICHAEL BLAESE *is Chief of the Molecular Immunology Section of the National Cancer Institute of the National Institutes of Health.*
W. FRENCH ANDERSON *is Chief of the Molecular Hematology Branch of the National Heart, Lung, and Blood Institute of the National Institutes of Health, Bethesda, Maryland.*

(Opposite page) Illustration by Jane Meredith

they are also unable to resolve completely such illnesses as common respiratory infections, chicken pox, and pneumonia. A comprehensive evaluation of their crippled immune system proves that there is a nearly complete failure of the body's ability to prevent and eliminate infections. This type of immunodeficiency is called severe combined immunodeficiency (SCID). The end result of the genetic defect is a child who has persistent viral and fungal infections, recurrent bacterial infections, and a markedly increased risk of early cancer. As a result, many of these children have died from overwhelming infections in their first months of life.

The treatment of choice for children with ADA(−)SCID is bone marrow transplantation with identically matched bone marrow from a brother or sister. Identically matched bone marrow is very important because when identical bone marrow is used, the transplant cures most of the children (70–90%). Unfortunately, however, only about 30% of patients will have a sibling with identically matched bone marrow. Parents typically have a 50% match with their children because children inherit one set of genes from each parent. Bone marrow transplantation with these 50%-matched bone marrow cells are much less successful in ADA(−)SCID (about 40%).

For ADA(−) children without a brother or sister with an identically matched marrow, there is an alternative therapy, called Adagen (PEG-ADA). Adagen is bovine (cow) ADA enzyme that has been united with polyethylene glycol (PEG) to allow survival and function of the cow ADA enzyme in the body for days. Without the PEG, injections of the ADA enzyme are ineffective because the enzyme is degraded in minutes. Injections of Adagen on a weekly basis have been helpful to many of the more than 20 children treated by this therapy, as evidenced by a decline in the number of infections and improved growth. Even with the use of Adagen, however, ADA(−)SCID children are not expected to live a normal life span without a curative bone marrow transplant or curative gene therapy.

Nearly 10 years ago three different investigators isolated the normal ADA gene from human T lymphocytes, white blood cells responsible for fighting off infections and cancer. Once the normal ADA gene had been identified, the next step was to develop a method that would allow its efficient transfer into human immune cells. In the early 1980s scientists developed an efficient method for the transfer of genes into mammalian cells using genetically altered mouse viruses called retroviral vectors. To create a vector, scientists remove the viral genes and replace them with the gene to be transferred. To transfer the gene, the vector is then mixed with growing cells in the laboratory. The vector enters the cells and deposits the new gene into the chromosome of the cell. The gene will then remain in that cell as long as the cell survives and will be passed to all daughter cells as the cell divides. This methodology allows the transfer of a new gene into as many as 90% of the cells. Extensive studies in the laboratory, in mice and monkeys, and, more recently, in humans have demonstrated that the use of this retroviral-mediated gene-transfer technology has a very low risk of causing problems.

Ideally, the genetic correction of ADA(−)SCID would involve insertion of a human ADA gene into a bone marrow cell called the pluripotent stem cell. The pluripotent stem cells are responsible for the production of all cells in the blood, which includes all cells that make up the immune system. The insertion of a normal ADA gene into the pluripotent stem cells would theoretically correct the ADA(−)SCID immunodeficiency, which would result in normal immunity and a lifetime cure. Many scientists had anticipated that the first use of gene therapy in humans would involve the genetic correction of ADA(−) bone marrow cells since the bone marrow would be a source of healthy cells for the lifetime of the patient.

Unfortunately, the isolation of the pluripotent stem cells in humans has proved very difficult. In addition, the insertion of normal, curative ADA genes into the pluripotent stem cells of monkeys and humans has not worked well, resulting in an insufficient number of gene-corrected cells in the peripheral blood. As a result, the use of retroviral-mediated gene transfer into bone marrow, a therapy that has the potential to cure a variety of genetic diseases (such as ADA(−)SCID, thalassemia, and sickle-cell disease), as well as other illnesses, is not yet technologically possible. Thus, for ADA deficiency, the isolation of the gene has not been the barrier to curative bone marrow gene therapy; instead, the gene-delivery system is insufficient. Researchers expect, however, that bone marrow gene therapy for ADA deficiency may become a reality soon.

Since the pluripotent stem cell cannot be used for gene therapy at this time, scientists considered the possibility of using other cell types, such as the T lymphocyte. T lymphocytes are easy to grow from the blood and are easy to alter genetically in the laboratory. The genetic correction of ADA(−) T lymphocytes is especially important because the transplantation of identical bone marrow to cure ADA(−)SCID completely requires only the T lymphocytes to survive and grow in the recipient. Engraftment of the other types of bone marrow cells is not necessary. Therefore, a series of experiments were initiated in which retroviral-mediated genes were transferred into T lymphocytes from the blood of children with ADA(−)SCID. These experiments demonstrated that the insertion of a normal human ADA gene into ADA(−) T lymphocytes corrected the ADA(−) and resulted in the production of normal amounts of functional ADA enzyme. In addition, the genetically corrected T lymphocytes grew like normal ADA(+) T lymphocytes in comparison with non-gene-corrected ADA(−) T lymphocytes, which had a shortened survival. These laboratory findings suggested that the intravenous infusion of the child's own genetically corrected ADA(−) T lymphocytes might improve the functioning of the immune system.

Prior to the initiation of this gene-therapy experiment in humans, the experimental plan had to be examined and approved by local and national review committees. These were the Institutional Review Board (IRB) and the Institutional Biosafety Committee (IBC) of the National Institutes of Health and the Recombinant DNA Advisory Committee (RAC) and its Human Gene Therapy Subcommittee, as well as the Food and

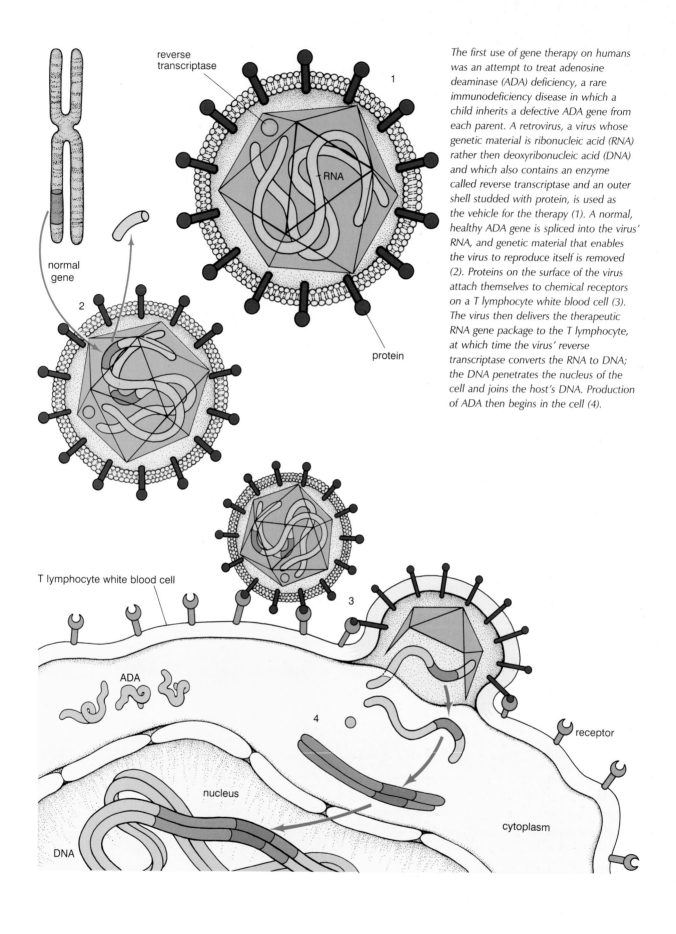

reverse transcriptase

1

RNA

normal gene

2

protein

The first use of gene therapy on humans was an attempt to treat adenosine deaminase (ADA) deficiency, a rare immunodeficiency disease in which a child inherits a defective ADA gene from each parent. A retrovirus, a virus whose genetic material is ribonucleic acid (RNA) rather then deoxyribonucleic acid (DNA) and which also contains an enzyme called reverse transcriptase and an outer shell studded with protein, is used as the vehicle for the therapy (1). A normal, healthy ADA gene is spliced into the virus' RNA, and genetic material that enables the virus to reproduce itself is removed (2). Proteins on the surface of the virus attach themselves to chemical receptors on a T lymphocyte white blood cell (3). The virus then delivers the therapeutic RNA gene package to the T lymphocyte, at which time the virus' reverse transcriptase converts the RNA to DNA; the DNA penetrates the nucleus of the cell and joins the host's DNA. Production of ADA then begins in the cell (4).

T lymphocyte white blood cell

ADA

3

4

receptor

nucleus

cytoplasm

DNA

Drug Administration (FDA). Following a series of extensive discussions, these committees decided that the proposed treatment of children with ADA(−)SCID with genetically corrected T lymphocytes posed no risk to society and that the treatments had the possibility of benefit to the patient. Final approval was given by the director of the National Institutes of Health and the FDA. Following the lengthy approval process, the first human gene-therapy experiment began on Sept. 14, 1990.

This experimental therapy began with the treatment of a four-year-old girl suffering from ADA(−)SCID. By the end of 1991 a second child, nine years old, had begun to receive infusions of ADA gene-corrected cells. Both children received infusions every one to two months during the year with no significant adverse effects. In fact, the children were able to return home several hours after the administration of the genetically corrected T lymphocytes. The early results of this experiment were encouraging for both children. As predicted by laboratory experiments, the ADA gene-corrected T lymphocytes appear to survive much longer in the human body than the T lymphocytes that have not received the gene. As a result, by late 1991 the two children had normal numbers of T lymphocytes in their blood, a key aspect in mounting a good fight against invading microorganisms and in preventing cancer. In addition, both children developed clear evidence of improved immune function.

The first evidence of improved immune function in the two children was the development of the ability to produce antibodies called isohemagglutinins. Normal individuals spontaneously produce isohemagglutinins, which are antibodies to blood types different from their own. For example, a person with type A blood will spontaneously make antibodies to type B blood. Children with ADA(−)SCID cannot make normal amounts of these antibodies. Following the infusion of their own gene-corrected T lymphocytes, both children developed the ability to make antibodies of the appropriate type in normal amounts. This is a very important result

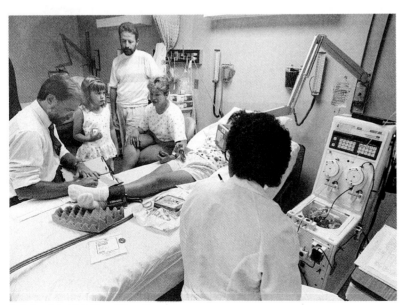

Ernie Cox, Jr. © 1991 Chicago Tribune Company

A 10-year-old girl, one of two young patients in the first trial of human gene therapy, undergoes apheresis to remove white blood cells for genetic correction. The girl was reported to be responding well in the early stages of the treatment.

Photos courtesy of the National Institutes of Health, Bethesda, Md.; photos, John T. Crawford

To prepare for gene therapy for ADA deficiency, white blood cells (T lymphocytes) are taken from a patient's own blood. In a laboratory the cells grow in culture (right), where retroviruses containing healthy ADA genes are mixed with them. The retroviruses deliver the healthy genes into the DNA of the cells. During the next few days the cells increase in number. They are then transferred to a gas-permeable bag (below left), where they continue to multiply. Later, the genetically corrected cells are reinfused into the patient (below right).

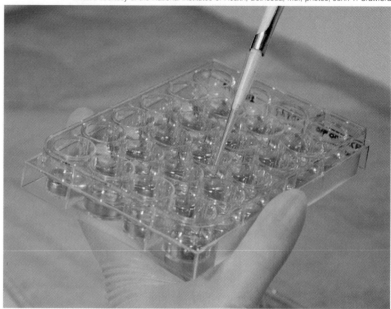

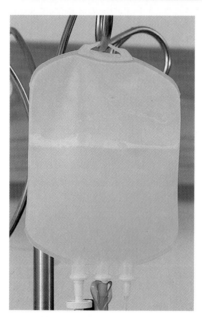

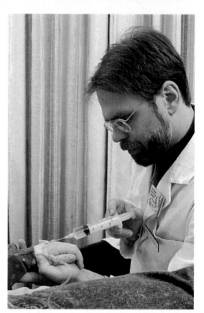

because the ability to make antibody is essential to mounting a protective immune response following infection and immunization. The youngest child, who has been treated the longest, has also experienced a dramatic decrease in the number of infections compared with her condition before gene therapy. This prompted the family to reduce the degree of her isolation at home, a common restriction used to help minimize the number of infections. By late 1991 she was able to attend school, swim, dance, and ice skate with her family and friends. She now tends to have infections only when other members of her family are ill.

The important and continuous immunologic improvement seen in these two children suggests that infusions of their genetically corrected

132

cells every several months may be sufficient to keep them healthy. While the use of T lymphocytes for the treatment of ADA(−)SCID is not a one-shot cure, it may provide continued good health in combination with Adagen. Once bone marrow stem-cell gene therapy becomes a reality, ADA(−)SCID children might be cured with a single treatment, eliminating the need for repeated infusions of ADA gene-corrected T lymphocytes.

Limitations of gene therapy

In their pursuit for curative, genetic treatments of genetic diseases, scientists must accomplish three goals. First, they must identify the gene responsible for the disorder. In 1989 an international collaboration was initiated by the United States to map all of the genes in the human cell. This international team is called the Human Genome Organization (HUGO). During the next two decades, as scientists identify each of the 50,000–100,000 genes in human cells, the overall understanding of health and disease will increase sufficiently to provide many new therapies. Once a gene has been identified, however, the next step is to learn to regulate it inside the body.

Approximately 2,500 human genes have been identified, but only a small number of gene-therapy experiments have begun. A major obstacle to the rapid increase in the number of gene-therapy trials in humans is the lack of the ability to control the new gene properly inside a cell. Gene therapy for ADA deficiency was tried first, even though it is a rare disease, because the normal production of the ADA enzyme is not complicated. The ADA gene makes the enzyme continuously, requiring no specific regulation. In addition, the risk that overproduction of the enzyme might be harmful is minimal. People with normal immune function have been identified with ranges between as little as 10% of normal and 50 times normal amounts of ADA in their T lymphocytes. This is in marked contrast to the possible use of the insulin gene for the treatment of diabetes mellitus. The insulin gene has been available for more than 10 years, but the ability to control the production of the insulin gene has not been decoded. If the normal insulin gene was inserted into the body of a person with diabetes mellitus, the amount of insulin made by that gene would need to be controlled. If the gene made only 10% of the amount needed or 50 times too much (such as is acceptable with the ADA gene), the person with diabetes could be adversely affected. Once the technology to specifically control more complicated genes such as insulin has been developed, gene therapy will be applicable to a larger number of diseases.

The third major obstacle to the use of gene therapy on a broad scale is the lack of an efficient method of gene transfer into the diseased cells of the body. There are no methods for routinely culturing a variety of tissues (such as nerves, muscle, and lung) in the laboratory that can be returned to the patient. Therefore, the gene transfer has to occur in the body. One example of this problem occurs in the treatment of cystic fibrosis (CF). CF is a common genetic disorder affecting as many as one in 2,500 births in families of central European background. The inheritance of two defective genes results in severe lung disease and poor growth due to chronic lung infections and an inability to absorb nutrients from the digestive tract. The CF gene has recently been isolated, and insertion of the normal CF gene into defective cells in the laboratory has corrected the genetic defect. However, there is no proven gene-transfer method that will insert the normal CF gene into diseased lung cells in the body. During recent months a number of investigators have been working on methods to transfer the CF gene into the lung cells of animals. These methods include genetically altering viruses that normally infect the human lung, such as adenoviruses, as well as wrapping the CF gene in lipid that will allow the gene to be blown into the lung to be absorbed into some of the lung cells. Once a suitable gene-delivery system has been identified in animal studies, the era of genetic healing for cystic fibrosis should begin.

AIDS and cancer

T lymphocytes have the potential for the genetic treatment of many diseases, including AIDS (acquired immune deficiency syndrome) and cancer. The experiment with ADA(−)SCID demonstrated that the genetic alteration of an ADA(−) T lymphocyte can make a "sick" T lymphocyte healthy. Since AIDS is caused by a virus, the human immunodeficiency virus (HIV), that makes T lymphocytes sick, genetically altering HIV-infected T lymphocytes may be a useful therapy. Many scientists are working on genetic methods of modifying body tissues so that they will decrease the spread of the virus and genetically turn off the ability of the AIDS virus to grow in the body. Gene-therapy experiments for the treatment of human HIV infection are likely to begin in the next year.

T lymphocytes are also critical for the prevention and elimination of tumors. Scientists have isolated from T lymphocytes genes that are responsible for the production of chemicals that will improve the body's ability to kill the tumor. Experiments in humans have used genetically modified T lymphocytes, called tumor-infiltrating lymphocytes or TIL, and genetically modified tumor cells. These experiments, conducted at the National Institutes of Health under the direction of Steven Rosenberg, involve the insertion of the human tumor necrosis factor (TNF) gene.

TNF is a chemical that is normally produced by T lymphocytes and in sufficient amounts can destroy tumors. Unfortunately, the intravenous infusion of TNF in humans has significant adverse side effects. The initial experiments with TIL aim to use genetically altered T lymphocytes to deliver high concentrations of TNF directly to the tumor. Following an intravenous infusion of these TNF-altered T lymphocytes into the patient, they migrate back to the tumor sites in the body. The researchers hope that the T lymphocytes will deliver more TNF to the tumor with minimal side effects compared with intravenous TNF therapy.

The genetic modification of a person's own tumor cells was approved in October 1991. The experiment was an attempt to immunize patients specifically against their own tumors by genetically altering the tumors with the TNF gene or the IL-2 gene (a chemical that improves the growth

134

Scanning electron micrograph reveals human tumor-infiltrating lymphocytes (TILs) growing inside an artificial hollow fiber. These cells may deliver into a patient high concentrations of the human tumor necrosis factor (TNF) gene. If infused into the body in sufficient amounts, TNF can destroy tumors. When delivered by TILs, TNF may cause fewer harmful side effects than it does when it is infused intravenously.

and function of T lymphocytes). Tumor cells (malignant melanoma, kidney cell cancer, or colon carcinoma) were surgically removed from the body and genetically altered in the laboratory. The tumor cells were reinjected under the skin, like a vaccination, in an effort to stimulate the immune system to better fight the remaining cancer cells in the body. This experiment was in its early stages, and no results were available. Gene-therapy experiments for the treatment of ovarian cancer and brain tumors were currently under investigation.

Other potential uses

A second human gene-therapy experiment for the treatment of genetic disease was approved in October 1991 for the treatment of a lethal liver disease. The experiment is to be conducted at the University of Michigan by James Wilson and colleagues. The disease, familial hypercholesterolemia, is a deficiency in the low-density lipoprotein (LDL) receptor that is necessary for the normal metabolism of cholesterol. Without a normal LDL receptor, individuals develop very high cholesterol levels (over 700) and often suffer from heart attacks during childhood. In this experiment, liver cells would be surgically removed, the LDL gene inserted into the cells in the laboratory, and the cells then infused intravenously back into the liver.

Scientists throughout the world were working vigorously on many other cell types to deliver genes into the body. These included endothelial cells, which are cells that coat the inside of blood vessels, and skin. The genetic modification of skin could have many applications because skin could theoretically secrete a large amount of gene product into the bloodstream. For example, hemophilia (a genetic disorder that results in

135

James M. Wilson, Mariann Grossman, and Dawn McKinley, The University of Michigan Medical Center, Ann Arbor

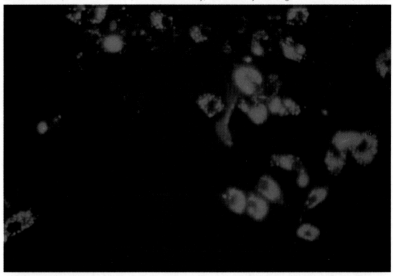

Rabbit liver cells that lack the receptor for low-density lipoprotein (LDL) start to manufacture the receptor (bright regions) after being infused with the LDL gene. Humans who lack the receptor have very high levels of LDLs in their serum cholesterol and often suffer fatal heart attacks during childhood. Scientists hoped that treating such people with the genetically altered cells would correct this condition.

severe bleeding because of an inability to make a normal clotting factor in the blood) potentially could be corrected by insertion of a normal clotting-factor gene into a patient's skin in the laboratory. The genetically altered skin could then be grafted back onto the patient, where the new skin would continuously secrete the needed factor into the bloodstream. Since the skin previously belonged to the patient, the skin graft should not be rejected. This has not yet been attempted in humans because gene-transfer methods into skin or other cell types have not resulted in the production of sufficient amounts of the normal blood-clotting factors to make this a feasible approach to the treatment of hemophilia.

The genetic alteration of cells that cannot be grown in the laboratory poses a more difficult problem. These tissues include lung, heart, spinal cord, and brain. In these situations the gene needs to be transferred into the correct location in the body. While retroviral vectors work reasonably well with T lymphocytes, liver cells, and skin, this method does not work with cells that are not growing, such as spinal cord and brain. Consequently, in order to treat a wide variety of neurological disorders such as Parkinson's disease, Alzheimer's disease, and neurofibromatosis, other types of gene-transfer methods need to be developed. This is a difficult problem. A number of years may pass before scientists understand enough about gene transfer into cells of the nervous system to begin gene-therapy trials for neurological diseases.

For many diseases the ability to block the function of a gene (such as one that causes arthritis) or turn on a gene (such as one that will produce a missing hormone) is all that is necessary. This differs from genetic defects, where one must insert a normal gene to correct the disease. There are many novel ideas for using gene therapy to cure diseases such as arthritis. Because each gene inside a cell is unique, scientists can build a gene that is the mirror image of a specific gene. When injected into a cell, this new piece of recombinant DNA will bind specifically to its mirror image (block it) and not to any of the other thousands of genes in the cell. This process has been termed, "antisense" or "triplexing." If the gene that is blocked is normally producing a protein, such as a hormone, the production of that hormone would cease. However, if the function of that gene was to suppress the production of a hormone, the hormone would now be made. With this type of genetic targeting it might be possible to turn off genes that are responsible for arthritis or other autoimmune diseases such as systemic lupus erythematosis.

The concept of antisense or triplexing genes is appealing, but accomplishing this in the human body poses a difficult challenge. Once again, the delivery system for antisense/triplexing genes is a major concern. The goal is to one day be able to simply inject the antisense/triplexing genes directly into patients, like a vaccination, on an outpatient basis. This is theoretically possible through the use of specific receptors on the surface of cells. Cell-surface receptors are protein structures on the surface of cells that bind specific proteins in the blood such as nutrients or bind to the surface of other cells. For example, there are cell-surface proteins found on liver cells that are not found on any other cells of the body. If a specific tag is attached to a gene that would allow specific binding to a special receptor on a cell, there would be the potential for gene transfer into specific cell types in the body. The development of injectable, targetable genes (the injected genes that will go to a specific tissue) will probably require 5–10 more years of research before the initiation of human trials.

Future prospects

During the 1990s the speed at which new therapies arrive at the bedside will not be primarily limited by the isolation and cloning of the genes or by the willingness of society to accept these new experimental therapies; instead, the rate will be limited by the ability to deliver and regulate the genes that are now available (such as insulin and hemoglobin). With continued determination and imagination, new methods for delivery in the body will be developed. As gene-therapy experiments become increasingly successful, there should be a welcome decrease in the amount of human suffering.

FOR ADDITIONAL READING

W. French Anderson, "Prospects for Human Gene Therapy," *Science* (Oct. 26, 1984, pp. 401–409).

Kenneth Culver *et al.,* "Lymphocytes as Cellular Vehicles for Gene Therapy in Mouse and Man," *Proceedings of the National Academy of Sciences* (1991, vol. 88, pp. 3155–59).

R. Michael Blaese, Kenneth Culver, and W. French Anderson, "The ADA Human Gene Therapy Clinical Protocol," *Human Gene Therapy* (1990, vol. 1, pp. 331–362).

Kenneth Culver, W. French Anderson, and R. Michael Blaese, "Lymphocyte Gene Therapy" *Human Gene Therapy* (1991, vol. 2, pp. 107–109).

Inder Verma, "Gene Therapy," *Scientific American* (November 1990, pp. 68–84).

137

The Biology and Culture of Human Odor

by D. Michael Stoddart

Odor-based communication, so important to most mammals for recognition and reproduction, lingers in greatly subdued form in modern humans. Understanding the subtle ways in which human odors still influence our biology and behavior presents scientists with an intriguing but difficult challenge.

A. Renee McGinnis

The scents of fresh-baked cookies, Christmas trees, wet paper and watercolors—for many people such smells are intimately connected with the memories of childhood. Experiencing them even decades later can stir emotions as well as recollections, for odors speak directly to the primitive part of the human brain.

(Top and bottom right) Cathy Melloan; (bottom left) James P. Dwyer—Stock, Boston

D. MICHAEL STODDART is Professor of Zoology and Department Head, Department of Zoology, University of Tasmania, Hobart, Australia.

(Overleaf) Illustration by M. Renee McGinnis

You are walking along your neighborhood street to the supermarket, thinking over your shopping list, when you catch a whiff of baking cinnamon cookies that takes you right back to your grandmother's kitchen. The force of it is almost overwhelming as your mind fills with childhood memories not recalled for decades. Similarly, you help your toddler open a box of crayons, and suddenly the distinctive waxy odor has you seated at your desk in your own first-grade classroom, coloring cutouts of circus animals.

As many people have learned firsthand, smells and scents can be extremely evocative. They are able to penetrate to the emotional side of one's being far more directly than sounds or sights. Strangely, however, humans regard themselves as having little use for the sense of smell. Ask 100 people at random about which one of their five senses—sight, touch, hearing, taste, and smell—they would part with most readily, and

140

the huge majority would say smell (and the remainder, probably taste). Some would claim that their allergies or sinus conditions keep them from smelling much anyway but that their lives are not greatly affected. Others might say that they sustained a car or sports injury some time in the past and have not been able to perceive odors for years. Paradoxically, if one were to ask the same 100 people whether they had either given or received a perfumed product like after-shave, body lotion, talc, toilet water, perfume, or scented soap in the past 12 months, the chances are good that they all would respond positively.

A look at the products in one's grocery bags will show that many of them are purposely perfumed by the manufacturer. Floor and furniture polishes, bathroom disinfectants, household cleaners, toilet paper, and—most particularly—laundry products all contain fragrances, many openly announcing the fact. "Sudz-O detergent makes your clothes *smell* clean!" intones the voice-over on the television commercial. What is not said is that one's clothes would be chemically cleaner *without* the extra substances used as perfume. People in Western nations live in a perfumed world, yet most folk would deny that their noses are of much use to them.

The ancient sense of smell

The fundamental reason for this seemingly contradictory situation is that in evolutionary terms the olfactory system, the network of nerves extending from the nose to the brain, is very old. The nose as one normally thinks of it—the structure associated with the air passage in terrestrial animals—is no older than life on land. But chemical communication, which is really the function of the sense of smell, is as old as life itself. Within every cell of the human body, chemical messengers coordinate the various activities that keep the cell functioning normally. At higher levels of organization the body's cells and tissues are in constant communication with one another, again relying on molecules as their

People generally regard the sense of smell as the most expendable of the senses, yet a look at the supermarket shelves indicates the attention that manufacturers and consumers pay to odors. Fragrances are added to products as diverse as soaps and detergents, furniture polish, bubble baths, antiperspirants, and personal hygiene articles. Deodorants are available to freshen rooms, cars, carpets, and trash cans. Some medicinal products and cleaners exploit the common belief that ingredients with strong flavors and smells are especially effective at eliminating germs.

Cathy Melloan

messengers. When sexual reproduction first evolved in lowly aquatic life forms, it was the release of chemicals into the water that brought the sexes together for mating.

Lowly organisms do not have the advanced kind of brain, dominated by large cerebral hemispheres, that is found in the higher vertebrates. In these more complex organisms, as a legacy of their evolutionary past, the olfactory system sends its sensory impulses into a primitive part of the brain called the rhinencephalon, a word that literally means "nose-brain." In humans the rhinencephalon is located within the central basal part of the cerebral hemispheres in a region called the limbic system (from *limbus,* a Latin word meaning "edge" or "threshold"). Research over the past century has revealed that the limbic system is the seat of emotion and an important center of memory. This explains why human reactions to odors can be so emotional and why the scent of cookies or crayons can fill one's head involuntarily with thoughts of the past. The sense of smell is the least intellectual of the human senses. We trust our eyes and ears to feed us information about the world to which we can react rationally, for visual and aural signals are processed in the cerebral hemispheres, the parts of the brain that make us human. But odors bypass the rational part of the brain and appeal directly to the primitive part to stimulate the emotions.

Smells are actually various airborne molecules that are swept into the upper part of the nasal cavity as a person inhales. The sensory part of each nostril, no larger than a fingernail, is found just beneath the bridge of the nose. There, nestling in a thin yellowish membrane, are specialized nerve cells, the scent-receptor cells. Humans have about 3 million receptor cells in each nostril; by comparison, rabbits and dogs have 10 million. Each cell terminates in a ring of tentacle-like hairs, or cilia, and it is onto the web of intertwined cilia that scent molecules are deposited. Despite much recent research, scientists are not exactly sure how a scent molecule triggers a nerve impulse. Nor do they know whether there are specific receptor sites for certain types of odors; for example, minty, fruity, burnt, or musky.

The receptor cells project into the outside world, protected only by a layer of mucus about a tenth of a millimeter (four thousandths of an inch) thick. They also send back long projections, called axons, into a paired part of the brain called the olfactory bulbs. In humans these are small, insignificant structures located just above the nasal cavity, but in fish and in primitive mammals like shrews they are dominating features of the brain. In the olfactory bulbs the receptor-cell axons enter spherical regions called glomeruli and terminate there. Secondary nerve cells of the olfactory system run laterally from the glomeruli; they connect with yet other, tertiary nerve cells that complete the chain by terminating in the region of the hypothalamus. The various structures of the hypothalamic region send out their own nerve-cell axons, some of which return to the olfactory bulbs while others connect with higher, cognitive centers in the cerebral hemispheres. It is these latter connections that stimulate one to think of the name of the perfume just smelled, to identify the

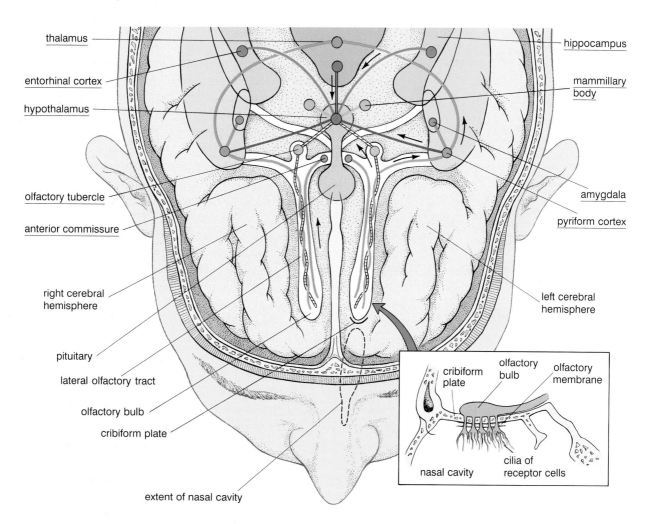

thalamus

entorhinal cortex

hypothalamus

olfactory tubercle

anterior commissure

right cerebral
hemisphere

pituitary

lateral olfactory tract

olfactory bulb

cribiform plate

extent of nasal cavity

hippocampus

mammillary
body

amygdala

pyriform cortex

left cerebral
hemisphere

cribiform
plate

olfactory
bulb

olfactory
membrane

nasal cavity

cilia of
receptor cells

rose by its fragrance, or to instigate a search of one's memory for the associations provoked by a particular odor.

A nose-to-gonad connection

The small clusters of brain cells collectively called the hypothalamus govern a great many physiological functions, including sexual reproduction. Chemicals secreted by the hypothalamus pass through tiny channels to the pituitary, a glandular structure just beneath the hypothalamus that directly controls the ebb and flow of sex hormones in women and men. The flow of chemical messages from the hypothalamus stimulates the pituitary to release hormones, known as gonadotropins, into the blood. These function to prompt the gonads—the ovaries in women and the testes in men—to produce the corresponding steroid sex hormones: the estrogens (mainly estradiol, estrone, and estriol) and the androgens (predominantly testosterone). It is the sex hormones, in turn, that bring about the secondary sexual characteristics that accompany puberty.

Laboratory studies of rodents suggest that there exists a chain of chemical signals linking the nose to the gonads, via the hypothalamus and pituitary, and that if the chain is broken, the normal course of

143

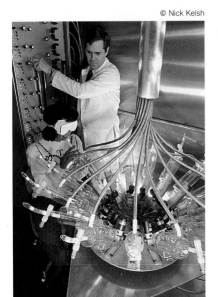

A subject is tested for her ability to detect low levels of odors at the University of Pennsylvania Taste and Smell Center. In certain medical conditions the inability to smell occurs along with disturbances in reproductive function or development. While much work remains to be done on a nose-to-gonad connection in humans, the evidence for its existence is substantial.

The apocrine glands associated with human hair are so abundant in the armpits, or axillae, that the area is called the axillary organ. Fresh axillary secretion is odorless, but in the presence of bacteria it takes on the familiar armpit smell.

sexual reproduction is severely disturbed. Yet it would be an oversimplification to say that sexual reproduction cannot occur if the chain is broken. For example, sexually mature but inexperienced male rats in which researchers had cut the olfactory nerves, *i.e.,* the bundles of axons projecting from the scent-receptor cells to the olfactory bulbs, showed no interest at all in sexually mature females. But when the same procedure was carried out on sexually experienced rats, normal courtship and mating occurred. This study, and others like it conducted on other kinds of rodents, indicate that reproductive behavior is not under the simple control of one sensory system and that, although the sense of smell predominates in sexually inexperienced individuals, it may be superseded in experienced subjects.

There is evidence to suggest that the message chain between nose and gonads also exists in humans and that it must be intact for normal sexual function. It is not uncommon for a whiplash injury sustained in a car accident to damage the olfactory nerves by stretching them, like elastic bands, to the breaking point. Not only does this kind of injury produce anosmia, the loss of the sense of smell, but in women it also results in an interruption of the menstrual cycle. The condition is usually temporary, however; as the olfactory nerve regrows, so normal menstruation and the ability to perceive odors return.

Some kind of relationship between the nose and sexual reproduction in humans has been suspected since ancient times. Students of the Greek physician Hippocrates admonished men to "abstain from warmth and women" at the first signs of a cold or catarrh, since venery was thought to irritate the nose. In fact, inflammation of the nasal membranes, sometimes severe to the point of bleeding, often occurs during pregnancy and puberty when levels of sex hormones are high. Some women suffer a degree of nasal irritation during each menstrual cycle around the time of ovulation. The extreme sensitivity of the nasal membranes to sex hormone levels in the blood has yet to be adequately explained.

There exists a rare inherited condition in humans known as Kallmann's syndrome, in which the gonads fail to develop and the person never enters puberty. In those afflicted with this condition, production of gonadotropins by the pituitary is very low. Particularly interesting is the observation that all sufferers are anosmic. Studies reported by Dietrich Klingmüller and co-workers in Bonn, Germany, revealed that a malformation of the olfactory part of the brain is associated with Kallmann's syndrome. Although much more work remains to be done, the anatomic and physiological evidence for the existence of a nose-to-gonad connection in humans is substantial.

Human scent glands

As described above, it is during puberty that hormones secreted by the testes and ovaries give rise to the secondary sexual characteristics of men and women. One feature of puberty is the appearance of dense hair growth in certain bodily locations, in particular, the pubic region and the axillae, or armpits. Another feature, which can be embarrassing for

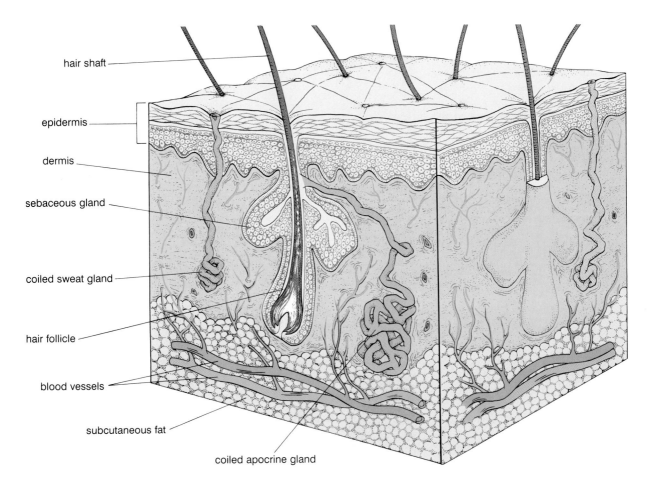

hair shaft

epidermis

dermis

sebaceous gland

coiled sweat gland

hair follicle

blood vessels

subcutaneous fat

coiled apocrine gland

teenagers, is the eruption of unsightly acne on the skin. Both phenomena are associated with the "switching on" of the body's countless thousands of scent-producing glands: the sebaceous and apocrine glands.

Every hair on the body, even the tiny, downy ones that cover the so-called hairless areas, has associated with it a gland that secretes a blend of fatty substances, called sebum, into the hair follicle. These sebaceous glands are particularly abundant around the nipples and surrounding areas (areolae) in females, on the scrotum in males, and on the face, scalp, and anogenital region in both sexes. As many as 140 glands per square centimeter (900 per square inch) have been recorded on the face and scalp.

Human hair is equipped with a second type of gland, which also empties its secretion into the hair follicle. Called apocrine glands, they are particularly abundant in the armpits, in the pubic region, and around the face. In the armpits they are so densely packed that the term *axillary organ* is a fitting description for this feature. The axillary organ of an adult man measures 50 millimeters (two inches) long and up to 20 millimeters (³/₄ inch) wide. It can be as much as five millimeters (³/₁₆ inch) thick, with the coiled vessels of the glands forcing up the skin surface into a raised platform. Curiously and for reasons not yet known, women have more apocrine glands in the axillary organ than do men, though

A cutaway diagram of the human skin shows the sebaceous and apocrine glands and their relation to the hair follicle, the tubular pocket in the skin that encloses the hair shaft and bulb. Both kinds of glands empty their secretions into the hair follicle, and individual human odor comes from a combination of apocrine secretion and sebum. By contrast, the eccrine, or true, sweat glands open directly to the skin surface; their secretion, mostly water, serves to keep the skin moist and to regulate body temperature.

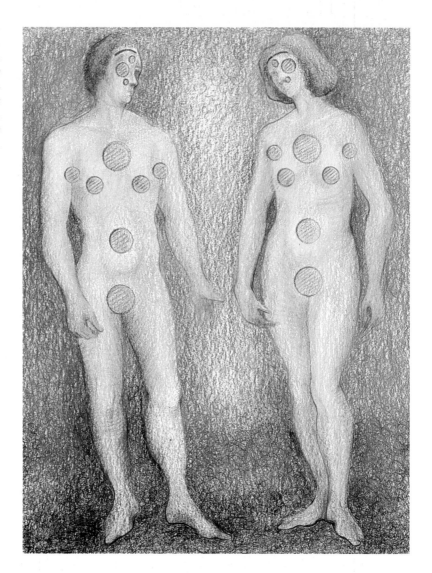

the glands themselves are generally smaller in size. Apocrine secretion is a viscid oily substance ranging in color from milky pale gray or clear white to red, yellow, or even black. The expression *to sweat blood* refers to a condition known as chromidrosis, in which the apocrine glands in the armpits produce a reddish secretion.

The human axillary organ is structurally very reminiscent of scent organs found in many species of mammals, though this is as far as the similarity extends. The bodies of nonhuman mammals are well endowed with scent organs, and much is known of their functions. The commonest use is in territorial marking, in which, for example, the scent organ is rubbed against branches or its content sprayed on rocks or tree trunks. Such scent posts seldom actually deter visitors from entering, but they serve to inform the visitor of the age and social status of the owner. Other species use emitted scent to announce their presence and sexual condition to members of the opposite sex. Owners of female dogs are well aware of the power of such scents to attract males from the whole

146

neighborhood. Contrary to popular literature—and as is discussed below—little is certain about the contributions of human scent to biological and social, particularly sexual, communication.

There is one area of human biology in which scientists seem to agree that bodily odors play an important part. Once newborn infants have been nursed by their mothers, they subsequently are able to orient themselves correctly to the smell of their mothers' breasts. If breast pads from a group of lactating women are held close, one at a time, to the nose of an infant of one of the women, the infant shows excited nipple-searching movements only to the pad from his or her own mother. To what extent this response is to the odor of the mother's milk or of the sebum secreted by areolar glands is not known. Mothers, too, are able to identify their own infants by odor after an exposure of as little as 10 minutes—an ability that can last as long as 30 months. Both phenomena resemble the odor imprinting that occurs between mother and offspring in sheep, mice, bats, and possibly all mammals.

Among adults, from the meager research done to date, identification of other adults by odor seems limited by a decline with age in the ability to discriminate between different human odors. In one study published in 1980 by Margret Schleidt, 25 German couples were given a simple cotton shirt to wear every night for a week. Each subject was then asked to sniff groups of 10 shirts and to identify his or her own, his or her partner's, and those worn either by males or by females. Only a small proportion could reliably discriminate between the sexes by shirt odor. Both men and women subjects generally described the men's shirts as unpleasant and the women's shirts as pleasant. Interestingly, men who were told that a particular shirt was their own, even if it was not, classified its odor as pleasant. That result illustrates one of the difficulties encountered in human odor research: one's own odor is usually reported as agreeable, while the odors of one's companions are perceived as disagreeable.

The culture of human odor

Compared with other primates, humankind is the species most richly endowed with scent glands, yet it is the primate species that relies least on odorous signals. Among humans in the West, where hot and cold water is available at the turn of a tap, concentrated efforts are made to remove all traces of body odor. Not only do people shower once or twice a day, but also in many societies the underarm region is shaved clean of hairs. Research conducted in the 1950s showed that shaved underarms remain free of detectable odors between 24 and 36 hours after washing, whereas unshaved underarms may be noticeable after as little as 4 hours. The reason for the difference is that shaving removes much of the surface area on which the normal bacterial population of the armpit resides. Freshly expressed axillary secretion is odorless, but after a few hours in the presence of underarm bacteria it takes on a typical armpit smell. The use of antibacterial soaps, which kill the microorganisms, and antiperspirant deodorants, which reduce axillary organ secretion, are effective agents in the control of unpleasant underarm odor.

Newborn infants who have been nursed by their mothers are able subsequently to orient themselves to the smell of their own mothers' breasts. To what extent the response is to the odor of the milk or of the sebum secreted around the nipples is not known. Mothers, too, are able to identify their own infants by odor after an exposure of only 10 minutes.

Spencer Grant—Stock, Boston

147

Much has been learned about chemical communication, and of the functions of scent and scent organs, in nonhuman animals. Among mammals the most common use of scent is in territorial marking. A cheetah (top left) proclaims its presence and social status by spraying a rock with its urine, while an African antelope known as a klipspringer (top right) defines its territory by coating a twig with a dark, sticky secretion from a special gland below the eye. Chemical communication also serves in reproduction. Chemicals on the skin of a female red-sided garter snake (right; the largest snake in the image) announce her sexual receptiveness to numerous courting males, who sample the chemicals by bringing them into the mouth with flicks of the tongue. (Bottom

right) The airborne scent emitted by a white-tailed deer doe informs a buck that she is in estrus and that his attentions will not be futile. The power of such scents to attract males of a species over considerable distances is familiar to any dog owner who has observed a female in heat. On the other hand—and contrary to popular literature— little is certain about the contributions of human scent to biological and social, particularly sexual, communication.

So basic to the Egyptians was the relationship between happiness and a beautiful odor that the hieroglyphic determinative for happiness was a nose (below). In a papyrus (left) Anubis, god of embalming, watches over a mummified body and jars of removed viscera. Mummification was a religious ritual, intended to assure immortality for the deceased. To please Osiris, god of the underworld, who was said to exude a fine odor, the embalmer dressed the body and viscera with scented oils and spices and poured more oil on the body wrappings. Small, narrow-necked bottles of aromatic oil were among typical materials to be found in an Egyptian embalmer's workshop (bottom).

(Top left) From the collection of the British Museum; photo, © Michael Holford; (bottom) The University Museum, University of Pennsylvania (neg. no. T4–354)

Paradoxically, although humans do not wish to smell of humans, they have the urge to smell of *something*. For thousands of years perfumed unguents have been used to give the body what has been deemed a proper odor, and many plant and animal products have been employed for the task. To the ancient Egyptians the relationship between happiness and a beautiful odor was so fundamental that the hieroglyphic determinative for happiness was a nose. In Egyptian society it was held that, in order to ascend to heaven, the deceased had to travel to the tomb of Osiris. The god of the underworld was said to exude a fine odor, and all who breathed his breath could be laid to rest in peace. To help its ascendency the mummified body was packed with incense and other perfumes, and pots of perfume were placed alongside it in the tomb. The exact basis for this belief is not clear, but it may be related to the idea of fine odor as an antidote to, and protection from, demonic influences.

During the scourge of the Black Death, which ravaged Europe in the

149

Throughout human history odors have been associated with beliefs ranging from the divine to the morbid. Ancient peoples hoped to please their gods by perfuming the air around them with incense, a ritual that is still carried out in modern religious rites. In a relief from an Egyptian chapel at Karnak (top), Queen Hatshepsut burns incense before a god. (Bottom) The smoke from burning incense liberally suffuses worshipers at a liturgical service at the Episcopal Cathedral Church of St. John the Divine in New York City. In Europe during the time of the great plagues, the odor of a sick person was thought to carry the disease to others, whereas pleasant smells were thought to protect against such transmission. Plague doctors held pomanders, fruits studded with dried cloves, to the nose when treating the diseased (opposite page, top). Others donned masks equipped with birdlike bills into which were placed dried flower petals and herbs (opposite page, bottom).

14th century, as well as during later outbreaks of the disease, plague doctors wore curious masks shaped like birds' bills into which was placed dried flower petals and herbs. They carried before them small braziers of smoldering incense to perfume the air and provide protection against the evil odor of the diseased. Others held pomanders, oranges studded with dried cloves, close to their noses as they approached an ill person. The 14th-century English nursery rhyme "Ring-a-ring of roses/A pocketful of posies/A-tishoo, a-tishoo/We all fall down" refers to the relationship between the plague, which produced dark rings and blotches on the skin, and the naive belief in the prophylactic power of sweet odor.

The 11th-century Arab physician Avicenna perceptively used his nose as an aid in diagnosis of disease, concluding that variations in urine

150

odor resulted from the body's expelling the evil influence that caused the malady. It was long held that disease was actually caused by bad air—the word *malaria* means just that. Today it is known that a change in urine odor, such as the sweet smell of the urine of a diabetic, signifies a metabolic abnormality associated with the disease.

There seems little doubt that the notion of sweet scent as a demonifuge is deeply rooted in the psyche of modern humans and explains why people are attracted to cleaning products that imbue the cleaned article with a particular odor. Despite the fact that we know much about the role of microorganisms in disease and about the substances that are effective against them, we still believe that disinfectants should have a strong smell, and manufacturers trade heavily on that belief.

Although most people from Western nations would hold that the human body does not smell appealing, many writers and poets have called attention to the fragrance of their lovers in beautiful and evocative ways. The writer of the biblical Song of Solomon describes the odor of his lover's garments as being "like the scent of Lebanon. A garden locked is my sister, my bride!" He calls upon the north wind to "blow upon my garden, let its fragrance be wafted abroad. Let my beloved come to his garden, and eat its choicest fruits." The 17th-century English poet Robert Herrick made frequent references to the skin fragrances of various imaginary mistresses, even entitling one poem "Upon Julia's Sweat." Émile Zola, Charles Baudelaire, Joris-Karl Huysmans, and other noted writers frequently probed the psyche for its deep-rooted awareness of the power of human body odor to effect arousal. The suggestion that emerges from the works of these aesthetes is that human scent may contribute to sexual interest and may be powerfully involved in sexual attraction. Is there any scientific support for such an idea, given the ancientness of the role of chemical communication in sexual reproduction and the evidence for the link between the nose and the sex glands?

The olfactory sense in mammalian reproduction

The mouse has proved to be a useful model for studying the function of the sense of smell in mammalian reproduction, and it will be helpful to review what is known about this species before examining what is known about humans. Shortly after the end of World War II, when laboratory colonies of mice were being built up to serve the nascent but growing pharmaceutical industry, Hilda Bruce, a researcher at the University of Cambridge, noticed that when newly pregnant female mice were brought into contact with male mice from a different colony, a high proportion of females resorbed their litters and were no longer pregnant. It soon became apparent that the physical presence of the male stranger was not required; a sample of his urine or his nesting material was sufficient to terminate pregnancy. About the same time, two Dutch biologists, S. van der Lee and L.M. Boot, observed that if female mice were kept together and totally isolated from males, their estrous cycles, normally four days long, gradually lengthened until eventually they ceased altogether. Australian researcher Wesley Whitten extended these observations, demon-

Photos, The Granger Collection, New York

151

"Here at the downy roots of every strand I stupefy myself on the mingled scent of musk and tar and coconut oil for hours . . . from which I gulp the wine of memory." So wrote Baudelaire on the occasion of smelling a woman's hair, an evocative recognition of the power of human fragrance to arouse mingled passions and recollections.

strating that if an adult male was introduced to females in this condition, their cycles all switched on again.

Since the 1960s careful investigations of these observations have uncovered a complicated picture of the chemical control of reproductive biology in the mouse. The chemical signals in question fall into a broad category of substances, called pheromones, that are now known to be widespread among vertebrates and insects. Today a pheromone—the word was coined to suggest "carried hormone"—is considered to be any chemical substance made and released by an organism that elicits a particular reaction from another organism of the same species. In mice the pheromones involved in reproduction may be carried as odors to the nose or dissolved in water, in which form they enter through the mouth. Dissolved chemicals are detected by a specialized sensory apparatus, the vomeronasal organ (Jacobson's organ), lying in the roof of the mouth. For all intents and purposes this organ is a secondary nose, the only difference being that it samples molecules that are drawn in aqueous solution into the oral cavity. Like the membrane-bound scent receptor cells in the nose, the vomeronasal organ sends its neural messages to the limbic system by way of a special series of nerve cells.

Once detected, pheromones cause levels of gonadotropins to rise, leading to the expression of various behavioral and physiological responses that are hormonally influenced, including the induction of estrus. Young female mice brought up in close contact with adult male odor grow faster and become sexually mature earlier than those kept in the company only of "maiden aunts." Scientists know of many of the effects of odors on the sexual development of mice, but they know less about the precise biochemical mechanisms responsible for the effects.

Although more is understood about pheromonal control of reproduction in mice than in any other mammal, such control appears to exist to some degree in most terrestrial mammalian species. Cattle and sheep farmers, horse owners, and dog and cat breeders know how readily their male animals sample the urine of females. After licking the urine, the

Female and male harvest mice direct their noses attentively toward one another. Studies since the late 1940s have uncovered a complicated picture of the role of chemical signals in the reproductive biology of the mouse and have made the animal a useful model for assessing the function of the sense of smell in mammalian reproduction.

male raises his head and sharply sucks in air through a partly open mouth, sometimes making a whistling noise, in order to bring the sampled chemicals to the vomeronasal organ. The behavior, known by the German word *flehmen,* is visible as a curling of the lips in a snarl-like grimace. It has been suggested that the secondary olfactory system, based on the vomeronasal organ, gives the individual animal its first insight into its partner's sexual condition. After that, the true nose takes over.

Until the early 1990s humans had been thought to lack a functional vomeronasal organ, but that view has now been challenged. Recent anatomic research has revealed a pair of blind-ended tubes that lie in the nasal septum and open onto its surface in small pits. The tubes measure between two and eight millimeters (about ³⁄₃₂ to ⁵⁄₁₆ inch) in length and are lined with specialized cells that may be sensory in function. A group of researchers in Utah led by David Berliner reported that the human vomeronasal organ is specifically sensitive to chemicals claimed by some to be human pheromones. This fascinating area of research can be expected to blossom in the near future. Humans may yet be found to have a functional pheromone-receiving system, like other terrestrial mammals.

Are there human pheromones?

The nearly universal involvement of odor in the reproductive control of nonhuman mammals might suggest that human reproductive biology is, to some extent, under odorous control. Do human pheromones exist, and do they play a part of any significance in reproduction?

The evidence on this matter remains equivocal. In 1971 Illinois researcher Martha McClintock claimed that women who roomed together in an all-female university residence hall experienced more synchronous menstrual periods than any pair of women chosen at random. Support for that observation came from a follow-up British study indicating that some interpersonal effect appeared to be operating, rather as it does in mice. M.J. Russell and his associates in California investigated the

Many mammalian species—from domesticated animals like the dog, sheep, and horse to "wild" animals like the lion and rhinoceros—demonstrate a particular interest in certain substances by displaying a behavior known as flehmen. After the animal samples the substance of interest, which may be the urine of an individual of the same species, it raises its head and sucks in air through a partially open mouth (top left and right) in order to bring the sampled chemicals to the vomeronasal organ, a specialized sensory apparatus that is essentially a second nose. Some researchers have suggested that this second olfactory system gives an individual animal its first insight into a prospective partner's sexual condition.

153

Some support for the existence of pheromones in humans comes from reports that young women who room together in college dormitories experience more synchronous menstrual periods than pairs of women chosen randomly. Other studies suggest that the underarm secretion of some women contains substances that can "drive" the cycles of others, putting them into synchrony with the cycle of the source of the secretion. While such results favor the notion of human pheromones, the lack of fully convincing evidence makes it wise to remain skeptical.

claimed ability of some women to "drive" the cycles of others. Their work concentrated on underarm secretion, since it contains steroidal compounds known to act as mating pheromones in pigs. On the upper lips of a group of female volunteers, the researchers daubed either an extract of underarm secretion of a supposed "driver" or a placebo several times a week. After three months the cycles of the women in the extract group had come almost into synchrony with that of the donor, while those of the placebo group showed no trend toward synchrony.

Other studies have endeavored to reveal what relationship, if any, exists between the steroidal, pheromone-like secretion of the armpit and human sexual physiology. Evidence has been presented in the scientific literature to show that underarm secretion from men, when applied periodically to the upper lips of women, reduces the variability of cycle length and the proportion of aberrant cycles. It must be noted that in all these studies the sample sizes were rather too small for the data to stand up to rigorous statistical testing. Such a drawback is encountered by many researchers who work with human subjects and is not specific to studies on human odor.

Research conducted on rhesus monkeys in England in the mid-1960s by Richard Michael indicated that the state of a female monkey's cycle was revealed in the nature of the cocktail of substances occurring in her vaginal secretion. These substances were named copulins, for it was shown that male monkeys would undertake quite exhausting tasks to gain access to females at the peak of their heats. Copulins are fatty acids, produced by the action of bacteria on glycogen or carbohydrates, and they reach their maximum abundance at the time of ovulation. Other studies showed that fatty acids also occur in human vaginal secretions but in quite variable amounts. Behavioral investigations in the laboratory revealed that humans, men and women alike, do not find the odor of vaginal secretion particularly pleasant, although it is least unpleasant

154

around the time of ovulation. Furthermore, there is no evidence at all that vaginal secretion extract, when applied to the body as a perfume, acts in any way as an aphrodisiac. In matters of libido, humans are clearly different from rhesus monkeys.

Women are generally most sensitive to odors during the middle phase of the menstrual cycle, *i.e.*, around the time of ovulation, an observation that has led some writers to conclude that the sense of smell is intimately involved in the reproductive cycle. The levels of the sex hormones estradiol and estrone also peak at ovulation, and these are known to increase the levels of other hormones that enhance the nose's sensitivity. Thus, lowering of the odor threshold of detectability at ovulation may be no more than an artifact of a more widespread hormonal change.

A critical appraisal of the now considerable body of literature concerning purported human pheromones leaves one less than fully convinced of their existence or their roles in sexual behavior or physiology. Some evidence in their favor cannot be denied, and while it is tempting, even fashionable, to conclude that human reproductive biology is driven by factors that drive reproduction in other animals, it is wise to remain skeptical. Research into this fascinating aspect of human biology is being pursued in various laboratories around the world, and the next decade should see many questions resolved.

The nose's loss, the family's gain

If it is so uncertain that odors play a part in human reproductive biology, why are scented personal products marketed largely on their sex appeal? And why do perfumes contain sex attractants and other chemical messengers from animals like civet cats, beavers, and musk deer or flowery scents made by plants to attract animal pollinators? In other publications I have advanced a theory to explain this enigmatic state of affairs.

When the far-distant ancestors of human beings still dwelled in forests, they likely lived in small groups based on the family, with a single male and possibly two or three females and some dependent young. As the females came into heat, they produced an estrus-advertising odor, as most primates and other mammals do today, which resulted in mating and pregnancy. Later in human evolution, about 10 million years ago, our hominid ancestors moved out of the forests and onto the open plains. On this landscape dwelled the ancestors of the large ungulates, the hooved mammals, but such fleet, powerful prey was inaccessible to a single hominid male or even to a single family. Gradually groups of hominids started to coalesce, such that bands of hunters were able to ambush large prey. This major gain in hunting ability may well have been the ecological imperative for the adoption of a gregarious life-style.

In a large multifamily community the continued production of estrus-advertising odors would have been counterproductive. It would have undermined evolution of the security, provided by pair-bonded parents, that was necessary for the slow-growing young to acquire cultural knowledge—for males would no longer be certain of the paternity of their bonded mate's offspring, as their nongregarious forebears would have

155

Advertisements frequently imply, sometimes with little subtlety, that scented personal products are sex attractants in a bottle, trading on the popular notion that what is known about the factors that drive reproductive biology in other animals also applies to humans.

ANIMALE
Pure Instinct

been. Sociobiologists hold that natural selection would have favored factors that encouraged persistence and continued development of the nuclear family within the gregarious group. It has been proposed, therefore, that the olfactory system became desensitized to the pheromonal action of estrous odors at some stage in human evolution in order to protect the genetic basis of the nuclear family. For the same reason, ovulation became visually concealed, and a suite of other anatomic and physiological adaptations evolved to strengthen the pair bond.

For modern humans odor no longer plays a central, controlling role in human reproduction, but memory traces of its importance remain deep within the psyche. Those traces can be stirred, and the emotions stimulated, by the scent of musk of rutting deer, of civet from civet cats, and probably of the secretions of a great many other species. Scent-producing organs in humans do not function in the manner observed in other mammalian species, for they do not attract a member of the opposite sex from afar. Their evolution is consistent with their being part of a complex suite of adaptations that helped maintain the bond between a single male and a single female long enough for the young to be reared. They act discretely, subtly, and only in the most intimate circumstances, their natural perfumes fulfilling an ancient need for odorous signals to trigger sexual reproduction.

Such a theory is not possible to confirm. It assumes circumstances that ceased to exist many millions of years ago and so must remain speculative. Its strength is that it is based on a critical examination of the ways in which odors are used in the animal kingdom. The human sense of smell is far from redundant. City life may drive it into retreat but cannot rob it of its power to exhilarate us with the smell of parched earth slaked with rain, of new-mown hay, or of the sepulchral depths of a tall forest. Neither can it take away some of the most exquisite and vibrant sensations we shall ever know.

FOR ADDITIONAL READING

Alain Corbin, *The Foul and the Fragrant: Odor and the French Social Imagination* (Berg Publishers Ltd., 1986).

Ellis Douek, *The Sense of Smell and Its Abnormalities* (Churchill Livingstone, 1974).

Aytoun Ellis, *The Essence of Beauty* (Secker and Warburg, 1960).

Max Lake, *Scents and Sensuality* (John Murray, 1989).

D. Michael Stoddart, *The Scented Ape: The Biology and Culture of Human Odour* (Cambridge University Press, 1990).

Steve Van Toller and George H. Dodd, *Perfumery: The Psychology and Biology of Fragrance* (Chapman and Hall, 1988).

High-quality perfumes typically include such ingredients as rose oil, distilled from flower petals (top) whose function is to attract insect pollinators; musk, extracted from the abdominal pouch of rutting male musk deer (above); and civet, a musklike secretion from the anal glands of the civet cat (above left). Why humans should be drawn to the odors of such products is addressed by a theory that proposes that while odor no longer plays a central role in human reproduction, as it did for our far-distant ancestors, memory traces of its importance linger in the psyche— and are stirred by the scents employed by plant and animal species for chemical communication.

Finding Tomorrow's Scientists:
50 Years of the Westinghouse Science Talent Search

by Charles F. Carroll

Beginning in 1942 high school students throughout the United States have developed their skills as scientists while competing in the prestigious Westinghouse Science Talent Search.

Calling the Westinghouse Science Talent Search just a science fair is like calling Albert Einstein just a physicist. For half a century this competition has identified and rewarded top students and encouraged untold thousands of other youngsters to pursue careers in science, engineering, and mathematics. Since 1942 more than 100,000 high school seniors have completed research projects and entered the competition, and 2,000 of them have been selected as national winners.

The achievements of these 2,000 as teenagers and adults are impressive. Alumni of the Science Talent Search (STS) have earned hundreds of honors in scientific and related fields. Five former STS winners have won Nobel Prizes. Two have earned Fields Medals, the mathematics equivalent of the Nobel. MacArthur Fellowships, the so-called genius awards that grant large sums for unrestricted use by the recipients, have gone to eight alumni. Fifty-two have been selected as Sloan research fellows, 29 elected to the National Academy of Sciences, and 3 chosen for the National Academy of Engineering.

More than 70% have earned Ph.D. or M.D. degrees. Well over half of the former STS winners who are old enough to have completed their education are either teaching or engaged in research on college and university campuses, where much of the world's basic scientific research is done. Career choices are about evenly distributed among the physical sciences, the biological sciences, and medicine.

Some writers have called the STS the "Oscars of science fairs," others "the farm club for Nobelists." Observers agree that it is the most prestigious no-strings-attached scholarship competition for U.S. high school seniors.

Origins

For a re-creation of how the notion of the STS came to be a reality, the clock must be turned back to 1939, when two former newspaper science

G. Edward Pendray (above) of the Westinghouse Electric Corp. established in 1938 a national competition sponsored by Westinghouse to identify 10 U.S. high school seniors who were talented in science. In 1939 he joined with Watson Davis (below, center), and the two began the planning that led to the first Westinghouse Science Talent Search in 1942. In the photograph below, Davis, a civil engineer and science writer, autographs the programs of the two winners of the 1942 competition, Paul Teschan of Shorewood, Wisconsin, and Marina Prajmovsky of Farmingdale, New York.

CHARLES F. CARROLL *is retired Director of Public Information at the Westinghouse Electric Corp., Pittsburgh, Pennsylvania.*

(Overleaf) Illustration by Kathryn Diffley

writers were discussing the sorry state of science education. G. Edward Pendray and Watson Davis met at the 1939 New York World's Fair.

Pendray had been a reporter and science editor for the *New York Herald Tribune* from 1925 to 1931 and science editor of the *Literary Digest* magazine from 1931 to 1936. He then joined the Westinghouse Electric Corp. as assistant to the president in charge of advertising and public relations. While on the *Herald Tribune*, Pendray had participated in an annual science fair put on by the American Institute of the City of New York. The event stimulated interest in science among the New York high schools, and Pendray obtained a series of annual grants from Westinghouse to help support it. In 1938 he established a national Westinghouse competition to identify 10 talented high school seniors, who were then awarded tuition, room, and board to attend Carnegie Institute of Technology (now Carnegie Mellon University) in Pittsburgh, Pennsylvania, the hometown of Westinghouse.

Pendray was well known for his writings on the possibilities of rocket power and spaceflight. He founded the American Rocket Society, which later became incorporated into the American Institute of Aeronautics and Astronautics. In 1931 he said in an interview, "If shooting rockets across the Atlantic Ocean is feasible, there is no obstacle to shooting them to another planet, with the Moon as a beginner."

Watson Davis was a civil engineer who became a science writer. He was the first science radio newscaster and for 33 years was director of Science Service, the organization that has administered the STS since it was founded. At Science Service, Davis directed a unique institution. The nonprofit organization was founded in 1921 by E.W. Scripps of the Scripps-Howard newspapers. For years, Scripps was concerned about the gulf between scientific achievement and public understanding of it. Intrigued by the challenge to interpret science to the public accurately, Davis joined Science Service in 1922; he became its director in 1933.

Eight eminent scientists constitute the board that chooses the finalists and winners of each year's Westinghouse Science Talent Search. The 1990 board consisted of (seated, left to right) Glenn T. Seaborg and J. Richard Gott and (back row, left to right) Charles Schwartz, Brigid Leventhal, Gilbert Castellan, Andrew Yeager, Stuart Hauser, and William Thurston.

Davis and Pendray thus shared a strong interest in fostering a better public understanding of science and in finding and stimulating young people whose scientific talents might otherwise be lost to society. It was at the New York World's Fair that they first began discussing ways of expanding this youth science work across the United States. They learned that of the 25,000 U.S. high schools then in existence, fewer than 1,000 had teachers who were trained in science or even offered basic science courses.

Pendray said, "Watson and I agreed that science was too important for the coming generation to be neglected in high schools. We perceived that the American Institute youth activity offered a practical way of calling broad attention to the need, as well as for stirring the enthusiasm of young people for science careers. The American Institute, being limited to New York City, could not do the national job, so Science Service, which was admirably suited to the task, agreed in 1940 to undertake it, with financial support from Westinghouse." That first year's grant, which was to cover scholarships and administrative costs in 1942, totaled $25,000.

Pendray and Davis agreed on a basic premise for STS: The best way to learn science is not from a textbook but by doing it, to participate actively in the inquiry process. The wisdom of that premise has stood the test of time.

Conducting the search

As a new school year begins in September, Science Service notifies the 20,000 high schools in the U.S. that the competition is under way. Any student in the senior year of secondary school is eligible to enter.

161

U.S. Pres. Dwight Eisenhower meets with the 40 finalists in 1955. Most presidents personally welcome the students during their stay in Washington, D.C.

Each student submits a written report on an independent research project in the physical sciences, behavioral and social sciences, engineering, mathematics, or biological sciences. What the judges hope to elicit from the report is evidence of student creativity and interest in science.

An entry form also must be completed, in part by the student, in part by the supervising scientist (if any), and by at least one science teacher. The entry includes a copy of the student's official high school transcript. Typically, close to 1,600 seniors meet the entry requirements each year.

Experiments on live vertebrate animals are not eligible. However, if a student is working in a laboratory where animal experimentation is taking place, the student's research is eligible for entry if the student has no physical contact with the animals.

The research project must be the work of a single individual, not a group project. The deadline for entries to be in the hands of Science Service is early December.

The first level of judging is conducted by a group of evaluators from leading scientific and academic institutions, such as Johns Hopkins University, Baltimore, Maryland, and the National Institutes of Health, Bethesda, Maryland. Entries are categorized by discipline and evaluated by at least two judges who are specialists in the relevant area. After all the entries have been evaluated, 300 semifinalists are selected. Admissions offices of every four-year college in the U.S. receive the names and addresses of the 300 students, along with letters of recommendation. Because of the impressive undergraduate track record of previous semi-

162

finalists and the reputation of the STS program, the colleges approach many of the students with admission and scholarship offers.

At the next level the entries are judged by a board of eight distinguished scientists, also from a variety of backgrounds. Among them are Glenn T. Seaborg, a Nobel Prize winner and university professor of chemistry at the University of California at Berkeley, and J. Richard Gott, professor of astrophysical sciences at Princeton University, a Sloan Fellowship recipient and second-place scholarship winner in the 1965 STS competition. Gott serves as chairman of the judges.

The judges are aided by other scientists in completing a careful evaluation of each entry. The 40 finalists are selected from the 300 semifinalists. These 40 receive a five-day, all-expense-paid trip to Washington, D.C.,

Westinghouse Electric Corporation

An exhibition of the projects of the 40 finalists is open to the public each year at the National Academy of Sciences in Washington, D.C.

Westinghouse Electric Corporation

U.S. Pres. George Bush addresses the 50th annual Westinghouse Science Talent Search awards banquet in Washington, D.C.

where the judges meet the students for the first time and interview them. Past winners have also met with U.S. presidents, vice presidents, and distinguished science advisers in government and universities.

The finalists display their projects for the public at the National Academy of Sciences and describe their work to hundreds of visitors, including important figures in government and science. They are also interviewed by national and international newspapers and magazines, press associations, television networks, and science and education journals.

The whirlwind in Washington culminates at an awards banquet at which Westinghouse distributes $205,000 in scholarships. As of 1991 the top prize was a $40,000 scholarship. Second- and third-place winners received $30,000 and $20,000, respectively. Three others won $15,000 each, and four $10,000 scholarships were awarded. The other 30 finalists received $1,000 scholarships.

The judges rank the 40 finalists in terms of scientific creativity and interest, partially on the basis of their projects but also equally on that of personal interviews. Questions in the interviews are unpredictable, ranging from "How many tennis balls would fit in this room?" to "How did you get interested in science?"

During the 50-year history of the STS, the kinds of projects that win scholarships have changed considerably as science itself has changed and advanced. Paul B. Teschan, in 1942, was the first to win the top prize. All he had to do was pass a special examination and write an essay entitled "How Science Can Help Win the War." That was good enough to win what was then the $2,400 top award.

Sister Mary Lauretta

New York City has produced more finalists in the Westinghouse Science Talent Search than any other area. The competition among city schools as well as between teachers within those schools is obvious in the results. Other big cities, with excellent laboratory facilities at hand, also are well represented among the finalists.

But occasionally an aberration occurs, usually traceable to a gifted and dedicated teacher. In the mid-1950s a small school in a semirural section of Wisconsin began turning out STS finalists on a consistent basis. Students from Columbus High in Marshfield reached the top 40 in seven of the eight years from 1955 to 1962. At first the judges were puzzled. "How could this little school turn out such fine young scientists year after year?" the judges wondered. Eventually they found that the key that had unlocked so much talent was a physics and chemistry teacher named Sister Mary Lauretta Bishop.

Before Sister Mary Lauretta became Columbus High's first science teacher in 1952, she had taught in a Milwaukee school and had tried, unsuccessfully, to find and encourage a talent search winner. "But when I got to Marshfield," she said, "I tried again. And I certainly was blessed with some wonderful students."

One of those students was Ronald Gates, who decided to study the chemistry of making vinegar, using 20 natural products as different sources for the acidic compound. The school had few laboratory resources, and so Gates collected his materials as best he could. He picked dandelions from the school's lawn; for cattails, he went to the pond on a local farm. Sister Mary Lauretta accompanied him to gather apples in an orchard. She remembered that the vivid color of Gates's cranberry vinegar was "as beautiful as red wine."

Just before Christmas of 1958, Gates abandoned

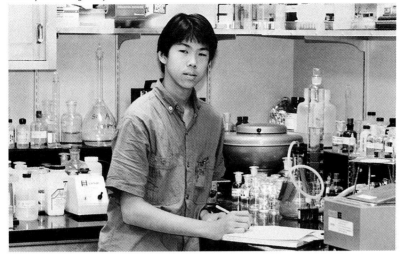

Clifford Lee Wang of Vero Beach, Florida, a finalist in the 1991 competition, conducted a study in biochemistry that led him to propose that seaweed can be grown in the ocean to remove metal pollutants and then harvested as biomass for producing energy. He used seaweed that he cultivated in the family garage to absorb trace metals and found that the metals served as biocatalysts, enhancing methane production from the seaweed.

Today's winning projects range from gene-splicing experiments done in national laboratories to backyard physics projects, from issue-oriented projects examining various aspects of the environment to purely theoretical projects in mathematics done with pencil and paper. Students in the 1990s have the advantage of sophisticated computer technology and modeling, which open up almost limitless possibilities for scientific investigation. It has been estimated that the level of scientific research conducted by the winning high school seniors is about equal to what a first-year graduate student is capable of doing.

the project in order to earn some extra spending money for the holidays. A few weeks later, urged by his father, he decided to resume work on it. During his hiatus, Sister Mary Lauretta disclosed, "I've fed your cultures. They're still going."

Gates would have had to start all over again if Sister Mary Lauretta had not kept the cultures alive.

The project earned Gates a trip to Washington as a finalist in the STS.

Just before Sister Mary Lauretta died at the age of 90, Gates told her in a letter that he had decided to give up his career as a biochemist and become a high school science teacher. "If I can be a teacher half as good as she was, it will be terrific," he said.

Sister Mary Lauretta Bishop produced finalists in seven of her eight years at Columbus High School in semirural Marshfield, Wisconsin.

Nobelists

Who are these remarkable people? What are their backgrounds? What motivates them? Brief biographies of the STS alumni who won Nobel Prizes disclose both similarities and differences.

Roald Hoffmann was just six years old when his father smuggled him and his mother out of a Nazi labor camp in Poland and hid them in a schoolhouse attic until they were freed in June 1944. His father was killed by the Nazis a year before liberation came. Most of his family suffered a similar fate.

Roald and his mother moved from Poland to Czechoslovakia in 1946 and then to displaced persons' camps in Austria and Germany. They finally arrived in the United States in 1949. At that time 11-year-old Roald learned English, his sixth language. After finishing grade school in Brooklyn, New York, he attended Stuyvesant High School in Manhattan, New York.

"In my day," Hoffmann recalled, "most of the students at Stuyvesant were Jewish immigrants, first or second generation. They were an in-

---

Immigrants

Immigration into the United States has had a major impact on the Westinghouse Science Talent Search. Prodigies uncovered in the early years of the STS included many children of Jewish immigrants, most of them refugees from Nazi-dominated Europe. Knowledge, they were reminded often by parents and teachers, was a passport to success in the U.S.

Just as Jewish refugees' children were in the forefront of the STS winners in its early history, the children of Asian birth or parents

The top five scholarships in 1986 were won by students born in Asia or of Asian parentage. They are (left to right) Anh Tuan Nguyen-Huynh, fifth; Yoriko Saito, third; Wei-Jing Zhu and Wendy Kay Chung, tied for first; and George Jer-Chi Juang, fourth.

credible group of young people. In fact, that run-down building held the largest concentration of intellectual talent that I ever experienced, including college at Columbia or graduate school at Harvard. Now nearly half are Asian-Americans. And just as bright."

He added: "When someone asks what America should do to keep up the flow of scientists for industry and universities, the answer is obvious. Liberalize the immigration laws. If we open our doors, we will never have trouble getting scientists and doctors."

Hoffmann was a winner in the 1955 STS. Through the STS he got his first job in science at the National Bureau of Standards. He went to Columbia University, New York City, as an undergraduate and earned a doctorate in chemistry from Harvard University. In 1981 the Polish lad who escaped from the Nazis and moved to the United States won the Nobel Prize for Chemistry, sharing it with a Japanese scientist from Kyoto. Since 1965 he has held an honored chair on the faculty at Cornell University, Ithaca, New York, as the John A. Newman professor of physical science.

---

began crowding the list in the 1980s. In the 10 years from 1979 to 1988, 88 students born in Asia or of Asian parents were among the 400 STS winners, including six first-place champions.

The first Asian-born student to win top STS honors, in 1973, was Arvind Srivastava, who moved from India to the U.S. at age three. He won with a mathematics project that examined the possibility that the universe is finite rather than infinite. The first native East Asian student to win first place was Paul Chih Ning, in 1983. Born in Taiwan, he also submitted and won with a math project.

Anh Tuan Nguyen-Huynh fled Vietnam with his widowed mother. While living for a year in refugee camps, he studied English to be prepared for life in the U.S. He won an STS scholarship in 1986 and four years later graduated from Harvard University.

The success of immigrants in the STS competition has been attributed to a number of factors, including a cultural emphasis on education and the desire of newcomers to succeed through intellectual achievement, with an emphasis on science. People who have traveled to the U.S. from great distances have often already displayed extraordinary courage and the determination that would bring them success in the academic world. In addition, they have found science a field where linguistic barriers are minimized and where talent and hard work are rewarded.

The second-place winner in 1991 was Denis Lazarev, who, with his parents, had been able to leave the Soviet Union only a year and a half earlier as a result of liberalized immigration policies. As events in the world unfold, new waves of immigration may come from different directions. The STS and the U.S. scientific establishment as a whole can expect to continue to be enriched by them.

How are young people first attracted to science? Sheldon L. Glashow's interest stemmed from the science-fiction books he found so fascinating as a boy during World War II and from a chemistry set his father gave him.

His father, Lev Glukhovsky, had left Czarist Russia in 1905 at the age of 16, a refugee seeking new opportunity in a new land. Renamed Lewis Glashow by an anonymous immigration official, he sent for his family

Females

How have young women fared in the Science Talent Search? Early in its history the STS made allowance for the fact that fewer females were going into the sciences by judging their entries apart from those of the males. In each of the first six years, a separate female winner was named. Then, as high schools in the U.S. began to produce more women interested in science, the separate classification was dropped. Beginning with the STS of 1948, all entrants competed on an equal footing—male and female.

It was not until 1972, however, that a female competing against all comers won the first-place scholarship. Since then, six more have captured first prize. The young women have asserted their presence in the top ranks of science.

They could not have had a better champion than the first one—Nina Tabachnik of Little Neck, Long Island, New York. This talented 16-year-old, with visions of a career in medical research, was the

daughter of parents who "took me on long weekends visiting museums, libraries and attending concerts." In this way Nina discovered intellectual and cultural things "as a game," long before she encountered them in any school curriculum.

She attended New York's Benjamin Cardozo High School. While not a specialized school, it offered advanced-placement courses and especially a two-year program in biological research that required a research report. Nina's report on a study of aldehyde air pollutants as an environmental hazard to plants that live in water won her first place among the 40 finalists in the STS.

After her triumph in Washington, Nina entered Yale. She found the university unique in that it offered a major that combined biology and chemistry. She earned her bachelor of science degree in molecular biophysics and biochemistry and then pursued simultaneously a Ph.D. in medical biochemistry at

a few years later. When Sheldon was a boy, his father agreed to build a small chemistry lab for him by converting a basement closet in their home in New York City. Through his two brothers—a physician and a dentist—Sheldon was able to obtain the test tubes, beakers, and other tools of the laboratory and, above all, the chemicals.

From the New York Public Library young Glashow copied procedures for exotic chemical syntheses from old textbooks and attempted to carry them out in his basement lab. It was his experimenting with powdered selenium metal that eventually led to his winning entry in the STS. He grew tomato seedlings in a hydroponic solution in his back yard, feeding some of the plants selenium to see if they would take it instead of sulfur in the growth process. He attended the Bronx (New York) High School of Science, where students then, as now, were encouraged to enter "the Westinghouse," accounting for the large number of STS winners from that school over the years.

"We had a wonderful week in Washington," Glashow recalls of his STS experience. "We shook hands with President Truman and met a lot of big-shot scientists. I was not selected for one of the big-money prizes and came away with a mere $100 scholarship award. Nevertheless, becoming an 'STSer' was a tremendous ego boost."

His outstanding career in theoretical physics, in search of the basic elements and secrets of the "stuff the world is made of," won Glashow a share of the 1979 Nobel Prize for Physics and many other honors. He told his personal story and the story of particle physics in the book *Interactions*, which was published in 1988.

(Opposite page) Roald Hoffmann, a finalist in the 1955 competition (left), shared the Nobel Prize for Chemistry in 1981 (right).

Rockefeller University, New York City, and an M.D. at Cornell University's medical college. She is now a scientist doing research in pediatric neurology at Children's Hospital in Pittsburgh.

In five of the eight years from 1980 to 1987, young women won top honors in the STS—Lisa Joy Randall of Stuyvesant High School, New York City; Amy Sue Reichel of New York City's Hunter College High School; Reena Beth Gordon of Midwood High School, Brooklyn, New York; Wendy Kay Chung of Miami (Florida) Killian Senior High School; and Louise Chia Chang of the University of Chicago Laboratory Schools High School. In 1991 another young woman, Ashley Melia Reiter of the North Carolina School of Science and Mathematics in Durham, captured first place in the competition.

Nina Tabachnik Schor, a research scientist in Pittsburgh, Pennsylvania, in 1972 became the first female to win first place in direct competition against males.

Westinghouse Electric Corporation

Leon Cooper (above right) was the first talent search finalist to win a Nobel Prize. His project, in 1947, was on bacterial resistance to penicillin; in 1972 he shared the Nobel Prize for Physics for his studies on the theory of superconductivity. Ben Mottelson (below) earned a finalist position in 1944 as a telescope maker. He shared the Nobel Prize for Physics in 1975 for his work in nuclear physics.

Westinghouse Electric Corporation

Walter Gilbert, another Nobelist from the STS ranks, offers a contrasting background to Hoffmann and Glashow. His parents were born in the U.S., and Walter was given his early education at home by his mother, who was a child psychologist. In 1939 the family moved from the Boston area to Washington, D.C., where his economist father joined the New Deal "brain trust" under Pres. Franklin D. Roosevelt.

Walter's interest in science surfaced early. He had a chemistry set by age six and was a collector of minerals and butterflies. A few years later members of the Mineralogical Society of Washington were startled to learn that their newest member was only 11 years old. Gilbert spent his high school years as a student at Sidwell Friends School in northwest Washington but describes his relationship with the school as "distant." "I spent most of my time playing hooky so I could read at the Library of Congress," he admits. There he pored over science books that were unavailable to him elsewhere, attending class just often enough to pass the tests. He was graduated from Sidwell with straight A's.

He completed a project in chemistry for his winning entry in the 1949 STS. It concerned a one-step separation of zirconium and hafnium—metals important to the new field of nuclear energy. But, for exhibit purposes, he pursued another of his interests—astronomy—and built a small telescope.

Gilbert studied both chemistry and physics at Harvard and at Cambridge. Gradually his interest in chemistry was overtaken by a fascination with physics. He taught theoretical physics at Harvard as an assistant professor until he again shifted gears in 1960 and moved into biological research.

His success in biophysics, biochemistry, and molecular biology firmly established him in the field of biology, and it was for his work in genetic engineering—techniques for sequencing and handling DNA—that he won the Nobel Prize for Chemistry in 1980. He shared the prize with a British scientist at Cambridge and another American, at Stanford.

Sheldon L. Glashow (left), a finalist in 1950 for his experiments with powdered selenium metal, shared the Nobel Prize for Physics in 1979 for his investigations in theoretical physics. Walter Gilbert (right), a 1949 finalist for a chemistry project involving a one-step separation of zirconium and hafnium, shared the 1980 Nobel Prize for Chemistry for his work in genetic engineering.

The first two Westinghouse Science Talent Search winners to capture the Nobel Prize were Ben Mottelson, STS 1944, and Leon Cooper, STS 1947. A graduate of Lyons Township High School in La Grange, Illinois, Mottelson was a young telescope maker when he won a place among the 40 STS winners. He earned his bachelor's degree in physics at Purdue University, West Lafayette, Indiana, and then continued at Harvard for his master's and doctor's degrees. After receiving his Ph.D. from Harvard in 1950, he joined the faculty of the Institute of Theoretical Physics at the University of Copenhagen. Mottelson's work in nuclear physics in Copenhagen won him his Nobel Prize in 1975. He shared the award with a Danish scientist and another American, from Columbia University.

Another product of the Bronx High School of Science, Leon Cooper captured a place in the STS winner's circle with research on bacterial resistance to penicillin. Cooper points out that this is an area of scientific effort that since that time has brought "incredible dividends." However, he did not pursue it after high school, turning instead to the study of physics. Following this interest, he earned a Ph.D. from Columbia in 1954. After several years on the faculty at the University of Illinois and at Ohio State University, he moved to Brown University, Providence, Rhode Island, in 1958.

Cooper shared the Nobel Prize for Physics in 1972 for his studies on the theory of superconductivity, completed while still in his 20s. In 1974 he was appointed the Thomas J. Watson, Sr., professor of science at Brown. His early years of research in nuclear physics and superconductivity were followed by investigations into neural networks and the biological basis of learning, working toward an understanding of memory and other brain functions.

As the STS begins its second half century, other bright, creative young minds will continue to point toward securing a better world. And the STS, in uncovering such talent, plays its part in crossing new thresholds of scientific discovery.

LIFE

AS WE DON'T KNOW IT

by Charles E. Taylor

Researchers in a fledgling field are working to determine what being alive actually means and to instill lifelike behavior in such traditionally nonliving media as computer programs, robots, and simple chemical processes.

What is alive and what is not? How large is the class of objects that possess life? The answer from humankind's deep past—from its oldest myths and ancient religions and cosmologies—has been that life extends beyond plants and animals and permeates all nature and the universe. "We are part of the earth and it is part of us. The perfumed flowers are our sisters. The bear, the deer, the great eagle, these are our brothers. The rocky crests, the juices of the meadow, the body heat of the pony, and man, all belong to the same family," said Seattle, chief of the Suquamish. As far as can be determined, most hunter societies have held similar beliefs.

For Western culture that traditional view began to change with the Greek philosophers, particularly Aristotle. Animate and inanimate came to be viewed as fundamentally different. Over the centuries the separation continued to grow, culminating in the theory of vitalism, which lasted well into the 20th century. During the 17th and 18th centuries, building on the discoveries of Galileo, Newton, and others, Descartes and other philosophers made various attempts to view animals as "nothing but" machines. None of their theories proved satisfactory, however, especially for biologists.

The trend toward separation has now reversed itself. The distinction between living and nonliving is thoroughly blurred. In fact, scientists are building artificial systems—some of them far removed from the common perception of living organisms—that possess most or all of the properties and behaviors that traditionally have been associated with life. These characteristics include self-assembly and self-reproduction, development and differentiation, adaptation and evolution, and complex ecological interactions. Such scientific efforts are defining a new area of research termed artificial life, or a-life. The field attempts to extract the logical

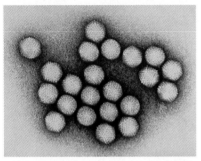

CHARLES E. TAYLOR is Professor of Biology at the University of California at Los Angeles and an artificial-life researcher.

(Overleaf) Illustration by Stephanie Motz

properties of life from naturally occurring organisms and then to provide them to characteristically nonliving systems, like computer processes or robots. It has also begun to seek signs of life in such seemingly unlikely places as the abstract realms of ideas and theories.

A variety of human-made systems now being studied have properties that one commonly attributes to living systems. Investigating these systems is making it possible to understand life in the broader sense, that is, life-as-it-can-be, and through this effort to better appreciate life-as-it-is. The consequences of research in artificial life are likely to be profound: they will challenge, perhaps fundamentally alter, our view of humankind's place in nature; they will dramatically enhance our ability to control our environment; and they may even endow other systems with the ability to control us. This article will elaborate on a few of the trends that are tearing down the barriers between the living and nonliving, then introduce some developments in artificial life that are providing a new way of examining what it means to be alive, and finally speculate on consequences that these endeavors may have in the intermediate future.

Animate or inanimate?

The past century has seen sharp changes in how biologists view life. One of them has been the demise of vitalism, the view that there are qualitative differences in the forces and laws governing living, as opposed to nonliving, systems. It is now well established that there is no "life force" unique to biological organisms, that the same physical and chemical forces are at work throughout all of nature.

A second change has been the blurring of just what distinguishes living systems from nonliving ones. It was traditional to begin textbooks on biology by listing the properties of living systems, with the aim of defining the subject matter. But with the discovery of more and more borderline cases—like viruses, which consist only of proteins and ribonucleic acid (RNA) or deoxyribonucleic acid (DNA) and cannot reproduce unless inside a bacterium or higher cell, and the infectious agents known as prions, which appear to be all protein and do not contain even nucleic acid—the task appears increasingly futile.

The properties that seem most characteristic of natural life are: (1) the ability to reproduce; (2) responsiveness to the environment; (3) metabolism; (4) chemical uniqueness; (5) a high degree of complexity and organization; (6) possession of a genetic program that directs development; and (7) a history shaped by natural selection. Others could be listed. But none of these properties, by itself or in combination, seems either necessary or sufficient to distinguish life. For example, consider mules, which are alive but do not reproduce; seeds, which are alive but need not metabolize; or frankfurters, which are not alive but are made of protein and DNA.

The revelations of molecular biology suggest that organisms are better regarded as processes than as objects. From this perspective, living organisms are complicated, ongoing chemical reactions that order the world around them. The atoms and molecules that constitute a partic-

174

ular human being today are different from those of a few years ago; furthermore, that individual looks and acts differently today—yet he or she is recognized as being the same person. The critical feature that provides continuity and identity across time is that the person comprises the same continuous, self-organizing process.

During the 1930s and '40s, when the first modern computers were being built, a few people with exceptional vision began to ask whether the processes that exist, or someday would exist, in computers might properly be thought to be alive and even to possess mental states. In particular, the English computer theorist Alan Turing speculated that thinking is really a process that links input with output, independent of the substrate (*e.g.*, a biological brain or an electronic device) that supports it. That view, which has its clearest statement in the physical-symbol system hypothesis of artificial intelligence pioneer Allen Newell and colleague Herbert Simon of Carnegie Mellon University, Pittsburgh, Pennsylvania, states that any system capable of manipulating symbolic information, be it a computer or a human being, has the necessary and sufficient means for general intelligent action. This theory, sometimes called functionalism, ultimately gave rise to the field of artificial intelligence.

At the same time that Turing was speculating about the abstract properties of thought, another founding father of computers, the American mathematician and theorist John von Neumann, was similarly speculating about the abstract properties of life. Might life, too, be properly regarded as a self-organizing and self-replicating process that is independent of the substrate that supports it? The subsequent development of that idea became the guiding principle for artificial life.

One may broadly distinguish between two categories of artificial life at present: "wet" and "dry." Wet a-life, alternately called in vitro a-life, is similar to natural nucleic-acid–based life, but it is explored in artificial systems. It is based on chemical reactions that occur in a liquid medium. Dry, or in silico, a-life refers to processes that are not liquid based but typically exist on computers or other systems capable of supporting the kinds of information regulation and transmission appropriate for producing lifelike behavior.

Life almost as it is

As early as the 1960s, molecular biologists mixed together the organic ingredients for self-replicating wet systems—precursors of the nucleotide building blocks of RNA molecules, inorganic molecules, an energy source, specialized enzymes to promote (or catalyze) the proper reactions for replication, and RNA primer to get the system started. The RNA replicated generation after generation, and it also began evolving. Once started, mutation and selection led to simpler and simpler systems having less extraneous baggage until an apparently minimal RNA evolved. This kind was adapted only to continued activity in a test tube and was unlikely to survive outside.

Since then, other types of RNA, termed ribozymes (for "ribonucleic acid enzymes"), have been discovered not only to serve as a blueprint

(Opposite page) Attempts to define life traditionally consist of listing those properties—e.g., metabolism, chemical uniqueness, the ability to reproduce, and the possession of a genetic program for directing development—that seem most characteristic of natural living systems. The weakness of that approach is apparent when one considers the many borderline cases and exceptions. Seeds, for example, are certainly alive but need not metabolize. Viruses cannot reproduce unless they take over the synthesis machinery of bacteria or higher cells. Sausages contain a genetic program and are made of protein and nucleic acids but are not alive. Such considerations suggest that living organisms may be better regarded as continuous, self-organizing chemical processes than as objects.

(Top) Cathy Melloan; (center) © CDC—Peter Arnold, Inc.; (bottom) © Edward L. Miller—Stock, Boston

175

for replication but also to catalyze reactions in the manner of enzymes. Some of these RNA sequences can cut themselves out of a longer RNA molecule, while others can cut other RNA sequences at specific locations in the molecule. If one creates a kind of test-tube "selection pressure" and permits only those ribozymes with a particular enzymatic activity to reproduce, it is possible to generate a set, or "population," of ribozymes suited to a specific task. In a recently reported case, an RNA-cutting ribozyme was induced to evolve into a form that cuts DNA instead. Eventually such artificial evolution may allow scientists to generate ribozymes for catalyzing chemical reactions that are beyond the abilities of natural enzymes to promote.

In addition to their practical applications, such studies are helping to illuminate what the earliest forms of protolife on Earth may have been like, about four billion years ago. Biological life today depends on DNA and RNA to carry the information for making proteins, but it also depends on proteins, in the form of enzymes, to drive the reactions that make DNA and RNA molecules. Consequently, biologists have been faced with a classic "chicken or egg" dilemma: which came first, nucleic acids or proteins? The realization that RNA molecules can work like enzymes has offered an attractive solution: RNA may first have served as both blueprint and catalyst, while the now-dominant roles for DNA and protein evolved later.

Developing simple chemical systems that mimic biochemical reactions or exhibit lifelike behavior has become an intense and challenging field of research. Chemists recently described their success at synthesizing an organic molecule that, given the proper conditions, brings two molecular building blocks of itself into close association and then promotes their coupling to form a new molecule identical with the first. In essence, the system mimics biological reproduction with a catalytic molecule that gives rise to the replication of its own structure. It, too, may shed light on the self-replicating chemical systems from which natural life originated.

Computer parasites

Dry a-life is being explored in a variety of systems, including computer viruses, evolving, self-regulating computer processes, and robots. It encompasses more extreme types of lifelike behavior than the wet variety and offers more exotic possibilities for study.

Computer viruses provide a simple example of the issues raised in artificial life. In popular usage the term *computer virus* refers to any of several software entities created for electronic mischief, not all of which are viruses in a more restricted sense. Technically computer viruses are programs, typically a few hundred to a few thousand bits long, that are embedded in larger programs and are able to duplicate and spread when the larger program is activated. They usually spread by changing other programs in the computer on which they are run. In distinction to viruses are computer worms, small programs that can run by themselves and are able to spread over computer networks. Worms do not insert themselves into other programs (although they might, themselves, contain computer

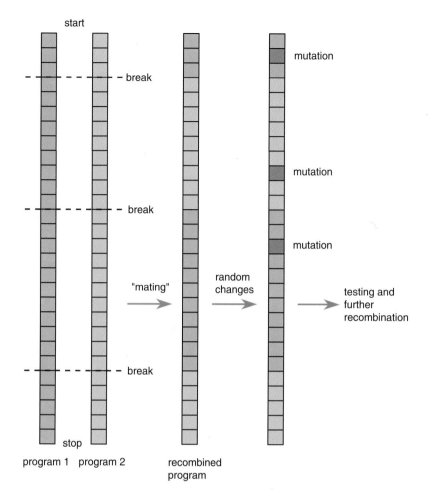

start

break

break

"mating"

break

stop

program 1 program 2

random
changes

recombined
program

mutation

mutation

mutation

testing and
further
recombination

Figure 1 (left) schematically diagrams a genetic algorithm, a systematic procedure for inducing the evolution of populations of computer programs. The procedure begins with an accumulation of hundreds or thousands of programs, each of which is more or less efficient at some common task. The programs are tested for their efficiency, and only the comparative few that do well enough to "survive" are paired up, like the two shown. In analogy with sexual reproduction and evolution in natural organisms, the pairs of programs are "mated," i.e., their component bit strings of 1s and 0s (represented by boxes) are cut apart and recombined, to form an "offspring" program. Furthermore, in analogy with mutation, a few bits in some of the recombined programs are changed at random to provide new variation. The programs are then tested, and the highest scorers enter into another round of pairing and recombination. The procedure is repeated for as many generations as desired, while the survivor programs continue to evolve in the ability to perform their task.

viruses that do). The Internet worm that severely disrupted the international computer networks in 1988 is an example. Computer bacteria are like computer worms in that they reproduce by themselves and do not alter existing programs, but they do not travel over networks; they typically reproduce on a single machine until the local resources (*e.g.*, memory) are exhausted.

Computer viruses and their kin possess many of the properties of biological life: they reproduce; they respond to their environment; they metabolize (they use up computer processing, memory, or both); they may be quite complex; and they function only as an integrated whole. In one case they were observed to exhibit the counterpart of genetic recombination when two slightly different types of virus infected the same machine and produced a new virus that differed from either "parent." Few people would regard computer viruses as actually being alive, but it will be recognized that their distinction from natural viruses is not particularly obvious.

Computer programs that evolve

One property of life that does seem significant, and that is typically lacking in computer viruses, is the ability of populations to reproduce

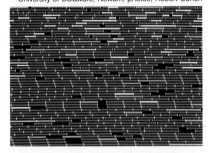

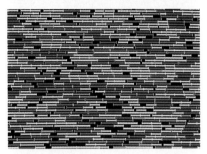

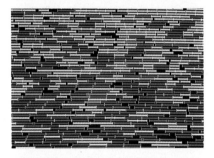

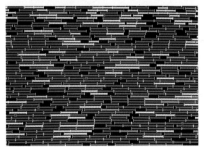

sexually and evolve. By itself this is nothing special; programs possessing this property date to the 1950s and were among the first ever to run on computers. The concept experienced a rebirth of interest in the late 1970s after John Holland of the University of Michigan had introduced the term *genetic algorithms* and begun to study the process in earnest.

A genetic algorithm is a systematic step-by-step procedure by which populations of computer programs are induced to evolve. An example of such a procedure is illustrated in Figure 1 on page 177. Imagine an initial collection of 1,000 programs, each of which is more or less efficient at some common task. At some basic level, each such program is a bit string, a sequence of 1s and 0s, similar to the nucleotide sequences in DNA that serve as genetic instructions for living organisms. For concreteness, suppose that the task is to sort a list of numbers in order from smallest to largest. Depending on how well each program sorts the list, it is assigned a fitness. The great majority of the worst-performing programs are discarded, and the comparative few that did best are retained. Next, in analogy with sexual reproduction and evolution in natural organisms, pairs of the best-performing survivors are chosen, copies of them are recombined, and thereby 1,000 more programs are generated for the next generation. Analogous to mutation, a few bits in a few of the programs are typically changed at random to provide new variation. The 1,000 new programs are then evaluated, and the procedure is repeated for as many generations as desired. In this way the programs evolve the ability to perform their task, *i.e.,* sort numbers, more effectively.

In practice genetic algorithm studies are typically performed on massively parallel computers, like the Connection Machine, having thousands of processors to which can be assigned small portions of the task, so that evolution proceeds at rates in the range of seconds to minutes per generation. Genetic algorithms have been used to evolve custom software that offers good solutions for a number of problems, including sorting, finding the shortest route for salespeople to travel among cities, and optimizing flow rates through complex systems. They have also produced computer simulations of food-foraging and trail-following behavior in ants and created programs for wall-following behavior for robots. Some biologists see the genetic algorithm process itself as a useful model for studying the roles of genetic recombination and mutation in biological evolution.

Thomas Ray, a biologist at the University of Delaware, has studied natural selection and evolution within whole "ecosystems" of such programs. A genetic algorithm as it is depicted in Figure 1 may be viewed as a search through all the possible bit strings that have some fixed length. While the number of possibilities may be quite large, they all can be enumerated, and evolution reduces to a search to find just which of them are optimal for the assigned task. Suppose, however, that the search allows the length of the bit strings to grow or contract. Suppose also that the criterion for success is not simply performance on a task arbitrarily assigned by the programmer but is instead the ability to compete for, and occupy, resources that are in short supply in the world of the programs themselves, such as memory within the computer. Ray constructed such

178

a world, which in its behavior is much closer to natural life. He observed that some programs evolved to parasitize others by appropriating parts of the host's code to make more parasites. Later, "hyperparasites"—parasites on parasites—emerged by effectively forcing the parasites on the host programs to replicate more of the hyperparasites than their own kind. This silicon variant of "nature red in tooth and claw" sometimes led, not surprisingly, to eventual extinction of the whole community. It is tempting to see lessons here about the need for prudently managing the Earth's ecosystem and what may happen if humankind does not.

Robots

Robots and autonomous vehicles are physical realizations of processes that might otherwise be confined to computers. They are, in fact, computers equipped with sensors and actuators—sensors to take in information about their environment and actuators to interact with the environment. It is customary to distinguish between industrial robots, which at present consist largely of stationary mechanical arms programmed to accomplish tasks like welding or assembling, and autonomous vehicles, which actually move around. The latter are under development for a variety of tasks; *e.g.,* working in high-radiation environments or exploring other planets. While industrial robots typically bear only a superficial resemblance to what are normally thought of as living systems, in some ways they provoke quite interesting questions. For example, NeXT workstations, which are a type of high-power personal computer, are constructed almost entirely by industrial robots, which in turn are controlled by other NeXT workstations. At just what point should NeXT workstations be regarded as self-reproducing?

In a 1964 landmark case about obscenity, U.S. Supreme Court Justice Potter Stewart observed that he did not know just how to define obscenity "and perhaps I could never succeed in intelligibly doing so. But I know it when I see it." Life and mind are quite like obscenity in that regard. Good definitions of these terms do not exist, but most people are confident that they know life and mind when they see them—at least in their developed forms. The reason for this confidence is tied to one's ability to observe how the relevant objects behave and then to reflect on what is required for generating that behavior. As a result, robots make extraordinary "lab animals" for testing theories about artificial life.

Lifelike robots have a long pedigree in the movies and television. Among the more memorable are the Madonna-like "material girl" of Fritz Lang's 1926 classic *Metropolis;* HAL of *2001: A Space Odyssey* (1968); C-3PO and R2-D2 of the *Star Wars* films; the android Data in the television series "Star Trek: The Next Generation"; and the creatures played by Arnold Schwarzenegger in the *Terminator* movies. Even the small robots and autonomous vehicles of today, although much less capable than these fictional creatures, do seem to share significant aspects of simple mind and life. It is illuminating to watch the current state-of-the-art autonomous vehicles investigate their environment. The Rocky III explorer, developed at the Jet Propulsion Laboratory, Pasadena,

Series of images on a display screen (opposite page) shows natural selection and evolution taking place among artificial organisms within one of biologist Thomas Ray's computer-based ecosystems. Individuals of each "species" appear as a characteristically colored rod whose length represents the length of the instruction program—analogous to the genome, or genetic endowment, of a natural organism. Early on (top), the resources of the ecosystem are dominated by the ancestor organism (red rods), the original 80-instruction program. After a number of generations (second from top), a smaller, fast-reproducing parasite program (yellow rods) proliferates at the expense of the ancestor population. Still later (second from bottom), a 79-instruction, parasite-resistant organism (blue rods) arises and eventually takes over the ecosystem (bottom).

179

Robots in movies and television—particularly those that mimic human form or behavior—date back to such classic silent-film characters as the evil mechanical duplicate of Maria (above) in Fritz Lang's Metropolis. More recent examples are C-3PO and R2-D2 (top left) of the Star Wars trilogy; Arnold Schwarzenegger's Terminator character (top right), whose metal skeleton is covered with living tissue; and the android Data (above right), another quasi-living creation of human technology, from the "Star Trek: The Next Generation" television series. Although these fictional creatures owe their impressively lifelike behavior to a human actor or human guidance via remote control, some true robots being developed today seem on their own merits to possess significant aspects of simple mind and life.

California, can move about and collect soil samples from simulated Martian surfaces; *i.e.*, the dry stream channels around the laboratory. Attila and Herbert from the Massachusetts Institute of Technology are indeed thought provoking as they explore their cluttered MIT laboratory environments, Herbert sometimes picking up empty soda cans as it does so.

A small autonomous vehicle, Attila was developed at the MIT Mobile Robotics Laboratory, directed by Rodney Brooks. It has 6 legs, 23 small motors, and up to 150 sensors of a dozen or more types that include accelerometers, inclinometers, a television camera, and a variety of proximity sensors. Needless to say, programming all of these parts in a manner that provides for continuous, coordinated action is not trivial. MIT researcher Pattie Maes programmed Attila such that it learned, on its own, how to walk. She provided a neural-net program—a program run on software inspired by the way nerve cells in the brain are interconnected—to coordinate its leg motion in such a fashion that those neural-net connections that led to successful behavior were strengthened while those that did not were weakened. In experimental trials, after several minutes of trying out different methods of leg coordination, Attila became able to walk.

While Attila's controlling programs were not themselves evolved in the manner of genetic algorithms described above, attempts to do so

180

are under way in various laboratories, and there is certainly no reason why they should not succeed. By giving robots the ability to learn, to evolve their own programming, and perhaps to transmit their knowledge to other robots (a key requisite in the development of culture), researchers may be able to increase vastly the repertoire of behaviors that these robots exhibit.

Seeking a universal structure for life

Computer viruses, robots, and evolving computer processes possess lifelike features, but just what substrates, or what interactions on those substrates, are capable of generating systems having the properties of life? In other words, just how broad are the possibilities for life? It is unlikely that the system of life that evolved on Earth is the only one possible. For example, it has long been recognized that many of the molecules made by and crucial to biological life have a handedness: one structural form is favored over its mirror-image counterpart. Virtually all amino acids used in the cellular synthesis of protein are left-handed, and virtually all sugars in natural nucleic acids are right-handed. Although molecules of mixed handedness do not work in the system of life on Earth, there are no theoretical principles that would prohibit life from exhibiting a handedness different from that observed. The particular handedness of Earthly life seems to have been an accident that became "frozen" in place arbitrarily in the distant past. If such is the case, how many other possibilities exist? Given a collection of chemicals and of laws relating them on a distant planet, might not that system support life? This same question can be extended from biological systems to nonbiological ones. Computer viruses, genetic algorithms, robots—what other computer-based systems might have lifelike properties? On just which computational systems can computers support computational life?

Stated more generally, if the exact substrate that supports life is not important, then what general features of the substrate are required? In

© Peter Menzel

Herbert (alias "The Collection Machine"), an autonomous vehicle developed at the Massachusetts Institute of Technology, nips a soda can from a desktop as it negotiates its cluttered laboratory environment.

Developed at MIT, Attila (shown in a variant form—Attila II, or Hannibal) behaves in a way highly reminiscent of an insect as it scuttles around and over obstacles in perpetual exploration of its surroundings. Attila sports a computer chip on each leg and more than 150 individual sensors, including an infrared range finder and a CCD (charged-coupled diode) camera in its tilt-pan head; proximity sensors, joint-angle sensors, and contact sensors in its legs; and a strain gauge sensor in the form of a forward-projecting, moving "feeler." In experiments Attila used a neural net program to learn by trial and error how to coordinate the motion of its six legs so that it could walk.

an effort to answer that question, von Neumann, working with ideas contributed by Polish-born mathematician Stanislaw Ulam, invented the mathematical theory of cellular automata. While von Neumann saw his theory as embracing a broad range of fields including biology, computers and control systems, mathematical logic, and the meaning of complexity, he chose to model the phenomenon of reproduction as a way of accessing all these other issues. He designed a hypothetical machine, or automaton, consisting of many identical, linked cells that changed their states over time according to a simple, unvarying set of rules. The automaton was, in effect, an artificial universe governed by a small set of physical laws. The laws operated on the cells—the raw materials of the environment—organizing them into patterns that, depending on the way the automaton was constructed, sometimes resembled reproduction and evolution in living organisms.

Setting up a cellular automaton is not at all difficult. Imagine an array of cells, as shown in Figure 2. In this example the array is one-dimensional, but there is no problem extending it to two, three, or more dimensions. Furthermore, the ends of the array wrap around, like a tape on a drinking glass, such that the rightmost cell is next to the leftmost cell and every cell has two neighbors. The array is then followed through a series of steps over time. At each step any given cell will be in one state or another. Again for simplification, assume that there are two possible states, red or yellow, corresponding to the numbers 1 and 0 of the binary system used in computer operations. At the next time step, the state of each cell might change or not, depending on the applicable rules and the states of the surrounding cells. One such rule might be: if the cells on the immediate left and right are both 1 (red), then go to state 1; otherwise go to state 0 (yellow). Following this rule, a cellular automaton pattern that starts out with a line of alternating red and yellow squares will "blink," each square going from yellow to red to yellow again. When

182

the array from each time step is placed immediately below that for the previous step, the resulting pattern resembles a chessboard. Other starting conditions will give other patterns, some of them much more varied, dynamic, and lifelike.

Two points emerge from the study of cellular automata. First, whether or not it is strictly true that all physical laws and behavior can be represented in the workings of cellular automata (with a three-dimensional array), it is certain that cellular automata can provide a useful approximation to them. Second, given automata whose cells have only a finite number of possible states, it is possible (in principle) to list all possible rule systems that can relate the cells and then to examine the rule systems to see just which ones give the substrate a lifelike pattern and which do not.

Christopher Langton, the "father" of artificial life and a scientist at New Mexico's Los Alamos National Laboratory and Santa Fe Institute, did just that. He examined a very large number of rules for one-dimensional and two-dimensional cellular automata with the goal of determining which rule systems support the basic operations of information transmission, storage, and modification and which do not; these systems presumably correspond to those that do or do not support life. He found that one large class of rule systems leads ultimately to stable or cyclical behavior (like the checkerboard pattern in Figure 2) analogous to the "frozen," or solid, state of matter. Another large class of systems leads to chaotic behavior analogous to the fluid phases of matter—liquid and gas. Only a small set of rule systems, at the interface between these two, or

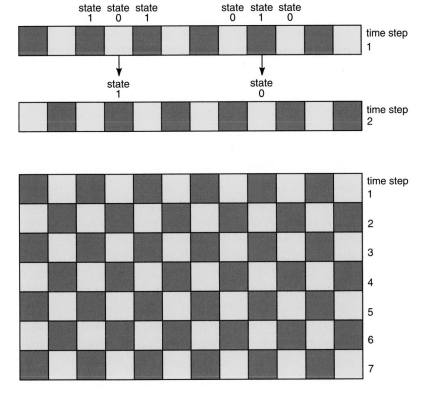

Figure 2 (left) shows the setting up of a cellular automaton as described on page 182. This particular pattern starts out with alternating red and yellow squares (corresponding to 1 and 0 in the binary system) and follows the rule: if the cells on the immediate left and right are both state 1 (red), go to state 1; otherwise, go to state 0 (yellow).

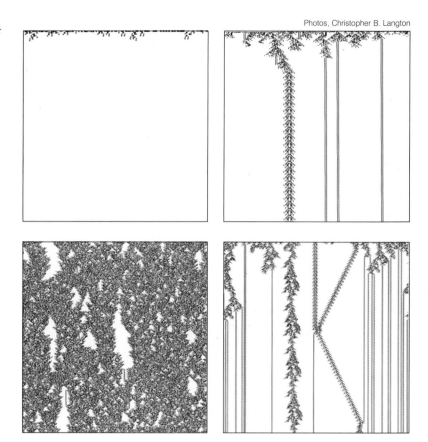

Photos, Christopher B. Langton

The computer-generated patterns of one-dimensional cellular automata at right exemplify the broad classes of rule systems that emerged from the study of a large number of such systems in one- and two-dimensional cellular automata. The pattern in each figure is generated from a single row of cells at the top: 128 cells for the top left figure, 256 for the top right figure, and 512 for the two bottom figures. Each cell can exist in four discrete states, indicated by four different colors including white. The rules governing the patterns as they progress from the top to the bottom of the figures depend on the states of the relevant cell and of its immediate neighbor on either side. One class of rules leads to homogeneous, one-color states (top left). Another class leads to unchanging points or stable periodic structures (top right). A third class produces chaotic patterns (bottom left). A fourth class, made up of a comparatively small set of rule systems at the interface between the second and third types, generates complicated, propagating structures. It has been speculated that any systems capable of supporting lifelike behavior must fall into the last class.

at the "phase transition" between solid and fluid, allows the automata to possess the sensitivity to initial conditions and long-term responsiveness that seem necessary for life. In his words, life is found only "at the edge of chaos."

If only those systems poised on the edge of chaos are able to support lifelike behavior, then will the outputs of those systems stay lifelike over time, or will they tend to drift off toward stability or chaos? This is not at all clear, but there are hints that certain persistent patterns, perhaps those that are properly regarded as lifelike, compensate by becoming more fluidlike when they drift toward solidification and more solidlike when they drift toward the fluid. Stuart Kauffman, also at the Santa Fe Institute, has referred to such systems as being poised, and maintained, between chaos and "antichaos." This intriguing idea invites further study.

Similar to the problems being addressed by cellular automata are questions about computer simulations of pools of mutually catalyzing chemicals. An example would be nucleic acids that regulate the production of other nucleic acids. At one extreme, when there is too little catalysis or chemical activity, not much will happen, and the system will move toward a more-or-less stable state. At the other extreme, when activity is too high, the system will be continually churning away, making virtually everything possible and then breaking it down again, remaining chaotic and developing little structure. Poised between these two extremes, however, are autocatalytic reaction systems in which certain participants in

184

the system, or constellations of participants, become more common while the others do not.

As a hypothetical example of such a system, one may think of a pool of five compounds, A through E. By means of catalysis A helps produce more B, B helps produce more C, and C helps produce more A; D and E do not benefit. In this system A, B, and C will become more common, while D and E will not. The ABC group has been termed a "hypercycle" by chemists Manfred Eigen and Peter Schuster. It may not be far wrong to think of these as the early, transitional stages in the origin of life on Earth, the bridge between "chemical soup" and primitive organisms. These first hypercycles became capable of building more complex ones and resisting perturbations, resisting the drifts to chaos or to solidification and thereby keeping themselves poised on the edge of chaos.

Mind viruses

Like biological organisms, ideas may arise, persist, die out, and, before doing so, give rise to others. Can some ideas—or languages or cultures—properly be thought to be dead while others are still living? Biologist Richard Dawkins has drawn attention to the similarities among natural viruses, computer viruses, and "mind viruses," by which he means ideas and fads like hula hoops, break dancing, and transient religious movements. He argues that these cultural entities can take over the "operating system" of humans, much as computer viruses take over the operating system of the computer or natural viruses take over the regulatory system of the cell nucleus.

Less metaphorically, theoretical physicist Murray Gell-Mann has suggested that a critical feature of systems that are living is their ability to go from expanded phenotype to compressed genotype and back again to phenotype in the next generation. For human life this corresponds to the process of going from the physical bodies of the parents to the genetic representations of those bodies as carried in the sperm and egg

Fads like the 3-D movie craze of the '50s and disco dancing in the '70s seem in some ways to resemble living systems. Such cultural entities can be viewed as infectious "mind viruses," taking over the "operating system" of humans in much the same way that computer viruses take over a computer's operating system or natural viruses take over the cell's regulatory system.

(Left) UPI/Bettmann Newsphotos; (right) © Archive Photos

cells and once again to the physical body of the child. If one brings the same idea to the process of science, a scientific theory would represent the compressed version of an expanded application to some general situation. Those familiar with the history of science cannot help but be impressed with the way theories seem to compete, produce offspring, die out, and so on. Looking at culture in the broad sense, Gell-Mann suggests that the collection of myths that are shared by members of a culture represents the compressed knowledge that has come down through time as part of that culture. The myths are the cultural equivalents of DNA. While still speculative, these theories about the way certain ideas outlast and outcompete others are intriguing. They suggest the possibility that a systematic treatment of culture may someday be possible, as part of a comprehensive theory of adaptive complex systems that encompasses all of life, both natural and artificial, known and yet to be discovered.

The future

It is difficult to predict what investigations of a-life will hold for the future. Social evolution is a complex, nonlinear system that is probably unpredictable for deep reasons related to chaos theory. Nonetheless, some broad trends may be anticipated. From chaos theory one knows that it is impossible to predict whether it will rain in Chicago on July 4 two years from now. On the other hand, it seems a good bet that the city will be colder on January 4 than July 4 of that year, global warming not withstanding. Likewise, whereas the exact ways in which genetic engineering, robots, or the ability to launch new forms of evolution will affect the future seems impossible to foresee, broad trends can still be anticipated. In particular, J. Doyne Farmer of the Santa Fe Institute and Alletta Belin suggest that development of some forms of artificial life is likely to have a profound effect on humanity, comparable to that of nuclear weapons, the Industrial Revolution, or possibly human evolution itself.

The ability to understand and manipulate the environment is the basis of human control over other parts of nature. At present, computers do not have the computational abilities of humans. On the basis of the number of computing units and connections, their speed, storage capacity, and other factors, it is estimated that humans have roughly 1,000 times more computational capacity than even the most powerful supercomputers. But it is also true that computers have been increasing in computational ability by a factor of approximately 1,000 every 20 years. With optical and biomolecular-based computers on the horizon, there is no reason to expect this rate to drop off soon. As a result, in 20–40 years computers likely will equal or exceed humans in computational ability. Another 20 years beyond that, well within the lifetime of many alive today, computers should outstrip humans by several orders of magnitude, in the same way that the mental ability of humans exceeds that of horses or dogs.

Up to now humans have controlled the programs of computers and the design of new molecules. It has been reasonable to accept the notion that "machines can do only what we tell them to do" and to anticipate that they will be governed by the kind of "laws of robotics" popularized in

186

Isaac Asimov's science-fiction writings—robots shall never harm humans and shall always carry out human orders. Most fictional robots adhere to these rules. Nevertheless, given the ability of computer programs to evolve on their own, and even to control their own evolution, computers may acquire much more power, including the ability to escape our control. Further, those that do so are likely to be favored by natural selection. Because the ability of such computer programs will greatly exceed that of the human brain, they may relate to people in very different ways than they do now. Such programs will be unlikely to share human and ethical values. Pain and moral obligations will be understood but not felt. Alternatively, humanity may find itself in a world populated with much less intelligent "creatures," like the brooms conjured by Mickey Mouse as the sorcerer's apprentice in *Fantasia,* and equally out of control.

If either of these scenarios is at all a reasonable possibility, then what steps should be taken now? The best guide from the past is probably the attempt over the last 50 years to grapple with the good and bad consequences of applied nuclear physics. (Genetic engineering is still quite new, and its applications are just beginning to be realized, so there is little guidance that it can offer.) Among others, Albert Einstein and J. Robert Oppenheimer both addressed the problem with great apprehension but also with reason and compassion. They stressed that people should deeply consider what is likely to come from their actions and should avoid those avenues that will court disaster. At the same time, neither argued that the entire field of nuclear physics should be abandoned because of its potential for harm. There are unlikely to be simple rules, except to be alert to the consequences and to act as wisely as one can.

In the next decade the study of artificial life should allow us to make exciting gains in understanding ourselves and our place in nature—and also in our control over it. History suggests, however, that the consequences will not be all good. It will be important to reflect on them, recognize them, and deal with them in a thoughtful and timely manner. The world likely will see a synthesis of complex adaptive systems, offering a view that places humans within a world teeming with other forms of life and lifelike entities. We may ultimately come to view nature in a way closer to that of Chief Seattle than to the worldview commonly held today.

FOR ADDITIONAL READING

Valentino Braitenberg, *Vehicles: Experiments in Synthetic Psychology* (MIT Press, 1984).

Stuart A. Kauffman, "Antichaos and Adaptation," *Scientific American* (August 1991, pp. 78–84).

Christopher G. Langton, *Artificial Life* (Addison-Wesley, 1989).

Christopher G. Langton, Charles E. Taylor, J.D. Farmer, and Steen Rasmussen, *Artificial Life II* (Addison-Wesley, 1991).

Steven Levy, *Artificial Life: The Quest for a New Creation* (Pantheon, 1992).

Pattie Maes, *Designing Autonomous Agents: Theory and Practice from Biology to Engineering and Back* (MIT Press, 1990).

THE MANY WORLDS OF
VIRTUAL REALITY

by John Rhea

*A variety of technologies—computer-generated imagery,
holography, liquid crystal displays, high-definition television,
and increasingly powerful computer hardware—are being
brought together to form the emerging field of virtual reality.*

When Neil Armstrong took his famous first "giant leap for mankind" on
July 20, 1969, the Moon was not entirely the alien place it might logically
have been expected to be. True, no human had ever set foot on it before,
but Armstrong and his fellow Apollo astronauts knew it well because
they had spent endless hours practicing landings on a "virtual Moon" at
the Manned Space Center of the U.S. National Aeronautics and Space
Administration (NASA) in Houston, Texas.

The astronauts trained rigorously for two years in a mission simulator
that would be considered primitive by today's technological standards.
They "landed" a replica of their lunar module, using actual flight controls, on a simulated area of the Sea of Tranquillity known as a model
board. This model board was a scale model of the lunar surface created from a composite of photos returned by NASA's Ranger, Surveyor,
and Lunar Orbiter unmanned reconnaissance spacecraft. The astronaut
trainees viewed this subscale world in their simulator via closed-circuit
television. As they manipulated their flight controls, the television camera
moved correspondingly toward the simulated lunar surface to give them
the experience of what it would be like to land on the Moon.

Until the past decade, when the computer revolution achieved its
present level of pervasiveness throughout all human activities, that is all
that simulators were: TV cameras, model boards, and replicas of flight
vehicles. Now, however, the outside world is being reproduced digitally
within computers and displayed to the trainees in a way that allows
them to interact with a broad range of situations—including imaginary
worlds as well as the real one. This new technology is called computer-
generated imagery (CGI), and it is the foundation of the emerging field
of virtual reality.

Apollo astronauts trained for their landings on the Moon in a mission simulator (above). At the top of the stairs behind the control console was a compartment that exactly duplicated an Apollo command module control area. Astronauts William Anders, Michael Collins, and Frank Borman (above right, left to right) were among those who spent many hours in the compartment responding to commands generated by operators at the control console. (Below right) A pilot operates a Link flight trainer, monitored by the instructor at the desk. Developed by Edwin Link in 1929, these simple mock-ups of aircraft cockpits and instruments taught a generation of pilots how to fly.

Origins, components, and challenges

The roots of virtual reality actually can be traced back to 40 years before the Apollo astronauts explored the Moon. In 1929 Edwin Link developed the first of his famous flight trainers, which were crude mock-ups of aircraft cockpits and flight instruments that taught a generation of pilots how to fly and how to use their flight instruments at night and during bad weather. These skills played a key role in the Allied victory in World War II.

The difference between those primitive, precomputer simulators and today's state-of-the-art virtual reality systems is the exponentially growing power of digital processing. This computer power can reproduce any scenario the human mind can imagine. Furthermore, today's computer-controlled systems do two things the Link trainers could never do. They simulate training tasks interactively and in real time. The Link trainers were limited to canned programs in which the students worked their way through a series of increasingly complex problems.

Virtual reality is actually a confluence of technologies. In addition to CGI, these include holography, which uses lasers to create three-dimen-

JOHN RHEA is a free-lance science writer in Woodstock, Virginia, and technologies editor of Government and Military Video *magazine.*

(Overleaf) Photograph, Evans & Sutherland/ © Peter Menzel

sional images; liquid crystal displays (LCDs), which replace conventional television picture tubes with more powerful solid-state electronic equivalents; high-definition television (HDTV), which promises to introduce advanced data processing methods to TV broadcasting; and multimedia techniques, which combine various types of displays in a single computer terminal.

Also, the computer revolution is spawning new hardware and software that will completely change the way people think about computers. Today's silicon-based electronics is evolving into more powerful devices built from gallium arsenide (GaAs) and indium phosphide (InP)—and is already beginning to evolve again to still more powerful photonic devices, in which photons, rather than electrons, are used to process information. The descendants of today's robots on the factory floor will provide future space explorers and others with a "telepresence" that will mechanically extend and enhance their ability to interact with the physical world. Meanwhile, scientists are creating new ways of organizing computers—the technical term is *system architecture*—such as "massive parallelism," a situation in which many processors work on a computing problem simultaneously instead of one in which a single processor works sequentially; neural networks, which emulate the human brain's learning ability; and distributed computing concepts, which enable computers to continue working, albeit in a slightly degraded mode, if any of the subsystems fail.

These emerging technologies constitute the technology base of virtual reality—which means that they also constitute the prerequisites for full implementation of virtual reality. Despite the widespread attention given to the entertainment prospects of virtual reality, the field is still in an embryonic state and will remain so until the supporting technologies can catch up with human expectations.

The public perception is that virtual reality is a kind of magic, electronically created world in which people can live out their most outrageous fantasies. This world even has its own name, "cyberspace," coined by science-fiction writer William Gibson in his novel *Neuromancer*. Visitors

A dome 8.5 meters (28 feet) in diameter is a principal component of the Weapon Systems Simulation Center of the Lockheed Aeronautical Systems Co. (below). In the center of this and another identical dome, test pilots seated in cockpit simulators engage enemy forces in real-time combat scenarios generated by computers and projected onto a 360° screen (bottom, left and right).

Photos, U.S. Department of Defense

191

to this mythical realm could, among other things, walk on the surface of the Moon (or Pluto), engage in hand-to-hand combat with gladiators (or dragons), and converse with famous people long dead, according to the proponents of virtual reality who saw its application as principally entertainment.

In conjunction with this better known future application of virtual reality, a growing number of technologists and businesspeople are exploring near-term, potentially profitable uses, such as industrial training and, inevitably, such military functions as rehearsing military missions before conducting them. Much of the basic research is under way at the Human Interface Laboratory at the University of Washington, headed by Thomas Furness, who spent 23 years in the U.S. Air Force developing advanced cockpit displays.

William Bricken, chief scientist at the laboratory, lists three requirements that still must be fulfilled before virtual reality can be fully developed. They are: the supporting technologies must be improved to make the computer-generated worlds look, sound, and feel more real; software must be developed to write the computer programs needed to organize the huge amounts of data that stream back and forth between people and the computers that are creating virtual worlds; and more basic research is needed on human perception so that the virtual reality developers can do a better job of "tricking the senses."

From this more business-oriented perspective, the term *virtual reality* has become somewhat embarrassing. "The term *virtual environments* better fits a field of scientific research," says David Zeltzer, associate professor of computer graphics at the Massachusetts Institute of Technology (MIT).

CGI-based systems
The transition to the modern era of virtual reality can be pinpointed to a single military program, Simnet (which stands for "simulator network"),

Researcher at the Human Interface Laboratory of the University of Washington wears both a black spandex glove equipped with fiber-optic sensors and glasses that can project computer-generated images onto his retina. By touching his glove to the image of the jet liner approaching him, he gains instant voice communication with the pilot.

launched by the U.S. Department of Defense's in-house think tank, the Defense Advanced Research Projects Agency (DARPA), in 1989. This is an experimental network of personal computer-based workstations, linked in a distributed system by broadband optical-fiber communications lines, that enables army and air force personnel to prepare for military operations on interactive, real-time training systems. It was used effectively in 1991 before the coalition drive to retake Kuwait from the Iraqi invaders.

In a typical Simnet tactical training exercise, ground forces and their close air support train together against "red" teams representing potential enemies, explained U.S. Air Force Col. Jack Thorpe, the program manager at DARPA. Their computers are mock-ups of their tanks and aircraft, and the warriors fight against other humans rather than against computers. This enables them to practice more dangerous military operations than would be possible in field exercises. For example, the pilots can learn how to dodge enemy surface-to-air missiles, and the infantry can call in artillery support to within 100 meters (328 feet) of their position in this electronic re-creation of the battlefield; in field exercises the distance is limited to one kilometer (0.62 mile).

Another early form of virtual reality is paying off today in multimedia training, which combines personal computers, modularized software, and videodiscs. An example of how interactive—and how engrossing—this computer-based training can be is the maintenance trainer for the navigation system in the Trident ballistic missile submarine that Paramax Systems Corp. (formerly Unisys Defense Systems) has developed at its Tactical Systems Unit in Reston, Virginia.

This trainer uses a standard personal computer to run students through simulated exercises with a series of menu-driven commands. The student goes to the "toolbox" screen to pick up the right tool and then switches screens to use that tool to perform simulated maintenance on the Trident navigation equipment selected for the exercise. The equipment appears on a videodisc that actually shows a bolt being tightened as the student uses his computerized "wrench" by touching the screen for each turn. If he turns it the right number of times, he can go on to the next problem. If not, he is given constructive feedback. The whole process has the fascination of a computer game, and the students are given scores based on their ability to perform complex maintenance.

A second type of interactive training is also employed for the navigation system in the Trident ballistic missile submarine. The Navigation Operational Trainer, also developed by Paramax, utilizes an array of simulated hardware built and physically arranged in a room to duplicate the Trident submarine's navigation system. The trainer is supported by computers containing software that enables, through the hardware simulators, total functional replication of all navigation system operations. All aspects of normal and emergency operations of the system can be simulated in the trainer for any location at which the submarine may operate. Submarine navigation crew members, led by experienced instructors, operate this trainer in the same manner as they would the real ship. The system interactively responds to all student activities just as the real shipborne

Student operates the maintenance trainer for the navigation system of the Trident II ballistic missile submarine. Developed by Paramax Systems Corp., the trainer employs a standard personal computer to run students through simulated exercises. In this example, the student goes to a "toolbox" menu on his right to select the proper tool as required by his procedure. He then "uses" that tool on a subsequent screen to perform simulated maintenance on the appropriate navigation equipment. If the student uses the tool correctly, he can continue his procedure; if not, he receives constructive feedback. The screen, with its accompanying keyboard, on his left replicates the tactical, man-machine interface found on board the submarine and is not used during this maintenance training exercise.

navigation system would. This type of virtual reality training has proved to be the most cost-effective method to achieve the interactive training requirements of these complex systems.

Computer power requirements

The computer power required for operating CGI-based virtual reality systems is immense. The MH-53J helicopter weapons system trainer that General Electric Co. developed for the U.S. Air Force's Special Operations Forces, for example, uses a combination of general- and special-purpose computers with processing speeds ranging from 10 billion to 50 billion instructions per second. The data-storage requirements are equally demanding. To simulate a 475,000-square kilometer (300,000-square mile) area of the United States used for air force training exercises (essentially from Arkansas to Kentucky and west to parts of California), GE used four 300 million-byte disk storage devices. (Simulating the 9.3 million square kilometers [3.6 million square miles] of the 50 states would require 12 times that amount.)

The key to future virtual reality systems is the visual fidelity of CGI. As a rough measure of the capability of the human eye, if the normal field of view is digitized, it amounts to about a million pixels (picture elements) of direct vision and roughly another million pixels of peripheral vision. Today's CGI simulators update such a scene 60 times a second to give the illusion of reality. The human eye cannot sense individual pictures at rates greater than 24 a second and, therefore, that is the rate used in motion pictures (although each frame is projected twice to eliminate the jerky motion of the early silent films). This rate of 60 frames per second made possible by modern computers provides a further smoothness of motion. That is essential in interactive mission simulations because conflicting visual cues can cause motion sickness among the trainees. Thus, the computational requirement for CGI is dictated by both the need to

194

provide at least a million digitized picture elements per scene and to do it 60 times a second.

The computational requirements are literally orders of magnitude more demanding for three-dimensional real-time images that are produced by holographic techniques. Scientists at the Media Lab at MIT estimated that in order to transmit a holographic image and update it 60 times a second so that the human eye could be tricked into believing it is moving, a commercial system would require data rates of 12 trillion bits per second. That is two million times faster than a home television set.

The situation is analogous to the current competition to develop an international standard for high-definition television, which requires at least nine megaHertz (million cycles per second) of bandwidth for the high-resolution picture. Yet the U.S. Federal Communications Commission decreed that bandwidth had to be limited to six megaHertz to be compatible with standard TV broadcasting. In order to stay within this bandwidth limitation, HDTV developers will have to find techniques that do not require the entire signal to be transmitted. Information that does not change from one frame to another can be represented by a single, much smaller signal. This technique is called data compression, and railroad telegraphers worked it out more than 100 years ago when they created sets of numbers for frequently sent messages.

Computer-generated scene, produced by General Electric's Compu-Scene 5 image-generation system, features the U.S. Air Force's MH-53J helicopter. The trainer, developed by GE for the MH-53J helicopter weapons system, uses a combination of general- and special-purpose computers with processing speeds ranging from 10 billion to 50 billion instructions per second.

GE Aerospace

Lasers, while still a leading-edge technology since their simultaneous invention in the United States and Soviet Union in 1960, are sufficiently understood to sustain real progress in holography. The coherent light made possible by lasers enables an object to be illuminated directly by one laser, which reflects that image onto a film, while another laser is focused on the film. The interference pattern created by the two beams gives the image its three-dimensional appearance. Researchers at the Media Lab early in 1991 created crude real-time holograms by using data-compression techniques and supercomputers operating at gigaHertz (billions of cycles per second) rates, but any commercial applications will require even more sophisticated techniques and computers capable of teraHertz (trillion cycles per second) speeds.

The computer problem may not be as formidable as it appears. Using the number of data-switching functions that can be built into a single chip (or other device) as a benchmark of raw computing power, one can see that that power has been growing consistently at a rate of two orders of magnitude per decade on a cumulative basis for the past 40 years. From one function per device for the first transistor demonstrated by Bell Laboratories in 1947 to the 64 million-bit dynamic random access memories (DRAMs) introduced in 1991 by several Japanese companies, that progress has been predictable. Even a conservative extrapolation of that progress into the future should yield a one-gigabit chip by the end of the century and one-terabit chips by at least the second decade of the next century.

Crude real-time hologram was created by the Media Lab of the Massachusetts Institute of Technology by the use of data-compression techniques and supercomputers operating at rates of billions of cycles per second. Scientists at the laboratory estimated that data rates of 12 trillion bits per second are required in order to transmit a holographic image and to update that image 60 times per second so that the human eye can be tricked into believing that the image is moving.

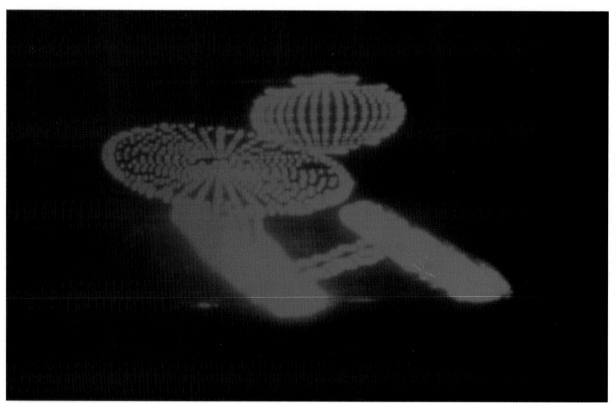

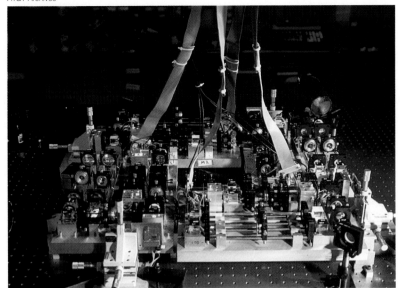

During those years today's silicon-based electronics will evolve into the more powerful gallium-arsenide and indium-phosphide devices until electronics gives way entirely to photonics, in which photons, or light particles, are used to switch the signals. In early 1990 Bell Labs demonstrated the first crude working model of an all-photonic computer. Furthermore, processing information as photons rather than electrons is compatible with the rapid progress under way in fiber optics. U.S. Air Force-sponsored research is aimed at achieving data rates of at least 100 billion bits per second in the next generation of optical fibers.

High-resolution displays

Another critical need for virtual reality is high-resolution displays to replace today's failure-prone, expensive cathode-ray tubes (CRTs), which are universally used in television sets and personal computers. CRTs have the additional disadvantage of requiring large amounts of electrical power. A leading solution is liquid crystals. This technology is proceeding in two overlapping phases: first, with the passive-matrix, or fixed format, LCDs, which are limited to small, monochromatic displays of alphanumeric and analog data; and second, with the more powerful active-matrix LCDs, which are capable of displaying a full range of video and computer-generated data in color. Both LCD technologies share two common features: the potential for reduced costs and improved performance.

In one of the first practical applications of active-matrix LCDs, Litton Systems Canada, Ltd., in Toronto began supplying prototype 15 × 20-centimeter (6 × 8-inch) displays to an upgrade of the U.S. Air Force C-130 transport aircraft. Each display unit has a resolution of 31.5 color pixels per centimeter (80 color pixels per inch) for a total of almost 1,000 per square centimeter (6,400 pixels per square inch) and produces luminance that allows the displays to be readable in sunlight. The brightness and high contrast of the displays greatly reduce the washout common

Active-matrix liquid crystal display (LCD) is a feature of an upgraded U.S. Air Force C-130 transport aircraft. Such LCDs can display a full range of computer-generated data in color. Their brightness and high contrast are advantageous in the sunlight of a cockpit. Active-matrix LCDs could eventually be used for optical computing applications for virtual reality.

to color CRT displays under the sunlight illumination conditions of a cockpit. For nighttime operation the displays are individually dimmable.

In its unenergized state the liquid crystal cell causes light passing through it to undergo a fixed rotation, or twist, in its plane of polarization. When used in conjunction with polarizing sheets external to the cell, this normally causes the display to block or absorb all the light emitted by the backlight. Once energized, the liquid crystal material no longer imposes this polarization rotation and therefore allows light to pass through to the color dot-sized filters, producing the required images. The display is capable of presenting full-color images with 16 shades of gray. The displays can present both computer-generated symbols and full camera/sensor video images.

But active-matrix LCDs are more than merely displays; they can be thought of as intelligent surfaces. The 960 × 1,280-line LCD used in the C-130 is actually a 1.2-megabit DRAM. The difference between an LCD and its semiconductor counterpart is that it is made from thin films on transparent substrates, with every memory cell having an output electrode. A 15 × 20-centimeter LCD thus is the equivalent of a DRAM on a 310-square centimeter (48-square inch) substrate. Furthermore, there is no reason why this giant semiconductor has to be limited to memory applications any more than microchips are. Logic applications are also possible. Active-matrix LCDs could eventually be used for optical computing applications for virtual reality.

Replicating the human brain

Another area of intense research in support of future virtual reality systems concerns the organization of computers so as to best replicate the functions of the human brain. These efforts fall under the catchall term *artificial intelligence,* although the focus is now shifting to what are known as expert systems. As the name implies, these systems capture the best available human expertise in computers and apply it more quickly and consistently to predefined problems than any human could.

James Ionson, former director of innovative science and technology projects for the Strategic Defense Initiative Organization and now a consultant, uses the analogy of a snail's brain to illustrate how the expert systems of the future will have to function. His point is not that snails are any smarter than computers—or humans—but that what little brain power they do have is organized to enable them to survive. The typical snail has the equivalent of four or five neurological gates, or brain cells, Ionson explained. "If those were all digital, it [the snail] could never find its prey or a mate—or get bored. Yet it can do more than the most advanced computer."

The reason is that the brain of a snail—or a human—is not entirely digital. Computers, with rare exceptions, are. The latter have to process all their information as a series of digits: ones and zeros. To do more than just process digital data, truly thinking mechanisms also must be able to handle complex analog data, as humans and other living things do to varying degrees with the five basic senses of sight, sound, touch,

198

taste, and smell. The difference between this and traditional computing is the ability to adapt to changing conditions and handle data of a type never before encountered.

Researchers are trying to develop high-reliability expert systems that embody two characteristics of the human brain that are beginning to find their way into computers: parallel processing and neural networks. Parallel processing is the opposite of the way most present-day computers work. Instead of tackling the processing jobs in serial fashion, working on them one at a time and completing each job before beginning on the next one, parallel processors break up the jobs into smaller parts and work on all the parts at the same time. This reduces the downtime, while the computer is waiting for the next data to process, but it requires a much more complex system architecture of many individual processors. Experimental machines used for the particularly demanding job of image processing, for example, consist of as many as 65,536 one-bit processors linked together in what is known as a "massively parallel" configuration. Computer scientists call these machines "connectionist" because they use a collection of permanent knowledge stored as a pattern of connections among the processing elements. This knowledge directly determines how the processing elements interact; they do not sit passively in a memory, waiting to be looked at by a single central processor. The connections can be symbols that represent the instructions needed to process the data.

Although the exact nature of the human brain is still something of a mystery, this is believed to be the way the brain's neural networks also work. The brain contains about 10 billion neurons representing the logic and memory functions, and they are organized in a complex, unknown structure in which each neuron is connected to several thousand other neurons. This results in more than 100 trillion synapses, which are the brain's subsystems for tackling different processing jobs. Even though this biological process is a million times slower than today's top-of-the-line electronic computers (operating at milliseconds, or thousandths of a second, instead of nanoseconds, or billionths of a second), the efficient routing scheme enables the brain to make tentative decisions based on partial information, while the computers must wait for the last bit of data before making any decision at all.

Some scientists, such as Carver A. Mead, professor of computer science at the California Institute of Technology, believe that these biological functions can be reproduced electronically—thus combining the efficiency of the brain with the speed of electronics. In the brain electrical impulses must have a high enough voltage to jump from one neuron through a connection known as an axon and across the synapse to another collector, known as a dendrite, of an adjoining neuron. This whole process must be completed in sequence for information to be processed. Mead proposed to replace the neurons with complex inte-grated circuits, the axons and dendrites with wires (or more likely optical fibers), and the synapse with variable resistors. The resistors would be set for a specific voltage and pass along to the neighboring neuron only those signals that met the requirement. The advantage is that, like the human brain, these electronic neural networks would develop patterns of routing signals and "remember" which ones to use the next time they had to tackle a similar problem.

One of the most promising applications of this humanlike machine intelligence is for remote control. The technical term for this concept is *teleoperation,* and it involves the use of robotic-like devices under human control to enhance, not replace, human performance. This means that they are optimized for a specific set of jobs rather than being all-purpose machines and are not intended to operate autonomously, explained Capt. Ronald G. Julian, manager of the human sensory feedback project at the Air Force's Harry G. Armstrong Aerospace Medical Research Laboratory at Wright-Patterson Air Force Base, Ohio.

This new generation of robotic devices, therefore, falls somewhere between the traditional industrial robots used for many years in such pre-programmed tasks as spot welding automobiles and assembling complex electronic components and the visions of future autonomous fighting vehicles and roving vehicles to explore the surface of Mars and other planets without human intervention. The thrust of current air force research, according to Captain Julian, is to create a "robotic telepres-ence" that will enable human operators to perform vital maintenance tasks in hazardous areas at a safe distance from the hazards. This is accomplished by what he called a "quasi-anthropoid" device that instan-taneously mimics all the motions of the human operator's arms, hands, and fingers. The human wears a sensor-laden exoskeleton that translates each of his movements into a series of signals that are transmitted to the robot for execution. The robot is equipped with visual and other sensors to inform the human operator about what is happening at the servicing location, which could be many kilometers away if radio communications are used. This two-way communication is known as a real-time feedback loop, and it synergistically combines the superior ability of the human to respond to unanticipated situations with the invulnerability of the robot in environments that would be lethal to humans.

Principal investigator for the Telepresence for Planetary Exploration Project of the U.S. National Aeronautics and Space Administration stands beside the Phantom 2 underwater remotely operated vehicle. The investigator's video headset allows her to see remote locations through a high-resolution video camera on the vehicle; she points the camera by moving her head and steers the vehicle with a pair of joysticks or with body motion. NASA hopes that the vehicle, already used for underwater research, can be modified for exploration of Mars.

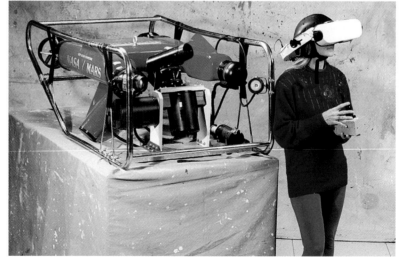

Data suit worn by its designer at VPL Research is adjusted (above left). It allows the wearer to use his or her entire body to interact with a program or with another person wearing a data suit. Autodesk researcher sees an image through his goggles (above) as he uses a real racket to hit a virtual racquetball on a virtual court. (Left) A person plays musical instruments on a virtual stage. A video camera captured an image of the person, and this was then passed through a matrix of software in a computer that transposed the person's mirror image into a world of computer animation and interactive video.

NASA has a near-term application for this concept of telepresence: enabling astronauts to repair the planned space station *Freedom* while remaining safely inside. To do this, robots equipped with TV cameras and other sensors would do the hazardous work under direct control of the astronauts via a feedback loop. This pioneering work at the space agency's Ames Research Center in Mountain View, California, is being spun off to a growing number of small entrepreneurships that are coalescing around California's Silicon Valley, including VPL Research in Redwood City and Autodesk across the Golden Gate Bridge in Sausalito. Their goal is to create the next major consumer product to follow in the wake of the successes of personal computers and VCRs. The marketing—and publicity—has begun, but the requisite supporting technology base is still taking shape.

THE FRUSTRATIONS OF
A PUSH-BUTTON WORLD

by Harold Thimbleby

People commonly expect that today's technology should make their lives easier, yet so many push-button devices are infuriatingly difficult to use. Perhaps even more infuriating is the realization that they need not be that way.

(Top) © Rhoda Sidney—Stock, Boston; (bottom left) © Stuart Cohen—Comstock, Inc.; (bottom right) © Bob Daemmerich—The Image Works

Whether shopping for a new stereo, buying train tickets, or making bank transactions, people frequently find themselves confronting push-button products that they do not understand how to operate.

HAROLD THIMBLEBY *is Professor of Information Technology at the University of Stirling, Scotland. He is often unable to work his own VCR, to redirect telephone calls through the university exchange, or to run films through his camera without ruining them. He believes that the reason is not because he is not clever enough but because modern technology is in a mess.*

(Overleaf) Illustration by Ron Villani

It was 1930, and the German physicist and future Nobel laureate Otto Stern had a visitor to his equipment-filled laboratory in Hamburg. The visitor remarked that there were a lot of controls on Stern's apparatus. The physicist replied that it was a pity humans had not kept the prehensile tails of their distant forebears, as they would have been useful in the laboratory now. The visitor retorted, "They wouldn't help you, Stern; you would just make your apparatus still more complicated!"

Today we live in a "push-button world," and it seems as if the people who built it had prehensile minds. We depend on things that we do not know how to use effectively. At worst the situation is dangerous—somebody may press the Red Button by mistake. At best it adds complications to our lives. There is a science of designing machines for human use, and in the 1990s the need to begin applying that science has become urgent. The frustration that people experience with overly complex gadgets must be understood as a failure to design the devices properly; it is not our failure in being too old and inflexible or too simpleminded.

204

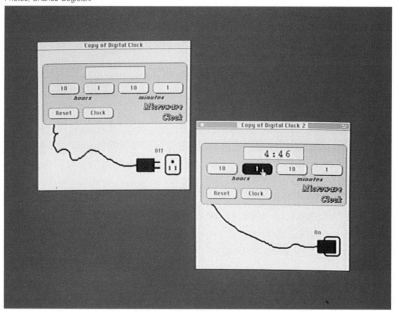

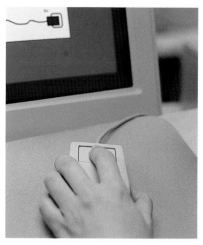

The screen of an Apple Macintosh computer (left) shows a pair of simulations for a digital clock design, which actually works when its cord is plugged in. All buttons on the clock can be pressed by means of a finger-shaped screen pointer directed by a mouse that has only one button (above). That such a simple interface as a mouse can operate simulations of devices having numerous buttons suggests that today's button-festooned products have taken the wrong path of development.

Button mania

The number of buttons on the remote controls of my own videocassette recorder and television set, added together, is 105 (there are another 34 on the machines themselves), more than the keys on some computer keyboards. In other words, computers, which are far more complicated than VCRs and TVs, can be controlled with fewer buttons. Indeed, since the mid-1980s the Apple Macintosh line of computers has made a point of being operable largely with a mouse; *i.e.*, a screen-pointer controller, equipped with a single button. Still, if one really wants buttons, everything that a computer mouse can do can be done instead with only five ordinary buttons: one to move the pointer in each of four directions on the screen and one to accept the selection indicated by the pointer (*see* Figure 1). Adding one more button as an on-off switch gives a grand total of six. Thus, having dozens or hundreds of buttons does not, in itself, make a product easy to use.

Equipped with a remote control for a TV-VCR combination that has 6 buttons, rather than 100 or more, a viewer would press each button more often and consequently would be less likely to forget what each one does. Every function that one wishes the remote control to perform could be displayed in the form of menus, or lists of choices, on the TV screen, in much the same way that Macintoshes and other computers employ menus. The viewer would move a pointer around a menu and make a selection. Menus allow the viewer to see all possible functions for the VCR and TV, yet, unlike physical buttons, they need show nothing confusingly irrelevant when some particular function happens to be unavailable in a given situation.

Many designers use the Macintosh as a quick way to simulate new product designs without having to go to the expense of building a prototype. That a computer, operated with as simple an interface as a mouse,

Figure 1: The capabilities of a computer mouse can be duplicated with a controller having only five buttons: four to move the screen pointer and one to select the choice indicated by the pointer. Adding a sixth "button," actually a slider, as an on-off switch makes the device a remote control for a TV or VCR that has been designed to display on-screen menus of functions.

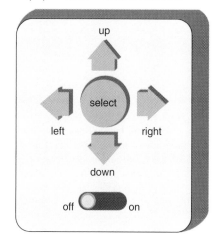

can simulate the pressing of, and the response from, the numerous buttons on a envisaged product is compelling evidence that domestic push-button products have taken an altogether different and worse path of development.

Although TVs and VCRs are the most frequently used push-button products at home, they are not the only ones to suffer from problems. A microwave oven can have 20 buttons, and a compact disc (CD) player more. If one cannot press the correct buttons in the correct order on the burglar alarm, it will protest deafeningly. Furthermore, most such systems have infuriatingly designed digital clocks. A common joke is that one can tell a house with no teenagers because the digital clocks are all flashing the wrong time.

Button mania extends to the modern automobile. In-car audio entertainment systems aspire to simulate the acoustical environment of the orchestra hall, church, or concert stage at the touch of a button—the correct button. A typical car radio-tape or radio-CD system now has more than 25 buttons, almost identical, and a display that shows characters as tiny as 1.5 millimeters (about 0.06 inch) in height. A driver cannot be expected to read the information displayed on the radio and drive safely, yet such products, regardless of their danger, sell well.

Although the mentality that designs car radios and VCRs also designs nuclear power stations and aircraft cockpits, there is an important difference. Power station operators and pilots are highly trained, whereas motorists have no schools to teach them how to work their entertainment systems.

On the job, people face button-studded photocopiers and facsimile machines that display "ERROR" but do not reveal what the error is or even whether it is the operator or the machine that is at fault. The "hold" and "transfer" functions of office telephone systems can be so intimidating that workers refuse to use them. On standard telephones having buttons for the 10 digits plus # (pound) and * (star), a call transfer might require pressing a sequence like *#1. Such a sequence may not come to mind— or may be confused with a similar sequence—just when one needs it.

The control panel of a typical modern in-car audio entertainment system has 25 or more buttons, many similar in appearance and some doubling up in function. Characters in the displays can be as small as 1.5 millimeters (about 0.06 inch) in height. In some designs the characters flash, which means that, whatever their size, they are invisible half the time.

An aircraft cockpit and the "mobile office" of an on-the-go businessperson bear strong similarities of push-button design. An important difference exists, however. Whereas pilots are highly trained to operate their complex controls, there is no one to train drivers how to deal with their car radios, portable phones, computers, and facsimile machines efficiently and safely.

Conversely, there is no guarantee that telephones having a dedicated transfer button, marked as such, will work quite as expected when the button is pushed.

Tedious as this list of frustrations has become, it will only grow longer. Why, consumers rightly ask, is life getting like this? Why does advanced technology, of which there is no shortage, seem to be of no assistance? Part of the answer is that products covered in buttons sell better than products that look simple. For something that can cost a few days' salary or more, one wants to see some buttons for it and a long list of features that will outdo the neighbors. The marketplace emphasizes styling, what things look like, rather than how they work. The customer usually finds out whether something is easy to use well after he or she has been seduced in the store. Some features may not be explored until weeks

A control board in a television studio carries an assortment of controls with different "affordances." Knobs that turn, buttons that press, and handles that swing up and down offer clues or reminders about their functions and help the user quickly locate the right one at the right time.

Today's office photocopiers, facsimile machines, and computer printers may offer dozens of special features and effects, but the design of their controls can deter the user from taking full advantage of those capabilities. Operators find it hard to glean the functions of buttons from their labels, which are usually symbolic icons or abbreviations, and they sometimes press the icons instead of the flat, membrane-style buttons next to them. Especially frustrating are machines that display obscure error messages without revealing the cause of the problem.

Cathy Melloan

after the purchase, and only then are they discovered to be impossible to understand or use.

A more important part of the answer involves the way products are fundamentally designed to interact with the people who are to use them. There exists plenty of science and engineering that could be applied in the design process to improve the usability of products. In the manufacturer's effort to get a product on the market as quickly and cheaply as possible, however, much of that knowledge gets overlooked—so much so that bad design often seems as if it could only have been deliberate.

The human factor

If sound science and engineering drove design, what principles would they espouse? Three main areas easily contribute answers: ergonomics, computer science, and plain common sense.

Ergonomics, also called human-factors engineering, is concerned with the interaction between people and the things they use. An ergonomist, for example, would question the readability of many car radio displays: the text is too small; block capital letters are harder to read than lowercase; the flashing display may not be visible at the specific instant that the user has a chance to look at it.

Knobs are for turning, buttons for pressing, switches for flicking, sliders for sliding. In other words, different types of controls have different "affordances," giving clues about what they do. Controls that feel different aid the user in operating the right one without having to look and, in the case of car radios, without having to divert attention from driving. Unfortunately, with the increase in digital electronics, more and more functions are controlled by buttons. Buttons, which are either pressed or not pressed, appeal to the binary thinking (0 or 1, off or on) of the computer designer. Although a VCR, microwave, or telephone may be built around a binary computer chip, what should that fact have to do

208

with the product's operation? It is apparently easier for the designer to use all buttons than to do a decent job.

The comprehensibility of instruction manuals is a particular ergonomic concern. Many manuals suffer from poor grammar, usage, and organization and from confusing illustrations. Often such defects are the result of translation to English from another language. A more inherent flaw is that manuals are written on the assumption that the user wants to know about the functions of each button on the product rather than about the things the product does. In fact, they typically require the user to learn a whole new technical vocabulary in order to look up the desired function. In other words, manuals are function-oriented, but they should be task-oriented. Still, the quality of manuals is subordinate to design, since no one can write good manuals for bad systems.

In addition to offering good design principles, ergonomics reveals a fundamental law: designers tend to design for themselves unless they make a conscious effort to design for users. For an electronics engineer, nothing is easier to comprehend than the functions of a few more buttons. Trained in the complexity of modern technology, technical people are least likely to appreciate the problems that others have with technology. Recall the visitor's good-natured criticism of Stern: having an extra hand simply would have led to more complicated controls.

Communicating with the computer chip

As ergonomics is to one's physical and physiological abilities and limitations, so computing is to one's intellectual abilities and limitations.

The acronym GIGO stands for an aphorism familiar to computer people: garbage in, garbage out. It means that computers, and the products that computers control, will function only as well as the instructions that humans give to them. A product whose design allows—or worse, encourages—the user to perform irrelevant actions will produce irrelevant, con-

Cathy Melloan

Exacerbating the difficulties caused by poor push-button product design are incomprehensible manuals. Instruction booklets can suffer from poor writing and organization and confusing illustrations. They also frequently approach their subject on the assumption that the user wishes to know about the function of each button rather than about the tasks the device can accomplish.

fusing responses. Computers do not have the flexibility of human beings; rather than making the best of a bad job, they just let things get worse.

A simple example of the GIGO principle involves the paired UHF tuning buttons found on some VCRs. Pressing one button increases the frequency, pressing the other decreases it. Their purpose is to let the user tune in the frequency of the desired UHF broadcasting station. The buttons, however, do not indicate when they have been pressed to the limit of their frequency range. A lack of response from pressing "increase" or "decrease" can mean either that the VCR has stopped looking for a station or that it is still looking. As the user starts to worry, he or she may start pressing both buttons randomly and may never find the station.

VCRs that tell the user exactly what they want and in what order are not immune to foul-ups. To record a TV program, say, later today, a VCR may first ask for today's date, then for the start time, then for the stop time, and then for the channel number. Finally it is ready to record, as long as one remembers to press the timer button. Several things are wrong with this design, all elementary programming faults. The VCR already knows today's date; it was probably displaying it a moment previously. It ought to default to today's date so that if the user wants to record something today, there is nothing extra to press. Although the VCR asks for date, times, and channel strictly in that order, it could easily be designed to allow the details to be entered in any order. If the hardest thing to remember, for example, is the start time, why not let the user enter it first, before it is forgotten? After finishing the settings the user certainly intends the VCR to record something, so why the need to press a timer button? Forgetting this task is one of the commonest mistakes users make. The machine would do better with a "cancel timer" button in case the user wishes to erase the settings.

When Samuel Morse invented his code, he had a given number of symbols (dots and dashes), detailed knowledge of the task (sending English messages), and a desire to make the code efficient. He knew that the letter E occurred frequently, whereas Q was rare. He realized that he should give E a short code (just a dot) and save one of the longer codes for Q (dash dash dot dash, which takes 10 times longer). Overall, he reduced the length of messages, making them less tedious to transmit.

In designing a VCR, therefore, one would expect the same approach to apply: find the probability of a user's performing a given task (like getting the machine to record), and pay attention to the symbols (combinations of button presses) available to get the message across to the VCR. There is even a formula, Zipf's Principle of Least Effort, that yields the relevant number of buttons to use. Given this principle, known qualitatively even to Morse, it is surprising to find that on one brand of VCR the "summer time adjust" is activated with a single button press, whereas setting a future recording time (which certainly is done more often than once a year) takes about 15 presses. The "summer time adjust" function wastes a button that would have been better used for a more frequent task. (Note also that having a "cancel timer" button instead of a timer button reduces the number of buttons to press for recording, a second good reason for the same design innovation.)

Many products have functions that designers have deliberately, and correctly, made harder for users to activate by accident. One example involves the standard audio tape recorder, which has long been designed to permit recording only if two buttons are pressed simultaneously. The intention is to keep the user from accidentally erasing what might already be on the tape. Nevertheless, many people find such finger gymnastics awkward, and even more so if the buttons are so widely separated as to require a finger from each hand. One manufacturer has responded to this complaint by adding yet another button that lets its machine be set "conveniently" to a permanent record mode—making it easy to wreck more than one tape before the user realizes what is going wrong. Thus, marketing encourages "solutions" to specious problems, ever lengthening "feature bouquets" to upstage the competition, and extra buttons to camouflage shortcomings that people have noticed.

If designers seriously wished to make things easier to use, they would add buttons not for new functions but rather as aids for operation—buttons for "help," "undo," or "cancel" being those most needed. Furthermore, they would add automatic verification so that button pressing was checked for being sensible. Some VCRs, for instance, will uselessly accept mistaken instructions to record something yesterday. VCRs should (and could very easily) verify that recording dates and times were plausible and, when they were not, point out the discrepancy immediately.

Common sense

Many principles of good design are so simple and sensible that they apply in any discipline, be it ergonomics, computer science, or even primary school problem solving. For example, if the user loses the VCR manual, is it possible to work out how to use the machine's "index search" function, or even to learn what the mysteriously labeled button is for? The answer is no. Why is the remote control totally different from the controls of the VCR or TV itself? Because of that inconsistency, the user must learn twice as much (for the set and the remote) from a manual twice as thick while getting only half the practice with each of two styles of controls than had there been one style.

In the 1960s consumer advocate Ralph Nader (above) alerted drivers to the realization that they are not at fault for accidents caused by poor automobile design. Today consumers are again mistakenly accepting blame for many of the usability problems they experience with push-button products.

It seems common sense to label a button for the job that it does, yet some manufacturers continue to give buttons unhelpful or obscure names. One VCR's "dpss" button is a sort of "play." Another machine's "standby" button allows setting the start time and length of a recording. On a particular model of TV, three quick presses of the "sound mute" button turn *on* the external speakers—neither a sound-muting function nor the first button one thinks of pressing when the speakers do not work.

Fallacy of the culpable user

In 1963 the American Association of Casualty and Surety Companies reported that parked cars sometimes rolled backward against the parking brake; a car parked on a slope might not be held by the brake. The solution suggested by the association was to educate the driver into the habit of applying the parking brake properly with the additional assistance of the foot brake. As it said, there would be "no problem . . . if a driver trains himself to do this." The solution to the safety problem was the driver's responsibility, and how to get the driver to read the car manual was a question of applied psychology.

That episode is reported in Ralph Nader's now classic book *Unsafe at Any Speed* (1965). With the benefits of nearly three decades of hindsight and of the perspective Nader did so much to promote, it is clear that the problem has nothing to do with drivers, their psychology, or their failure to read manuals. If a parking brake does not hold a car on a slope, the brake is at fault. The solution is not to get the driver to read the manual but to design the braking system so that nothing has to be said in the manual about special precautions. The insurance industry of the 1960s preferred to see usability problems with cars as the drivers' responsibility. Nader exposed the fallacy and put car manufacturers on course toward greatly improved design standards. Today the push-button product industry chooses to blame users for not reading manuals and argues that many of the difficulties that users experience are their own fault. That line of reasoning, although apparently no less attractive to industry than it was in the 1960s, remains no less fallacious.

VCR users do not sacrifice their lives for designers' sins, but they do have problems that even reading the manual cannot solve. One of the better examples centers on the time-out, which could well be described as "machine impatience." A time-out is a short period of time, started with a button press, in which the user must begin making more button presses to set desired functions; otherwise the equipment resets to its previous state. My own VCR has some time-outs only two seconds long, which means that even if I do use the manual, I still cannot read and comprehend fast enough. The machine is designed such that I cannot work through the controls step by step while studying the instructions.

If confrontations with the home VCR are humorous, buttons in cars are killing people. The distraction and frustration caused by fiddling with car radios and telephones make drivers have accidents. Today's campaigns for car safety should be obliged to include the dangers of in-car entertainment and communications.

212

Fallacy of the obsolete adult

Advertisements that emphasize how easy a push-button product is to use often suggest, by word or image, that "even a child can operate it." That idea, in combination with the user blame fostered by manufacturers, leads to perhaps the most pervasive false assumption about push-button technology: adults have trouble with it because they are too old.

Children do find VCRs easier to work than adults do. On the other hand, there are many things that children find easy, but VCRs are not designed specifically for children. If anything, VCRs are adult "toys," which adults should be able to use as effortlessly as possible. Adults have neither the time nor the inclination to expend the hours that children do "playing" at conquering a new gadget. More important, however, adults spend their childhoods learning rules and developing expectations about the way the world works. When they encounter products whose designs do not follow those expectations, they are justifiably baffled. Children, by contrast, are still learning. When dealing with new consumer technology, they are not disadvantaged by the otherwise useful knowledge and skills that adults have acquired. Adults find push-button products hard to use because the products do not conform to adult presumptions; children find things easier because they have fewer such presumptions.

The secret of the microwave clock

Ian Witten, professor of computer science at the University of Waikato, Hamilton, New Zealand, and I once spent a weekend in a friend's empty house. Because the power had been switched off, we had to restart the appliances, which included a microwave oven. The microwave, a popular brand, had a cute model name suggesting high intelligence—an apt description since it resisted our own intellects for 45 minutes. Later, after discussion with other people and from our own experiments, my colleague and I concluded that our difficulty was not unusual. The only advantage our professions gave us was that we did not blame ourselves.

Courtesy of Morgan Moss; photo, Cathy Melloan

Children are undisputed champions at such tasks as programming VCRs and setting digital clocks. It would be hasty to conclude, however, that adults have trouble with push-button technology because they are too old. Children find mastering a new gadget fun and satisfying and have much more time than adults do to explore all of its secrets. More important, they are not hampered by the expectations that adults have acquired over a lifetime about the way devices should work.

Figure 2: The design of this digital clock, from a microwave oven, allows it to be set to invalid times, making it unnecessarily difficult to understand how it works. (The layout shown is greatly simplified from the controls of the actual microwave, which in fact has another 18 buttons, all arranged on a smooth panel in a gridlike design.)

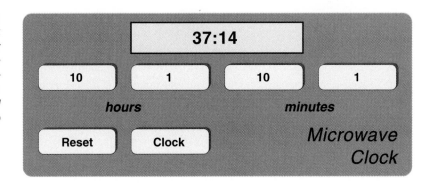

We discovered early on that the microwave's electronic digital clock (*see* Figure 2) allowed entering any number between 00:00 and 99:99. Consequently, we thought that the clock had been designed to accept 24-hour times. Since it was then 22:02 hours (10:02 PM), we tried setting that time. The clock refused to run. As time passed, we tried 22:05, 22:15, and so on, until much later we accidentally set the time to 1:00. The clock finally worked. We realized that we had been misled by what numbers the clock would accept; it was secretly a 12-hour clock. (We had a wager about what the manual, when we eventually found it, would say. We were both wrong; the manual did warn about the 12-hour-clock problem, but in a footnote.)

We had expected the clock to work a certain way. Indeed, it had led us to believe that, since it could count high enough to be a 24-hour clock, it indeed must be one. Given that expectation and the time of night, we would never have been able to set the clock. The experience exemplifies what happens with many push-button systems. When users do not understand how gadgets work, they become completely stuck. They give up even on such a "simple" thing as a digital clock. It becomes easier to let the clock be an hour ahead or behind for half the year than to risk a seasonal adjustment that might make it go totally awry. And, if the manual is mislaid, failure seems certain.

If manufacturers cannot design a digital clock properly, what hope is there for the thousands of other push-button products? Even the evidence of users' misfortune apparently is not sufficient to improve designs. Today, years after that microwave oven was introduced, and presumably in the face of an accumulated catalog of users' difficulties, microwave ovens containing clocks with identical flaws are still on the market. Some of the more recent manuals merely mention the difficulty more prominently. Again, the manufacturers have resorted to putting the burden on the user.

Unfortunately, designers have too many opportunities to misunderstand users. The designer of the microwave clock may have assumed that everyone used the 12-hour time system and that the extended range of the settings would confuse no one. In this case, fewer assumptions about users' behavior would have helped. In other cases, rather than trying to predict how users might behave, it is better to admit that they can behave in any way possible; *i.e.*, at random. A random model of a

214

user embodies all possible wrong—and right—ways of using a product. With a random user, the designer cannot fall into the trap of assuming too much and thereby being misled.

Consider again the infamous microwave clock. If asked how many button presses it takes to set it, its designer might reply that it takes as little as three: if, for example, 1:00 is desired, the user presses "clock" to enter the clock-setting mode, then the 1-hour button to advance its digit from 0 to 1, and finally "clock" again to start the clock running with the new time. On the other hand, if a random user were asked the same question, the answer would be 9.6 on average, a much larger value. Figure 3 helps explain why.

Each circle in the diagram corresponds to a state for the actual microwave clock. Because there are only five circles, it is a finite state model, and because it is not specific about the exact times or displays represented by each circle, it is a nondeterministic model. The numbers linking the circles show the approximate probabilities of being able to get from one state to another (straight arrows) or of remaining in the same state (curved arrows). If the diagram were a game board, the object would be to get a playing piece from the starting circle (power up) to the finish (clock running).

A user who knows how to set the clock simply follows the best route—reset, valid time, clock running—which corresponds to the minimal number of button presses that the designer expects. A user who has no idea of what to do will take different routes having different probabilities for advancing toward the finish. It is clear from the diagram that a random user takes so much longer because of the high probability of remaining in the invalid time circle; once there, a person is likely to waste button presses trying to get out.

What is striking, however, is that there is absolutely no design reason for the invalid time state or the reset state (in which the clock shows

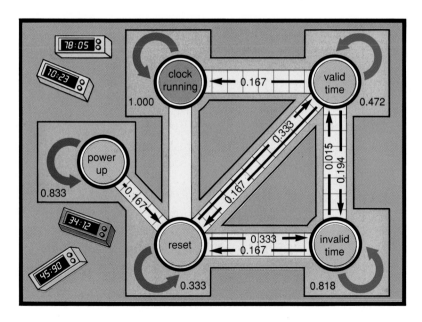

Figure 3: The diagram shows a nondeterministic finite state model of the digital clock discussed in text. The numbers show the approximate probabilities of being able to move from state to state or of remaining in the same state. For example, a probability of 0.333 indicates a 33% (a 1-in-3) chance, while a probability of 1.000 represents certainty, or no other alternative. The high probability (more than an 8-in-10 chance) of remaining in the invalid time state means that a random user—a user who does not know how to set the clock—is likely to be trapped in that state a long time. And when the user does get out, he or she is over 10 times more likely to reset the clock than get a valid time.

00:00, also an unacceptable time). Removing those states (*see* Figure 4) dramatically lowers the random user's score to about five button presses (the random user still takes longer than the designer's ideal). A user of the redesigned clock cannot get it to display a time beyond 12:59 and so would never be misled in the way we were.

The advantage of a random exploration of a design is that it presupposes no knowledge of the user. Although a good designer will consider the possible wrong ways in which the design might be used, he or she can think of only a limited number of them. Even a field trial of a design on a group of real users will, at best, reveal their own few and fixed preconceptions. A random process, however, embodies all possible wrong ways of using a system and is a remarkably effective way of testing out designs.

It is revealing that the random user can set the original microwave clock in about 10 button presses, whereas my colleague and I took many more. We would have worked out what to do more efficiently if we had simply rolled a die or tossed a coin. Being random is a better way of getting things to work than having the wrong ideas. This observation returns to the notion of why children are much better than adults at operating push-button products. Since they start off with fewer preconceptions, they press buttons at random more often. Such an approach gets results faster than a systematic one.

Error blocking

From the perspective of computer science, the trouble with the microwave clock is that its computer program is childishly trivial. There are four digits in the time display, each adjustable by its own button through a range of 0 to 9. The 10-minute button, for instance, moves the setting of minutes through the valid times, then into the 70s, 80s, and 90s. The programmer, apparently pleased with the neat plan of every button behaving exactly the same, forgot that the only button that should range

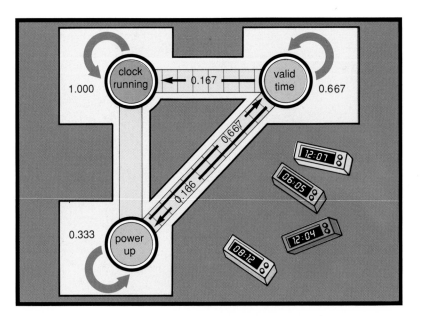

Figure 4: The diagram shows a model for a modified clock in which the invalid time and reset states have been removed. A random user finds it much easier to get such a clock running.

Arteria Blood Pressure Monitor designed for Paramed Technology
by IDEO Product Development. Industrial design by Tim Parsey, interaction design by
Peter Spreenberg, ergonomics by Jane Fulton, mechanical engineering by Bob Yuan; photo, Rick English

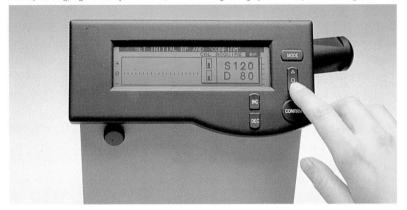

The design principle of commensurate effort is effectively incorporated into the Paramed Arteria, a blood pressure monitor made for medical institutions. The "inc" and "dec" buttons raise or lower the blood pressure threshold level that is needed to set off the alarm. To change the threshold setting by a large amount, the operator must press a button and hold it down a long time, making it impossible to set potentially dangerous threshold levels accidentally with a quick button press.

that freely is the 1-minute button. (The 1-hour button, for example, should not be able to advance its digit beyond a 2 if the 10-hour digit is a 1, because the clock should not be adjustable to 13 o'clock or beyond.) It is extremely easy to program the clock's computer such that a setting outside the 1:00-to-12:59 window is impossible to make. This technique, called error blocking, is standard in good product design.

The range of design options for blocking errors is wide. The simplest, and worst, option is for the designer to assume that the user will block errors. Only slightly better would be a note in the user's manual: Do not set 24-hour times. Next, the system itself could block the error; the clock's computer could be programmed so that, for example, 4:59 increased to 5:00 rather than to 4:60. Best of all, the entire clock design could be carefully thought out so that errors of any kind were far less likely and, when they did happen, were circumvented by programming.

The parking brake problem from the 1960s also can be analyzed in terms of error blocking. The American Association of Casualty and Surety Companies would have had the public believe that error blocking should occur in the driver, which in turn depended on the driver's learning the nature of the error and taking appropriate action. However, error blocking will be most effective in the design stage—*i.e.*, a parking brake that works properly—before users are involved.

Designing for safety and sanity

The importance of a microwave clock that blocks errors is "merely" that the user can easily set the correct time. In other situations incorporation of error blocking can be lifesaving.

In 1988 the London-based design company IDEO was asked to design a blood pressure monitor, which ultimately reached the market as the Paramed Arteria. Made for use in medical institutions, the device continually keeps tabs on a patient's blood pressure and sounds an alarm when the pressure exceeds or falls below a prescribed level. IDEO's designers initially made it easy to adjust the threshold pressure level on the device by assigning one button per digit, like the arrangement on the microwave clock. Being good at ergonomics, the company decided to test its design idea on the final users, medical personnel. Experiments revealed, as is

In translation of a product from old to new technology, good design principles sometimes are lost. For the digital clock discussed in text, in which each digit is controlled by its own button, single button presses can lead to invalid time settings. Even the better-designed digital clocks and watches that allow only valid times still let the user make a large change, and thus a large possible error, with one touch. By contrast, on a clock with an increment-decrement design, making a large deviation from the previous setting takes deliberate effort. Paradoxically, such a design has been around for centuries in the form of dial-face timepieces equipped with single adjustment knobs.

Cathy Melloan

217

obvious with hindsight, that the ability to change the numbers so easily was dangerous. With a single button touch a medical technician could introduce an error of 100 millimeters of mercury in the settings and thus allow potentially fatal blood pressure levels to pass undetected. The monitor was redesigned to have only two buttons for the threshold setting, one to increase it and one to decrease it. If a user really wants a high upper limit, he or she has to hold down the button a long time. It is no longer possible to make huge errors easily and unnoticeably. Such a design principle, in which greater changes require the user to try correspondingly harder, is called commensurate effort.

The principle of commensurate effort holds a lesson for the microwave clock. In the original clock the one-button-per-digit design caused errors; pressing the 10-hour button led to a sequence of such impossible increases as 10:00, 20:00, 30:00. By contrast, in a clock having a two-button increment-decrement design, the time naturally increases from 10:00 to 10:01 to 10:02. No errors are possible. Indeed, this is exactly how all dial-face clocks have been adjusted for centuries. They have knobs, with better affordances than buttons, for doing it.

A need for consumer action

One of the advantages of science is that a good theory has wide applicability. Scientifically developed designs that improve digital clocks and blood pressure monitors will also improve other number-setting devices, whether they be on one's wrist or in one's kitchen, family room, car, or office. The analysis of the microwave clock strongly suggests that the manufacturers considered neither human nor computer science. Had they tested their design on people or drawn a simple finite-state machine diagram, it is inconceivable that they could have left the clock in such an appalling state.

The flawed microwave clock embodies the impoverished state-of-the-art approach to designing modern push-button devices. Science is ignored in favor of marketing, while attempts to improve usability consist mainly of the addition of extra buttons to solve problems that should not have existed. If this year's push-button world is frustrating, next year there will be more intimidating telephones in the stores, more complex automatic teller machines on the street, and more confusing electronic games in the hands of children.

Nader's contribution to car safety was in raising public consciousness of the needless dangers designed into cars. Although it is now clear that drivers were being exploited, drivers at the time did not know better. Today the inhabitants of the push-button world are in an analogous situation. Manufacturers seem happy to keep on blaming consumers for their inability to use ineptly designed products. They hope that people can evade principles of computer science, physiology, and psychology. People cannot, of course, and are frustrated.

The car industry lost its complacency when consumers realized that it could be blamed for many of their problems. The push-button product industry is overdue for the same kind of revelation. Manufacturers have access to the science that will help them design things properly. They just need their customers to motivate them to use it.

FOR ADDITIONAL READING

Brenda Laurel (ed.), *The Art of Human-Computer Interface Design* (Addison-Wesley, 1990). Covers some of the background and design considerations involved in creating the Apple Macintosh computer.

Ralph Nader, *Unsafe at Any Speed* (Knightsbridge Publishing Co., 1991). The classic exposé of poor design in the car industry.

Donald A. Norman, *The Psychology of Everyday Things* (Basic Books, 1988). Readable and enjoyable, it argues that the reason for our errors in using consumer technology is invariably bad design and that a better understanding of humans is essential for improvement.

Dick Powell, *Presentation Techniques,* 2nd ed. (Macdonald, 1990). Provides insight into how products are designed and how graphic artists influence the final form of products.

Harold Thimbleby, "Can Humans Think?" (the 1991 Ergonomics Research Society Lecture), *Ergonomics* (October 1991). Expands on the principles discussed in the article and explores the future effects of interactive home entertainment coupled with multimedia systems.

Harold Thimbleby, "The Undomesticated Video Recorder," *Image Technology: Journal of the BKSTS* (June 1991, pp. 214–216). Considers specific design faults of VCRs.

Harold Thimbleby, *User Interface Design* (Addison-Wesley, 1990). Aimed at technically competent designers, it stresses the role of science and design principles.

Harold Thimbleby and Ian H. Witten, "New Techniques for User Modelling," in Rex Hartson and Debby Hix (eds.), *Advances in Human-Computer Interaction*, vol. iv (Ablex, 1992). Provides a complete discussion of the microwave clock example.

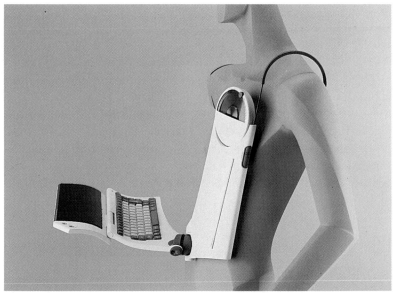

NEC

The design of the Lapbody, one of a line of prototype wearable computers, suggests that the evolution of information and communications technology will bring human and machine into even more intimate contact than at present. Should that vision prove true, it is imperative that manufacturers incorporate good science and engineering into their designs and that consumers demand products that are truly fit for use.

NEW VIEWS OF OLD SCIENCE

by Mary Jo Nye

Once dominated by inspirational accounts of heroes and of cumulative progress in the sciences, the history of science has since undergone striking changes in focus. Recent work has explored social, religious, and economic influences on scientists and has even questioned the objectivity of scientific knowledge.

A rapidly expanding discipline of teaching and research, the history of science has merged with philosophical and sociological studies of science and technology into a broader field now often referred to as "studies of science, technology, and society" (STS). Its practitioners work to further science literacy among non-science college students and the general public, to develop new materials for science teaching, and to study the historical past of science and technology in order to understand the dynamics of scientific change and the implications of science and technology in different historical periods and different cultures.

As a field of research and writing, the history of science has flourished since the late 19th century. Now, as then, its scholars and contributors include a diverse array of scientists, historians, philosophers, journalists, and popularizers, among them Stephen Jay Gould, Carl Sagan, Jeremy Bernstein, Daniel Boorstin, William Broad, Gina Kolata, Natalie Angier, and the late Isaac Asimov. Since the 1960s the history of science has become a well-established professional discipline within universities, museums, archives, and other institutions. Today advanced degrees, national and international meetings, and public programs in the history of science, the history of science and technology, and the social studies of science have become common from Berkeley to Cambridge to Tokyo.

The aims and uses of the history of science are many. At its best, it inspires students to emulate the achievements of past scientists. It explains how scientific theories have developed out of abstract thinking, practical problems, observation, and experiments. It describes the social institutions, political environments, and customs that have provided favorable or hostile settings for scientific work. It examines relationships between science and technology and between science and medicine. And it explores the aesthetic, moral, and practical implications of the sciences, many of which have so radically transformed intellectual and material culture. In our modern, specialized world, the history of science has become a bridge, providing common intellectual and social space between what British scientist and novelist C.P. Snow called the "two cultures" of the humanities and the sciences.

MARY JO NYE *is George Lynn Cross Professor of the History of Science at the University of Oklahoma, Norman.*

220

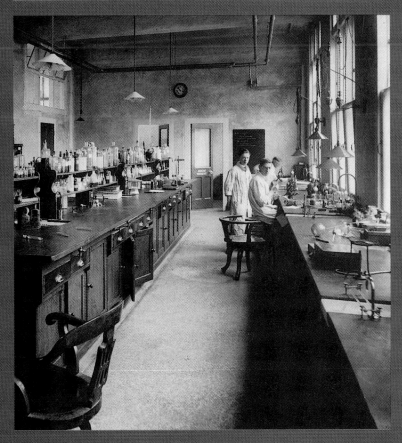

The history of science also can be entertainment, but entertainment of an enlightening variety, providing lively anecdotes and vignettes of scientific personalities and historical situations. Successful television series like Jacob Bronowski's "The Ascent of Man" and various miniseries like that on the life of Robert Oppenheimer have given millions of viewers a sense of the excitement and achievements of scientists. While cartoonist Sidney Harris would not make most people's lists of "historians of science," some of his best work fits into the anecdotal genre.

The history of science has sometimes been used by scientists to further self-interest. Histories have been written to settle priority disputes for scientific discoveries or theories, to discredit scientific opponents or ideological enemies, or simply to narrate chronologies of discoveries and inventions in an uncritical, celebratory way. Like all histories, the history of science sometimes has been falsified and misused for frightening ends, as in the 1930s when some Germans made historical claims that Jewish contributions to relativity theory and quantum physics had undermined scientific progress.

As a field, the history of science is still expanding. Some of its attention remains centered on reiterations and reinterpretations of very traditional topics; for example, the 16th- and 17th-century Copernican revolution, the trial of Galileo, the mechanical physics of Isaac Newton, the oxygen theory of Antoine Lavoisier, controversies over Darwinian evolutionary biology, and, more recently, Einstein's theory of relativity. Long-term projects are under way at Boston University for editing and publishing the papers of Albert Einstein and at the University of Cam-

222

bridge for publishing the letters of Charles Darwin. On the other hand, in recent decades the field has also experienced striking changes in focus and methodology.

The ideas, theories, and personalities of scientists used to dominate histories of science. Much attention was given to the logic of scientific argument and to facts used by scientists to support one theory over another. During the decade of the 1960s, when the discipline of the history of science became firmly established, philosopher Karl Popper's preoccupation with the demarcation of science (exemplified by Newton) from "pseudoscience" (alchemy, astrology, and psychoanalysis) received much attention. The majority of studies in the history of science dwelled on physics and on the sciences of the 17th and 18th centuries, while such topics as Charles Darwin, Gregor Mendel, and Louis Pasteur were notable exceptions.

Since the early 1970s all this has changed. Much of recent research has explored 19th- and 20th-century science, especially the genetic and behavioral sciences, with new emphasis on the sciences of animal behavior, ecology, and environmentalism, as well as on nuclear and high-

The dedication page of Galileo's Dialogue on the Two Chief World Systems, *(above), first edition in Italian (1632), can be taken to depict both Aristotle, Ptolemy, and Copernicus and the three speakers in the* Dialogue: Simplicio, *who defends the old system;* Sagredo, *who is undecided; and* Salviati, *who offers arguments in favor of the Earth's motion. Galileo was prosecuted by the Inquisition in 1633 for favoring Copernicus over Ptolemy in the* Dialogue, *which by papal instruction was supposed to have presented the Earth- and Sun-centered systems noncommittally. Galileo's trial (above left) and the events surrounding it remain among traditional subjects for history-of-science studies.*

A typical 17th-century European chemical laboratory is shown in an illustration dating from that era. Chemistry, physics, and other disciplinary specialties of the 17th and 18th centuries served as subjects for the majority of studies in the history of science until the past two or three decades, when the field embarked on a tremendous expansion and broadening of focus.

energy physics. These studies not only delve into facts illuminating past social and ethical effects of the technological applications of modern science but also sometimes pay considerable attention to the ways in which the social and moral attitudes of individual scientists may have affected their very understanding of the natural world. Some studies have reached a broad audience; for example, Daniel J. Kevles' annals of eugenics in the United States and Great Britain, which was serialized in *The New Yorker* in 1984.

Not only has it been the increased emphasis on very recent science that has changed the history of science in the last two decades. There also has been a shift away from the history of ideas to the history of institutions, laboratories, and research schools. In addition, influenced by new trends in the sociology and philosophy of science, the field has been the stage for lively and sometimes angry debate about the premise that science is rationally objective knowledge and is privileged in its possession of the truth, in contrast to religion, metaphysics, and ideology. To the dismay of many scientists and proponents of scientific values, the irrational and social roots of some scientists' work have been explored, including Newton's persistent pursuit of alchemy into his old age and anthropologists' use of human values and norms as a basis for evaluating the behavior of ape communities. Historians who have applied economic metaphors to science, describing past scientists as "producers" or "manufacturers" of knowledge, also have challenged some of the distinctions that formerly were made between the history of science and the history of technology.

The history of science as a history of ideas

During the 18th and 19th centuries it was mostly philosophers, scientists, and mathematicians who recounted or analyzed the emergence and development of the sciences. They did so in three principal genres of writing, which remain important today. First, there were biographical essays or books on the great men of science; for example, mathematician Vincenzo Viviani's account of the life of Galileo published in the early 1700s and physicist David Brewster's 19th-century biography of Newton. Most of the scientific heroes were legends in their own times, men who were leaders in scientific academies and who received much attention when they died. Even lesser heroes were remembered and revered by having their names tied to hypotheses, procedures, and laws, as in the naming of Avogadro's hypothesis, Boyle's law, or Mendeleyev's periodic table of the elements. Legend-building anecdotes, like Viviani's telling of Galileo's weight-dropping experiments before a crowd at the Leaning Tower of Pisa, have loomed large in such histories and have become part of the mythology and iconography of science.

A second kind of writing about science has been the historical paragraph or larger historical introduction prepared for a science lecture course or textbook. This pedagogical tradition in science has been perhaps oldest and strongest in mathematics and chemistry. One of the first significant histories of mathematics was the two-volume work published by Jean-Étienne Montucla in 1758. And when Lavoisier published his

Scottish physicist David Brewster's account of Isaac Newton exemplifies the early biographies on the great names in science, one of the principal genres of writing wherein the history of science was recounted and analyzed during the 18th and 19th centuries.

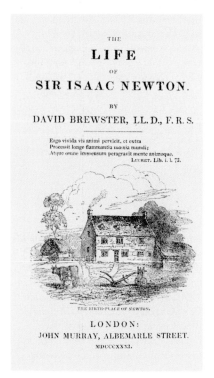

THE

LIFE

OF

SIR ISAAC NEWTON.

BY

DAVID BREWSTER, LL. D., F. R. S.

Ergo vivida vis animi pervicit, et extra
Processit longe flammantia mœnia mundi;
Atque omne immensum peragravit mente animoque.
LUCRET. Lib. i. 73.

THE BIRTH-PLACE OF NEWTON.

LONDON:
JOHN MURRAY, ALBEMARLE STREET.
MDCCCXXXI.

Elements of Chemistry in 1789 without a historical introduction to the subject, the omission was taken by contemporaries as proof of his arrogance in claiming to have invented a new chemistry and his meanspirited attitude in failing to give anyone else credit.

Historical introductions, like full-scale "special" histories written by scientists about their disciplinary specialties, tend to provide pictures of the cumulative advance of an individual science through a continuous chain of right thinking and observation generally devoid of confusion, false paths, and misassumptions. Such works serve to demonstrate the scientific method in operation not only in individual discoveries and advances but also over the history of an entire field.

In an introductory science lecture course, a history's purpose is to instill admiration for a tradition that the apprentice is to carry on and advance. The idea that a history can be told to students in a different way, for example, that Newton fudged his data on the Moon or that James Clerk Maxwell persisted in working on the kinetic theory of gases despite contradictory results, led one physicist historian of science in the 1970s to title a paper with the puckish question, "Should the History of Science Be Rated X?" One reason that James Watson's account of the discovery of the double-helix structure for DNA occasioned such scandal when it was published in 1968 was his abandonment of the inspirational mode of specialist history in favor of an account of the self-interested and careerist character of his early scientific work.

ELEMENTS

OF

CHEMISTRY.

PART I.

Of the Formation and Decomposition of Aeriform Fluids—of the Combustion of Simple Bodies—and the Formation of Acids

CHAP. I.

Of the Combinations of Caloric, and the Formation of Elastic Aeriform Fluids.

THAT every body, whether solid or fluid, is augmented in all its dimensions by any increase of its sensible heat, was long ago fully established as a physical axiom, or universal proposition, by the celebrated Boerhaave. Such facts as have been adduced for controverting the

VOL. I.   A   generality

Cold Spring Harbor Laboratory Archives

On the first text page of his Elements of Chemistry (above, English edition published in 1790), Antoine Lavoisier begins his subject without a historical introduction. So strong a tradition was the inclusion of such an introduction in chemistry textbooks at the time that the omission was taken by contemporaries as an indication of Lavoisier's arrogance in wanting to credit himself for the entire field. (Left) James Watson, left, and Francis Crick pose with their model of the DNA molecule in a photo from Watson's book The Double Helix (1968). One reason that the book aroused controversy was its departure from the inspirational mode of specialist history in favor of an account showing that scientists allow the same less-than-lofty motives to influence their work as anyone else.

A third long-standing tradition of writing about science is exemplified in the "general" histories, standardized by Auguste Comte's Positivist history and philosophy of science, first published in Paris in the 1830s. Comte, who had been an engineering student at the École Polytechnique, drew upon the recent successes in mechanics and natural history of Parisian mathematicians and scientists like Pierre-Simon Laplace and Georges Cuvier as well as upon 18th-century histories like the Marquis de Condorcet's *Sketch of a Historical Tableau of the Progress of the Human Mind*. In what became a standard account of the history of the sciences, Comte described the *necessary* pathway by which a pyramid of scientific, or "positive," knowledge was being constructed, with mathematics, astronomy, and mechanics first established at the base, followed by chemistry and physiology, and to be crowned by the development of what is known today as sociology. Comte excluded psychology and theology from the scientific edifice.

Late 19th and early 20th centuries

It was Comte's disciple, the Positivist, secular, and anti-Catholic philosopher Pierre Laffitte, who was appointed to the first academic professorship in the history of science, at the Collège de France in Paris in 1893. At the time, the finest historians of science in France were the Catholic engineer Paul Tannery and the Catholic physicist and physical chemist Pierre Duhem. Tannery had lectured at the Sorbonne on the history of mathematics, breaking with tradition by arguing that the ancient Greeks had good reasons to treat the Earth as the mathematical focus of planetary orbits and as the unmoved center of the universe.

Duhem also broke with tradition, following discoveries of manuscripts at the French National Library, which allowed him to demonstrate that the Middle Ages was not the "dark ages" ridiculed by Enlightenment and modern philosophers. Duhem found evidence to support what later was called the continuity thesis about the relationship between medieval philosophy and the new science of the Renaissance. Duhem argued that Galileo had not created an entirely new mechanics in the late 1500s and early 1600s but that medieval teachers in Paris beginning in the 13th century had first posed the fundamental problems of mechanics that Galileo took up. Duhem's work combated the claims in best-selling 19th-century books, like John W. Draper's *History of the Conflict Between Religion and Science,* that religion, and especially Roman Catholicism, was the enemy of science. It was not until later in the 20th century, however, that "natural theology" and religious inspiration for scientific work began to be studied by historians of science, demonstrating how very closely religious sensibility and scientific curiosity often were linked.

What is significant about the influence of Positivism within the history of science was not simply its anticlericalism but its idealism and its emphasis on mind or espirit. Comte's Positivist legacy was the historical point of view that the world is governed and overturned by ideas and that no ideas have been as important as scientific ones. This emphasis in the history of science was to dominate until the 1960s. Very few works

The Collège de France, Paris, established the first academic professorship in the history of science with the appointment of the Positivist philosopher Pierre Laffitte to the position in 1893.

Mary Jo Nye

in the history of science took a Marxist or economic view that material conditions are at the heart of scientific advance, and very few examined the social or political conditions and effects of scientific work.

Of course, there were exceptions. A notable and controversial one was Boris Hessen's paper on the social and economic roots of Newton's *Principia* delivered from the Soviet delegation to the second International Congress of the History of Science in London in 1931. This paper and its approach became an inspiration for British left-wing scientists, among whom the physicist and historian of science J.D. Bernal was a leader. Another controversial but non-Marxist book was University of Cambridge historian G.N. Clark's *Science and Social Welfare in the Age of Newton* (1937). Like Hessen, Clark argued the role of practical needs of transport, industry, and warfare in advancing 17th-century science while adding to these sources of scientific invention the medical and fine arts, as well as religion and "love of truth."

For the most part, however, the history of science during the 1920s and '30s was dominated by the concerns of what still was called the Positivist tradition, in particular the preoccupations of a circle of Parisian intellectuals led by the philosopher and historian Henri Berr and organized as the Centre International de Synthèse (International Center for Synthesis), a foundation "Pour la Science" ("for the sake of science"). Berr's early colleagues in this venture included the historian Lucien Febvre, the physicist Paul Langevin, and the philosopher Abel Rey. The Paris group attacked very big questions: the meaning of evolutionary biology; concepts of space, time, and relativity; and the roles of reductionism and determinism in quantum mechanics. Their interests and methods

Illustration of mining techniques from Denis Diderot's Encyclopédie, *one of the principal achievements of the Enlightenment, reflects the rationalist intentions of the work to bring out the essential principles and applications of every art and science. In the 1930s Boris Hessen of the Soviet Union and G.N. Clark of England both argued that practical needs of transport, industry, and warfare had played a role in scientific advancement in the age of Newton.*

were dedicated to the integration of science, history, and philosophy. In the early 1930s Émile Meyerson, Gaston Bachelard, Hélène Metzger, and Alexandre Koyré were among those pursuing this kind of history of science in Paris, along with Ernst Cassirer in Germany, Robin Collingwood in England, and Arthur Lovejoy in the United States.

Among histories of the great figures of science, no book written during the 1920s or '30s was more influential in the academic field of the history of science than Koyré's *Galileo Studies*, which appeared in 1939. It was a study not of Galileo the man but of Galileo the mind. Koyré argued that the 17th-century scientific revolution was a revolution in ideas resulting from Galileo's adoption of Platonic metaphysics, which identified truth about the natural world with ideal forms epitomized in mathematics rather than with ordinary experiences limited by the senses. Koyré took the view that there was a sharp break, a real discontinuity, between medieval Aristotelian philosophy and modern mathematical science, and he denied that experiment played a role comparable to Platonic metaphysics in Galileo's new scientific philosophy. Galileo's great achievement, according to Koyré, lay in recognizing that mathematical laws are true but can fit only an idealized physical world.

Among French-speaking scholars, George Sarton became a pivotal figure in the international definition and professionalization of the history of science, not so much because of his writing but because of his proselytizing the need for study and research in the field. The history-of-science professorship at the Collège de France was not replaced when it fell vacant in 1913, two years before Sarton emigrated from Belgium to the United States. Sarton took with him his recently founded journal *Isis*, which has remained in continuous publication since 1912, becoming the official journal of the History of Science Society founded in 1924 and still the central journal of the discipline. The intensity of Sarton's Positivist vision is nowhere clearer than in his *Introduction to the History of Science,* in which he wrote, "The history of science is the history of mankind's unity, of its sublime purpose, of its gradual redemption."

After World War I Sarton began teaching at Harvard University, where the biochemist L.J. Henderson already was teaching undergraduates about science from the Greeks to Galileo. The chemist and Harvard president James B. Conant was a strong advocate of the teaching of the history of science in the arts and sciences curriculum, and in 1936 he oversaw the creation at Harvard of a master's and doctoral program in the field. A primary aim of members of the program became the development of materials for improving science education by the use of historical case studies in science teaching. In 1941 the University of Wisconsin at Madison established an independent department of the history of science, and Cornell University, Ithaca, New York, followed with a program in 1945. Gradually survey courses in the history of science were instituted at many universities, in addition to the teaching of long-established courses in the history of special sciences like mathematics and chemistry.

Growth and new direction in the post-Sputnik era

During the 1950s the first generation of self-consciously professional historians of science emerged in the United States and Great Britain, for the most part committed to the Positivist vision of the history of science as the history of ideas and objective knowledge. Charles Gillispie's book *The Edge of Objectivity,* based on the course he gave undergraduates at Princeton University in the late 1950s, expressed in many ways the credo of this generation. Its members included A. Rupert Hall and Marie Boas Hall, René Taton, I. Bernard Cohen, Gerald Holton, Marshall Clagett, Richard S. Westfall, and A.C. Crombie, with Holton one of the few doing research in the history of 20th-century science.

Following World War II an influx of servicemen into American universities, in combination with the war-engendered cooperative arrangements among military agencies, industrial laboratories, and universities, transformed higher education. The launching of Sputnik by the Soviet Union in 1957 inspired rapid infusion of new funds into science education, scientific research, and science policy studies. In this environment the study of the history of science offered an important avenue for interesting young people in science and for furthering public understanding of science. It also offered to aid the development of science policy through a better-founded comprehension of the ways in which science and technology have developed in the past. The pace of postwar scientific developments and their effect on modern societies made imperative the professionalization of the history of science and technology for a generation well placed to implement it.

Both expansion and specialization within the field were results. In 1958 some members of the U.S.-based History of Science Society withdrew from the group, organized a Society for the History of Technology, and began publishing the journal *Technology and Culture* in 1960. Other new journals and national history-of-science societies began to appear

229

immediately after World War II, in eastern and western Europe and elsewhere. New national committees for the history of science (and for the history of technology and the philosophy of science) were organized under the auspices of Unesco. In many cases these committees were supported within national academies of science; for example, the Soviet Academy of Sciences. In the United States the National Science Foundation implemented a program for the history and philosophy of science in 1958, providing an entirely new source of funding for research and for graduate training.

At the very time that study and research in the history of science were becoming professionalized, two Americans were to transform the field conceptually. Although it first appeared as a journal monograph in 1938, Robert Merton's Harvard Ph.D. thesis, *Science, Technology and Society in Seventeenth-Century England* (reissued by Harper and Row in 1970), was to exert its real impact in the 1960s and '70s. This impact occurred simultaneously with that of perhaps the single most influential book in the field, Thomas Kuhn's *The Structure of Scientific Revolutions* (1962). Paradoxically, Kuhn's book, which some said undermined the tradition of the objectivity and cumulative progress of scientific knowledge, initially appeared in a series founded by Positivist thinkers in the 1930s, the International Encyclopedia of Unified Science. Like Merton's earlier work, this small monograph by a young physicist was conceived under the influence of the history-of-science community at Harvard, while Kuhn was a member of the Society of Fellows.

Both Merton's and Kuhn's work reintroduced into the history of science the social structure and the social history of science. Drawing upon Hessen and Clark, Merton argued the influence on past scientific work of economic and material conditions, the organization of scientific institutions, and what he called Puritan religious values. Largely because of the continued suspicion in the West of economic interpretations of history, Merton's reiteration of relations between 17th-century science and practical needs in architecture, canal building, ocean navigation, mining, and ballistics still received little interest. In any case, critics said, Newton had not had these practical needs in mind.

Nevertheless, Merton's claims that 30–60% of the papers presented to the Royal Society in the 1600s concerned topics of practical utility convinced some historians of the need to study social demands more closely. Merton's work also confirmed some sociologically minded scholars like Derek de Solla Price at Yale University in the belief that they were right in wanting to introduce quantitative methods, which compare numbers of papers published on different topics or count citations to earlier scientific works, into the history of science in order to gauge changing research fronts and important scientific advances in the past.

What became known specifically as Merton's thesis was that part of his Ph.D. thesis that dealt with religion and science; namely, the claim that many members of the Royal Society were Puritans in religion or espoused Puritan values. Drawing upon earlier studies by the German political economist Max Weber and the English economic historian R.H.

In the mid-20th century American sociologist Robert Merton helped transform the field of the history of science conceptually with his monograph Science, Technology and Society in Seventeenth-Century England, *in which he argued the influence on past scientific work of economic and material conditions, the organization of scientific institutions, and Puritan religious values. Merton's controversial claims encouraged historians of science to study social demands more closely and provided an important testing ground for new kinds of research.*

230

Tawney, Merton argued that the so-called Protestant ethic contains some of the core values of scientific behavior—diligence and industry, individual experience of God and nature, derogation of enthusiasm in favor of sober reason, distrust of organized authority, and belief in doing good works as proof of God's grace. He further emphasized the cooperative and consensus aspects of scientific organization. These distinguish the new science from older, more mystical and secretive inquiries into natural knowledge, like alchemy.

It is not surprising that Merton's thesis was controversial. For the expanding field of the history of science in the early 1960s, it provided an important testing ground for new kinds of research: on the religious concerns of scientists; on the organization and memberships of scientific institutions; and on scientists' involvement in practical matters of industry, agriculture, and engineering. Merton conceded to the historians of ideas that their approaches could illuminate short-term fluctuations in the history of science, but he advised that long-term changes were to be analyzed differently, by taking into account how scientists have selected problems that are vital to dominant values and interests of their culture.

Whereas Merton's thesis remained a model for research and testing within the confines of the field of the history and sociology of science, Thomas Kuhn's notion of the "scientific paradigm" has become much more popular and widely known. (Among the bumper stickers for sale at street stalls in Berkeley in the early 1990s was "Subvert the Dominant Paradigm.") When it appeared, Kuhn's account of the history of science

231

In 1962 American physicist Thomas Kuhn published The Structure of Scientific Revolutions. *This small monograph, which some regard as the single most important book in the field of the history of science, introduced the notion of the scientific paradigm, an accepted model that defines how scientists see the world and approach their research.*

was taken to be the kind of revolutionary theory that one might expect from a 1960s Berkeley professor, a colleague of California philosophers like Paul Feyerabend and Herbert Marcuse, who were teaching that science is nothing more or less than another ideology.

Demonstrating his interpretation by case histories, Kuhn argued that a well-established scientific community normally works within an accepted model or pattern—the paradigm—which defines how scientists see the world, the kinds of questions they ask, and the sorts of answers they expect to find. Aristotle's theory of motion, Ptolemy's astronomy, Newton's gravitational theory, Lavoisier's concept of the conservation of weight all provided such paradigms for normal science at different times. What was novel in Kuhn's argument was his emphasis on the conservatism seen in scientists' hesitation about abandoning a paradigm, their willingness to live with a paradigm despite ill-fitting observations and logical anomalies, the influence on scientists of cultural and psychological forces as they decide whether to abandon one paradigm in favor of a new one, and the incommensurability of successive paradigms with one another. By incommensurability Kuhn meant, for example, that the classical, or Newtonian, concept of mass (which is conserved) is not the same as the relativistic, or Einsteinian, view of mass (which can increase and is interchangeable with energy) or that the language systems of different paradigms (*e.g.,* Newtonian mechanics and relativistic mechanics) are translatable but not identical.

The psychological terminology of Kuhn's history appalled many historians and philosophers of science accustomed to worrying only about the logic of science. The notion of incommensurability introduced the idea that science is not cumulative. The role of factors external to the internal, technical (*i.e.,* so-called purely scientific) concerns of scientists threatened the autonomy of scientific knowledge and its objectivity. The emphasis on successive revolutions in science conjured up visions of chaos and relativism in what seemed the only bastion of rationality.

In response to criticisms and debates during the 1960s and 1970s, Kuhn denied extreme interpretations of his account, reemphasized in his later work the role of technical factors in scientific change, and reiterated the progressive character of science. Among those who addressed Kuhn's ideas, many social scientists debated among themselves whether their disciplines were in pre-paradigmatic or paradigmatic states; *i.e.,* whether their fields were "really" sciences. More self-confidently, many geologists claimed that the theory of plate tectonics constituted a Kuhnian-type "revolution" in science. Whereas the apparent coincidence that the Atlantic coastlines of Africa and South America fit together like pieces of a jigsaw puzzle was cited as an "anomaly" inexplicable by earlier geodynamics, which held that landmasses only move vertically, it was neatly explained by a theory of plates moving horizontally with respect to each other.

The social studies of science movement

At the time that Merton's work was rediscovered and Kuhn's work first appeared, enrollments, courses, and graduate study in the history of science were rapidly expanding throughout the Western and industrialized countries. In the United States, Western Europe, and Japan, many students entering universities in the 1960s were experiencing anxiety about the implications of what retiring U.S. Pres. Dwight Eisenhower had called the military-industrial complex. Influenced strongly by the social and political controversies centered on the war in Vietnam, this '60s generation began writing histories, and training students to write histories, of very modern science and "big" science in which academic science, engineering science, and industrial science are analyzed as overlapping networks of personalities, funding, and institutions.

The results included some very influential studies of national scientific traditions. Examples dealing with American science and technology are David Noble's *America by Design: Science, Technology and the Rise of Corporate Capitalism* (1977), Daniel J. Kevles' *The Physicists: The History of a Scientific Community in Modern America* (1978), and Richard Rhodes's Pulitzer Prize-winning *The Making of the Atomic Bomb* (1986). A Japanese historian of science, Yasu Furukawa, has written one of the more recent and comprehensive studies of the social history of science from the Renaissance to the 20th century, *Kagaku no shakaishi* ("A Social History of Science," 1989).

One of the important venues for these kinds of studies has been the journal *Minerva*, founded in 1962 as a politically conservative and historically oriented publication for international studies and comparisons of science, science education, and science policy. A more radical approach was the aim of the review *Science Studies*, founded in 1971 by David Edge and Roy Macleod in Great Britain. Collaboration among research units and academic groups in England, Scotland, France, Germany, and elsewhere in Europe resulted in two new organizations, the Society for Social Studies of Science (4-S) and the European Association for the Study of Science and Technology. At the University of Edinburgh, so-

Los Alamos National Laboratory

A photo featured in Richard Rhodes's The Making of the Atomic Bomb *(1986) shows the raising of the Trinity device, the first nuclear weapon, to the top of its test tower in New Mexico prior to detonation on July 16, 1945. The book, a Pulitzer Prize winner, is an example of the kinds of histories about "big" science that have been written since the 1970s by a generation influenced by concerns about the military-industrial complex and by the social and political controversies engendered by the war in Vietnam.*

ciologists embarked upon what they called the "strong program" in the sociology of science. This effort created forceful reverberations in the history of science.

Applying the anthropologist's notion of "culture" and "tribe" to the scientific laboratory and draping himself in the mantle of the anthropological observer, one of the strong-program proponents, the French philosopher Bruno Latour, spent two years at the Salk Institute for Biological Studies, La Jolla, California, watching scientists, assistants, and clerical staff in their physiology and chemistry laboratories, offices, workrooms, library, and conference area. Latour wrote up the results with the English sociologist Steve Woolgar in the book *Laboratory Life: The Social Construction of Scientific Facts* (1979).

Drawing not only upon anthropological theories but also upon the premises of the strong program of sociology, the two authors argued that there is no difference between scientific activity and any other kind of human activity or between scientific thinking and any other kind of thinking. They described the scientific laboratory as a "workplace" subject to sets of productive forces, the purpose of which is the "production" or "construction" of an account of the natural world, which sometimes may be no more than a fiction. While recognizing that scientists themselves have continued to make a distinction between "intellectual" and "social" elements in scientific activity, Latour and Woolgar denied the validity of the distinction. For them, as for others contributing to this "social constructivist" view of science, there is no distinction between "internal" and "external" approaches to the history of science, as had been maintained by Merton and Kuhn and previously by Koyré and Sarton.

Nor has the so-called strong program been the only challenge to the old tradition of Positivist assumptions in the history of science. The prosperity and baby boom of the 1950s and '60s brought into the universities

The laboratories, offices, and other work areas of the Salk Institute for Biological Studies were the target of a two-year anthropological-style study by French philosopher Bruno Latour, who with English sociologist Steve Woolgar presented the results in Laboratory Life: The Social Construction of Scientific Facts *(1979). The two authors described the scientific laboratory as a "workplace" subject to sets of productive forces and concluded that there was no more distinction between "intellectual" and "social" elements in scientific activity than in any other kind of human activity, even though scientists themselves continued to make such a distinction.*

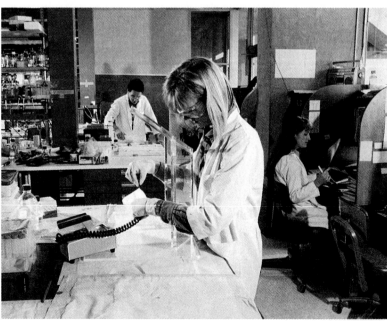

The Salk Institute

A racially integrated but sexually segregated class attends a physics lecture at the University of Michigan near the end of the 1800s. Some recent studies in the history of science have focused on the particular problems historically faced by women in gaining access to science education and achieving careers in various scientific fields. Margaret Rossiter's Women Scientists in America: Struggles and Strategies to 1940 *(1982), for example, has become a landmark both in the history of women in science and in the detailed archival history of science in American universities and governmental agencies.*

substantially larger numbers of lower-middle-class students and, later, female and minority students. Not only in the United States but also in Great Britain, Europe, Japan, and elsewhere, many of these students in the history of science chose for their doctoral and postgraduate research to study the history of individuals and institutions that earlier historians most often had labeled peripheral to a hero-oriented history of science. The new scholars recovered the history of human beings rather than of heroic geniuses, and they discovered technicians, women, and people of diverse ethnic backgrounds in observatories, museums, laboratories, and patent offices. Some quantitatively inclined historians also began using the method of prosopography, or group biography, in order to construct detailed portraits of the memberships, social backgrounds, religious affiliations, and research interests of large scientific communities and organizations. In a remarkable variation of the prosopographical method, MacArthur fellowship recipient and historian of science Frank Sulloway has developed a computer data base of materials on "revolutionary scientists" and defends the thesis that, on the whole, second-born children have been the scientists most prone to break with traditions of normal science and adopt a revolutionary new theory.

Careful study by historian of science Margaret Rossiter, another MacArthur fellowship winner, of the records of women's colleges and organizations in the late 19th and 20th centuries demonstrated that women historically have had easier access to such scientific fields as biology, home economics, and anthropology than to physics and engineering. Contrary to what one might think, women were more successful in achieving careers in scientific teaching and research in the 1920s and '30s than in the '50s and early '60s. Rossiter's book *Women Scientists in America: Struggles and Strategies to 1940* (1982) is a landmark both in the history of women in science and in the detailed archival history of science in American universities and governmental agencies.

235

More radically feminist in analysis have been other studies by women writing the history of science in the late 1970s and '80s. Some of the first startling and challenging work in what has come to be called gender studies appeared in historian Carolyn Merchant's book *The Death of Nature*, published in 1980. Merchant, whose 1967 doctoral thesis was a technical study of the concept of the conservation of energy in the tradition of the history of ideas, argued in *The Death of Nature* that the new scientific philosophy of the 17th century was a patriarchal and exploitative one that dehumanized Mother Nature with an aggressive masculine vision aimed at demystifying, mastering, and mechanizing the natural world. Similarly, in her essays and her book *A Feeling for the Organism: The Life and Work of Barbara McClintock* (1983), physicist and mathematical biologist Evelyn Fox Keller argued that science has evolved under an ideal of masculine ideals and values, and she has encouraged contemporary readers to look again at Aristotle, Francis Bacon, Robert Boyle, and their successors from the feminist standpoint.

Even more radically, historian of science Donna Haraway detailed the organization and exhibits of the African Hall in the American Museum of Natural History, New York City, in order to show how the museum's

A statue on the theme of Nature revealing herself to science, by 19th-century sculptor Louis-Ernst Barrias, was among photos featured in Carolyn Merchant's book The Death of Nature *(1980). An early contributor to what has come to be called gender studies, Merchant argued that the new philosophy of 17th-century science was a patriarchal and exploitative one that dehumanized Mother Nature with an aggressive masculine vision.*

Barbara McClintock, whose pioneering work in genetics during the 1940s and '50s was finally recognized with a Nobel Prize in 1983, is shown surrounded by students in a photo from Evelyn Fox Keller's A Feeling for the Organism (1983). In the book and in other writings, Keller has maintained that science has evolved in an environment of masculine ideals and values, and she has encouraged readers to reexamine the classic works of science from the feminist standpoint.

Cold Spring Harbor Laboratory Research Library Archives; photo, Herb Parsons

activities reflected white, male, patriarchal, and capitalist assumptions about race, sex, morality, and the achievement of manhood. Her book *Primate Visions* (1989), drawing upon this material, has been provocative and controversial.

Continuing expansion and evolution

The diversity of, and controversies over, approaches and interpretations within the history of science indicate both numerical growth and conceptual evolution for the field. The field is not only larger but also more mature, self-confident, and complex. Programs and departments in the history of science proliferated in the 1960s and '70s, with different universities developing characteristic styles, agendas, and specializations. Whereas the history of the physical sciences dominated early work in many of these programs, increased emphasis on the history of the biological sciences and the history of medicine characterizes much recent teaching and research. By 1990 there were more than 50 graduate-degree-granting programs and many more undergraduate programs in the history of science, including the history of technology and the history of medicine, in the United States and Canada.

In the late 1940s annual meetings of the History of Science Society convened 30 or 40 people. In the early 1990s membership in the society, about one-quarter of it resident outside the United States, reached approximately 3,500. Total combined membership of the History of Science

237

Society, the Philosophy of Science Association, and the Society for the History of Technology increased from about 2,000 in 1970 to 5,000 in 1990. Over 2,000 members of the American Physical Society signed on as members of its recently formed Division of History of Physics.

New research centers for the history of science have been established; for example, the Center for the History of Physics at the American Institute of Physics, New York City, and the Beckman Center for the History of Chemistry, Philadelphia. These institutions make available to researchers extraordinary collections of photographs, taped interviews, and unpublished correspondence and papers, as well as libraries of published materials. The new Dibner Institute for the History of Science and Technology will coordinate activities in a consortium of institutions in the Boston area from its home on the campus of the Massachusetts Institute of Technology.

Such growth has been by no means restricted to the United States. From 1932 to 1966 Sweden supported two university positions in the field. In 1991 the history of science was taught at all six Swedish universities by 25 full-time faculty members, and some 100 doctoral students were studying the history of science and technology. A research center for the history of science was established at the Royal Swedish Academy of Sciences in Stockholm in 1988. In France some 800 people responded in 1986 to questionnaires designed to construct a register of research workers in the history and philosophy of the sciences, and many researchers in specialized *équipes* (working groups) of the Centre Nationale des Recherches Scientifiques devote themselves to the history of science.

The field has expanded in Latin-American countries, where the Sociedad Latinoamericana de Historia de las Ciencias y la Tecnologia, based in Mexico City, began publishing the journal *Quipu* in 1984. The Sociedad Latinoamericana, the Sociedad Española de Historia de las Ciencias y Técnicas, and the History of Science Society cosponsored a

A historian gathers material in the Othmer Library of the Beckman Center for the History of Chemistry, Philadelphia. The Beckman Center is one of several new institutions that have been established to make available to researchers not only published materials but also unique collections of photographs, taped interviews, and unpublished correspondence and papers.

The National Foundation for the History of Chemistry

Participants at the 1990 session of the International Summer School in the History of Science hold an informal discussion on the grounds of Uppsala (Sweden) University. Arranged for doctoral and postdoctoral students, the school varies its location every second year among Uppsala; Bologna, Italy; and Berkeley, California.

congress in 1991 in Madrid where new topics in research were discussed. These ranged from historical research on the Rockefeller Foundation's efforts to build a distinctive school of genetics in Brazil in the 1930s to a study of the connections between scientific practice and movements for political independence in Mexico and Colombia.

Indeed, the meeting in Madrid is typical of increased international collaboration in the field. The International Summer School in the History of Science, which met in Bologna, Italy, in 1988 and in Uppsala, Sweden, in 1990, assembled in Berkeley in July 1992, where scholars from around the world, most of them advanced graduate students and experts, heard lectures for two weeks by American, Swedish, and French scholars on recent historical research on the sciences and their applications between the two world wars. A one-week meeting cosponsored by the History of Science Society, the British Society for the History of Science, and the Canadian Society for the History and Philosophy of Science convened in Toronto in July 1992 to bring together scholars whose recent research has concentrated on the history of laboratories and laboratory science.

While the field of the history of science has become a more thoroughly professionalized discipline of teaching, research, and public service in the last two decades, it nonetheless remains broad and eclectic in its array of practice and practitioners. The history of anorexia nervosa from medieval saints to fashion models, the story of the Hubble Space Telescope even before launch, a history of the *idea* and *ideal* of objectivity, a study of politics and physics in revolutionary Russia, essays by Hans Bethe on nuclear debates, an upcoming biography of Bethe by a historian of science, and a new history of biochemistry by a biochemist all suggest the diversity of directions and points of view in the history of science.

Public involvement

Such diversity is having increasingly broad effects on the public, bringing to popular attention the achievements and benefits of science as well

239

as its imminent responsibilities and perils. In June 1991 riders of London's subway system were encouraged by a Dada-like, pop-art poster to reflect on the bicentenary of Michael Faraday's birth and the revolution wrought by electricity. The poster was an advertisement for the Science Museum, where, as in other science-and-technology museums throughout the world, historians are using their expertise ever more frequently to present scientific issues to the public.

Traveling exhibits are taking the history of science to large audiences, including schoolchildren. The synthesis of quinine for treating malaria during World War II and other triumphs of synthetic chemistry are the subject of a 12-panel exhibit on the American chemist Robert B. Woodward and the art of organic synthesis. Sponsored by the National Center for the History of Chemistry and the American Chemical Society, the exhibit in 1992 was just beginning its tour of cities around the United States.

Public lectures offer perspectives on science's past that can help individuals think more clearly about the future. The annual meeting of the American Association for the Advancement of Science is now a huge public gathering. At the 1992 conference, held in Chicago, 10% of the 5,000 registrants were journalists, and 10,000 local students participated in science activities on the first day of the meeting. One of the principal public lectures, given by historian of physics Spencer Weart, used the 1896 discoveries of radioactivity and human contributions to the greenhouse effect as a starting point for reflections on the ways in which scientists and the public have reacted to the prospect of global catastrophes, like nuclear war and global warming. In such lectures, as in museums and traveling exhibits, and through the media of television and popular journalism, the history of science and technology is taking an increasingly visible place both in the academic world and in the public view.

FOR ADDITIONAL READING

Stephen G. Brush, "Should the History of Science Be Rated X?" *Science* (March 22, 1974, pp. 1164–72).

Stephen G. Brush, *The History of Modern Science: A Guide to the Second Scientific Revolution, 1800–1950* (Iowa State University Press, 1988).

Charles C. Gillispie (ed.), *Dictionary of Scientific Biography* (Charles Scribner's Sons, 1970–80).

F.L. Holmes (ed.), *Dictionary of Scientific Biography,* 2-vol. supplement (Charles Scribner's Sons, 1990).

Thomas S. Kuhn, *The Structure of Scientific Revolutions*, 2nd ed. (University of Chicago, 1970).

David C. Lindberg and Robert S. Westman (eds.), *Reappraisals of the Scientific Revolution* (Cambridge University Press, 1990).

R.C. Olby, G.N. Cantor, J.R.R. Christie, and M.J.S. Hodge (eds.), *Companion to the History of Modern Science* (Routledge, 1990).

Steven Shapin, "History of Science and Its Sociological Reconstructions," *History of Science* (vol. 20, 1982, pp. 157–211).

Encyclopædia

Britannica

Science Update

Major Revisions from the 1992 *Macropædia*

The purpose of this section is to introduce to continuing *Yearbook of Science and the Future* subscribers selected *Macropædia* articles or portions of them that have been completely revised or written anew. It is intended to update the *Macropædia* in ways that cannot be accomplished fully by reviewing the year's events or by revising statistics annually, because the *Macropædia* texts themselves—written from a longer perspective than any yearly revision—supply authoritative interpretation and analysis as well as narrative and description.

Two articles have been chosen from the 1992 printing: MINERALS AND ROCKS (in part) and TELESCOPES. Each is the work of distinguished scholars, and each represents the continuing dedication of the *Encyclopædia Britannica* to bringing such works to the general reader.

Minerals and Rocks

METAMORPHIC ROCKS

Metamorphic rocks are, as noted above, those rocks that have recrystallized in response to changes in pressure, temperature, and the composition of fluids percolating through them. The word metamorphism is taken from the Greek for "change of form"; metamorphic rocks are derived from igneous or sedimentary rocks that have altered their form (recrystallized) as a result of changes in their physical environment. Metamorphism comprises changes both in mineralogy and in the fabric of the original rock. In general, these alterations are brought about either by the intrusion of hot magma into cooler surrounding rocks (contact metamorphism) or by large-scale tectonic movements of the Earth's lithospheric plates that alter the pressure-temperature conditions of the rocks (regional metamorphism; see also PLATE TECTONICS). Minerals within the original rock, or protolith, respond to the changing conditions by reacting with one another to produce a new mineral assemblage that is thermodynamically stable under the new pressure-temperature conditions. These reactions occur in the solid state but may be facilitated by the presence of a fluid phase lining the grain boundaries of the minerals. In contrast to the formation of igneous rocks, metamorphic rocks do not crystallize from a silicate melt, although high-temperature metamorphism can lead to partial melting of the host rock.

Because metamorphism represents a response to changing physical conditions, those regions of the Earth's surface where dynamic processes are most active will also be regions where metamorphic processes are most intense and easily observed. The vast region of the Pacific margin, for example, with its seismic and volcanic activity, is also an area in which materials are being buried and metamorphosed intensely. In general, the margins of continents and regions of mountain building are the regions where metamorphic processes proceed with intensity. But in relatively quiet places, where sediments accumulate at slow rates, less spectacular changes also occur in response to changes in pressure and temperature conditions. Metamorphic rocks are therefore distributed throughout the geologic column.

Because most of the Earth's mantle is solid, metamorphic processes may also occur there. Mantle rocks are seldom observed at the surface because they are too dense to rise, but occasionally a glimpse is presented by their inclusion in volcanic materials. Such rocks may represent samples from a depth of a few hundred kilometres, where pressures of about 100 kilobars (3,000,000 inches of mercury) may be operative. Experiments at high pressure have shown that few of the common minerals that occur at the surface will survive at depth within the mantle without changing to new high-density phases in which atoms are packed more closely together. Thus, the common form of SiO_2, quartz, with a density of 2.65 grams per cubic centimetre, transforms to a new phase, stishovite, with a density of 4.29 grams per cubic centimetre. Such changes are of critical significance in the geophysical interpretation of the Earth's interior.

In general, temperatures increase with depth within the Earth along curves referred to as geotherms. The specific shape of the geotherm beneath any location on Earth is a function of its corresponding local tectonic regime. Metamorphism can occur either when a rock moves from one position to another along a single geotherm or when the geotherm itself changes form (see Figure 139). The former can take place when a rock is buried or uplifted at a rate that permits it to maintain thermal equilibrium with its surroundings; this type of metamorphism occurs beneath slowly subsiding sedimentary basins and also in the descending oceanic plate in some subduction zones. The latter process occurs either when hot magma intrudes and alters the thermal state of a stationary rock or when the rock is rapidly transported by tectonic processes (*e.g.*, thrust faulting or large-scale folding) into a new depth-temperature regime in, for example, areas of collision between two continents. Regardless of which process occurs, the result is that a collection of minerals that are thermodynamically stable at the initial conditions are placed under a new set of conditions at which they may or may not be stable. If they are no longer in equilibrium with one another under the new conditions, the minerals will react in such a way as to approach a new equilibrium state. This may involve a complete change in mineral assemblage or simply a shift in the compositions of the preexisting mineral phases. The resultant mineral assemblage will reflect the chemical composition of the original rock and the new pressure-temperature conditions to which the rock was subjected.

Because protolith compositions and the pressure-temperature conditions under which they may be placed vary widely, the diversity of metamorphic rock types is large. Many of these varieties are repeatedly associated with one another in space and time, however, reflecting a unifor-

Sources of metamorphic changes

Geotherms

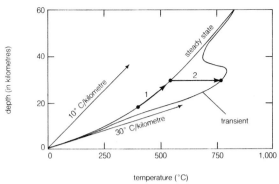

Figure 139: Depth-temperature diagram showing a typical steady-state geotherm through stable continental crust and a transient geotherm produced in response to magma intrusion at a depth of 30–40 kilometres. The heavier lines represent paths that show (1) metamorphism during burial along a single geotherm and (2) metamorphism as a result of a change in the geotherm at a fixed depth. Geothermal gradients of 10° C/km and 30° C/km are shown for reference.

After B. Yardley, *An Introduction to Metamorphic Petrology* (1989), Longman Earth Science Series, Longman Group Ltd., Essex, England

mity of geologic processes over hundreds of millions of years. For example, the metamorphic rock associations that developed in the Appalachian Mountains of eastern North America in response to the collision between the North American and African lithospheric plates during the Paleozoic are very similar to those developed in the Alps of south-central Europe during the Mesozoic-Cenozoic collision between the European and African plates. Likewise, the metamorphic rocks exposed in the Alps are grossly similar to metamorphic rocks of the same age in the Himalayas of Asia, which formed during the continental collision between the Indian and Eurasian plates. Metamorphic rocks produced during collisions between oceanic and continental plates from different localities around the world also show striking similarities to each other (see below *Types of metamorphism and their associated facies: Regional metamorphism*) yet are markedly different from metamorphic rocks produced during continent-continent collisions. Thus, it is often possible to reconstruct tectonic events of the past on the basis of metamorphic rock associations currently exposed at the Earth's surface.

Metamorphic variables

Metamorphism results from a complex interplay between physical and chemical processes that operate on a scale ranging from micrometres (*e.g.*, fine mineral grain sizes, thickness of intergranular fluid, diffusion distances for chemical species) to tens or hundreds of kilometres (*e.g.*, crustal thickness, width of collision zone between lithospheric plates, depth to subducting plate). Despite this wide range and the many processes involved in the recrystallization of sedimentary and igneous protoliths into metamorphic rocks, there are relatively few variables that effect metamorphic changes. Those of greatest importance are temperature, pressure, and the original chemical composition of the protolith; each is briefly discussed below.

TEMPERATURE

Temperatures at which metamorphism occurs range from the conditions of diagenesis (approximately 150°–200° C) up to the onset of melting. Rocks of different compositions begin to melt at different temperatures, with initial melting occurring at roughly 650°–750° C in rocks of granitic or shaley composition and approximately 900°–1,200° C in rocks of basaltic composition. Above these temperatures, metamorphic processes gradually give way to igneous processes. Hence, the temperature realm of metamorphism spans an interval of about 150°–1,000° C and is strongly dependent on the composition of the protolith.

The temperature at any point within the Earth's crust is controlled by the local heat-flow regime, which is a composite function of heat flow upward from the mantle into the crust, heat generated by radioactive decay

in nearby regions of the crust, heat transported into the crust by silicate melts, and tectonic transport of hot or cold rocks at rates faster than those needed to maintain thermal equilibrium with the surrounding rocks. The temperature gradient at any location in the Earth, known as the geothermal gradient, is the increase in temperature per unit distance of depth; it is given by the tangent to the local geotherm. The magnitude of the geothermal gradient thus varies with the shape of the geotherm. In regions with high surface heat flow, such as areas of active volcanism or mantle upwelling beneath thinned continental crust, geothermal gradients of 40° to 100° C (104° to 212° F) per kilometre (0.6 mile) prevail, giving rise to high temperatures at relatively shallow levels of the crust. Within the stable interiors of old continents, geothermal gradients of 25° to 35° C per kilometre are more typical, and in zones of active subduction, where the relatively cold oceanic crust is rapidly transported to great depths, geothermal gradients range from 10° to 20° C per kilometre. These large variations in geotherms and geothermal gradients give rise to different metamorphic regimes, or combinations of pressure-temperature conditions, associated with the different tectonic provinces. **Geothermal gradient**

In addition to the variation of geotherms as a function of position in the Earth, individual geotherms at a single location can vary with time. Geotherms are at steady state (*i.e.*, do not change with time) in tectonically quiescent areas of the Earth, such as the middle regions of large continents, and also in areas where tectonic processes like subduction have operated at similar rates over long periods. Transient geotherms, on the other hand, are generated in tectonically active regions, such as zones of continent-continent collision or rapid uplift and erosion, in which the tectonic processes are relatively short-lived; in these areas, the temperature at a given depth in the Earth is time-dependent, and individual geotherms can have very complex shapes that with time approach smooth curves (see Figure 139). These complex geotherms can produce wide temperature fluctuations at a given depth within the Earth; rocks metamorphosed in response to these variations may show considerable textural and chemical evidence of disequilibrium, reflecting the fact that temperatures changed at rates that were more rapid than reaction rates among the constituent minerals.

PRESSURE

The pressure experienced by a rock during metamorphism is due primarily to the weight of the overlying rocks (*i.e.*, lithostatic pressure) and is generally reported in units of bars or kilobars. For typical densities of crustal rocks of two to three grams per cubic centimetre, one kilobar of lithostatic pressure is generated by a column of overlying rocks approximately 3.5 kilometres high. Typical continental crustal thicknesses are on the order of 30–40 kilometres but can be as great as 60–80 kilometres in mountain belts such as the Alps and Himalayas. Hence, metamorphism of continental crust occurs at pressures from a few hundred bars (adjacent to shallow-level intrusions) to 10–20 kilobars at the base of the crust. Oceanic crust is generally 6–10 kilometres in thickness, and metamorphic pressures within the oceanic crust are therefore considerably less than in continental regions. In subduction zones, however, oceanic and, more rarely, continental crust may be carried down to depths exceeding 100 kilometres, and metamorphism at very high pressures may occur. Metamorphic recrystallization also occurs in the mantle at pressures up to hundreds of kilobars.

Changes in lithostatic pressure experienced by a rock during metamorphism are brought about by burial or uplift of the sample. Burial can occur in response either to ongoing deposition of sediments above the sample or tectonic loading brought about, for example, by thrust-faulting or large-scale folding of the region. Uplift, or more properly unroofing, takes place when overlying rocks are stripped off by erosional processes or when the overburden is tectonically thinned. **Burial and uplift**

Fluids trapped in the pores of rocks during metamorphism exert pressure on the surrounding grains. At depths greater than a few kilometres within the Earth, the magnitude of the fluid pressure is equal to the lithostatic pressure, reflecting the fact that mineral grain boundaries recrystallize in such a way as to minimize pore space and to seal off the fluid channelways by which solutions rise from depth. At shallow depths, however, interconnected pore spaces can exist, and hence the pressure within a pore is related to the weight of an overlying column of fluid rather than rock. Because metamorphic fluids (dominantly composed of water and carbon dioxide) are less dense than rocks, the fluid pressure at these conditions is lower than the lithostatic pressure.

Deformation of rocks during metamorphism occurs when the rock experiences an anisotropic stress—*i.e.*, unequal pressures operating in different directions. Anisotropic stresses rarely exceed more than a few tens or hundreds of bars but have a profound influence on the textural development of metamorphic rocks (see below *Textural features; Structural features*).

ROCK COMPOSITION

Common metamorphic rock types have essentially the same chemical composition as what must be their equally common igneous or sedimentary precursors. Common greenschists have essentially the same compositions as basalts; marbles are like limestones; slates are similar to mudstones or shales; and many gneisses are like granodiorites. In general, then, the chemical composition of a metamorphic rock will closely reflect the primary nature of the material that has been metamorphosed. If there are significant differences, they tend to affect only the most mobile (soluble) or volatile elements; water and carbon dioxide contents can change significantly, for example.

Despite the wide variety of igneous and sedimentary rock types that can recrystallize into metamorphic rocks, most metamorphic rocks can be described with reference to only four chemical systems: pelitic, calcareous, felsic, and mafic. Pelitic rocks are derived from shale protoliths and are rich in potassium (K), aluminum (Al), silicon (Si), iron (Fe), magnesium (Mg), and water (H_2O), with lesser amounts of manganese (Mn), titanium (Ti), calcium (Ca), and other constituents. Calcareous rocks are formed from a variety of chemical and detrital sediments such as limestone, dolostone, or marl and are largely composed of calcium oxide (CaO), magnesium oxide (MgO), and carbon dioxide (CO_2), with varying amounts of aluminum, silicon, iron, and water. Felsic rocks can be produced by metamorphism of both igneous and sedimentary protoliths (*e.g.*, granite and arkose, respectively) and are rich in silicon, sodium (Na), potassium, calcium, aluminum, and lesser amounts of iron and magnesium. Mafic rocks derive from basalt protoliths and some volcanogenic sediments and contain an abundance of iron, magnesium, calcium, silicon, and aluminum. Ultramafic metamorphic rocks result from the metamorphism of mantle rocks and some oceanic crust and contain dominantly magnesium, silicon, and carbon dioxide, with smaller amounts of iron, calcium, and aluminum. For the purposes of this discussion, ultramafic rocks are considered to be a subset of the mafic category.

The particular metamorphic minerals that develop in each of these four rock categories are controlled above all by the protolith chemistry. The mineral calcite ($CaCO_3$), for example, can occur only in rocks that contain sufficient quantities of calcium. The specific pressure-temperature conditions to which the rock is subjected will further influence the minerals that are produced during recrystallization; for example, at high pressures calcite will be replaced by a denser polymorph of $CaCO_3$ called aragonite. In general, increasing pressure favours denser mineral structures, whereas increasing temperature favours anhydrous and less dense mineral phases. Many of the minerals developed during metamorphism, along with their chemical compositions, are given in alphabetical order in Table 55. The most common metamorphic minerals that form in rocks of the four chemical categories described above are listed in Table 56 as a function of pressure and temperature. Although some minerals, such as quartz, calcite, plagioclase, and biotite, develop under a variety of conditions, other minerals are more restricted in occurrence; ex-

Mafic rocks

Table 55: Common Minerals of Metamorphic Rocks

mineral	composition
Actinolite	$Ca_2(Mg, Fe)_5(Si_8O_{22})(OH)_2$
Adularia†	$KAlSi_3O_8$
Albite*	$NaAlSi_3O_8$
Andalusite†	Al_2SiO_5
Anorthite	$CaAl_2Si_2O_8$
Anthophyllite	$Mg_7Si_8O_{22}(OH)_2$
Aragonite†	$CaCO_3$
Biotite*	$K_2(Mg, Fe^{2+})_{6-4}Fe^{3+}, Al, Ti)_{0-2}(Si_{6-5}Al_{2-3}O_{20})(OH, F)_4$
Calcite*†	$CaCO_3$
Chlorite*	$(Mg, Al, Fe)_{12}[(Si, Al)_8O_{20}](OH)_{16}$
Chloritoid	$(Fe^{2+}, Mg, Mn)_2(Al, Fe^{3+})Al_3O_2(SiO_4)_2(OH)_4$
Cordierite	$Al_3(Mg, Fe^2)_2(Si_5AlO_{18})$
Diopside	$CaMgSi_2O_6$
Dolomite*	$CaMg(CO_3)_2$
Enstatite	$MgSiO_3$
Epidote*	$Ca_2Fe^{3+}Al_2Si_3O_{12}(OH)$
Forsterite	Mg_2SiO_4
Garnet*	a complex solid solution of
	pyrope $Mg_3Al_2Si_3O_{12}$
	almandine $Fe_3^{2+}Al_2Si_3O_{12}$
	spessartine $Mn_3Al_2Si_3O_{12}$
	grossular $Ca_3Al_2Si_3O_{12}$
	andradite $Ca_3Fe_2^{3+}Si_3O_{12}$
Glaucophane	$Na_2Mg_3Al_2(Si_8O_{22})(OH, F)_2$
Hornblende*	$(Na, K)_{0-1}Ca_2(Mg, Fe^{2+}, Fe^{3+}, Al)_5(Si_{6-7}Al_{2-1}O_{22})(OH, F)_2$
Hypersthene	$(Mg, Fe)SiO_3$
Jadeite	$NaAlSi_2O_6$
Kaolinite	$Al_4Si_4O_{10}(OH)_8$
Kyanite†	Al_2SiO_5
Lawsonite	$CaAl_2(Si_2O_7)(OH)_2 \cdot H_2O$
Magnesite	$MgCO_3$
Microcline†	$KAlSi_3O_8$
Muscovite*	$KAl_2(AlSi_3O_{10})(OH)_2$
Omphacite*	a complex solid solution mainly of
	$NaAlSi_2O_6$-$CaMgSi_2O_6$-$NaFeSi_2O_6$
Orthoclase†	$KAlSi_3O_8$
Plagioclase*	$NaAlSi_3O_8$; $CaAl_2Si_2O_8$
Prehnite	$Ca_2Al(AlSi_3O_{10})(OH)_2$
Pumpellyite	$Ca_4(Mg, Fe^{2+})(Al, Fe^{3+})_5O(OH)_3(Si_2O_7)_2(SiO_4)_2 \cdot 2H_2O$
Quartz*†	SiO_2
Sanidine†	$KAlSi_3O_8$
Scapolite	$(Na, Ca, K)_4[Al_3(Al, Si)_3Si_6O_{24}](Cl, SO_4, CO_3)$
Serpentine†	$Mg_3(Si_2O_5)(OH)_4$
Sillimanite†	Al_2SiO_5
Staurolite	$(Fe^{2+}, Mg)_2(Al, Fe^{3+})_9O_6(SiO_4)_4(O, OH)_2$
Stilpnomelane	$(K, Na, Ca)_{0-1.4}(Fe^{3+}, Fe^{2+}, Mg, Al, Mn)_{5.9-8.2}(Si_8O_{20})$
	$(OH)_4(O, OH, H_2O)_{3.6-8.5}$
Talc	$Mg_3(Si_4O_{10})(OH)_2$
Tremolite	$Ca_2Mg_5(Si_8O_{22})(OH)_2$
Wollastonite	$CaSiO_3$

*Indicates wide range of stability.   †Indicates more than one form (polymorph) exists.

amples are lawsonite, which is produced primarily during high-pressure, low-temperature metamorphism of basaltic protoliths, and sillimanite, which develops during relatively high-temperature metamorphism of pelitic rocks.

Despite the large number of minerals listed in Table 56 for each of the four bulk compositions, the actual number of minerals present in an individual metamorphic rock is limited by the laws of thermodynamics. The number of mineral phases that can coexist stably in a metamorphic rock at a particular set of pressure-temperature conditions is given by the Gibbs phase rule: number of mineral phases = number of chemical components − number of degrees of freedom + 2, where the 2 stands for the two variables of pressure and temperature. The degrees of freedom of the system are the parameters that can be independently varied without changing the mineral assemblage of the rock. For example, a rock with no degrees of freedom can only exist at a single set of pressure-temperature conditions; if either the pressure or the temperature is varied, the minerals will react with one another to change the assemblage. A rock with two degrees of freedom can undergo small changes in pressure or temperature or both without altering the assemblage. Most metamorphic rocks have mineral assemblages that reflect two or more degrees of freedom at the time the rock recrystallized. Thus, a typical pelitic rock made up of the six chemical components silica (SiO_2), aluminum oxide (Al_2O_3), ferrous oxide (FeO), magnesium oxide (MgO), potash (K_2O), and water would contain no more than six minerals; the identity of those minerals would be controlled by the pressure and temperature at which recrystallization occurred. In such a rock taken from the Earth's surface, the identity

Table 56: Common Metamorphic Minerals as a Function of Pressure, Temperature, and Protolith Composition*

protolith	high P/low T	medium P and T	low P/high T
Shale, mudstone (*pelitic*)	paragonite, muscovite kyanite Mg-chloritoid Mg-carpholite jadeite chlorite pyrope garnet talc coesite	muscovite, paragonite chlorite biotite chloritoid garnet staurolite andalusite, kyanite, sillimanite plagioclase alkali feldspar cordierite orthopyroxene	muscovite biotite andalusite, sillimanite cordierite plagioclase orthopyroxene microcline, sanidine mullite spinel tridymite
Limestone, dolostone, marl (*calcareous*)	aragonite magnesite lawsonite zoisite jadeite talc	calcite dolomite tremolite diopside epidote, clinozoisite grossular garnet	wollastonite grossular garnet diopside plagioclase vesuvianite clinozoisite forsterite brucite talc
Granite, granodiorite, arkose (*felsic*)	jadeite paragonite	plagioclase alkali feldspar muscovite biotite garnet sillimanite	plagioclase alkali feldspar sillimanite cordierite
Basalt, andesite (*mafic*)	glaucophane lawsonite garnet omphacite epidote albite chlorite	plagioclase chlorite biotite garnet epidote actinolite hornblende diopside orthopyroxene	plagioclase biotite garnet hornblende diopside

*Quartz may be present in all categories. Minor phases such as oxides and sulfides have been omitted.

of the six minerals could be used to infer the approximate depth and temperature conditions that prevailed at the time of its recrystallization. Rocks that contain more mineral phases than would be predicted by the phase rule often preserve evidence of chemical disequilibrium in the form of reactions that did not go to completion. Careful examination of such samples under the microscope can often reveal the nature of these reactions and provide useful information on how pressure and temperature conditions changed during the burial and uplift history of the rock.

Metamorphic rocks only rarely exhibit a chemical composition that is characteristically "metamorphic." This statement is equivalent to saying that diffusion of materials in metamorphism is a slow process, and various chemical units do not mix on any large scale. But occasionally, particularly during contact metamorphism, diffusion may occur across a boundary of chemical dissimilarity, leading to rocks of unique composition. This process is referred **Meta-** to as metasomatism. If a granite is emplaced into a lime- **somatism** stone, the contact region may be flooded with silica and other components, leading to the formation of a metasomatic rock. Often such contacts are chemically zoned. A simple example is provided by the metamorphism of magnesium-rich igneous rocks in contact with quartz-rich sediments. A zonation of the type serpentine-talc-quartz may be found such as:

$$Mg_6(Si_4O_{10})(OH)_8 \text{-} Mg_3(Si_4O_{10})(OH)_2 \text{-} SiO_2.$$

In this case the talc zone has grown by silica diffusion into the more silica-poor environment of the serpentine. Economic deposits are not uncommon in such situations— *e.g.,* the formation of the $CaWO_4$ (calcium tungstate) scheelite when tungstate in the form of WO_3 moves from a granite into a limestone contact. The reaction can be expressed as:

$$CaCO_3 + WO_3 \text{ (solution)} \rightarrow CaWO_4 + CO_2 \text{ (gas)}.$$

calcite   scheelite

Metamorphic reactions

A very simple mineralogical system and its response to changing pressure and temperature provide a good illustration of what occurs in metamorphism. An uncomplicated sediment at the Earth's surface, a mixture of the clay mineral kaolinite $[Al_4Si_4O_{10}(OH)_8]$ and the mineral quartz (SiO_2), provides a good example. Most sediments have small crystals or grain sizes but great porosity and permeability, and the pores are filled with water. As time passes, more sediments are piled on top of the surface layer, and it becomes slowly buried. Accordingly, the pressure to which the layer is subjected increases because of the load on top, known as overburden. At the same time, the temperature will increase because of radioactive heating within the sediment and heat flow from deeper levels within the Earth.

In the first stages of incremental burial and heating, few chemical reactions will occur in the sediment layer, but the porosity decreases, and the low-density pore water is squeezed out. This process will be nearly complete by the time the layer is buried by five kilometres of overburden. There will be some increase in the size of crystals; small crystals with a large surface area are more soluble and less stable than large crystals, and throughout metamorphic processes there is a tendency for crystals to grow in size with time, particularly if the temperature is rising.

Eventually, when the rock is buried to a depth at which temperatures of about 300° C obtain, a chemical reaction sets in, and the kaolinite and quartz are transformed to pyrophyllite and water:

$$Al_4Si_4O_{10}(OH)_8 + 4SiO_2 \rightarrow 2Al_2Si_4O_{10}(OH)_2 + 2H_2O.$$

kaolinite   quartz   pyrophyllite   water

The exact temperature at which this occurs depends on the fluid pressure in the system (see Figure 140), but in general the fluid and rock-load pressures tend to be rather similar during such reactions. The water virtually fights its way out by lifting the rocks. Thus, the first chemical reaction is a dehydration reaction leading to the formation of a new hydrate. The water released is itself a solvent for silicates and promotes the crystallization of the product phases.

If heating and burial continue, another dehydration sets in at about 400° C, in which the pyrophyllite is transformed to andalusite, quartz, and water: *A second dehydration reaction*

$$Al_2Si_4O_{10}(OH)_2 \rightarrow Al_2SiO_5 + 3SiO_2 + H_2O.$$

pyrophyllite   andalusite quartz water

After the water has escaped, the rock becomes virtually anhydrous, containing only traces of fluid in small inclusions in the product crystals and along grain boundaries. Both of these dehydration reactions tend to be fast, because water, a good silicate solvent, is present.

Although the mineral andalusite is indicated as the first product of dehydration of pyrophyllite, there are three minerals with the chemical composition Al_2SiO_5. Each has unique crystal structures, and each is stable under definite pressure-temperature conditions (Figure 140). Such differing forms with identical composition are called polymorphs. If pyrophyllite is dehydrated under high-pressure conditions, the polymorph of Al_2SiO_5 formed would be the mineral kyanite (the most dense polymorph). With continued heating, the original andalusite or kyanite will invert to sillimanite, the highest-temperature Al_2SiO_5 polymorph (see Figure 140):

$$Al_2SiO_5 \rightarrow Al_2SiO_5$$

andalusite   sillimanite
or kyanite

The kinetics of these polymorphic transformations are sufficiently sluggish, however, that kyanite or andalusite may persist well into the stability field of sillimanite.

Owing to the very simple bulk composition of the protolith in this example (a subset of the pelitic system containing only SiO_2-Al_2O_3-H_2O), no other mineralogical changes will occur with continued heating or burial. The original sediment composed of kaolinite, quartz, and water

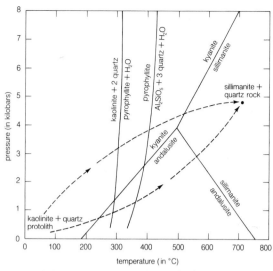

Figure 140: Pressure-temperature diagram showing the positions of the following reactions: kaolinite + 2 quartz = pyrophyllite + H_2O and pyrophyllite = Al_2SiO_5 + 3 quartz + H_2O, as well as the regions where the three polymorphs of Al_2SiO_5 are stable. Dashed lines show possible burial paths that would produce either kyanite or andalusite before sillimanite.

Calculated with the GEO-CALC software package, as described in T.H. Brown, R.G. Berman, and E.H. Perkins, "GEO-CALC: Software Package for Calculation and Display of Pressure-Temperature-Composition Phase Diagrams Using an IBM or Compatible Personal Computer," *Computers and Geosciences*, vol. 14 (1988)

will thus have been metamorphosed into a rock composed of sillimanite and quartz, and perhaps some metastable andalusite or kyanite, depending on the details of the burial and heating history. In the case of a more typical pelite containing the additional chemical components potash, ferrous oxide, and magnesium oxide, the reaction history would be correspondingly more complex. A typical shale that undergoes burial and heating in response to continent-continent collision would develop the minerals muscovite, chlorite, biotite, garnet, staurolite, kyanite, sillimanite, and alkali feldspar, in approximately that order, before beginning to melt at about 700° C. Each of these minerals appears in response to a chemical reaction similar to those presented above. Most of these reactions are dehydration reactions, and the shale thus loses water progressively throughout the entire metamorphic event. As discussed above, the total number of minerals present in the rock is controlled by the Gibbs phase rule, and the addition of new minerals generally results from the breakdown of old minerals. For example, the following reaction,

garnet + muscovite + chlorite →
staurolite + biotite + quartz + water,

occurs at temperatures of about 500°–550° C and typically consumes all the preexisting chlorite in the rock, introduces the new mineral staurolite, and adds more biotite and quartz to the biotite and quartz generated by earlier reactions. Some garnet and muscovite usually remain after the reaction, although examination of the sample under the microscope would probably reveal partial corrosion (wearing away due to chemical reactions) of the garnets resulting from their consumption.

Reactions that introduce new minerals in rocks of a specific bulk composition are referred to as mineral appearance isograds. Isograds can be mapped in the field as lines across which the metamorphic mineral assemblage changes. Caution must be exercised to note the approximate bulk composition of the rocks throughout the map area, however, because the same mineral can develop at quite different sets of pressure-temperature conditions in rocks of dissimilar chemical composition. For example, garnet generally appears at a lower temperature in pelitic rocks than it does in mafic rocks; hence, the garnet isograd in pelitic rocks will not be the same map line as that in metabasaltic (*i.e.,* metamorphosed basalt) compositions. Isograd patterns are discussed further in *Structural features* below.

Isograds

PRINCIPAL TYPES

Metamorphic reactions can be classified into two types that show different degrees of sensitivity to temperature and pressure changes: net-transfer reactions and exchange reactions. Net-transfer reactions involve the breakdown of preexisting mineral phases and corresponding nucleation and growth of new phases. (Nucleation is the process in which a crystal begins to grow from one or more points, or nuclei.) They can be either solid-solid reactions (mineral A + mineral B = mineral C + mineral D) or devolatilization reactions (hydrous mineral A = anhydrous mineral B + water), but in either case they require significant breaking of bonds and reorganization of material in the rock. They may depend most strongly on either temperature or pressure changes. In general, devolatilization reactions are temperature-sensitive, reflecting the large increase in entropy (disorder) that accompanies release of structurally bound hydroxyl groups (OH) from minerals to produce molecular water. Net-transfer reactions that involve a significant change in density of the participating mineral phases are typically more sensitive to changes in pressure than in temperature. An example is the transformation of albite ($NaAlSi_3O_8$) to the sodic pyroxene jadeite ($NaAlSi_2O_6$) plus quartz (SiO_2); albite and quartz have similar densities of about 2.6 grams per cubic centimetre, whereas jadeite has a density of 3.3 grams per cubic centimetre. The increased density reflects the closer packing of atoms in the jadeite structure. Not surprisingly, the denser phase jadeite is produced during subduction zone (high-pressure) metamorphism. Net-transfer reactions always involve a change in mineral assemblage, and textural evidence of the reaction often remains in the sample (see below *Textural features*); isograd reactions are invariably net-transfer reactions.

In contrast to net-transfer reactions, exchange reactions involve redistribution of atoms between preexisting phases rather than nucleation and growth of new phases. The reactions result simply in compositional changes of minerals already present in the rock and do not modify the mineral assemblage. For example, the reaction

Exchange reactions

$$Fe_3Al_2Si_3O_{12} + KMg_3AlSi_3O_{10}(OH)_2 \rightarrow$$

almandine garnet   magnesium-biotite

$$Mg_3Al_2Si_3O_{12} + KFe_3AlSi_3O_{10}(OH)_2$$

pyrope garnet   iron-biotite

results in redistribution of iron and magnesium between garnet and biotite but creates no new phases. This reaction is limited by the rates at which iron and magnesium can diffuse through the garnet and biotite structures. Because diffusion processes are strongly controlled by temperature but are nearly unaffected by pressure, exchange reactions are typically sensitive to changes only in metamorphic temperature. Exchange reactions leave no textural record in the sample and can be determined only by detailed microanalysis of the constituent mineral phases. The compositions of minerals as controlled by exchange reactions can provide a useful record of the temperature history of a metamorphic sample.

The types of reactions cited here are typical of all metamorphic changes. Gases are lost (hydrates lose water, carbonates lose carbon dioxide), and mineral phases undergo polymorphic or other structural changes; low-volume, dense mineral species are formed by high pressures, and less dense phases are favoured by high temperatures. Considering the immense chemical and mineralogical complexity of the Earth's crust, it is clear that the number of possible reactions is vast. In any given complex column of crustal materials some chemical reaction is likely for almost any incremental change in pressure and temperature. This is a fact of immense importance in unraveling the history and mechanics of the Earth, for such changes constitute a vital record and are the primary reason for the study of metamorphic rocks.

RETROGRADE METAMORPHISM

In general, the changes in mineral assemblage and mineral composition that occur during burial and heating are referred to as prograde metamorphism, whereas those that occur during uplift and cooling of a rock represent retrograde metamorphism. If thermodynamic equilibrium were always maintained, one might expect all the reactions that occur during prograde metamorphism to be reversed during subsequent uplift of the rocks and reexposure at the Earth's surface; in this case, metamorphic rocks would never be seen in outcrop. Two factors mitigate against complete retrogression of metamorphic rocks, however, during their return to the Earth's surface. First is the efficient removal of the water and carbon dioxide released during prograde devolatilization reactions by upward migration of the fluid along grain boundaries and through fractures. Because almost all the water released during heating by reactions such as

$$Fe_9Al_6Si_5O_{20}(OH)_{16} + 4SiO_2 \rightarrow 3Fe_3Al_2Si_3O_{12} + 8H_2O$$

chlorite   quartz   garnet   water

is removed from the site of reaction, the reaction cannot be reversed during cooling unless water is subsequently added to the rock. Thus, garnet can be preserved at the Earth's surface even though it is thermodynamically unstable at such low temperatures and pressures. The second reason that metamorphic reactions do not typically operate in reverse during cooling is that reaction rates are increased by rising temperatures. During cooling, reaction kinetics become sluggish, and metastable mineral assemblages and compositions can be preserved well outside their normal stability fields. Thus, prograde reactions are generally more efficient than retrograde reactions, and metamorphic assemblages indicative of even extremely high temperatures or pressures or both are found exposed throughout the world. It is common, however, to find at least some signs of retrogression in most metamorphic rocks. For example, garnets are often rimmed by small amounts of chlorite and quartz, indicating that limited quantities of water were available for the reverse of the reaction given above to proceed during cooling. Retrograde features such as these reaction rims can be mapped to yield information on pathways of fluid migration through the rocks during uplift and cooling. In other rocks, such as high-temperature gneisses, mineral compositions often reflect temperatures too low to be in equilibrium with the preserved mineral assemblage; in these samples, it is clear that certain exchange reactions operated in a retrograde sense even when the net-transfer reactions were frozen in during prograde metamorphism.

Reaction rims

Textural features

The fabric of a metamorphic rock results from the combined effects of mineral reactions and deformation throughout the metamorphic event and the subsequent return of the rock to the terrestrial surface. The study of metamorphic fabrics in outcrop and under the microscope has become a highly specialized subject aimed at revealing the nature and direction of the forces acting during dynamic processes within the Earth. Much of this work is an outgrowth of a classic investigation conducted in 1930 by the Austrian geologist Bruno Sander, coupled with more recent experimental work on the pressure-temperature stabilities of metamorphic minerals and their responses to deformation.

Observations show that pressure is only rarely hydrostatic (equal in all directions) at any point within the Earth's crust. In real cases, consequently, anisotropic stresses operate that may lead to flow or fracture of materials. Such occurrences produce certain characteristic fabrics or structures in metamorphic rocks that may be observed at the scale of the orientation of small crystals in a rock or as a pattern of folds in a mountain range. One of the principal characteristics of most metamorphic rocks is that the arrangement of crystals is not isotropic, or random, but that there is a strong preferred orientation related to the direction of stress components of pressure. Such preferred orientation of crystals and mineral grains is perhaps the most striking difference between metamorphic rocks and other rock types.

The most obvious features of metamorphic rocks are certain planar features that are often termed s-surfaces. The simplest planar features may be primary bedding (akin to the layering in sedimentary rocks). As the rock crystallizes or recrystallizes under directed pressure, new crystals may grow in some preferred direction, sometimes subparallel to the primary bedding but often at new angles defining new planar structures. At the same time, folding of layers may occur, leading to folds with amplitudes on scales of kilometres or millimetres. Fabric symmetry may be represented by the nature of deformed fossils, pebbles in a conglomerate, or any objects with a known shape prior to deformation (Figure 141).

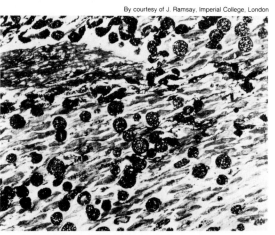

Figure 141: A deformed dolomite-calcite marble from Sardinia containing spherical fossil objects (oölites) about 3 millimetres (0.12 inch) in size. Oölites made of dolomite (black circles) are not deformed. Oölites made of calcite (gray), a weaker solid, are smeared out in S forms.

A few terms that commonly are used to describe several types of preferred orientation in metamorphic rocks include foliation, a general term describing any type of s-surface, bedding, or crystal orientation; slaty cleavage, a planar structure leading to facile cleavage that is normally caused by the preferred orientation of mica crystals; schistosity, a term used to describe repetitive and pronounced foliation of the type that is present in schists; and lineation, which is any linear structure, such as the axis of the fold, grooves on a fault plane, or the direction of stretching of pebbles.

The various mineral phases of a metamorphic rock have different physical properties and symmetries. When a rock is subjected to recrystallization in a stress field, different substances will behave differently according to such physical properties and symmetries. Some minerals always tend to grow in better-formed crystals than others; rates of nucleation may differ, and this can lead to different patterns of growth of crystals—there may be a few large crystals or a mass of small crystals. Minerals can be arranged in order of their tendency to form crystals showing planar surfaces—namely, magnetite, garnet, epidote, mica, calcite, quartz, and feldspar. Minerals that have a tendency to form large single crystals (*e.g.*, garnet) are termed porphyroblasts.

Porphyroblasts

Porphyroblastic crystals may grow before, during, or after an episode of deformation (pre-, syn-, and postkinematic growth, respectively); the relative timing of mineral growth and deformation can often be determined by examining the sample under a microscope. Prekinematic porphyroblasts may be fractured by subsequent deformation; the orientation of the fractures and any offset of the grains along them provide information on the directed stresses responsible for the deformation. Prekinematic grains may also be surrounded by pressure shadows produced by minerals such as quartz that dissolve in zones of maximum compressive stress and reprecipitate in zones of lesser compressive stress adjacent to the rigid porphyroblasts. The texture of the shadows is different from that of the host rock. Samples exhibiting asymmetric pressure shadows around porphyroblasts can yield information on the orientation of shear stresses during deformation. A spectacular example of synkinematic prophyroblast growth is provided by the so-called snowball garnets, which have spiral trails of inclusions that indicate rotation of either the garnet or the matrix foliation during garnet growth (see Figure 142). Postkinematic porphyroblasts typically overgrow all previous fabrics in the rock and may contain trails of mineral inclusions that define microfolds or an earlier schistosity.

In some samples, it is possible to use the compositions of the porphyroblasts to calculate the depth and temperature conditions at which they grew and thereby constrain the conditions at which deformation occurred. Studies of this sort add immeasurably to the understanding of crustal rheologies and the response of rocks to large-scale orogenic events. Because a particular metamorphic event may be accompanied by either several isolated episodes of deformation or a single continuum of deformation, there may be many fabric generations recorded in one sample; individual minerals may be postkinematic with respect to the earliest deformation but prekinematic relative to younger deformation in the same rock. Thus, the study of porphyroblast fabrics in metamorphic rocks can be complex but has the potential to yield important information on the structural history of metamorphic regions (see below *Structural features*).

By courtesy of J. Ramsay, Imperial College, London

Figure 142: A large garnet crystal (enlarged; 1 centimetre [0.4 inch]) growing in a quartz-mica matrix. The garnet contains trails of inclusions and has rotated during growth in the flowing rock medium.

Because changes in pressure and temperature often occur at faster rates than those of mineral reaction and recrystallization, metamorphic rocks may display fabrics that result from incomplete reactions. Such disequilibrium features provide a wealth of information on the reaction history of the sample and, by comparison with experimental studies of mineral stabilities, can also constrain the quantitative pressure-temperature history of the rock during metamorphism. An example of a reaction texture is shown in Figure 143, in which a corroded garnet is surrounded by a corona (reaction rim) of the mineral cordierite; other minerals present in the matrix include sillimanite, quartz, biotite, and alkali feldspar. The sample does not contain garnet in contact with sillimanite or quartz. These textural features suggest the following reaction relationship between garnet, sillimanite, quartz, and cordierite:

$$2Mg_3Al_2Si_3O_{12} + 4Al_2SiO_5 + 5SiO_2 \rightleftharpoons 3Mg_2Al_4Si_5O_{18}.$$

garnet   sillimanite quartz cordierite

This reaction has been shown experimentally to occur at temperatures of approximately $725° \pm 50°$ C and to be very sensitive to pressure, with cordierite occurring under low-pressure conditions. The textural evidence that preexisting garnet was partially replaced by cordierite thus implies that the rock underwent decompression while still at high temperatures and that the decompression occurred too rapidly for the rock to recrystallize completely (*i.e.*, for garnet to be totally replaced by cordierite).

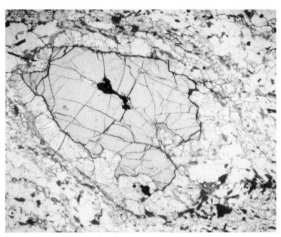

Figure 143: Photomicrograph showing corroded garnet (gray) surrounded by a corona of cordierite produced during uplift of the sample (see text). Other minerals present are biotite, plagioclase, sillimanite, alkali feldspar, and ilmenite. The garnet is two millimetres across.
Jane Selverstone

There is also a tendency for many types of metamorphic rocks to become laminated, and the separate laminae may have distinct chemical compositions. A macroscopically rather homogeneous sediment may prove to be inhomogeneous on a minute scale. When graywackes are metamorphosed within the greenschist facies, for example, laminae rich in quartz and feldspar alternate with others rich in epidote, chlorite, and muscovite. The precise causes of this process are not well known, but it must result from a combination of extensive deformation accompanied by recrystallization. In a sense, it is a type of flow unmixing. It is important to recognize that this type of structure need have no relation to original bedding in the unmetamorphosed sediments.

Lamination

Structural features

Metamorphic rocks are often intimately related to large-scale (kilometres of tens of kilometres) structural features of the Earth. Such features include folds, nappes, and faults with a wide variety of geometries. In many cases, the correlation of metamorphic isograds and their position in the structure implies a genetic relationship between the two. For example, one of the major structural features in the Himalayan mountain belt is the Main Central Thrust, a thrust fault that runs for hundreds of kilometres from east to west and was responsible for the transportation of rocks belonging to the Eurasian Plate southward over those of the Indian Plate. Along much of the length of this fault, the metamorphic rocks in the hanging wall (located above the fault) display a pattern of inverted isograds; *i.e.*, the rocks that reached the highest temperatures of metamorphism overlie rocks that record lower temperatures, implying that metamorphic temperatures decreased with depth to the fault. Several explanations have been proposed to account for this anomalous distribution of temperature with depth. One model suggests the fault transported hot Asian rocks over cooler Indian rocks, which caused cooling of the Asian rocks in the vicinity of the fault. Another model proposes that fluids circulating along the fault zone caused retrograde metamorphism and thus reset the rocks located nearest to the fault to lower temperatures. Although neither of these models provides an adequate explanation for the entire length of the Main Central Thrust, they both emphasize the significant control that structural features can exert on the development of metamorphic rocks.

Metamorphism associated with nappes (large recumbent folds) in the Alps and the Appalachians provides strong evidence that the tectonic transport of rocks typically occurs at rates faster than those of thermal equilibration—in other words, that the nappes can transport hot rocks for large distances without significant cooling. Nappe formation is a major process of crustal thickening during

Nappes

continent-continent collision; emplacement of the nappes results in burial and heating of the underlying rocks. Isograd distributions associated with nappe structures can be either normal or inverted, depending on the relative rates of nappe emplacement and heat transfer.

Isograd maps can provide information on the relative timing of structural and metamorphic events in much the same way that fabric studies constrain the relative timing of deformation episodes and prophyroblast growth. For example, isograd patterns that are cut by faults clearly indicate that metamorphism predated fault displacement, whereas isograd sequences that overprint structural discontinuities imply the reverse. Isograds that parallel major structures suggest some cause-and-effect relationship between the structural and metamorphic development of the region. Since the 1980s, metamorphic petrologists and structural geologists have increasingly worked together to correlate metamorphic and tectonic events and thereby increase understanding of crustal dynamics in tectonically active regions of the Earth.

Metamorphic facies

Metamorphic petrologists studying contact metamorphism early in the 20th century introduced the idea of metamorphic facies to correlate metamorphic events. The concept was first defined in 1914 by a Finnish petrologist, Pentti Eelis Eskola, as any rock of a metamorphic formation that has attained chemical equilibrium through metamorphism at constant temperature and pressure conditions, with its mineral composition controlled only by the chemical composition. In current usage, a metamorphic facies (Figure 144) is a set of metamorphic mineral assemblages, repeatedly associated in space and time, such that there is a constant and therefore predictable relation between mineral composition and chemical composition.

The facies concept is more or less observation-based. In a single outcrop, for instance, layers of different chemical composition will display different mineral assemblages despite having all experienced the same pressure and temperature history. A pelitic layer might contain the assemblage garnet + chlorite + biotite + muscovite + quartz, whereas a basaltic horizon a few centimetres away would contain the assemblage chlorite + actinolite + albite. Both of these rocks belong to the same facies, meaning that, in another region, a geologist who observed the assemblage chlorite + actinolite + albite in a metabasalt could predict that associated pelitic rocks would contain the garnet + chlorite + biotite + muscovite + quartz assemblage.

Experimental work on the relative stabilities of metamorphic minerals and assemblages has permitted correlation of the empirically derived facies with quantitative pressure and temperature conditions, as shown in Figure 144. The names of metamorphic facies in common usage are derived from the behaviour of a rock of basaltic bulk composition during metamorphism at various sets of pressure-temperature conditions. For example, a basalt metamorphosed by subduction to high pressures at low temperatures recrystallizes into a rock containing glaucophane, lawsonite, and albite; glaucophane is a sodic amphibole that is blue to black in hand sample and lavender to blue under the microscope. Because of their distinctive bluish coloration, such samples are called blueschists. The same rock type metamorphosed at more moderate pressures and temperatures in the range of 400°–500° C would contain abundant chlorite and actinolite, minerals that are green both in hand sample and under the microscope, and would be referred to as a greenschist. At somewhat higher temperatures, the rock would become an amphibolite, reflecting a mineralogy composed predominantly of the amphibole hornblende along with plagioclase and perhaps some garnet. At still higher temperatures, a metabasalt recrystallizes into a rock containing hypersthene, diopside, and plagioclase; in general, these minerals form relatively equant crystals and hence do not develop a preferred orientation. The granular texture of these rocks has resulted in the name granulite for a high-temperature metabasalt. A pelitic or calcareous rock will develop very different mineral assemblages from a metabasalt, yet the same facies names apply. Thus, one can refer to a greenschist facies pelitic schist, an amphibolite facies calcsilicate rock, or a granulite facies garnet gneiss.

The boundaries between the different facies are regions of pressure and temperature in which chemical reactions occur that would significantly alter the mineralogy of a rock of basaltic bulk composition. For example, the boundary between the greenschist and amphibolite facies marks a transition from amphibole of actinolitic composition to hornblende and of a sodic plagioclase into a more calcic plagioclase. The reactions that bring about these transformations depend on the specific composition of the rock and hence are denoted by broad bands rather than single lines on the pressure-temperature diagram in Figure 144.

Facies boundaries

FACIES SERIES

Different types of tectonic processes produce different associations of metamorphic facies in the field. For example, regions associated with subduction of oceanic material beneath either oceanic or continental crust are characterized by blueschist, greenschist, and eclogite facies rocks, whereas areas thought to reflect continent-continent collision are more typically distinguished by greenschist and amphibolite facies rocks. Still other regions, usually containing an abundance of intrusive igneous material, show associations of low-pressure greenschist, amphibolite, and granulite facies rocks. These observations led a Japanese petrologist, Akiho Miyashiro, working in the 1960s and '70s, to develop the concept of baric types, or metamorphic facies series. Miyashiro described the three facies associations given above as high-pressure, medium-pressure, and low-pressure facies series, respectively, and correlated the development of these characteristic series with the shape of the geotherm in different tectonic settings. Subsequent thermal modeling studies have shown that metamorphism generally occurs in response to tectonically induced perturbation of geotherms rather than along steady-state geotherms and, hence, that the facies series do not record metamorphic geotherms. Nonetheless, the concept of metamorphic facies series is a useful one in that it emphasizes the strong genetic relationship between metamorphic style and tectonic setting.

PRESSURE-TEMPERATURE-TIME PATHS

Interaction between metamorphic petrologists and geophysicists in the 1980s led to the realization that each metamorphic rock follows its own unique path through pressure- (depth-) temperature space during metamorphism and that these paths bear little or no resemblance to

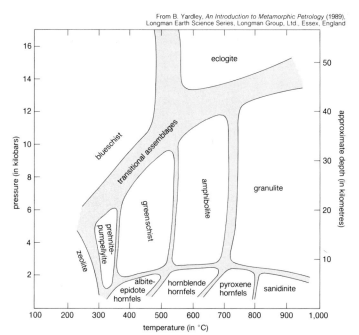

From B. Yardley, *An Introduction to Metamorphic Petrology* (1989),
Longman Earth Science Series, Longman Group, Ltd., Essex, England

Figure 144: Approximate pressure-temperature regions of the major metamorphic facies (see text).

steady-state geotherms. The specific shape of a pressure-temperature-time (P-T-t) path depends on the tectonic setting in which the rock was metamorphosed, which in turn controls the relative rates at which burial or uplift and heating or cooling occur. For example, a rock that is uplifted rapidly from depth, perhaps in response to extensional faulting (that caused by the stretching of the Earth's crust), may transport heat with it to near-surface depths. Its P-T-t path would show a phase of nearly isothermal decompression (uplift at approximately constant temperature), reflecting the fact that uplift rates were more rapid than those of heat transfer. In contrast, if the same rock remained at depth for a long period of time and then experienced very slow uplift, its P-T-t path would show cooling during uplift or even a phase of isobaric (constant-pressure) cooling. Rocks belonging to medium-pressure facies series generally follow P-T-t paths that are clockwise loops on a pressure-temperature diagram, reflecting rapid burial during a collisional event followed by heating and relatively rapid uplift. In contrast, low-pressure facies series rocks may follow counterclockwise P-T-t paths in response to rapid heating of the crust due to magma intrusion prior to uplift (Figure 145). P-T-t paths followed by rocks of a high-pressure facies series are less predictable and depend strongly on the mechanism by which the rocks are transferred from the subducting slab to the overlying continental crust. In general, the mineral assemblage preserved in a metamorphic rock is frozen at the highest temperature experienced during metamorphism (see above *Retrograde metamorphism*), and thus the facies and facies series to which the rock would be assigned reflect only a single point on its P-T-t path.

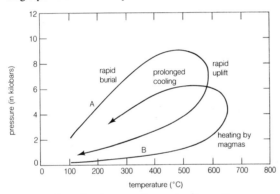

Figure 145: Examples of pressure-temperature-time paths that would be followed by rocks metamorphosed in different environments. (A) represents the rapid burial and uplift paths typical of areas of continental convergence. (B) represents heating and burial in response to regional-scale magma intrusion, followed by prolonged cooling and slow uplift.

Recon-
struction of
P-T-t paths
    One of the principal goals of much of the work that is done on metamorphic rocks is the reconstruction of the P-T-t paths followed by rocks presently exposed at the Earth's surface. Because these paths are so strongly linked to dynamic processes, their reconstruction provides a means by which tectonic processes operative in the geologic past may be understood. Owing to the continuous recrystallization of rocks that occurs during progressive metamorphism, much of the early record of metamorphic changes within a sample is eradicated by later events. It is, therefore, not possible to determine the entire P-T-t path followed by an individual sample, but often enough disequilibrium features are preserved to permit reconstruction of a few thousand bars and a couple of hundred degrees of the path; such a portion may represent anywhere from a few million to a hundred million years of Earth history, as revealed by geochronologic determinations involving different minerals or fabric generations in the sample. Techniques for determining the pressure-temperature history of a metamorphic rock include using compositions of coexisting minerals to calculate pressures and temperatures of equilibration (geobarometry and geothermometry, respectively), comparing the mineral assemblage to experimentally determined stability fields for the phases, utilizing mineral inclusions enclosed within porphyroblasts to

constrain assemblages present in the early history of the sample, and making use of the densities of small inclusions of fluids trapped within the minerals to determine possible pressures and temperatures experienced at different stages in the burial and uplift history.

Origin of metamorphic rocks: types of metamorphism

It is convenient to distinguish several general types of metamorphism in order to simplify the description of the various metamorphic phenomena. Recognized here are hydrothermal, dynamic, contact, and regional metamorphism, each of which will be described in turn.

Hydrothermal metamorphism.   Changes that occur in rocks near the surface, where there is intense activity of hot water, are categorized as hydrothermal metamorphism. Such areas include Yellowstone National Park in the northwestern United States, the Salton Sea in California, and Wairakei in New Zealand. It is now generally recognized that the circulating groundwaters that often become heated by their proximity to igneous materials produce the metamorphism. Migration of chemical elements, vein formation, and other kinds of mineral concentration may be extreme on account of the large volumes of water circulated.

Dynamic metamorphism.   When directed pressure or stress is the dominant agent of metamorphism, it is termed dynamic; other terms are dislocation, kinematic, and mechanical metamorphism. Mineralogical changes occurring on a fault plane provide an obvious example. In some such cases, the action may simply be a grinding up of existing grains or realignment of minerals that have nonequant crystals. If the action is intense, friction may even lead to melting.

Contact metamorphism.   Whenever silicate melts (magmas, from which igneous rocks crystallize within the Earth) invade the crust at any level, they perturb the normal thermal regime and cause a heat increase in the vicinity. If a mass of basaltic liquid ascending from the upper mantle is trapped in the crust and crystallizes there, it will heat the surrounding area; the amount of heating and its duration will be a direct function of the mass and shape of the igneous material. Contact-metamorphic phenomena thus occur in the vicinity of hot igneous materials and at any depth. Under such circumstances, pressure and temperature are not simply correlated. Thermal gradients are often steep unless the igneous mass is extremely large. Contact aureoles—the surrounding zones of rock that become altered or metamorphosed—vary in thickness from several centimetres (around tabular bodies such as dikes and thin sills) to several kilometres (around large granitic intrusions). The contact metamorphic rocks of the aureole zone often lack any obvious schistosity or foliation.

Contact-
aureole
thickness

The facies associated with contact metamorphism include the sanidinite, pyroxenite-hornfels, hornblende-hornfels, and albite-epidote-hornfels facies.

Sanidinite facies.   Rocks of the sanidinite facies are represented by small fragments of aureole materials that have often been totally immersed in silicate liquids or by the aureole rocks surrounding volcanic pipes. Very high temperatures are attained, often at very low pressures. The dominant feature of the mineralogy of this facies is an almost complete lack of minerals containing water or carbon dioxide. Many of the minerals show similarity to those of igneous rocks themselves. If the duration of heating is short, adjustment to the imposed temperature is often imperfect.

Pelitic rocks (high in aluminum oxide) contain minerals such as mullite, sillimanite, sanidine, cordierite, spinel, hypersthene, anorthite, tridymite, and even glass. One of the classic localities of such rocks is the island of Mull, off the west coast of Scotland, but these rocks can be found in most regions of volcanism.

Calcareous rocks (originally impure limestones or dolomites) tend to lose nearly all their carbon dioxide, but pure calcite may survive. Typical metamorphic minerals are quartz, wollastonite, anorthite, diopside, periclase, and in some places (the classic is Scawt Hill in Northern

Ireland) an array of complex calcium silicates such as spurrite, larnite, rankinite, melilite, merwinite, and monticellite. These minerals result from the addition of varying amounts of silica to impure mixtures of calcite and dolomite. In a general way the minerals of this facies are reminiscent of those of industrial slags.

Pyroxene-hornfels facies. Rocks of the pyroxene-hornfels facies are characteristically formed near larger granitic or gabbroic bodies at depths of a few kilometres or at pressures of a few hundred bars. The mineral assemblages are again largely anhydrous, but, unlike the sanidinite facies, the minerals reflect distinctly lower temperatures. One of the classic descriptions of such rocks is from the Oslo district of Norway.

In pelitic rocks, minerals such as quartz, orthoclase, andalusite, sillimanite, cordierite, hypersthene, and plagioclase occur. Sometimes the hydrate biotite is developed. In calcareous rocks the minerals found include plagioclase, diopside, grossularite, vesuvianite (a hydrate), wollastonite, and sometimes the more complex calcium silicates monticellite, melilite, spurrite, tilleyite, and clinohumite.

Hornblende-hornfels facies. A generally deeper level of contact metamorphism where pressures of a few kilobars may be active is represented by the hornblende-hornfels facies. Hydrated phases become stable, and the transition to regional metamorphism becomes apparent. Because of the generally greater depth, this type of aureole is often superposed on a metamorphism at more normal pressure-temperature conditions, and the rocks may appear schistose and exhibit new thermally generated minerals on a preexisting assemblage. This type of metamorphism develops the classic "spotted" texture in which new porphyroblasts grow in slates and phyllites of a previous episode of metamorphism. Typically, such rocks are developed near most of the world's large granite batholiths, where these have moved to higher levels in the Earth's crust.

Typical minerals of pelitic assemblages include quartz, muscovite, biotite, andalusite, sillimanite, cordierite, plagioclase, microcline, and staurolite. Calcareous assemblages include calcite, quartz, diopside, grossularite, plagioclase, wollastonite, brucite, talc, forsterite, tremolite, and clinozoisite. Basaltic compositions include plagioclase, hornblende, diopside, quartz, biotite, and almandine garnet.

Formation of skarns

When rather pure limestone and dolomite come into direct contact with granitic rocks, elements such as silicon, iron, magnesium, and aluminum diffuse into the limestone, forming spectacular rocks termed skarns. These rocks often consist of large garnet crystals (grossularite) with green diopside and vesuvianite or epidote.

Albite-epidote-hornfels facies. Rocks of the albite-epidote-hornfels facies are characteristically found as the outer zones of contact aureoles where the thermal episode fades out and the rocks pass into their regional grade of metamorphism. The mineral assemblages are quite similar to those found in regional greenschist-facies metamorphism, except for the presence of low-pressure phases such as andalusite. Characteristic minerals include quartz, muscovite, biotite, chlorite, andalusite, actinolite, calcite, dolomite, albite, and epidote.

Regional metamorphism. Regional metamorphism is associated with the major events of Earth dynamics, and the vast majority of metamorphic rocks are so produced. They are the rocks involved in the cyclic processes of erosion, sedimentation, burial, metamorphism, and mountain building, events that are all related to major convective processes in the Earth's mantle.

Most regionally metamorphosed rocks develop primarily in response to continent-continent collision and to collision between oceanic and continental plates. As a result, young metamorphic belts aligned roughly parallel to the present-day continental margins (*e.g.,* the Pacific margin) as well as older metamorphic belts are used to infer the geometries of the continental margins at earlier periods in Earth history. Most of the world's mountain belts are at least partially composed of regionally metamorphosed rocks, with spectacular examples provided by the Alps, the Himalayas, the northern Appalachians, and the Highlands of Scotland. Although the processes that formed each of these mountain belts are broadly similar, in almost all

such crustal events at different times and places, there is uniqueness as well as conformity to a general pattern. Metamorphic events in the Alps, the Urals, and the Himalayas all show specific differences: to unravel such differences and their significance is one of the major tasks of metamorphic petrology.

In areas of collision between oceanic and continental lithospheric plates such as the circum-Pacific region, the denser oceanic plate is subducted (carried into the Earth's mantle) beneath the more buoyant continental lithosphere. Rapid subduction of the cool oceanic lithosphere perturbs the thermal regime in such a way that high pressures can be obtained at relatively low temperatures (see Figure 146), thereby generating blueschists and eclogites (high-

After A. Miyashiro, *Metamorphism and Metamorphic Belts* (1973), George Allen and Unwin, Ltd., London

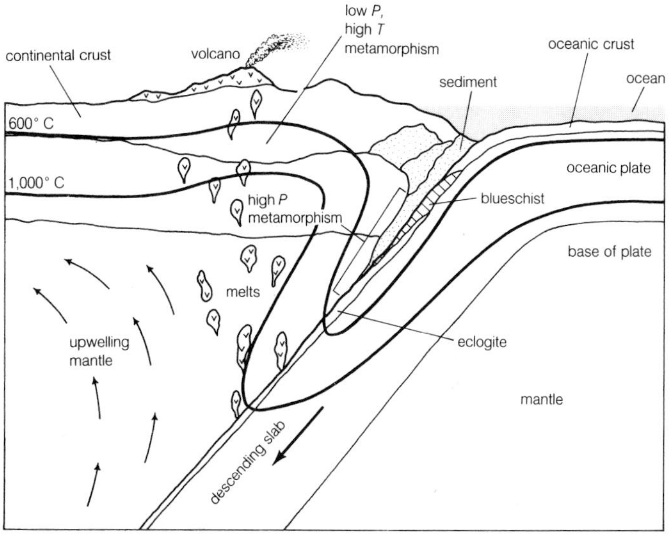

Figure 146: Schematic cross section of a collision zone between oceanic and continental lithospheric plates showing development of a paired metamorphic belt. Oceanic crust subducts rapidly and perturbs the thermal regime of the mantle. Rocks in the oceanic crust are progressively metamorphosed to blueschists and eclogites at high pressure. Subsequent melting in or above the descending crust causes a rise of magma to the surface and low-pressure, high-temperature metamorphism in the continental crust.

pressure facies series) from ocean-floor basalts transported down the subduction zone. Continued subduction of these rocks to great depth may eventually result in partial melting in response to rising temperatures; these melts contribute to the formation of the volcanoes that overlie subduction zones in areas such as the Andes of South America, Japan, and the Aleutian Islands. Upward migration of subduction-related magmas also contributes to the development of paired metamorphic belts, in which high-pressure, low-temperature metamorphic rocks are flanked on the continental side by a parallel belt of low-pressure, high-temperature rocks. The latter rocks are thought to reflect perturbation of the crustal thermal regime by the passage of silicate melts generated above the subducting slab. Continued intrusion of magma over a period of time would cause an increase in crustal temperatures at relatively shallow depths and produce the high-temperature rocks adjacent to the high-pressure rocks generated in the subduction zone (see Figure 146). Well-developed paired metamorphic belts are exposed in Japan, California, the Alps, and New Zealand.

Paired metamorphic belts

Data obtained from deep earthquakes in subduction zones indicate that a descending slab of oceanic lithosphere can remain intact to depths of several hundred kilometres before undergoing complete melting or fragmentation or both and being incorporated into the surrounding mantle. Clearly, the blueschists and eclogites exposed in orogenic belts around the world did not undergo such a process and were instead returned to the Earth's surface. Most of the high-pressure rocks that have been studied from Japan, California, New Caledonia, the Alps, and Scandinavia record maximum pressures of 10–20 kilobars, corresponding to subduction to depths of approximately 35–70 kilometres. A few samples have been discovered in Norway, the Alps, and China that contain the mineral coesite, a high-pressure polymorph of quartz. Experimental studies on the stability of coesite imply minimum pressures of 30 kilobars for these rocks, indicating burial or subduction to depths of approximately 100 kilometres. These pressures are particularly noteworthy in that they are recorded in rocks derived from sedimentary rather than basaltic protoliths. Because of the low density, and hence greater buoyancy, of sediments relative to basalts, many geologists have argued that sediment subduction must be a rather limited process; the coesite-bearing metapelites (metamorphosed pelites) provide important evidence that sediment subduction can and does occur under certain circumstances.

The processes by which rocks that have been partially subducted are returned to the surface are not well understood. Models have been proposed to account for uplift and exposure of these high-pressure, high-density rocks; they include scraping material from the subducting plate against the overlying crustal lithosphere, upward flow of material in response to forced convection above the subducted slab, and removal of overlying thickened crust by low-angle extensional faulting. Testing these models requires considerable petrologic and structural work in areas where high-pressure rocks are exposed.

High-pressure rocks

Most of the high-pressure rocks that are currently displayed in metamorphic belts around the world were metamorphosed in Mesozoic or Cenozoic time (*e.g.*, the circum-Pacific belt, the Alps, the Greek Cyclades, and the Cordillera Betica in Spain). Older high-pressure rocks are known from only a few isolated occurrences in, for example, Wales, Bavaria, the Île de Groix off the coast of Brittany, and the Norwegian Caledonides (on the west coast of Norway). The general absence of high-pressure samples in the early rock record raises a number of interesting questions concerning Earth history. Some geologists have argued that the lack of well-developed Precambrian and Paleozoic high-pressure belts indicates that plate tectonic processes have changed significantly throughout geologic time. Specifically, they claim that greater heat production in Archean time (about 3.8 to 2.5 billion years ago) would have produced hotter crustal geotherms, resulting in thin, hot lithospheric plates whose mechanical behaviour may have been quite different from that of the present-day plates and hence may not have permitted formation of subduction zones. The increasing abundance of subduction-related metamorphic rocks with decreasing age in the rock record would thus reflect the gradual onset of plate tectonics as operative today. Others argue that the rock record is biased owing to preferential erosion or thermal overprinting (development of a new mineralogy that may obliterate the original one) of old blueschists and eclogites. Thermal modeling studies suggest that blueschists will generally undergo heating and be converted to greenschist assemblages if exposure at the Earth's surface does not occur within 100 million to 200 million years after high-pressure metamorphism. Early exposure at the surface also increases the chances for removal by erosion, however, resulting in a low probability for preserving blueschists greater than 100 million to 200 million years old. Geologists favouring generation of blueschists throughout Earth history but only selective preservation of these rocks also point to crustal rocks more than 2.5 billion years old that record metamorphism at depths of 25–40 kilometres; these medium-pressure facies series rocks imply that crustal thicknesses in the early Earth were similar to those of the present day and thus that modern plate tectonic processes may have operated from the early Precambrian to the present. This debate, though unresolved, emphasizes the substantial knowledge of the thermal structure of the Earth and plate tectonic processes that can be obtained from the study of metamorphic rocks.

Continent-continent collision

Depending on the original geometry of the Earth's lithospheric plates, subduction of oceanic crust beneath continental lithosphere may result in complete consumption of an ocean basin and subsequent collision between two continents. Collisions of this type have a long and complex history that may include initial formation of a paired metamorphic belt followed by extreme crustal thickening in response to the actual collision of the continents. The overthickened crust produced by the collision event will be gravitationally unstable and will undergo subsequent rapid erosion and possibly extensional faulting in order to return to a normal crustal thickness. Rocks metamorphosed in the early stages of collision may belong to a high-pressure facies series, reflecting the final stages of subduction of oceanic lithosphere, whereas the younger facies more typically belong to medium-pressure facies series. Metamorphic rocks exposed in former collision zones may thus have followed a variety of pressure-temperature-time paths, but paths showing rapid burial followed by heating and subsequent unroofing at moderate to high temperatures have been reported from many mountain belts around the world. Owing to the strong directed forces operative during collision, deformation typically accompanies metamorphism; rocks metamorphosed in response to continent-continent collision generally have fabrics showing a strong preferred orientation of mineral grains, folds on a variety of scales, and pre-, syn-, and postkinematic porphyroblasts. Examples of metamorphic belts produced in response to this type of collision include the Paleozoic Appalachian and Caledonides belts and the Mesozoic-Cenozoic Alpine and Himalayan belts.

Regionally metamorphosed rocks are also exposed in areas where the crust has been thinned by extensional faulting, such as the Basin and Range province of the western United States. In this type of occurrence, areas of medium- and low-pressure facies series rocks that measure a few tens of kilometres in diameter are juxtaposed against unmetamorphosed sediments or very low-grade metamorphic rocks along low-angle extensional faults. (Metamorphic grades refer to the degree and intensity of the metamorphism: they are determined by the pressure and temperatures to which the rock has been subjected.) Such areas are generally referred to as metamorphic core complexes. Metamorphism in these complexes may or may not be related to the extensional event. In some instances, metamorphic rocks produced during much earlier events are simply unroofed and exposed by the faulting but show little or no recrystallization related to extension. In other cases, prolonged extension has resulted in an increased crustal geotherm, and relatively high-temperature metamorphism and magmatism is thus directly related to the extensional event. Immediately adjacent to the faults, the rocks may also be affected by dynamic metamorphism.

The facies associated with regional metamorphism include, at low grade, the zeolite and prehnite-pumpellyite facies. In areas belonging to high-pressure facies series, the rocks are predominantly in the blueschist and eclogite facies. Medium- and low-pressure facies series are typified by rocks belonging to the greenschist, amphibolite, and granulite facies.

Zeolite facies. In the zeolite facies, sediments and volcanic debris show the first major response to burial. Reactions are often not complete, and typical metamorphic fabrics may be poorly developed or not developed at all. This is the facies of burial metamorphism.

The zeolite facies was first described from southern New Zealand, but similar rocks have now been described from many younger mountain regions of the Earth, particularly around the Pacific margin and the European Alps. Typically, the rocks are best developed where reactive volcanic materials (often partly glassy) are common and the characteristic minerals include zeolites, which are low-density, hydrated silicates, stable at temperatures rarely exceeding 300° C. Typical mineral assemblages include heulandite, analcite, quartz with complex clay minerals (montmorillonite), micaceous phases such as chlorite and celadonite, and the potassium feldspar, adularia. At higher grades of metamorphism, the zeolite laumonite and the feldspar albite dominate the mineral assemblage. In New Zealand these are developed in a rock column that is about 15 kilometres thick. Calcareous rocks (impure limestones) show very little response to this grade of metamorphism.

Prehnite-pumpellyite facies. Along with the zeolite facies, the prehnite-pumpellyite facies received little attention until about 1950. The first rocks of the facies were described in New Zealand and Celebes. The facies is transitional, bridging the path to the blueschist facies or the greenschist facies. It is particularly well developed in graywacke-type sediments. The two minerals prehnite and pumpellyite replace the zeolite minerals of the zeolite facies and are themselves replaced by epidote minerals in the greenschist facies and by lawsonite and pyroxenes in the blueschist facies. Typical minerals in this facies are quartz, albite, prehnite, pumpellyite, chlorite, stilpnomelane, muscovite, and actinolite. Almost all the minerals are hydrated, and, except for chlorite, they bear little resemblance to the minerals of sediments. Again, the facies has been most described from younger mountain ranges of the Pacific margin.

Blueschist facies. Rocks of the blueschist facies represent deep metamorphism under conditions of a low thermal gradient. The characteristic locale for this type of metamorphism appears to be along a continental margin being underthrust by an oceanic plate. Regions in which blueschists are found are also regions of great seismic and volcanic activity, such as the Pacific margin. The best described examples of this class of metamorphism come from California, Japan, New Caledonia, Celebes, the Alps, and the Mediterranean region. At present there are no confirmed examples of glaucophane schists predating the Paleozoic Era. Because of the presence of the blue amphibole glaucophane and minerals such as garnet and jadeite, these schists are among the most attractive of metamorphic rocks.

Characteristic minerals of the facies include quartz, glaucophane, lawsonite, jadeite, omphacite, garnet, albite, chlorite, muscovite, paragonite, epidote, and kyanite. In calcareous rocks, calcite may be replaced by the high-pressure polymorph aragonite. In general, the facies is characterized by many high-density minerals reflecting a high pressure of formation.

Eclogite facies. The eclogite facies was initially recognized in rocks only of basaltic composition, which are transformed at the pressure-temperature conditions of the eclogite facies into spectacular red and green rocks composed of the anhydrous mineral assemblage garnet plus omphacite. The garnet is rich in the high-pressure species pyrope, and the omphacite is rich in the high-pressure pyroxene jadeite. Small amounts of minerals such as kyanite, the hydrate zoisite, and hornblende may be present. The rocks are of high density and frequently show little or no schistosity. It is now known that protoliths other than basalt also can be metamorphosed to pressures and temperatures characteristic of the eclogite facies, and a wide variety of mineral assemblages can be stable at these conditions, including several hydrous mineral phases. Minerals that have been observed in metapelites include magnesium-rich chloritoid and staurolite, kyanite, garnet, phengite (a muscovite mica with high magnesium and silicon and low aluminum content), chlorite, and talc. Experimental work shows that pelitic rocks composed primarily of talc and kyanite, which are referred to as whiteschists, can be stable from pressures of approximately 6 kilobars up to greater than 30 kilobars. Minerals observed in eclogite-facies calcareous rocks include magnesite, dolomite, zoisite or epidote, and omphacite.

Because of the high density and composition, it was proposed long ago that part of the upper mantle might be made of eclogite. Such a view is supported by eclogitic intrusions in volcanic rocks and by eclogitic inclusions in diamond-bearing kimberlite, which must come from the upper mantle. Some workers also think that eclogites found in metamorphic terrains in Norway, California, U.S., and the European Alps could also come from the mantle by tectonic processes.

Early experimental work on eclogites of basaltic bulk composition suggested that eclogites could generally only be stable if water pressure was much lower than the lithostatic pressure, and the facies was thus thought to represent dry, high-pressure metamorphism of basaltic protoliths. Subsequent work on the more diverse protolith compositions reveals, however, that a wide range of water pressures are possible in the eclogite facies and

that fluid compositions in equilibrium with the eclogite minerals also probably vary greatly. Indeed, fluid inclusions (tiny bubbles of fluid trapped within mineral grains) in eclogite samples provide evidence of fluids containing nitrogen, salts, and carbon dioxide in addition to water. Eclogite metamorphism is therefore not confined to dry environments but results instead from metamorphism of a variety of rock types at pressures above about 10 kilobars, corresponding to burial to approximately 35 kilometres, and at temperatures ranging from about 400° to 1,000° C. The temperatures of the eclogite facies overlap those of the greenschist, amphibolite, and granulite facies, but the higher pressures result in distinctly different mineral assemblages characterized by high-density mineral phases.

Greenschist facies. The greenschist facies was once considered the first major facies of metamorphism proper. The name comes from the abundance of the green mineral chlorite in such rocks. Because chlorite and muscovite are ubiquitous and because both exhibit a platy crystal habit, these rocks normally show a highly developed foliation and often exhibit strong metamorphic differentiation. They have been described from practically every metamorphic terrain on Earth, from earliest Precambrian to the young mountain regions. In fact, many of the Earth's oldest rocks (about three billion years old) of the continental-shield areas are in this facies, classic examples of which are in the Appalachians, the Highlands of Scotland, New Zealand, the European Alps, Japan, and Norway.

The dominant minerals of greenschists formed from silicate-rich sediments include quartz, albite, muscovite, chlorite, epidote, calcite, actinolite, magnetite, biotite, and paragonite. Minerals less common include the manganese-rich garnet spessartine, stilpnomelane, kyanite, rutile, sphene, pyrophyllite, and chloritoid. Calcareous rocks are dominated by calcite, dolomite, and quartz; the major carbonate minerals are thermally stable. It is only when large quantities of water flush away carbon dioxide or keep its partial pressure low that carbonate-silicate reactions take place and liberate carbon dioxide. The typical minerals of this facies have low water contents as compared to the zeolite facies minerals.

Amphibolite facies. The amphibolite facies is the common high-grade facies of regional metamorphism, and, like the greenschist facies, such rocks are present in all ages from all over the world. Their characteristic feature is the development of the most common amphibole, hornblende, in the presence of a plagioclase feldspar and garnet. The rocks are normally highly foliated or schistose. Many zones or isograds subdividing the facies have been recognized, and classic studies have been made in the Highlands of Scotland, New Hampshire and Vermont in the United States, Switzerland, and the Himalayas.

Characteristic minerals derived from pelitic rocks are quartz, muscovite, biotite, garnet, plagioclase, kyanite, sillimanite, staurolite, and orthoclase. Minerals derived from basaltic rocks include hornblende, plagioclase, garnet, epidote, and biotite. Those derived from calcareous rocks are calcite, diopside, grossularite (garnet), zoisite, actinolite (hornblende), scapolite, and phlogopite. Minerals from magnesium-rich ultrabasic rocks are chlorite, anthophyllite, and talc. In most common types, water is present in minerals only of the mica and amphibole families, and, with their water contents of only about 1 to 3 percent, dehydration is nearing its metamorphic climax.

Granulite facies. In rocks of basaltic composition, the granulite facies is an anhydrous facies that results from progressive dehydration of amphibolites at high temperature. Rocks of other bulk compositions may retain some hydrous minerals, such as biotite and hornblende, but it is likely that water pressure is lower than lithostatic pressure during most granulite facies metamorphism. Evidence for relatively low water pressures comes from fluid inclusion data indicating carbon dioxide-rich fluid compositions and from preservation of some bulk compositions that should have undergone nearly total melting at granulite temperatures if water pressure had been equal to lithostatic pressure.

Rocks of this facies frequently have a granular texture quite similar to plutonic igneous rocks. Schistosity is only weakly developed. Typical minerals of the facies are quartz, alkali feldspar, garnet, plagioclase, cordierite, sillimanite, and hypersthene. In calcareous members, dolomite, calcite, diopside, and forsterite occur; and it is in this facies that minerals of the scapolite family are best developed. Small amounts of hornblende are often present. A rare mineral occurring in this facies is sapphirine. The rock type charnockite (from Tamil Nādu, India), essentially a hypersthene granite, is normally included in this facies.

It appears from experimental studies that during ultrametamorphism, when melting starts, the basic reactions which take place are of the type

$$\text{biotite} + \text{other minerals} \rightarrow \text{melt} + \text{residue}$$
$$\text{hornblende} + \text{other minerals} \rightarrow \text{melt} + \text{residue.}$$

The probable process of granulite formation

The first melts to form are partly wet granitic or granodioritic melts, and phases such as biotite and hornblende break down by producing a partly wet melt from the least refractory phases in the rocks. They would persist to much higher temperatures in other systems of their own composition. The residue in the above equations is a granulite-facies metamorphic rock containing phases such as pyroxene and sillimanite. Thus it is probable but certainly not universally proved that many granulites are formed only in the presence of a silicate liquid. This liquid may, of course, move to higher crustal levels.

Large areas of granulite facies rocks are confined almost entirely to Precambrian areas of the continents (those areas that were formed more than 570 million years ago), with well-developed areas exposed in Canada, India, Africa, Antarctica, Greenland, and the Adirondack Mountains of New York in the northeastern United States. Smaller areas of granulite facies rocks occur in younger mountain belts, with Paleozoic examples in New England (U.S.) and Brittany and Tertiary examples (those formed between 66.4 and 1.6 million years ago) in British Columbia (Can.) and Timor. The apparent decrease in the volume of granulite facies rocks with decreasing age of metamorphism has led some geologists to postulate, as mentioned above, that plate tectonic processes might have changed significantly with time—specifically that steady-state continental geotherms were hotter in the Precambrian than at the present time. Some work on pressure-temperature-time paths in granulites also suggests that Precambrian granulites were metamorphosed along distinctly different paths than younger granulites, lending credence to models invoking changes in tectonic processes. An alternative hypothesis is that large volumes of granulites have been formed throughout Earth history but that they have not yet been exposed by erosion. Pressures calculated from fragments of granulite-facies metamorphic rocks carried to the surface in young volcanic eruptions suggest that the fragments were derived from the lower crust. It is likely that the lower crust is currently composed largely of granulite-facies rocks that may be exposed by future episodes of mountain building, but it is also possible that these granulites will prove to be different from their Precambrian counterparts. In order to resolve some of the controversies surrounding the origin and composition of granulites, it is necessary that considerable studies of these rocks be conducted in the future.

Distribution of metamorphic rocks

A high-grade metamorphic rock is one that formed at a depth of tens of kilometres and later returned to the surface. Hence, metamorphic regions are also regions of former or recent intense orogeny. More stable regions of the Earth's crust tend to be covered with sediments, and only deep drilling will reveal the metamorphic rocks below.

The Earth's crust is made up of two basic units, the continents and ocean basins. Exploration of ocean floors has revealed that old, thick sedimentary piles are missing. Doubtless this is related to the processes of continental drift or seafloor spreading; sediments are continuously swept up by continental motion and are added to the continents or returned to the upper mantle (see also PLATE TECTONICS). Nearly all studies of metamorphic rocks have concentrated on the continents for this reason.

There are few large areas of the Earth's crust that are not affected by some type of igneous event from time to time. Although the intensity of volcanism may be focused in certain geographic regions (*e.g.,* the Pacific margin), volcanism appears to be a rather random phenomenon, at times even occurring in the stable shield areas of the continents. In this sense, contact-metamorphic events may be found almost everywhere at almost any time on Earth. But these metamorphic events are of trivial volumetric significance compared to those of regional metamorphism.

During the past 500 million years or so of Earth history, major tectonic, seismic, igneous, and metamorphic events have been concentrated on continental margins (Figure 147). This has been a period of depression and uplift of the Earth's crust associated with the formation of the present continental distribution. The processes are still going on at dramatic rates in ocean trench environments. These modern regions of activity form immense linear

Belts of mountain building and shield areas

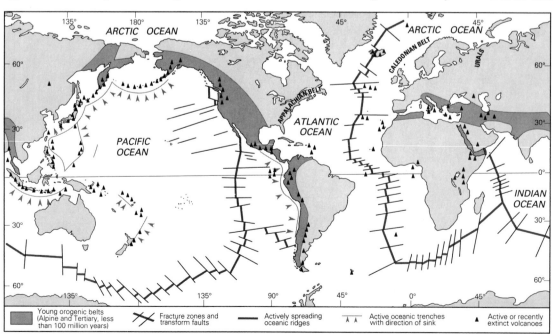

Figure 147: Tectonic units of the continents: shields and the present-day configuration of the continents and the Earth's major lithospheric plates (see text).

belts. One such belt runs around virtually the entire Pacific margin and another through the Mediterranean and southern Asia to fuse with the circum-Pacific belt. It is in these belts that the spectacular development of zeolite facies, prehnite-pumpellyite facies, blueschist facies, and, occasionally, eclogite facies, as well as the more universal facies of regional metamorphism, have occurred. The granulite facies is almost missing.

The central and often dominant feature of most continents is their vast Precambrian-shield area; examples include the Canadian Shield, Brazilian Shield, African Shield, and Australian Shield. In these rocks, dating reveals ages of 1 to 3.5 billion years, and they have been little affected by tectonic events postdating the Cambrian. But these shield areas are themselves complex. They consist of vast areas of granitic or granodioritic gneisses. Inside them, between them, and overlapping onto them are belts of sedimentary rocks quite like those in modern sedimentary belts of the Pacific margin or European Alps. These rocks are frequently metamorphosed in the greenschist, amphibolite, and granulite facies. Low-temperature facies and, in particular, low-temperature–high-pressure facies are missing—or have not yet been found. From marginal areas of these stable shield areas, a complex array of processes has been documented covering the past few hundred million years. The Caledonian orogeny (at the close of the Silurian Period) produced tectonic-metamorphic events along the east coast of North America, Greenland, the British Isles, Fennoscandia, Central Asia, and Australia. The Hercynian, or Variscan, orogeny followed about 300 million years ago, affecting subparallel regions and the Urals and European Alps. In fact, the shield margins appear to have been subjected to a more or less constant battering by forces both destroying and rebuilding the margins of these protocontinents. As geologists study Precambrian areas in greater detail, the number of metamorphic and orogenic events recognized on a global scale increases.

Tectonic-metamorphic events associated with the Caledonian orogeny

It is the great task and problem of those who study metamorphic rocks to deduce the record of Earth dynamics and thermal history from metamorphic rocks. Among the questions to be answered are (1) whether the pattern of facies development through time—*e.g.,* the granulite facies in the Archean to blueschist facies in the Tertiary—is a reflection of a cooling Earth and the decline of radioactivity in the crust, and (2) whether the increase in size of global tectonic-metamorphic belts through time reflects changes in convective patterns in the mantle.

As understanding of the pressure-temperature regimes of metamorphism increases, and as knowledge of rock mechanics and fluid motion during metamorphism also increases through field and laboratory studies, it may become possible to understand the details of the motion of the chemical elements during such processes and hence much of the subject of economic geology, or the search for man's essential raw materials.

Classification of metamorphic rocks

Because of the diverse chemistry, mineralogy, and primary origin of metamorphic rocks and because of the diverse fabrics or textures that may develop depending on the stresses that may operate during their formation, there is no simple, universally used classification of these rocks. Any classification of metamorphic rocks tends to stress either their fabric, mineralogy, or primary origin. Some common metamorphic rock types are described here.

Schist. Rocks in which metamorphic minerals are easily seen by eye or hand lens and in which the mineral grains have a highly orientated fabric are called schists. Grains of acicular (needlelike) or platy minerals (*e.g.,* amphiboles and micas) tend to lie with their long directions parallel or their planar directions parallel. Often the rocks show a pronounced mineralogical layering; quartz layers a few millimetres or centimetres in thickness may lie between mica layers, for example. Other words often qualify schist: as described above, greenschist is a schist rich in the green mineral chlorite; blueschist is rich in the blue amphibole, glaucophane; mica-schist is rich in mica; and a graphite-

Pronounced mineralogical layering in schists

schist is rich in graphite. Schists that are rich in the amphibole hornblende and are often derived by metamorphism of common igneous rocks of the basalt-gabbro type are called amphibolites.

Slate. A very fine-grained metamorphic rock (usually developed from clay-rich sediments) exhibiting perfect planar layering and perfection of splitting into layers (slaty cleavage) is slate. Such rocks are normally rich in micas and chlorites. As the intensity of metamorphism increases, porphyroblasts may grow; such slates are sometimes called spotted slates. As metamorphism proceeds, the average crystal size increases, and mineral segregation develops; the rock then may be termed a phyllite.

Gneiss. A gneiss is produced by intense metamorphism, at high temperature and pressure. The grain size is coarser than that in schists, and layering is often well developed (see Figure 148); mineral orientation is less perfect than in schists, however. Very common granitic gneisses of Precambrian areas have been derived from metamorphism of granitic igneous rocks.

Jane Selverstone

Figure 148: Banded gneiss produced by metamorphism of quartzofeldspathic sediments in Scotland. White bands have undergone partial melting and recrystallized into granite. Dark bands represent material composed predominantly of biotite and minor hornblende.

Hornfels. The hornfels are formed by contact metamorphism and typically show little sign of the action of directed pressure. They are fine-grained rocks in which crystals display little orientation.

Marble. Rocks derived from the metamorphism of carbonate sediments containing calcite or dolomite are marbles. The main result of metamorphism is an increase in grain size. Because of the rather equidimensional habit of calcite and dolomite crystals, they rarely appear schistose unless they contain other minerals such as mica.

Hornfels as a product of contact metamorphism

Mylonites and cataclastites. These are rocks in which the texture is the result of ductile shearing or mechanical shattering of grains. They often show only slight, if any, development of new minerals. They form on fault planes or in zones of intense shearing. If the crustal rocks have an appropriate composition, phyllonites may develop where new mica crystals grow parallel to the shearing direction. If shearing is extreme, melting may occur, locally producing a pseudo-tachylite. Tachylite is a term applied to certain types of glass formed by rapid cooling of molten rocks.

Other classes. Most of the above terms indicate structural or fabric classification of metamorphic rocks. Sometimes terms are used to indicate chemical features. Several types of schists, for example, include the following: pelitic schists contain much aluminum oxide and often are derivatives of clay-rich sediments; quartzofeldspathic schists are high in quartz and feldspars and often are derivatives of sandstones or quartz-rich igneous rocks; calcareous schists have a high content of lime (CaO) and often are derivatives of impure limestones, dolomites, or calcareous muds; and basic schists contain the elements of basic igneous rocks—namely, calcium, magnesium, and iron.

(William S. Fyfe/Jane Selverstone)

Telescopes

The telescope is undoubtedly the most important investigative tool in astronomy. It provides a means of collecting and analyzing radiation from celestial objects, even those in the far reaches of the universe.

Galileo revolutionized astronomy when he applied the telescope to the study of extraterrestrial bodies in the early 17th century. Until then, magnification instruments had never been used for this purpose. Since Galileo's pioneering work, increasingly more powerful optical telescopes have been developed, as has a wide array of instruments capable of detecting and measuring invisible forms of radiation, such as radio, X-ray, and gamma-ray telescopes. Observational capability has been further enhanced by the invention of various kinds of auxiliary instruments (*e.g.,* the camera, spectrograph, and charge-coupled device) and by the use of electronic computers, rockets, and spacecraft in conjunction with telescope systems. These developments have contributed dramatically to advances in scientific knowledge about the solar system, the Milky Way Galaxy, and the universe as a whole.

The article is divided into the following sections:

GENERAL CONSIDERATIONS

Today, the telescope is used to explore every region of the electromagnetic spectrum from the shortest wavelengths (gamma rays) to the longest (radio waves; see Figure 1). The wavelengths of the spectrum are measured in three different units: angstroms (Å), micrometres (μ), and metres (m). Each of these units is customarily used for specific wavelength ranges, as shown in the figure. For example, the wavelengths for gamma rays and X rays are given in angstroms, those for infrared rays in micrometres, and those for intermediate radio waves in metres. (Centimetres are often used for short radio waves [microwaves] and kilometres for long radio waves.)

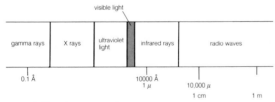

Figure 1: The electromagnetic spectrum.

Astronomical observations were restricted to visible wavelengths until the 1930s, when Karl Jansky and Grote Reber of the United States opened the radio "window." Since the 1960s the use of Earth-orbiting telescope systems has enabled astronomers to make observations in all other spectral regions as well.

OPTICAL TELESCOPES

Refracting telescopes. Commonly known as refractors, telescopes of this kind are used to examine the visible-light region of the electromagnetic spectrum. Typical uses include viewing the Moon, other objects of the solar system such as Jupiter and Mars, and double stars. The name refractor is derived from the term refraction, which is the bending of light when it passes from one medium to another of different density—*e.g.,* from air to glass. The glass is referred to as a lens and may have one or more components. The physical shape of the components may be convex, concave, or plane-parallel. Figure 2 illustrates the principle of refraction and the term focal length. The focus is the point, or plane, at which light rays from infinity converge after passing through a lens and traveling a distance of one focal length. In a refractor, the first lens through which light from a celestial object passes is called the objective lens. It should be noted that the light will be inverted at the focal plane. A second lens, referred to as the eyepiece lens, is placed behind the focal plane and enables the observer to view the enlarged, or magnified, image. Thus, the simplest form of refractor consists of an objective and an eyepiece, as illustrated in Figure 3.

The diameter of the objective is referred to as the aperture; it typically ranges from a few centimetres for small spotting telescopes up to one metre for the largest refractor in existence. The objective, as well as the eyepiece, may have several components. Small spotting telescopes may contain an extra lens behind the eyepiece to erect the image so that it does not appear upside-down. When an object is viewed with a refractor, the image may not appear sharply defined, or it may even have a predominant colour in it. Such distortions, or aberrations, are sometimes introduced when the lens is polished into its design shape. The major kind of distortion in a refractor is chromatic aberration, which is the failure of the differently coloured light rays to come to a common focus. Chromatic aberration can be minimized by adding additional components to the objective. In lens-design technology,

Aperture

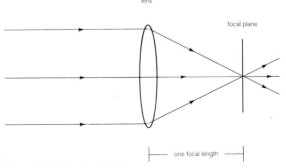

Figure 2: Focal length of a lens.

the coefficients of expansion of different kinds of glass are carefully matched to minimize the aberrations that result from temperature changes of the telescope at night.

Figure 3: Refracting telescope.

Eyepieces, which are used with both refractors and reflectors (see below *Reflecting telescopes*), have a wide variety of applications and provide observers with the ability to select the magnification of their instruments. The magnification, sometimes referred to as magnifying power, is determined by dividing the focal length of the objective by the focal length of the eyepiece. For example, if the objective has a focal length of 254 centimetres (100 inches) and the eyepiece has a focal length of 2.54 centimetres (1 inch), then the magnification will be 100. Large magnifications are very useful for observing the Moon and the planets; however, since stars appear as point sources owing to their great distances, magnification provides no additional advantage when viewing them. Another important factor that one must take into consideration when attempting to view at high magnification is the stability of the telescope mounting. Any vibration in the mounting will also be magnified and may severely reduce the quality of the observed image. Thus, great care is usually taken to provide a stable platform for the telescope. This problem should not be associated with that of atmospheric seeing, which may introduce a disturbance to the image due to fluctuating air currents in the path of the light from a celestial or terrestrial object. Generally, most of the seeing disturbance arises in the first 30 metres of air above the telescope. Large telescopes are frequently installed on mountain peaks in order to get above the seeing disturbances.

The most important of all the powers of an optical telescope is its light-gathering power. This capacity is strictly a function of the diameter of the clear objective—that is, the aperture—of the telescope. Comparisons of different-sized apertures for their light-gathering power are calculated by the ratio of their diameters squared; for example, a 25-centimetre objective will collect four times the light of a 12.5-centimetre objective $[(25 \times 25) \div (12.5 \times 12.5)] = 4$. The advantage of collecting more light with a larger-aperture telescope is that one can observe fainter stars, nebulas, and very distant galaxies.

Resolving power Resolving power is another important feature of a telescope. This is the ability of the instrument to distinguish clearly between two points whose angular separation is less than the smallest angle that the observer's eye can resolve. The resolving power of a telescope can be calculated by the formula

resolving power $= 11.25$ seconds of arc$/d$,

where d is the diameter of the objective expressed in centimetres. Thus, a 25-centimetre-diameter objective has a theoretical resolution of 0.45 second of arc and a 250-centimetre telescope has one of 0.045 second of arc. An important application of resolving power is in the observation of visual binary stars. Here, one star is routinely observed as it revolves around a second star. Many observatories conduct extensive visual binary observing programs and publish catalogs of their observational results. One of the major contributors in this field is the United States Naval Observatory in Washington, D.C.

Most refractors currently in use at observatories have equatorial mountings. (The mounting describes the orientation of the physical bearings and structure that permits a telescope to be pointed at a celestial object for viewing.) In the equatorial mounting, the polar axis of the telescope is constructed parallel to the Earth's axis. The polar axis supports the declination axis of the instrument. Declination is measured on the celestial sky north or south from the celestial equator. The declination axis makes it possible for the telescope to be pointed at various declination angles as the instrument is rotated about the polar axis with respect to right ascension. Right ascension is measured along the celestial equator from the vernal equinox (*i.e.*, the position on the celestial sphere where the Sun crosses the celestial equator from south to north on the first day of spring). Declination and right ascension are the two coordinates that define a celestial object on the celestial sphere. Declination is analogous to latitude, and right ascension is analogous to longitude. Graduated dials are mounted on the axis to permit the observer to point the telescope precisely. To track an object, the telescope's polar axis is driven smoothly by an electric motor at a sidereal rate—namely, at a rate equal to the rate of rotation of the Earth with respect to the stars. Thus, one can track or observe with a telescope for long periods of time if the sidereal rate of the motor is very accurate. High-accuracy, motor-driven systems have become readily available with the rapid advancement of quartz-clock technology. Most major observatories now rely on either quartz or atomic clocks to provide accurate sidereal time for observations as well as to drive telescopes at an extremely uniform rate.

A notable example of a refracting telescope is the 66-centimetre refractor of the U.S. Naval Observatory (see Figure 4). This instrument was used by the astronomer Asaph Hall to discover the two moons of Mars, Phobos and Deimos, in 1877. Today, the telescope is used primarily for observing double stars. The 91-centimetre refractor at Lick Observatory on Mount Hamilton, Calif., U.S., and the one-metre instrument at Yerkes Observatory in Williams Bay, Wis., U.S., are the largest refracting systems currently in operation (Table 1).

Another type of refracting telescope is the astrograph, which usually has an objective diameter of approximately 20 centimetres. The astrograph has a photographic plate-holder mounted in the focal plane of the objective so that photographs of the celestial sphere can be taken. The photographs are usually taken on glass plates. The principal application of the astrograph is to determine the positions of a large number of faint stars. These positions are then

Astrographs

Figure 4: The 66-centimetre refractor of the U.S. Naval Observatory.

Table 1: Some Important Ground-Based Optical Telescopes

name	aperture and type	observatory and location
Bolshoi Teleskop	6-metre reflector	Special Astrophysical Observatory, Zelenchukskaya, Russian S.F.S.R.
George Ellery Hale Telescope	5-metre reflector	Palomar Observatory, Palomar Mountain, Calif., U.S.
William Herschel Telescope	4.2-metre reflector	Roque de los Muchachos Observatory, La Palma, Canary Islands, Spain
	4-metre reflector	Cerro Tololo Inter-American Observatory, Cerro Tololo, Chile
Anglo-Australian Telescope	3.9-metre reflector	Anglo-Australian Observatory, Siding Spring Mountain, N.S.W., Australia
Nicholas U. Mayall Telescope	3.8-metre reflector	Kitt Peak National Observatory, Kitt Peak, Ariz., U.S.
Canada-France-Hawaii Telescope	3.6-metre reflector	Canada-France-Hawaii Telescope Corporation, Mauna Kea, Hawaii, U.S.
	3.6-metre reflector	European Southern Observatory, La Silla Hill, Chile
Multiple Mirror Telescope	six 1.8-metre paraboloid mirrors mounted in a single framework	Whipple Observatory, Mount Hopkins, Ariz.
	1.2-metre Schmidt	Palomar Observatory, Palomar Mountain, Calif.
	1-metre refractor	Yerkes Observatory, Williams Bay, Wis., U.S.
	91-centimetre refractor	Lick Observatory, Mount Hamilton, Calif.
	83-centimetre refractor	Meudon Observatory, Meudon, Fr.

published in catalogs such as the *AGK*3 and serve as reference points for deep-space photography.

Reflecting telescopes. Reflectors are used not only to examine the visible region of the electromagnetic spectrum but also to explore both the shorter- and longer-wavelength regions adjacent to it (*i.e.,* the ultraviolet and the infrared). The name of this type of instrument is derived from the fact that the primary mirror reflects the light back to a focus instead of refracting it. The primary mirror usually has a concave spherical or parabolic shape, and, as it reflects the light, it inverts the image at the focal plane. Figure 5 illustrates the principle of a concave

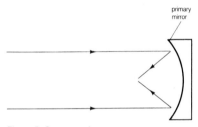

Figure 5: Concave mirror.

reflecting mirror. The formulas for resolving power, magnifying power, and light-gathering power, as discussed for refractors, apply to reflectors as well.

The primary mirror is located at the lower end of the telescope tube in a reflector and has its front surface coated with an extremely thin film of metal, such as aluminum. The back of the mirror is usually made of glass, although other materials have been used from time to time. Pyrex (trademark) was the principal glass of choice for many of the older large telescopes, but new technology has led to the development and widespread use of a number of glasses with very low coefficients of expansion. A low coefficient of expansion means that the shape of the mirror will not change significantly as the temperature of the telescope changes during the night. Since the back of the mirror serves only to provide the desired form and physical support, it does not have to meet the high optical quality standards required for a lens.

Reflecting telescopes have a number of other advantages over refractors. They are not subject to chromatic aberration because reflected light does not disperse according to wavelength. Also, the telescope tube of a reflector is shorter than that of a refractor of the same diameter, which reduces the cost of the tube. Consequently, the dome for housing a reflector is smaller and more economical to construct. So far only the primary mirror for the reflector has been discussed. In examining Figure 5, one might wonder about the location of the eyepiece. The primary mirror reflects the light of the celestial object to the prime focus

near the upper end of the tube. Obviously, if an observer put his eye there to observe with a modest-sized reflector, he would block out the light from the primary mirror with his head. Isaac Newton placed a small plane mirror at an

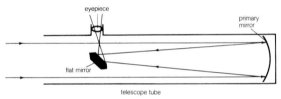

Figure 6: The Newtonian reflector.

angle of 45° inside the prime focus and thereby brought the focus to the side of the telescope tube. The amount of light lost by this procedure is very small when compared to the total light-gathering power of the primary mirror. The Newtonian reflector, shown in Figure 6, is popular among amateur telescope makers.

A contemporary of Newton, N. Cassegrain of France, invented another type of reflector. Called the Cassegrainian telescope, this instrument employs a small convex mirror to reflect the light back through a small hole in the primary mirror to a focus located behind the primary. Figure 7 illustrates a typical Cassegrain reflector. Some large telescopes of this kind do not have a hole in the primary mirror but use a small plane mirror in front of the primary to reflect the light outside the main tube and provide another place for observation. The Cassegrain design usually permits short tubes relative to their mirror diameter.

Cassegrainian telescope

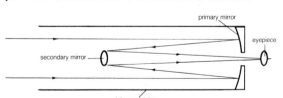

Figure 7: The Cassegrain reflector.

One more variety of reflector was invented by another of Newton's contemporaries, the Scottish astronomer James Gregory. Gregory placed a concave secondary mirror outside the prime focus to reflect the light back through a hole in the primary mirror. Notable is the fact that the Gregorian design was adopted for the Earth-orbiting space observatory, the Solar Maximum Mission (SMM), launched in 1980.

Most large reflecting telescopes currently in use have a cage at their prime focus that permits the observer to sit inside the telescope tube while operating the instrument. The five-metre reflector at Palomar Observatory, near San

Figure 8: The astrometric reflector of the U.S. Naval Observatory.
Official U.S. Navy photograph

Diego, Calif., is so equipped. While most reflectors have equatorial mounts similar to refractors, the world's largest reflector, the six-metre instrument at the Special Astrophysical Observatory in Zelenchukskaya, Russian S.F.S.R., has an altitude-azimuth mounting. The significance of the latter design is that the telescope must be moved in both altitude and azimuth as it tracks a celestial object. Equatorial mountings, by contrast, require motion in only one coordinate while tracking, since the declination coordinate is constant. Reflectors, like refractors, usually have small guide telescopes mounted parallel to their main optical axis to facilitate locating the desired object. These guide telescopes have low magnification and a wide field of view, the latter being a desirable attribute for finding stars or other remote cosmic objects.

The parabolic shape of a primary mirror has a basic failing in that it produces a narrow field of view. This can be a problem when one wishes to observe extended celestial objects. To overcome this difficulty, most large reflectors now have a modified Cassegrain design. The central area of the primary mirror has its shape deepened from that of a paraboloid, and the secondary mirror is configured to compensate for the altered primary. The result is the Ritchey-Chrétien design, which has a curved rather than a flat focus. Obviously, the photographic medium must be curved to collect high-quality images across the curved

Ritchey-Chrétien design

focal plane. The one-metre telescope of the U.S. Naval Observatory in Flagstaff, Ariz., was one of the early examples of this design. The 1.54-metre astrometric reflector of the Naval Observatory is shown in Figure 8.

The Schmidt telescope. The above-mentioned Ritchey-Chrétien design has a good field of view of about 1°. For some astronomical applications, however, photographing larger areas of the sky is mandatory. In 1930 Bernhard Schmidt, an optician at the Hamburg Observatory in Bergedorf, Ger., designed a catadioptric telescope that satisfied the requirement of photographing larger celestial areas. A catadioptric telescope design incorporates the best features of both the refractor and reflector—*i.e.,* it has both reflective and refractive optics. The Schmidt telescope has a spherically shaped primary mirror. Since parallel light rays that are reflected by the centre of a spherical mirror are focused farther away than those reflected from the outer regions, Schmidt introduced a thin lens (called the correcting plate) at the radius of curvature of the primary mirror. Since this correcting plate is very thin, it introduces little chromatic aberration. The resulting focal plane has a field of view several degrees in diameter. Figure 9 illustrates a typical Schmidt design.

The *National Geographic Society–Palomar Observatory Sky Survey* made use of a 1.2-metre Schmidt telescope (Figure 10) to photograph the northern sky in both the

Palomar Observatory photograph

Figure 10: The 1.2-metre Schmidt telescope of the Palomar Observatory near San Diego, Calif.

red and blue regions of the visible spectrum. The survey produced 900 pairs of photographic plates (about 7° by 7° each) taken between 1949 and 1956. Schmidt telescopes of the European Southern Observatory in Chile and of the observatory at Siding Spring Mountain in Australia have photographed the remaining part of the celestial sky that cannot be observed from Palomar Mountain. (The survey undertaken at the latter included photographs in the infrared as well as in the red and blue regions of the spectrum.)

Multimirror telescopes. The main reason astronomers build larger telescopes is to increase light-gathering power so that they can see deeper into the universe. Unfortunately, the cost of constructing larger single-mirror telescopes increases rapidly—approximately with the cube of the diameter of the aperture. Thus, in order to achieve the goal of increasing light-gathering power while keeping

Figure 9: The Schmidt telescope.

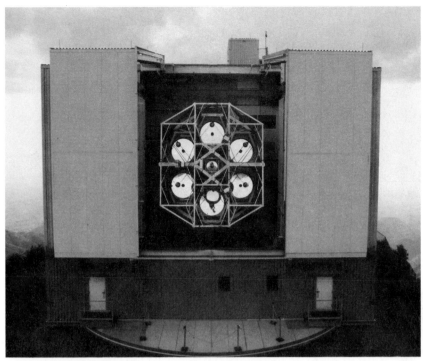

Figure 11: The Multiple Mirror Telescope of the Whipple Observatory, Mount Hopkins, Ariz.

costs down, it has become necessary to explore new, more economical and nontraditional telescope designs.

The Multiple Mirror Telescope

The American-built Multiple Mirror Telescope (MMT), located at the Whipple Observatory in Arizona (Figure 11), represents such an effort. The MMT has six 1.8-metre paraboloid mirrors mounted in a single framework; the light from all the mirrors is concentrated into a single focus. The mirrors, under computer control, are automatically aligned at regular intervals during an observing tour. A 10-metre multimirror telescope is expected to be installed on Mauna Kea on the island of Hawaii by the early 1990s. When completed, this instrument, called the Keck Telescope, will comprise 36 contiguous, adjustable mirror segments, all under computer control. Even larger multimirror instruments are currently being planned by American, western European, and Soviet astronomers.

Special types of optical telescopes. *Solar telescopes.* Either a refractor or reflector may be used for visual observations of solar features, such as sunspots or solar prominences. The main precaution that needs to be taken is to reduce the intensity of the image so that the observer's eye will not be damaged. Generally, this is done with a tinted eyepiece. Special solar telescopes have been constructed, however, for investigations of the Sun that require the use of such ancillary instruments as spectroheliographs and coronagraphs. These telescopes are mounted in towers and have very long focus objectives. Typical examples of tower solar telescopes are found at the Mount Wilson Observatory in California and the McMath-Hulbert Observatory in Michigan. The long focus objective produces a very good scale factor, which in turn makes it possible to look at individual wavelengths of the solar electromagnetic spectrum in great detail. A tower telescope has an equatorially mounted plane mirror at its summit to direct the sunlight into the telescope objective. This plane mirror is called a coelostat. Bernard Lyot constructed another type of solar telescope in 1930 at Pic du Midi Observatory in France. This instrument was specifically designed for photographing the Sun's corona (the outer layer), which up to that time had been successfully photographed only during solar eclipses. The coronagraph, as this special telescope is called, must be located at a high altitude to be effective. The high altitude is required to reduce the scattered sunlight, which would reduce the quality of the photograph. The High Altitude Observatory in Colorado and the Sacramento Peak Observatory in New Mexico have coronagraphs.

Corona-graph

Earth-orbiting space telescopes. While astronomers continue to seek new technological breakthroughs with which to build larger ground-based telescopes, it is readily apparent that the only solution to some scientific problems is to make observations from above the Earth's atmosphere. A series of Orbiting Astronomical Observatories (OAOs) has been launched by the National Aeronautics and Space Administration (NASA); the OAO launched in 1972 (later named Copernicus) had an 81-centimetre telescope on board. The most sophisticated observational system placed in Earth orbit so far is the Hubble Space Telescope (HST; see Figure 12). Launched in 1990, the HST is essentially an optical-ultraviolet telescope with a 2.4-metre primary mirror. It has been designed to enable astronomers to see into a volume of space 300 to 400 times larger than that permitted by other systems. At the same time, the HST is not impeded by any of the problems caused by the atmosphere. It is equipped with five principal scientific instruments: (1) a wide-field and planetary camera, (2) a faint-object spectrograph, (3) a high-resolution spectrograph, (4) a high-speed photometer, and (5) a faint-object camera. The HST was launched into orbit from the U.S. Space Shuttle at an altitude of more than 570 kilometres above the Earth. Shortly after its deployment in Earth orbit, HST project scientists found that a manufacturing error affecting the shape of the telescope's primary mirror severely impaired the instrument's focusing capability. The flawed mirror causes spherical aberration, which limits the ability of the HST to distinguish between cosmic objects that lie close together and to image distant galaxies and quasars. Project scientists expect to devise measures that will enable them to compensate for the defective mirror and correct the imaging problem.

Astronomical transit instruments. These small but extremely important telescopes play a vital role in mapping the celestial sphere. Without the transit instrument's very accurate determination of stellar and planetary positions, the larger deep-space telescopes would not be able to find their desired celestial object.

Astronomical transit instruments are usually refractors with apertures of 15 to 20 centimetres. (Ole Rømer, a Danish astronomer, is credited with having invented this type of telescope system.) The main optical axis of the instrument is aligned on a north-south line such that its motion is restricted to the plane of the meridian of the observer. The observer's meridian is a great circle on the celestial sphere that passes through the north and south

Figure 12: Cutaway of the Hubble Space Telescope, revealing the Optical Telescope Assembly (OTA), the heart of this orbiting observational system.
By courtesy of the Hughes Aircraft Company

Principal types of transit telescopes

points of the horizon as well as through the zenith of the observer. Restricting the telescope to motion only in the meridian provides an added degree of stability, but it requires the observer to wait for the celestial object to rotate across his meridian. The latter process is referred to as transiting the meridian, from which the name of the telescope is derived. There are various types of transit instruments, as, for example, the transit circle telescope, the vertical circle telescope, and the horizontal meridian circle telescope. The transit circle determines the right ascension of celestial objects, while the vertical circle measures only their declinations. Transit circles and horizontal meridian circles measure both right ascension and declination at the same time. The final output data of all transit instruments are included in star or planetary catalogs.

One of the most accurate astronomical transit instruments in the world is the U.S. Naval Observatory's 15-centimetre transit circle telescope (see Figure 13). Other notable examples of this class of telescopes include the transit circle of the National Astronomical Observatory in Tokyo, the meridian circle of the Bordeaux Observatory in France, and the automatic meridian circle of the Roque de los Muchachos Observatory in the Canary Islands.

Astrolabes. Another special type of telescopic instrument is the modern version of the astrolabe. Known as a prismatic astrolabe, it too is used for making precise determinations of the positions of stars and planets. It may sometimes be used inversely to determine the latitude and longitude of the observer, assuming the star positions are accurately known. The aperture of a prismatic astrolabe is small, usually only 8 to 10 centimetres. A small pool of mercury and a refracting prism make up the other principal parts of the instrument. An image reflected off the mercury is observed along with a direct image to give the necessary position data. The most notable example of this type of instrument is the French-constructed Danjon astrolabe. During the 1970s, however, the Chinese introduced various innovations that resulted in a more accurate and automatic kind of astrolabe, which is now in use at the Peking Observatory. (B.L.Klock)

RADIO TELESCOPES

Radio telescopes are used to study naturally occurring radio emissions from stars, galaxies, quasars, and other astronomical objects between wavelengths of about 10 metres (30 megahertz [MHz]) and 1 millimetre (300 gigahertz [GHz]). At wavelengths longer than about 20 centime-

Official U.S. Navy photograph

Figure 13: The 15-centimetre transit circle instrument of the U.S. Naval Observatory.

tres (1.5 GHz), irregularities in the ionosphere distort the incoming signals. This causes a phenomenon known as scintillation, which is analogous to the twinkling of stars seen at optical wavelengths. The absorption of cosmic radio waves by the ionosphere becomes more and more important as wavelength increases. The ionosphere becomes opaque to incoming signals of wavelengths longer than about 10 metres. Radio observations of the universe at these wavelengths are difficult from ground-based radio telescopes. Below wavelengths of a few centimetres, absorption in the atmosphere becomes increasingly critical. At wavelengths shorter than 1 centimetre (30 GHz), observations from the ground are possible only in a few specific wavelength bands that are relatively free of atmospheric absorption.

Principles of operation. Radio telescopes vary widely, but they all have two basic components: (1) a large radio antenna and (2) a radiometer or radio receiver. The sensitivity of a radio telescope—*i.e.,* the ability to measure weak sources of radio emission—depends on the area and efficiency of the antenna, the sensitivity of the radio receiver used to amplify and detect the signals, and the duration of the observation. For broadband continuum emission the sensitivity also depends on the receiver bandwidth. Because some astronomical radio sources are extremely weak, radio telescopes are usually very large and only the most sensitive radio receivers are used. Moreover, weak cosmic signals can be easily masked by terrestrial radio interference, and great effort is taken to protect radio telescopes from man-made interference.

Power gain   The power gain of a radio antenna is usually measured in terms of the improved sensitivity over a simple dipole antenna. For any given antenna the gain varies with the surface area of the antenna and inversely with the square of the wavelength of operation. In a high-gain antenna, radiation is accepted only from a very narrow beam in the sky; the width of the beam depends on the ratio of the wavelength of operation to the diameter of the antenna.

The most familiar type of radio telescope is the radio reflector consisting of a parabolic antenna—the so-called dish—which operates in the same manner as a television-satellite receiving antenna to focus the incoming radiation onto a small antenna referred to as the feed, a term that originated with antennas used for radar transmissions (see Figure 14). In a radio telescope the feed is typically a waveguide horn and is connected to a sensitive radio receiver. Cryogenically cooled solid-state amplifiers with very low internal noise are used to obtain the best possible sensitivity.

In some radio telescopes the parabolic surface is equatorially mounted, with one axis parallel to the rotation axis of the Earth. Equatorial mounts are attractive because they allow the telescope to follow a position in the sky as the Earth rotates by compensating motion about a single axis, but they are difficult and expensive to build. In most cases, a digital computer is used to drive the telescope about the azimuth and elevation axes to follow the motion of a radio source across the sky.

Observing times up to many hours are expended and sophisticated signal-processing techniques are used to detect astronomical radio signals that are as much as one million times weaker than the noise generated in the receiver. Signal-processing and analysis are usually done in a digital

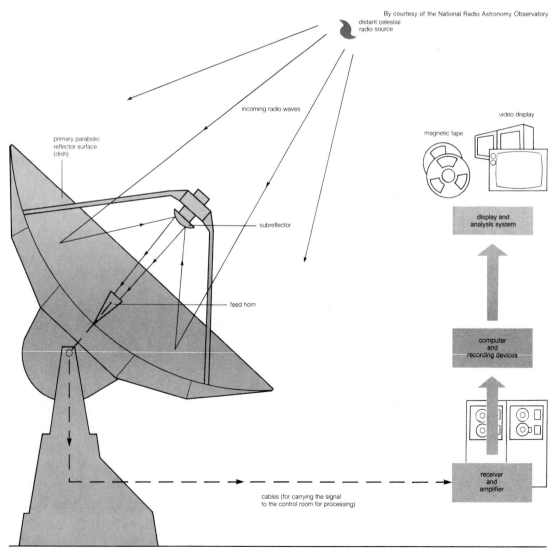

By courtesy of the National Radio Astronomy Observatory

distant celestial radio source

incoming radio waves

primary parabolic reflector surface (dish)

subreflector

feed horn

cables (for carrying the signal to the control room for processing)

magnetic tape

video display

display and analysis system

computer and recording devices

receiver and amplifier

Figure 14: Radio telescope system.

computer. Although some of the computations may be carried out by microcomputers (*i.e.,* those of the personal-computer class), other tasks require large, high-speed machines to translate the raw data into a form useful to the astronomer.

In the simplest form of radio telescope, the receiver is placed directly at the focal point of the parabolic reflector, and the detected signal is carried by cable along the feed support structure to a point near the ground where it can be recorded and analyzed. However, it is difficult in this type of system to access the instrumentation for maintenance and repair, and weight restrictions limit the size and number of individual receivers that can be installed on the telescope. More often, a secondary hyperbolic reflector is placed near the focal point of the paraboloid to focus the radiation to a point near the vertex of the main reflector where multiple receivers may be more readily accommodated with less stringent weight restrictions and access is more straightforward. Secondary focus systems also have the advantage that both the primary and secondary reflecting surfaces may be carefully shaped so as to improve the gain over that of a simple parabolic antenna.

Perfor-
mance-
limiting
factors

The performance of a radio telescope is limited by various factors: the accuracy of a reflecting surface that may depart from the ideal shape because of manufacturing irregularities; the effect of wind load; thermal deformations that cause differential expansion and contraction; and deflections due to changes in gravitational forces as the antenna is pointed to different parts of the sky. Departures from a perfect parabolic surface become important when they are a few percent or more of the wavelength of operation. Since small structures can be built with greater precision than larger ones, radio telescopes designed for operation at millimetre wavelength are typically only a few tens of metres across, whereas those designed for operation at centimetre wavelengths range up to 100 metres in diameter.

Traditionally, the effect of gravity has been minimized by designing the movable structure to be as stiff as possible in order to reduce the deflections resulting from gravity. A more effective technique, based on the principle of homology, allows the structure to deform under the force of gravity, but the cross section and weight of each member of the movable structure are chosen to cause the gravitational forces to deform the reflecting structure into a new paraboloid with a slightly different focal point. It is then necessary only to move the feed or secondary reflector to maintain optimum performance. Homologous designs have become possible only since the development of computer-aided structural analysis.

Some radio telescopes, particularly those designed for operation at very short wavelengths, are placed in protective radomes that can nearly eliminate the effect of both wind loading and temperature differences throughout the structure. Special materials that exhibit very low absorption and reflection of radio waves have been developed for such structures, but the cost of enclosing a large antenna in a suitable temperature-controlled radome may be almost as much as the cost of the movable antenna itself.

The cost of constructing a very-large-aperture antenna can be greatly reduced by fixing the structure to the ground and moving either the feed or the secondary reflector to steer the beam in the sky. For parabolic reflecting surfaces, the beam can be steered in this way over only a limited range of angle without introducing aberration and a loss of power gain. For operation at relatively long metre wavelengths where the reflecting surface need not have an accuracy better than a few centimetres, it becomes practical to build very large fixed structures in which the reflecting surface is made of simple "chicken wire" fencing or even parallel rows of wires.

Radio telescopes are used to measure broad-bandwidth continuum radiation as well as spectroscopic features due to atomic and molecular lines found in the radio spectrum of astronomical objects. In early radio telescopes, spectroscopic observations were made by tuning a receiver across a sufficiently large frequency range to cover the various frequencies of interest. This procedure, however, was extremely time-consuming and greatly restricted observations. Modern radio telescopes observe simultaneously at a large number of frequencies by dividing the signals up into as many as several thousand separate frequency channels that may range over a total bandwidth of tens to hundreds of megahertz.

The most straightforward type of radio spectrometer employs a large number of filters, each tuned to a separate frequency and followed by a separate detector to produce a multichannel, or multifrequency, receiver. Alternatively, a single broad-bandwidth signal may be converted into digital form and analyzed by the mathematical process of autocorrelation and Fourier transformation (see below). In order to detect faint signals, the receiver output is often averaged over periods of up to several hours to reduce the effect of noise generated in the receiver.

Radio interferometry and aperture synthesis. Angular resolution, or ability of a radio telescope to distinguish fine detail in the sky, depends on the wavelength of observations divided by the size of the instrument. Yet even the largest antennas, when used at their shortest operating wavelength, have an angular resolution of only about one arc minute, which is comparable to that of the unaided human eye at optical wavelengths. Because radio telescopes operate at much longer wavelengths than do optical telescopes, it was thought for many years that the

Angular
resolution

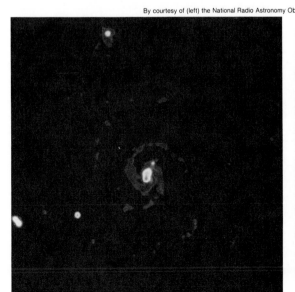 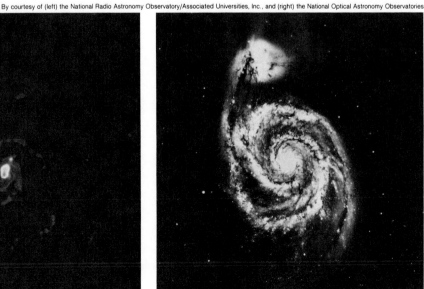

Figure 15: Comparison of a radiograph (left) and a photograph (right) of a spiral galaxy.

resolution of radio telescopes must be much poorer than that of optical instruments. In actuality, this is not the case, for several reasons.

First, although the theoretical resolution of an optical telescope may be as good as a few hundredths of a second of arc, distortions of the incoming light signal by the Earth's atmosphere, known as seeing, diffuse the image, so that even at a good mountain site under good observing conditions the best angular resolution is only a little better than one arc second. At the much longer radio wavelengths, the distortions introduced by the atmosphere are less important, and so the theoretical angular resolution of a radio telescope can in practice be achieved (Figure 15). Because radio signals are easier than light signals to distribute over large distances without distortion, it is possible to build radio telescopes of essentially unlimited dimensions. In fact, the history of radio astronomy has been one of solving engineering problems to construct radio telescopes of continually increasing angular resolution.

The high angular resolution of radio telescopes is achieved by using the principles of interferometry to synthesize a very large effective aperture from a number of small elements. In a simple two-element radio interferometer, the signals from an unresolved, or "point," source alternately arrive in phase and out of phase as the Earth rotates and causes a change in the difference in path from the radio source to the two elements of the interferometer. This produces interference fringes in a manner similar to that in an optical interferometer. If the radio source has finite angular size, then the difference in path length to the elements of the interferometer varies across the source. The measured interference fringes from each interferometer pair thus depend on the detailed nature of the radio "brightness" distribution in the sky.

During the late 1940s Australian radio astronomers realized that each interferometer measurement is one "Fourier component" of the brightness distribution of the radio source. Further developments during the 1950s by Martin Ryle and his colleagues in Cambridge, Eng., involved the use of movable-element interferometers and the rotation of the Earth to sample a sufficient number of Fourier components with which to synthesize the effect of a large aperture and thereby reconstruct high-resolution images of the radio sky. The laborious computational task of doing Fourier transforms to obtain images from the interferometer data is accomplished with high-speed computers and the fast Fourier transform (FFT), a mathematical technique that entails the application of a group of algorithms specially suited for computing discrete Fourier transforms (see ANALYSIS: *Fourier analysis: Harmonic analysis and integral transforms: The Fourier transform*).

Use of fast Fourier transform

In recognition of their contributions to the development of the Fourier synthesis technique, more commonly known as aperture synthesis, Ryle and Antony Hewish were awarded the 1974 Nobel Prize for Physics. During the 1960s the Swedish physicist Jan Hogbom developed a technique called "clean," which can be used to remove spurious responses from a celestial radio image caused by the use of discrete, rather than continuous, spacings in deriving the radio image. Further developments, based on a technique introduced in the early 1950s by the British scientists Roger Jennison and Francis Graham Smith, led to the concept of self-calibration, which is used to remove errors in a radio image due to uncertainties in the response of individual antennas as well as small errors introduced by the propagation of radio signals through the terrestrial atmosphere.

The combination of up to millions of data points to form a single image, together with the lengthy calculations required to clean and self-calibrate, is a formidable computational task. For more complex images, such calculations are made practical only by using large, high-speed computers.

Very long baseline interferometry. In conventional interferometers and arrays, coaxial-cable, waveguide, or even fibre-optic links are used to distribute a common local oscillator reference signal to each antenna and also to return the received signal from an individual antenna to a central laboratory where it is correlated with the signals from other antennas. For antenna spacings greater than a few tens of kilometres, however, it becomes prohibitively expensive to employ real physical links to distribute the signals. Very high frequency (VHF) or ultrahigh frequency (UHF) radio links can be used, but the need for a large number of repeater stations makes this impractical for spacings greater than a few hundred kilometres.

Interferometer systems of essentially unlimited element separation can be formed by using the technique of very long baseline interferometry, or VLBI (see Figure 16). In a VLBI system the signals received at each element are recorded by broad-bandwidth videotape recorders located at the element. The recorded tapes are then transported to a common location where they are replayed and the signals combined to form interference fringes. The successful operation of a VLBI system requires that the tape recordings be synchronized within a few millionths of a second and that the local oscillator reference signal be stable to better than one part in a trillion. For the most precise work, hydrogen maser frequency standards are used to give a timing accuracy of only a few billionths of a second and a frequency stability of one part in a quadrillion.

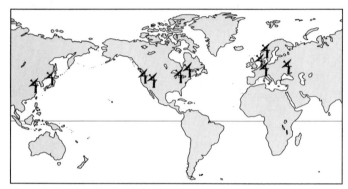

Figure 16: A portion of a gigantic interferometer system formed by linking together individual radio telescopes located many hundreds or even thousands of kilometres apart.

For many VLBI applications, modified consumer-type videocassette recorders (VCRs) provide adequate performance, and the low cost and widespread availability of these devices have allowed as many as 18 radio telescopes throughout the world to be used simultaneously to obtain high-resolution images. The most sensitive observations, however, require the use of special recorders that are able to record up to several hundred megabits of data per second. A single magnetic tape capable of recording for several hours can contain one trillion bits of information, which is roughly equivalent to storing the entire contents of a modest-sized library.

Radar techniques. Techniques analogous to those used in military and civilian radar applications are employed with radio telescopes to study the relatively nearby objects in the solar system. By measuring the spectrum and the time of flight of signals reflected from planetary surfaces, it is possible to examine topographical features, deduce rates of rotation, and determine with great accuracy the distance to the planets. Nonetheless, radio signals reflected from the planets are weak, and high-power radar transmitters are needed in order to obtain measurable signal detections. The time it takes for a radar signal to travel to Venus and back, even at the closest approach of the planet to the Earth, is about five minutes. For Saturn, it is more than two hours.

Planetary radar astronomy

Major applications of radio telescopes. Radio telescopes permit astronomers to study many kinds of extraterrestrial radio sources. These astronomical objects emit radio waves by one of several processes, including (1) thermal radiation from solid bodies such as the planets, (2) thermal, or bremsstrahlung, radiation from hot gas in the interstellar medium, (3) synchrotron radiation from relativistic electrons in weak magnetic fields, (4) line radiation from atomic or molecular transitions that occur in the interstellar medium or in the gaseous envelopes around stars,

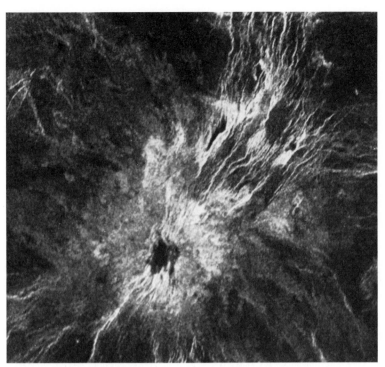

Figure 17: High-resolution radar image of a large topographic rise on Venus' surface known as Beta Regio. The summit of the volcano Theia Mons can be seen at the lower centre of the image.

By courtesy of D.B. Campbell, National Astronomy and Ionosphere Center, Cornell University, and *Science*, vol. 246, p. 375, Oct. 20, 1989, copyright 1989 by the American Association for the Advancement of Science

and (5) pulsed radiation resulting from the rapid rotation of neutron stars surrounded by an intense magnetic field and energetic electrons.

Radio telescopes enabled investigators to discover intense radio emissions from Jupiter and have been used to measure the temperature of all the planets. Astronomers have relied on radar observations to map the large-scale features on the surface of Venus, which is completely obscured from visual scrutiny by the heavy cloud cover that permanently enshrouds the planet (Figure 17). In addition, radar studies have shown that Venus is rotating in the retrograde, or reverse, direction from that of the other planets. Radar measurements also have revealed the rotation of Mercury, which was previously thought to keep the same side toward the Sun. Accurate measurements of the travel time of radar signals reflected from Venus near superior conjunction have indicated that radio waves passing close to the Sun slow down owing to gravity and have thereby provided a new independent test of Albert Einstein's general theory of relativity.

Broadband continuum emission throughout the radio-frequency spectrum is observed from a variety of stars (especially binary, X-ray, and other active stars), from supernova remnants, and from magnetic fields and relativistic electrons in the interstellar medium. The discovery of pulsars (from *pulsating radio stars*) in 1967 revealed the existence of rapidly rotating neutron stars throughout the Milky Way Galaxy and led to the first observation of the effect of gravitational radiation.

Utilizing radio telescopes equipped with sensitive spectrometers, researchers have discovered more than 50 separate molecules, including familiar chemical compounds like water vapour, formaldehyde, ammonia, methanol, ethanol, and carbon dioxide. The important spectral line of atomic hydrogen at 1421.405 MHz (21 centimetres) is used to determine the motions of hydrogen clouds in the Milky Way Galaxy and other spiral systems. This is done by measuring the change in the wavelength of the observed lines arising from Doppler shift. It has been established from such measurements that the rotational velocities of the hydrogen clouds vary with distance from the galactic centre. The mass of a spiral galaxy can, in turn, be estimated using this velocity data.

Radio telescopes have discovered powerful radio galaxies and quasars beyond the Milky Way system. These cosmic objects have intense clouds of radio emission that extend hundreds of thousands of light-years away from a central energy source located in an active galactic nucleus (Figure 18), or quasar. VLBI observations made with worldwide networks of radio telescopes have revealed apparent faster-than-light motion in many quasars. (For more specific information about quasars and other extragalactic radio

Discovery of molecules in interstellar space

Table 2: Some Notable Radio Telescope Systems		
size and type	designation or institution	location
305-metre fixed spherical dish	Arecibo Observatory	Arecibo, P.R.
27 25-metre dishes in 36-kilometre array	Very Large Array (VLA)	near Socorro, N.M., U.S.
100-metre steerable dish	Max Planck Institute for Radio Astronomy	Effelsberg, near Bonn, Ger.
76-metre steerable dish	Jodrell Bank Experimental Station (also called Nuffield Radio Astronomy Laboratories)	Jodrell Bank, Cheshire, Eng.
64-metre steerable dish	Australia Telescope National Facility	Parkes, N.S.W., Australia
14 25-metre dishes in 3.2-kilometre array	Westerbork Synthesis Radio Telescope	Westerbork, Neth.
30-metre fully steerable precision dish	Institut de Radio Astronomie Millimetrique (IRAM)	Veleta Peak, Spain
45-metre steerable dish	National Astronomy Observatory	Nobeyama, Japan
36-metre, radome-enclosed, fully steerable dish	Haystack Observatory	Westford, Mass., U.S.

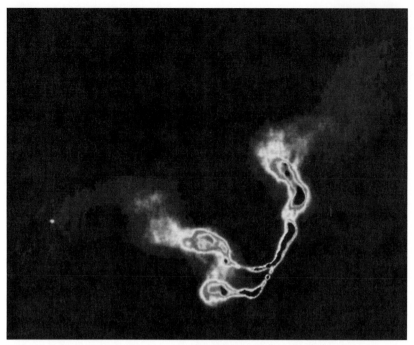

Figure 18: VLA (Very Large Array) image of an interacting twin-jet radio galaxy. The two black dots (at the bottom centre) are each associated with one of the twin nuclei of a distant galaxy. The jets appear to interact and wrap around one another.

By courtesy of the National Radio Astronomy Observatory/Associated Universities, Inc.

sources, see COSMOS, THE: *Components of the universe: Quasars and related objects.*)

Measurements made by Arno Penzias and Robert W. Wilson with an experimental communications antenna at Bell Telephone Laboratories detected the existence of cosmic background radiation at a temperature of 3 K. This radiation, which comes from all parts of the sky, is thought to be the remaining radiation from the hot big bang, the primeval explosion from which the universe presumably originated some 15 billion years ago.

Important radio telescopes. The first really large fully steerable radio telescope was completed in 1957 at Jodrell Bank, Eng. This 76-metre instrument is still used for a number of research programs (Table 2). The world's largest fully steerable radio telescope is the 100-metre-diameter antenna operated by the Max Planck Institute for Radio Astronomy at Effelsberg, near Bonn, Ger. (Figure 19). It is used in a number of different wavelength bands as short as one centimetre for atomic and molecular spectoscopy and for other galactic and extragalactic studies. Because of its large collecting area and full sky coverage, the Effelsberg radio telescope is frequently used for worldwide VLBI observations.

The Commonwealth Scientific and Industrial Research

By courtesy of the Max-Planck-Institut fur Radioastronomie; photographer, G. Hutschenreiter

Figure 19: The 100-metre radio telescope at Effelsberg, near Bonn, Ger.

Figure 20: The 305-metre rigid dish of the Arecibo Observatory in Puerto Rico, operated by Cornell University under a cooperative agreement with the National Science Foundation.

Organization (CSIRO) in Australia maintains near Parkes, N.S.W., a 64-metre radio telescope that is the largest of its kind in the Southern Hemisphere. The world's largest radome-enclosed radio telescope is the 36-metre Haystack antenna operated by the Northeast Radio Observatory Corporation under agreement with the Massachusetts Institute of Technology (MIT).

A 91-metre fixed-azimuth radio telescope with limited elevation motion was operated by the National Radio Astronomy Observatory in Green Bank, W.Va., U.S., until its unexpected collapse in late 1988. A 43-metre equatorially mounted radio instrument, however, remains in operation in Green Bank; this telescope is used primarily for molecular spectroscopy at wavelengths as short as one centimetre. Green Bank is located in the national Radio

Quiet Zone, which offers unique protection for radio telescopes from sources of man-made interference.

The largest single radio telescope in the world is the 305-metre fixed spherical reflector operated by Cornell University near Arecibo, P.R. (Figure 20). The 305-metre antenna has an enormous collecting area, but the beam can be moved through only a limited angle of about 20° from the zenith. It is used for planetary radar astronomy as well as for studying pulsars and other galactic and extragalactic phenomena. The Soviet RATAN-600 telescope (RATAN stands for Radio Telescope of the Academy of Sciences), located near Zelenchukskaya in the Caucasus Mountains, has 895 reflecting panels, each 7.4 metres high, arranged in a ring 576 metres in diameter. Using long parabolic cylinders or dipole elements, researchers in Australia, France, India, Italy, and the Ukrainian S.S.R. have also built antennas with very large collecting areas.

Several smaller, more precise radio telescopes for observing at millimetre wavelength have been installed high atop mountains, where clear skies and high altitudes minimize absorption from the terrestrial atmosphere. A 45-metre radio dish near Nobeyama Plateau, Japan, is used for observations at wavelengths as short as a few millimetres. The French-German Institut de Radio Astronomie Millimetrique (IRAM) in Grenoble, Fr., operates a 30-metre antenna at an altitude of 2,850 metres on Veleta Peak in the Spanish Sierra Nevada for observations at wavelengths as short as one millimetre. Radio telescopes having a diameter of 10 to 15 metres that operate at submillimetre wavelengths are positioned near the summit of Mauna Kea, Hawaii, U.S., at an elevation of about 4,250 metres and on La Silla Hill in Chile at an elevation of 2,350 metres. Millimetre interferometers and arrays are operated at the Owens Valley Radio Observatory of the California Institute of Technology, the Hat Creek Observatory Laboratories of the University of California at Berkeley, the IRAM Plateau de Bure facility in France, and the Nobeyama Observatory.

The world's most powerful radio telescope is the Very Large Array (VLA) located on the Plains of San Agustin near Socorro, N.M., U.S. The VLA consists of 27 parabolic antennas, each measuring 25 metres in diameter. The total collecting area is equivalent to a single 130-metre antenna. Each element of the VLA can be moved by a transporter along a Y-shaped railroad track; it is possible to change the length of the arms between 600 metres and 21 kilometres to vary the resolution of the system (Figure 21). Each antenna is equipped with receivers that operate in six different bands from wavelengths of approximately one centimetre to one metre. When used at the shorter wavelength in the largest antenna configuration, the angular resolution of the VLA is several tenths of one arc second. The VLA is operated by the U.S. National Radio Astronomy Observatory as a national facility and is used by more than 500 astronomers each year for a wide vari-

Very Large Array

Figure 21: The Very Large Array near Socorro, N.M.

ety of research programs devoted to the study of the solar system, Milky Way Galaxy, and extragalactic systems.

There are a number of other large radio telescope arrays around the world. The Netherlands Foundation for Radio Astronomy operates the Westerbork Synthesis Radio Telescope in continental Europe (see Table 2). The Commonwealth Scientific and Industrial Research Organization maintains the six-element Australia Telescope at Culgoora, N.S.W., for studies of the southern skies. A number of smaller arrays are operated by the Mullard Radio Astronomy Observatory near Cambridge, Eng., including the pioneering One-Mile Radio Telescope and a simple yet very powerful array of Yagi antennas operating at 151 MHz.

The Multi-Element Radio-Linked Interferometer Network (MERLIN), operated by the Nuffield Radio Astronomy Laboratories at Jodrell Bank, employs microwave radio links to connect seven antennas separated by up to 200 kilometres in the southern part of England. It is used primarily to study compact radio sources associated with quasars and active galactic nuclei.

The Very Long Baseline Array (VLBA), which will consist of ten 25-metre dishes spread across the United States from the Virgin Islands to Hawaii upon completion in the early 1990s, is expected to yield radio images of quasars and other compact radio sources of unprecedented angular resolution and quality. Other radio telescopes being constructed in such countries as Italy and Australia will be dedicated to VLBI research programs. When used together with the VLBA and other radio telescopes throughout the world, the effective resolution of the system will be comparable to that of a single antenna whose diameter is roughly equivalent to the Earth's. Future space-based radio antennas are expected to increase the resolution still further to produce images of cosmic radio sources in even finer detail. (Kenneth I. Kellermann)

OTHER TYPES OF TELESCOPES

Infrared telescopes. Telescopic systems of this type do not really differ significantly from reflecting telescopes designed to observe in the visible region of the electromagnetic spectrum. The main difference is in the physical location of the infrared telescope, since infrared photons have lower energies than those of visible light. The infrared rays are readily absorbed by the water vapour in the Earth's atmosphere, and most of this water vapour is located at the lower atmospheric regions—*i.e.,* near sea level. Earth-bound infrared telescopes have been successfully located on high mountaintops, as, for example, Mauna Kea in Hawaii. The other obvious placement of infrared instruments is in a satellite such as the Infrared Astronomical Satellite (IRAS), which mapped the celestial sky in the infrared in 1983. The Kuiper Airborne Observatory, operated by NASA, consists of a 0.9-metre telescope that is flown in a special airplane above the water vapour to collect infrared data. The majority of the data collection in the infrared is achieved with some type of electronic camera, since ordinary film is unable to register the low-energy photons.

Another example of an infrared telescope is the United Kingdom Infrared Telescope (UKIRT), which has a 3.8-metre mirror made of Cer-Vit (trademark), a glass ceramic that has a very low coefficient of expansion (see above; Figure 22). This instrument is configured in a Cassegrain design and employs a thin monolithic primary mirror with a lightweight support structure. This telescope is located at Mauna Kea Observatory. The 3-metre Infrared Telescope Facility (IRTF), also located at Mauna Kea, is sponsored by NASA and operated by the University of Hawaii.

Ultraviolet telescopes. These telescopes are used to examine the shorter wavelengths of the electromagnetic spectrum immediately adjacent to the visible portion. Like the infrared telescopes, the ultraviolet systems also employ reflectors as their primary collectors. Ultraviolet radiation is composed of higher-energy photons than infrared radiation, which means that photographic techniques as well as electronic detectors can be used to collect astronomical data. The Earth's stratospheric ozone layer, however, blocks all wavelengths shorter than 3000 angstroms from

Use of electronic cameras

Figure 22: The United Kingdom Infrared Telescope located on Mauna Kea, Hawaii.

reaching ground-based telescopes. As this ozone layer lies at an altitude of 20 to 40 kilometres, astronomers have to resort to rockets and satellites to make observations from above it. Since 1978 an orbiting observatory known as the International Ultraviolet Explorer (IUE) has studied celestial sources of ultraviolet radiation. The IUE telescope is equipped with a 45-centimetre mirror and records data electronically down to 1000 angstroms. The IUE is in a synchronous orbit (*i.e.,* its period of revolution around the Earth is identical to the period of the planet's rotation) in view of NASA's Goddard Space Flight Center in Greenbelt, Md., and so data can be transmitted to the ground station at the end of each observing tour and examined immediately on a television monitor.

International Ultraviolet Explorer

Another Earth-orbiting spacecraft, the Extreme Ultraviolet (EUV) Explorer satellite, which is scheduled to be launched in the early 1990s, is designed to survey the sky in the extreme ultraviolet region between 400 and 900 angstroms. It has four telescopes with gold-plated mirrors, the design of which is critically dependent on the transmission properties of the filters used to define the EUV band passes. The combination of the mirrors and filters has been selected to maximize the telescope's sensitivity to detect faint EUV sources. Three of the telescopes have scanners that are pointed in the satellite's spin plane. The fourth telescope, the Deep Survey/Spectrometer Telescope, is directed in an anti-Sun direction. Its function is to conduct a photometric deep-sky survey in the ecliptic plane for part of the mission and then to collect spectroscopic observations in the final phase of the mission.

X-ray telescopes. The X-ray telescope is used to examine the shorter-wavelength region of the electromagnetic spectrum adjacent to the ultraviolet region. The design of this type of telescope must be radically different from that of a conventional reflector. Since X-ray photons have so much energy, they would pass right through the mirror of a standard reflector. X rays must be bounced off a mirror at a very low angle if they are to be captured. (This technique is referred to as grazing incidence.) For this reason, the mirrors in X-ray telescopes are mounted with their surfaces only slightly off a parallel line with the incoming X rays, as seen in Figure 23. Application of the grazing-incidence principle makes it possible to focus X rays from a cosmic object into an image that can be recorded electronically (see Figure 24).

NASA launched a series of three High-Energy Astronomy Observatories (HEAOs) during the late 1970s to explore cosmic X-ray sources. HEAO-1 mapped the X-ray sources with high sensitivity and high resolution. Some of the more interesting of these objects were studied in detail by

Space-based X-ray telescopes

HEAO-2 (named the Einstein Observatory). HEAO-3, on the other hand, was used primarily to investigate cosmic rays and gamma rays.

The European X-ray Observatory Satellite (EXOSAT), developed by the European Space Agency (ESA), was capable of greater spectral resolution than the Einstein Observatory and was more sensitive to X-ray emissions at shorter wavelengths. EXOSAT remained in orbit from 1983 to 1986. A much larger X-ray astronomy satellite was

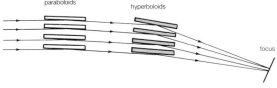

Figure 23: The grazing-incidence principle of the X-ray telescope.

launched in June 1990 as part of a cooperative program involving the United States, West Germany, and the United Kingdom. This satellite, called the Röntgenstrahlen Satellit (ROSAT), has two parallel grazing-incidence telescopes. One of them, the X-ray telescope (XRT), bears many similarities to the equipment of the Einstein Observatory but has a larger geometric area and better mirror resolution. One of the focal plane instruments, the high-resolution imager (HRI)—supplied by the Smithsonian Astrophysical Observatory—is expected to show considerable improvement over similar Einstein Observatory instrumentation. The other telescope, the extended ultraviolet wide-field camera, has an imaging detector much like the X-ray HRI. A positive sensitive proportional counter will make it possible to survey the sky at X-ray wavelengths for the purpose of producing a catalog of 100,000 sources with a positional accuracy of better than 30 arc seconds. A wide-field camera with a 5°-diameter field of view is also part of the ROSAT instrument package. It is designed to produce an extended ultraviolet survey with arc minute source positions in this wavelength region, making it the first instrument with such capability. The ROSAT mirrors are gold-coated and will permit detailed examination of the sky from 6 to 100 angstroms.

By courtesy of Dr. Frederick Seward, Harvard–Smithsonian Center for Astrophysics

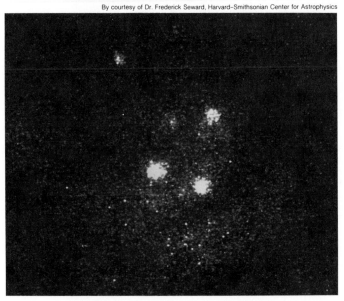

Figure 24: X-ray image of the Eta Carinae nebula.

Gamma-ray telescopes. These instruments require the use of grazing-incidence techniques similar to those employed with X-ray telescopes. Gamma rays are the shortest (about 0.1 angstrom or less) known waves in the electromagnetic spectrum. As mentioned above, HEAO-3 was developed to collect data from cosmic gamma-ray sources. NASA and collaborative international agencies have numerous ongoing and planned projects in the area of gamma-ray astronomy. The scientific objectives of the

programs include determining the nature and physical parameters of high-energy (up to 10 gigaelectron volts) astrophysical systems. Examples of such systems include stellar coronas, white dwarfs, neutron stars, black holes, supernova remnants, clusters of galaxies, and diffuse gamma-ray background. In addition to satellite investigations of these cosmic high-energy sources, NASA has an extensive program that involves the design and development of gamma-ray telescope systems for deployment in high-altitude balloons. All mirrors in gamma-ray telescopes have gold coatings similar to those in X-ray telescope mirrors.

THE DEVELOPMENT OF THE TELESCOPE AND AUXILIARY INSTRUMENTATION

Evolution of the optical telescope. Galileo is credited with having developed telescopes for astronomical observation in 1609. While the largest of his instruments was only about 120 centimetres long and had an objective diameter of 5 centimetres, it was equipped with an eyepiece that provided an upright (*i.e.,* erect) image. Galileo used his modest instrument to explore such celestial phenomena as the valleys and mountains of the Moon, the phases of Venus, the Milky Way, and the four largest satellites of Jupiter, which had never been systematically observed before.

The reflecting telescope was developed in 1668 by Newton, though John Gregory had independently conceived of an alternative reflector design in 1663. Cassegrain introduced another variation of the reflector in 1672. Near the end of the century, others attempted to construct refractors as long as 61 metres, but these instruments were too awkward to be effective.

The most significant contribution to the development of the telescope in the 18th century was that of Sir William Herschel. Herschel, whose interest in telescopes was kindled by a modest 5-centimetre Gregorian, persuaded the king of England to finance the construction of a reflector with a 12-metre focal length and a 120-centimetre mirror. Herschel is credited with having used this instrument to lay the observational groundwork for the concept of extragalactic "nebulas"—*i.e.,* galaxies outside the Milky Way system.

Reflectors continued to evolve during the 19th century with the work of William Parsons, 3rd Earl of Rosse, and William Lassell. In 1845 Lord Rosse constructed in Ireland a reflector with a 185-centimetre mirror and a focal length of about 16 metres. For 75 years this telescope ranked as the largest in the world and was used to explore thousands of nebulas and star clusters. Lassell built several reflectors, the largest of which was on Malta; this instrument had a 124-centimetre primary mirror and a focal length of more than 10 metres. His telescope had greater reflecting power than that of Rosse, and it enabled him to catalog 600 new nebulas as well as to discover several satellites of the outer planets—Triton (Neptune's largest moon), Hyperion (Saturn's 8th moon), and Ariel and Umbriel (two of Uranus' moons).

Refractor telescopes, too, underwent development during the 18th and 19th centuries. The last significant one to be built was the 1-metre refractor at Yerkes Observatory. Installed in 1897, it remains the largest refracting system in the world. Its objective was designed and constructed by the optician Alvan Clark, while the mount was built by the firm of Warner & Swasey.

The reflecting telescope has predominated in the 20th century. The rapid proliferation of larger and larger instruments of this type began with the installation of the 2.5-metre reflector at the Mount Wilson Observatory near Pasadena, Calif., U.S. The technology for mirrors underwent a major advance when the Corning Glass Works (in Steuben county, N.Y., U.S.) developed Pyrex. This borosilicate glass, which undergoes substantially less expansion than ordinary glass, was used in the 5-metre Hale reflector built in 1950 at the Palomar Observatory. Pyrex also was utilized in the main mirror of the world's largest telescope, the 6-metre reflector of the Special Astrophysical Observatory in Zelenchukskaya. In recent years, much better materials for mirrors have become available. Cervit, for example, was used for the 4.2-metre William

The reflectors of Rosse and Lassell

Development of new materials for mirrors

Herschel Telescope of the Roque de los Muchachos Observatory in the Canary Islands, and Zerodur (trademark) for the 3.5-metre reflector at the German-Spanish Astronomical Center in Calar Alto, Spain. (B.L. Klock)

Development of the radio telescope. Extraterrestrial radio emission was first reported in 1933 by Karl Jansky, an engineer at the Bell Telephone Laboratories, while he was searching for the cause of shortwave interference. Jansky had mounted a directional radio antenna on a turntable so that he could point it at different parts of the sky to determine the direction of the interfering signals. He not only detected interference from distant thunderstorms but also located a source of radio "noise" from the centre of the Milky Way Galaxy. This first detection of cosmic radio waves received much attention from the public but only passing notice from the astronomical community.

Grote Reber, a radio engineer and amateur radio operator, built a 9.5-metre parabolic reflector in his backyard in Wheaton, Ill., U.S., to continue Jansky's investigation of cosmic radio noise. In 1944 he published the first radio map of the sky. After World War II ended, the technology that had been developed for military radar was applied to astronomical research. Radio telescopes of increasing size and sophistication were built first in Australia and Great Britain and later in the United States and other countries (see above *Radio telescopes: Important radio telescopes*). (Kenneth I. Kellermann)

Advances in auxiliary instrumentation. Almost as important as the telescope itself are the auxiliary instruments that the astronomer uses to exploit the light received at the focal plane. Examples of such instruments are the camera, spectrograph, photomultiplier tube, charge-coupled device (CCD), and charge injection device (CID). Each of these instrument types is discussed below.

Cameras. John Draper of the United States photographed the Moon as early as 1840 by applying the daguerreotype process. The French physicists A.-H.-L. Fizeau and J.-B.-L. Foucault succeeded in making a photographic image of the Sun in 1845. Five years later, astronomers at Harvard Observatory took the first photographs of the stars.

The use of photographic equipment in conjunction with telescopes has benefited astronomers greatly, giving them two distinct advantages: first, photographic images provide a permanent record of celestial phenomena and, second, photographic plates integrate the light from celestial sources over long periods of time and thereby permit astronomers to see much fainter objects than they would be able to observe visually. Typically, the camera's photographic plate (or film) is mounted in the focal plane of the telescope. The plate (or film) consists of glass or of a plastic material that is covered with a thin layer of a silver compound. The light striking the photographic medium causes the silver compound to undergo a chemical change. When processed, a negative image results—*i.e.,* the brightest spots (the Moon and the stars, for example) appear as the darkest areas on the plate or the film.

Spectrographs. Newton noted the interesting way in which a piece of glass can break up light into different bands of colour, but it was not until 1814 that the German physicist Joseph von Fraunhofer discovered the lines of the solar spectrum and laid the basis for spectroscopy. The spectrograph, as illustrated in Figure 25, consists of a slit, a collimator, a prism for dispersing the light, and a focusing lens. The collimator is an optical device that produces parallel rays from a focal plane source—*i.e.,* gives the appearance that the source is located at an infinite distance. The spectrograph enables astronomers to analyze

the chemical composition of planetary atmospheres, stars, nebulas, and other celestial objects. A bright line in the spectrum indicates the presence of a glowing gas radiating at a wavelength characteristic of the chemical element in the gas. A dark line in the spectrum usually means that a cooler gas has intervened and absorbed the lines of the element characteristic of the intervening material. The lines also may be displaced to either the red end or the blue end of the spectrum. This effect was first noted in 1842 by the Austrian physicist Christian Johann Doppler. When a light source is approaching, the lines are shifted toward the blue end of the spectrum, and when the source is receding, the lines are shifted toward its red end. This effect, known as the Doppler effect, permits astronomers to study the relative motions of celestial objects with respect to the Earth's motion.

The slit of the spectrograph is placed at the focal plane of the telescope. The resulting spectrum may be recorded photographically or with some kind of electronic detector, such as a photomultiplier tube, CCD, or CID. If no recording device is used, then the optical device is technically referred to as a spectroscope.

Photomultiplier tubes. The photomultiplier tube is an enhanced version of the photocell, which was first used by astronomers to record data electronically. The photocell contains a photosensitive surface that generates an electric current when struck by light from a celestial source. The photosensitive surface is positioned just behind the focus. A diaphragm of very small aperture is usually placed in the focal plane to eliminate as much of the background light of the sky as possible. A small lens is used to focus the focal plane image on the photosensitive surface, which, in the case of a photomultiplier tube, is referred to as the photocathode. In the photomultiplier tube a series of special sensitive plates are arranged geometrically to amplify or multiply the electron stream. Frequently, magnifications of a million are achieved by this process.

The photomultiplier tube has a distinct advantage over the photographic plate. With the photographic plate the relationship between the brightness of the celestial source and its registration on the plate is not linear. In the case of the photomultiplier tube, however, the release of electrons in the tube is directly proportional to the intensity of light from the celestial source. This linear relationship is very useful for working over a wide range of brightness. A disadvantage of the photomultiplier tube is that only one object can be recorded at a time. The output from such a device is sent to a recorder or digital storage device to produce a permanent record.

Charge-coupled devices. The charge-coupled device uses a light-sensitive material on a silicon chip to electronically detect photons in a way similar to the photomultiplier tube. The principal difference is that the chip also contains integrated microcircuitry required to transfer the detected signal along a row of discrete picture elements (or pixels) and thereby scan a celestial object or objects very rapidly. When individual pixels are arranged simply in a single row, the detector is referred to as a linear array. When the pixels are arranged in rows and columns, the assemblage is called a two-dimensional array.

Pixels can be assembled in various sizes and shapes. The Hubble Space Telescope has a CCD detector with a $1,600 \times 1,600$ pixel array. Actually, there are four 800×800 pixel arrays mosaicked together. The sensitivity of a CCD is 100 times greater than a photographic plate and so has the ability to quickly scan objects such as planets, nebulas, and star clusters and record the desired data. Another feature of the CCD is that the detector material may be altered to provide more sensitivity at different wavelengths. Thus, some detectors are more sensitive in the blue region of the spectrum than in the red region.

Today, most large observatories use CCDs to record data electronically. Another similar device, the charge injection device, is sometimes employed. The basic difference between the CID and the CCD is in the way the electric charge is transferred before it is recorded; however, the two devices may be used interchangeably as far as astronomical work is concerned.

Marginal notes:
Studying spectral lines

Pixel arrays

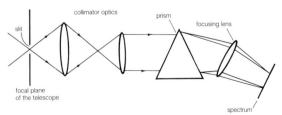

Figure 25: A spectrograph and its components.

collimator optics
prism
focusing lens
slit
focal plane of the telescope
spectrum

Figure 26: Mars's Utopian Plain as photographed by the Viking 2 lander.
By courtesy of the National Aeronautics and Space Administration

Impact of technological developments. *Computers.* Besides the telescope itself, the electronic computer has become the astronomer's most important tool. Indeed, the computer has revolutionized the use of the telescope to the point where the collection of observational data is now completely automated. The astronomer need only identify the object to be observed, and the rest is carried out by the computer and auxiliary electronic equipment.

A telescope can be set to observe automatically by means of electronic sensors appropriately placed on the telescope axis. Precise quartz or atomic clocks send signals to the computer, which in turn activates the telescope sensors to collect data at the proper time. The computer not only makes possible more efficient use of telescope time but also permits a more detailed analysis of the data collected than could have been done manually. Data analysis that would have taken a lifetime or longer to complete with a mechanical calculator can now be done within hours or even minutes with a high-speed computer.

Improved means of recording and storing computer data also have contributed to astronomical research. Optical disc data storage technology, such as the compact disc-read only memory (CD-ROM) or the write once-read many times memory (WORM), has provided astronomers with the ability to store and retrieve vast amounts of telescopic and other astronomical data. A 12-centimetre CD-ROM disc, for example, may hold up to 600 megabytes of data—the equivalent of 20 nine-track magnetic tapes or 1,500 floppy discs. A 13-centimetre WORM disc typically holds about 300 to 400 megabytes of data.

Rockets and spacecraft. As noted earlier, the quest for new knowledge about the universe has led astronomers to study electromagnetic radiation other than just visible light. Such forms of radiation, however, are blocked for the most part by the Earth's atmosphere, and so their detection and analysis can only be achieved from above this gaseous envelope.

During the late 1940s, single-stage sounding rockets were sent up to 160 kilometres or more to explore the upper layers of the atmosphere. From 1957, more sophisticated

multistage rockets were launched as part of the International Geophysical Year; these rockets carried artificial satellites equipped with a variety of scientific instruments. Beginning in 1959, the Soviet Union and the United States, engaged in a "space race," intensified their efforts and launched a series of unmanned probes to explore the Moon. Lunar exploration culminated with the first manned landing on the Moon by the U.S. Apollo 11 astronauts on July 20, 1969. Numerous other U.S. and Soviet spacecraft were sent to further study the lunar environment until the mid-1970s.

Since the early 1960s both the United States and the Soviet Union have also launched a multitude of unmanned deep-space probes to learn more about the other planets and satellites of the solar system. Carrying television cameras, detectors, and an assortment of other instruments, these probes have sent back impressive amounts of scientific data and close-up pictures. Among the most successful missions have been those involving the Soviet Venera probes to Venus and the U.S. Viking 1 and 2 landings on Mars (see Figure 26) and Voyager 2 flybys of Jupiter, Saturn, Uranus, and Neptune. When the Voyager 2 probe flew past Neptune and its moons in August 1989, every known planet except Pluto had been explored by spacecraft. Many long-held views, particularly those about the outer planets, were altered by the findings of the Voyager probe. These findings included the discovery of several rings and six additional satellites around Neptune, all of which are undetectable to ground-based telescopes.

Specially instrumented spacecraft have enabled astronomers to investigate other celestial phenomena as well. The Orbiting Solar Observatories (OSOs) and Solar Maximum Mission, Earth-orbiting U.S. satellites equipped with ultraviolet detector systems, have provided a means for studying solar activity. Another example is the Giotto probe of the European Space Agency, which enabled astronomers to obtain detailed photographs of the nucleus of Comet Halley during the 1986 passage of the comet.

(B.L. Klock)

Optical
disc data
storage

Planetary
exploration
with
unmanned
probes

Science

Year in

Review

Contents

The Year in Science: An Overview

by Robert P. Crease

The case of Zachary Taylor haunts my recollections of events of the past year in science. Taylor, 12th president of the United States, died in office on July 9, 1850, apparently the victim of gastroenteritis, or inflammation of the stomach and intestines. A century and a half later, however, a historical novelist and former professor who had studied the circumstances surrounding Taylor's death became convinced that Taylor may have been assassinated by pro-slavery advocates outraged at his plan to admit California and New Mexico to the Union as free states. This scenario was plausible enough to persuade Taylor's descendants and the local county coroner to look into the possibility of poisoning. On June 17, 1991, Taylor's remains were exhumed from a crypt at the Zachary Taylor National Cemetery in Louisville, Ky., and examined for traces of arsenic, the poison of choice for assassins of the era. The Kentucky medical examiner then ruled that Taylor had died of natural causes. The story made headlines, partly because the subject was a former president, partly because the theme was a suspected assassination, and partly because the episode suggested that when a person takes a secret "to the grave," it may be to a less secure sanctum than previously had been supposed.

What intrigued me, however, was the examination itself, which was all but ignored by the press. A key part took place at the Oak Ridge (Tenn.) National Laboratory. A sample of hair that had been removed from the corpse was cleaned, inserted into a "rabbit" (a small polyethylene container), and shot by pneumatic tube into Oak Ridge's high-flux isotope reactor, where it was bombarded with neutrons. Naturally occurring arsenic has one stable isotope, ^{75}As; by the process called neutron activation, a fraction of the ^{75}As atoms in the hair sample absorbed a single neutron each to become ^{76}As. This isotope is radioactive and decays by emitting beta radiation and, almost simultaneously, a 559-kilovolt gamma ray. After a few minutes' exposure, the "rabbit" containing Taylor's hair was pulled from the reactor and the sample was studied by a gamma-ray spectrometer, which detects gamma rays and measures their energy. Researchers could then estimate the amount of arsenic in the original sample: about 0.8 parts per million, or about that in a normal hair specimen. Had Taylor been

ROBERT P. CREASE *is an Assistant Professor of Philosophy at the State University of New York, Stony Brook, and Historian at the Brookhaven National Laboratory, Upton, N.Y.*

poisoned by arsenic, the amount would have been hundreds or thousands of times greater.

I found the episode fascinating on two counts. One was the way in which it illustrated the ability of science to transform our knowledge of the world by allowing us to revisit questions or issues we thought closed or beyond our ability to solve. Historians, no doubt, had abandoned hope for conclusive evidence regarding Taylor's death long ago. The other cause for fascination was the way the story illustrated how invisible science can be even while it is playing crucial roles in events. The high-flux isotope reactor was the unsung hero of the case of Zachary Taylor. Yet in all the newspaper stories I read about the episode, none showed a picture of the reactor or of the Oak Ridge laboratory, nor did they mention the gamma-ray spectrometer or the telltale 559-kilovolt signal (of which I learned only by speaking to scientists at the laboratory). These two characteristics illustrated by the case—the ability of science to again pose apparently defunct questions and science's near invisibility—I noted again and again in other stories of the year.

Headline stories. The year, of course, did have its share of stories in which science was prominent and not at all invisible. Consider all those photo shoots of various locations in the solar system—pictures of Mercury produced by Earth-based radio antennas suggesting the presence of ice in the polar regions of that planet or the space probe Magellan's radar images of Venus revealing dramatic volcanoes, rivers of lava, and a channel 6,800 km (4,200 mi) in length, longer than the Nile River and the longest known channel in the solar system (*see* Feature Article: DE-MYSTIFYING THE MISTY PLANET). Another space probe, Galileo, sent back an unusual "bottom-up" image of the Earth taken en route to its 1995 flyby of Jupiter. That spacecraft also turned in the first-ever photograph of the asteroid Gaspra, an object 20 km (12 mi) long and 13 km (8 mi) wide—a black-and-white picture, half in shadow, that looked like, depending upon the sources of one's imagination, an upside-down shark's head, a partly deflated football, or a pockmarked and lumpy fossilized Idaho potato.

And who could forget July's solar "eclipse of the century" that swept across the Pacific Ocean and the Americas, the longest total eclipse until the 22nd century? Astronomers in mountain observatories and amateurs watched the Moon slowly move in front of the Sun, first reducing it to a crescent-shaped sliver

Right, researchers Larry Robinson (left) and Frank Dyer at Oak Ridge (Tennessee) National Laboratory examine a sample of hair removed from the body of U.S. Pres. Zachary Taylor (above). After the hair was analyzed in the laboratory's high-flux isotope reactor, the researchers concluded that Taylor had not been poisoned by arsenic.

and then eradicating even that. The sliver's horns grew closer and closer together, and—just at the moment when the Sun seemed about to vanish entirely—the picture was abruptly transformed: a hoop of fire appeared with reddish jets streaking dramatically outward. Frame by frame, pictures of the event were splashed across the front pages of newspapers around the country.

Other fields, too, had prominent though less photogenic stories. *Science* magazine awarded "buckyballs," 60-piece molecules of carbon shaped like miniature soccer balls, its Molecule of the Year Award for their promise to revolutionize superconductors, optical transmission, lubrication, crystallography, and other fields. Physicists developed the first atom switch, or device turned on and off by the action of a single atom. Mathematicians computed pi to a record 2,160,000,000 decimal places. A computer discovered a winning line of attack, 223 moves long, in a chess endgame experts had long thought could only be drawn.

Answering defunct questions. I found the case of Zachary Taylor more engrossing, however, and each of its two features that I had found fascinating occurred in other stories of the year. For example, by identifying individuals believed to have vanished without a trace, scientific techniques allowed the resolution of questions long thought impossible to answer. As a case in point, U.S. forensic anthropologist Clyde Collins Snow spent time in several countries identifying the remains of torture victims

by using computer-assisted technology. A team of historians and scientists thought they had finally located the remains of Robert LeRoy Parker and Harry Longabaugh, alias Butch Cassidy and the Sundance Kid, in a cemetery in the mining village of San Vicente, Bolivia.

Some truly prehistoric discoveries, though, made the Zachary Taylor case seem like it happened at breakfast. One was the discovery of a mummified human body more than 4,600 years old in a glacier in the Tirolean Alps in Austria. Scientific techniques were expected to be able to determine whether the man died of exposure, exhaustion, or illness and to disclose information about his diet and life-style; analyses of his DNA would reveal his genetic makeup; and the artifacts found along with the body—an ax, a stone knife, a bow, a quiver, 14 arrows, a flint lighter, and a leather pouch—would give archaeologists an unprecedented and unexpected perspective on human life in the late Stone Age. Here again was the case of Zachary Taylor redux—only with the time elapsed since death not a century and a half but several millennia, and the answers anthropologists received to questions they once thought unanswerable bore not upon an individual's manner of death but upon entire aspects of early human life and culture.

Even that happened only yesterday compared with what science has revealed about dinosaurs. Pieces of teeth and bone and DNA from intact protein molecules disclosed to researchers a trove of infor-

275

mation about the food chain of the era, the injuries and diseases that dinosaurs sustained, their biology, and the climate and character of the world in which they lived. In this case, the time elapsed since the death of the subject was not hundreds or thousands but millions of years, and the questions thought unanswerable concerned the character of life in an entire geologic era (*see* Feature Article: THE DINOSAUR RENAISSANCE). And if one is allowed to place the discovery by astronomers of a gas cloud at the edge of the universe in this category of forensic science—given that the "evidence" (the telltale light it produced) has been en route for most of the time since the Big Bang—then the era we are peering into is billions of years ago, and the previously unanswerable questions concern basic processes in the formation of the universe.

Black boxes. The past year also had its share of events illustrating the invisibility of science. An example is the riddle of the Sphinx's age. A controversy erupted over how long the "Father of Terror," the inscrutable creature with human head and lion's body, had stared over the Giza plateau in Egypt, with traditionalists asserting 4,500 years and mavericks arguing several thousand years more.

The controversy, which made headlines because of the celebrity of the subject, hinges on the interpretation of less newsworthy seismological techniques. Traditional methods involve the detection of sound waves created by explosions of dynamite and were, of course, out of the question. Therefore, recently developed seismological instruments that allow the detection of very-low-energy waves were employed. One of the parties to the Sphinx controversy, for instance, placed a series of geophones around the structure and wired them all to a knapsack-sized computer. When a 2.5-cm (1-in)-thick steel plate was placed on the Sphinx and struck with a sledgehammer, the geophones were sufficiently sensitive to detect the sound waves as they refracted and reflected through the Sphinx's insides, and the information was recorded on a floppy disk. When that information was processed, it produced an image of the interior, which bore upon the question of the Sphinx's age. None of the articles I read about the controversy, however, spoke about or carried pictures of the instruments used to produce the evidence whose interpretation was at stake.

Another example of invisible science was the affair of the bootlegged scrolls. For nearly four decades a handful of individuals, mostly based at the École Biblique in Jerusalem, have held tight rein over the Dead Sea Scrolls and denied other scholars access to them. They did issue a concordance providing the occurrence and location of the 59,000 significant words in the text, which is like taking a puzzle and breaking it into 59,000 catalogued pieces. Martin Abegg, Jr., a biblical graduate student at Hebrew Union College in Cincinnati, Ohio, realized, however, that the concordance process could be reversed, and he programmed a computer to piece together a transcript of the scrolls from the information in the concordance. The computer-generated transcript was published by the Biblical Archaeology Society in Washington, D.C., in September 1991; the next month, with the cat out of the bag, the Jerusalem publication group agreed that scholars could have open access to the documents.

A total eclipse of the Sun in July 1991 (above), the longest total eclipse until the 22nd century, was viewed by many observers in Hawaii (right).

The story was widely publicized as an example of the triumph of academic freedom. But the unsung hero was Abegg's Macintosh SE personal computer with a Motorola 68030 chip, which ran the program to put the 59,000 puzzle pieces back together again.

The Sphinx's knapsack ultrasound device and the Macintosh illustrate the presence of science in the form of "black boxes," devices whose operation may be taken for granted and be all but invisible even while executing important tasks. Black boxes come in many types. Materials science is a regular producer of another kind of "black box." In April *The Atlantic* ran a feature story about concrete. One wonders what were the first thoughts of the editors of this national magazine upon glancing for first time at a proposal for an article about the subject. Yet concrete is one of the foundations of civilization. Even this article managed to overlook what I take to be the real story behind concrete, its bizarre chemistry, concentrating instead on concrete's history, maintenance, calamities, and "glamour problem."

Transforming the world. Hence the reason that the case of Zachary Taylor haunted me; it was a dramatic illustration both that the world is slowly being transformed by science and its instruments and that it is all too easy to overlook the transformation and take it for granted. For science and technology do more than simply add new items and new information to the existing stock or make things cheaper and more efficient. Even such mundane instruments as pencils, cigarette lighters, and sunglasses—not to mention more advanced technologies of energy, information, and transportation—transform the world itself: the kind of things we can do, the kinds of decisions we face, and our interactions with the environment and each other.

When cell biologists recently learned how to grow in the laboratory almost every type of cell the human eye comprises, it was hailed as a major breakthrough that would lead to cures for previously untreatable eye diseases. But when a biotechnology company in New Jersey announced during the year that it had genetically altered pigs to produce human hemoglobin, the oxygen-carrying component of blood, it was more than a medical breakthrough—it added a new dimension (unremarked in the reports I read) to the complex interaction between the animal and the human world.

Or consider the patent applications submitted by scientists associated with the U.S. National Institutes of Health for basic knowledge arising from the Human Genome Project. The action was called by some a reasonable protection of intellectual labor and by others as outrageous as attempting to patent a star. The controversy has implications for the evolution of the Human Genome Project but, more important, it seems likely to inaugurate a rethinking of fundamental issues involving patentability, freedom of information, and the legal status of knowledge about nature.

The past year even saw the birth of a novel kind of ethical dilemma when scientists reported a discovery that the gene causing the most common form of muscular dystrophy becomes larger each time it is passed on, meaning that the disease becomes more severe with each generation. Afflicted couples may now confront the choice of either not having children or passing on a disease that, though harmless to their immediate offspring, may be fatal to great-great-grandchildren.

All these examples—culled from the past year's stories alone—illustrate the kinds of new philosophical, legal, ethical, and sociological issues that technologies can produce, even while the operation of the "black boxes" that create them remain relatively invisible.

Magical thinking. The increasing presence of science in the world, however, has barely put a dent in magical thinking, the belief in the existence of animistic forces and powers in nature. Despite all the scientific attention paid to July's "eclipse of the century," individuals in some areas donned red paint, ribbons, safety pins, and red underwear as protection against "eclipse rays." Despite studies of the planets by Magellan and Galileo, astrology remained popular, with professional astrologers far outnumbering professional astronomers. During the past year human gullibility in regard to such pseudoscience was epitomized by the "crop circle" affair, in which two British pranksters claimed that they used wooden boards and a piece of string to create patterns in wheat fields that attracted international media attention and pilgrimages by occultists. Before the hoax was exposed, some pilgrims solemnly declared that they had detected intensified "energy fields" in the vicinity of the patterns and that the work was of such scale and precision that only alien spacecraft and superior intelligences could have been responsible.

Fighting superstition and pseudoscience takes patient work, does not advance one's professional reputation, and can be costly, as James Randi, a magician and one of the great debunkers of pseudoscience, discovered. During the year psychic spoon bender Uri Geller filed a $15 million defamation lawsuit against Randi for his references to Geller's "tricks." Randi already had spent more than $150,000 defending himself successfully against two previous lawsuits by Geller; this time, out of money, he had to seek assistance from a special legal fund established by scientists and other supporters throughout the world.

The impulse for magical thinking seems to be created by the feeling that science has stripped us of our dignity. Modern science has told us that we

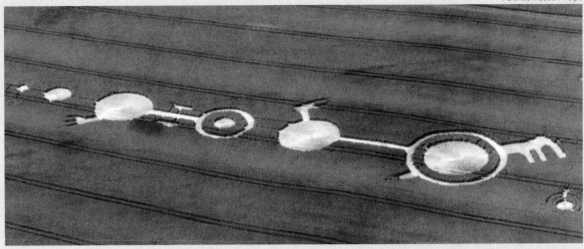

An elaborate pattern of "crop circles" in the county of Wiltshire, England, was believed by some to be the work of aliens from another world. In September 1991, however, two British landscape painters claimed that they had crafted these and other circles with a plank, a wire sight, and string.

are not the creatures who contemplate the rest of creation from the center of the universe, as we once believed, but are instead residents of an insignificant planet in the anonymous reaches of space. Magical thinking would put us back in the celestial center of things. It would have us believe that the planets play a personal role in our destiny, that thoughts can be communicated across space, that superior intelligences roam our world leaving only minor clues to their presence, and that minds can levitate objects and control matter. However, it is the ability of human beings to learn their way around in nature through science, rather than merely fantasize about it as supernaturalists do, that truly testifies to the nobility of the human spirit.

Era swap. Daniel E. Koshland, Jr., the editor of *Science* magazine, once proposed what he called the "era swap experiment." Imagine that you could be transported back to a previous era, Koshland proposed, but only on the condition that you accept all features of that era, including the available medicine (recall that until relatively recently all medical operations were done without anesthetics), education, mortality rate, the existence of plagues, life ex-

pectancy, transportation, and so forth. Which era would you choose?

If one stressed the word *swap*, one might interpret Koshland's thought experiment as an exhibition of scientific braggadocio, vaunting the progress of modern science and challenging anyone to suggest that a better time existed than the present; but the salient word is *era*. The entire texture of human experience changes over time, and science plays a role in that transformation. Some utopians find the role of science a blessing ("No revolution without science," declared French Marxists in the mid-1950s), while some find it a curse, thinking that science distances human beings from nature and from each other.

Nevertheless, science is only one of the forces responsible for the transformation of human experience. And one of the ways it effects this transformation is by allowing us to return again to questions and issues that at one time were thought to be beyond human ability to answer. Era to era, however invisibly, advances in science have made features of the world speak when they previously were mute.

Just ask Zachary Taylor.

—Robert P. Crease

Anthropology

The excitement and growth of anthropology noted during recent years continued throughout 1991 and into 1992. New opportunities for anthropologists increased in various governmental agencies, in areas related to economic development in the Third World, and as marketing or human-resource consultants in business and industry. A significant increase in the number of anthropologists serving on National Academy of Science boards and working on various legislative amendments, environmental initiatives, and public health issues on national and local levels also could be noted.

During the past year several continuing issues and topics held the attention of anthropologists, and some new ones made their appearance. The current emphasis on multiculturalism, ethnicity, and cultural sensitivity in government, in social service delivery agencies, in business, and throughout education raised significant issues for anthropologists. Ethnic and cultural diversity in education was expected to dominate both education and anthropology for some time to come. Another major concern of anthropologists in the 1990s was the widespread perception of their discipline as esoteric and irrelevant. That anthropologists had already moved to counter this idea was seen in the work of William Leap with the Task Force on AIDS; the landfill project of William Rathje; in Annalou de Havenon's Action Research on Hunger, the Homelessness and Family Health in New York City; and in Joan Weibell-Orlando's work on drugs, alcoholism, and aging.

Events in Europe stimulated interest by anthropologists in that part of the world. European nationalism was the major topic of a conference held at the Catholic University of Leuven, Belgium, and the "Challenge of Europe's Emerging Order" was the theme of the plenary session of the American Anthropological Association at its annual meeting. At this meeting Marvin Harris presented the Distinguished Lecture, entitled "Anthropology and the Theoretical and Pragmatic Implications of the Collapse of Soviet and East European Communism."

A new policy was announced by the Smithsonian Institution on the question of American Indian remains. Its general thrust was that such remains were to be handled according to the wishes of Native Americans. The commission established to deal with this question issued a report calling for sensitivity and respect between anthropologists and Native Americans regarding human remains. The Smithsonian policy seemed in keeping with the sentiments expressed in that report.

Concern with the rapid decline and disappearance of indigenous peoples continued in 1991. Anthropological interest in the plight of the Yanomamö (often called Yanomami) was regenerated when the government of Brazil did not honor promises it had made to create a special refuge for these people. Resolution of the problem came toward the end of 1991 as the government of Brazil reaffirmed the terms of the original agreement.

In response to the rapid merging of such indigenous peoples into the nations of the world, anthropologists were joining with population geneticists and medical researchers to collect, analyze, and preserve human DNA as part of a survey of genetic diversity. Molecular anthropologist Allan Wilson teamed with population geneticists Luigi Luca Cavalli-Sforza and Kenneth Kidd to propose this ambitious project.

The debate over the origins of modern humans appeared to be far from over. The long-held belief that modern humans originated in many different areas of the world had by 1992 become the minority opinion. Most anthropologists agreed that the human lineage began about 2.5 million years ago with *Homo habilis*. Many of these same researchers believed that modern *Homo sapiens* arose about 100,000 to 200,000 years ago in Africa and quickly replaced all other forms of humanlike creatures. Neanderthal was presented as little more than a side branch of the human family tree. The debate was rekindled during the past year as new research and studies were reported. Physicist Norbert Mercier of France convincingly demonstrated that Neanderthals and anatomically modern humans lived side by side for thousands of years. Evidence from sites in the Middle East also suggested that Neanderthal was contemporary with modern humans. The question of modern human origins was also fueled by Christy Turner II, who reported on a study of more than 250,000 teeth. Contrary to the idea of African origins, Turner's work supported a Southeast Asian origin for modern humans. Turner argued that at the very least Asia could no longer be ignored. Given the latest contributions, there were in 1992 three theories on the origins of modern humans: the "Multiregional Theory" of Milford Wolpoff, suggesting that modern humans made their appearance in several different areas of the world simultaneously; the "Out of Africa Theory," espoused by many anthropologists; and the "Asian Theory," supported by Turner's research.

Developments in locating and interpreting data might contribute to the ultimate resolution of the debate. One is related to the mitochondrial "Eve" work of Allan Wilson and others. (Mitochondria are organelles within a cell that lie outside the cell's nucleus.) From this research came the suggestion that the "mother of us all" lived about 200,000 years ago in Africa. A refinement of this study led to the suggestion that this common ancestor lived between 166,000 and 249,000 years ago somewhere south of the Sahara. Researchers involved with the original project argued that the study reflected the "maternal history of the human species." By 1992 researchers were searching for "Adam," the consort to Eve and "father of us all." Judging from the chromosome work of David Page of the Massachusetts Institute of Technology, Gérard Lucotte in Paris, and Michael Hammer of Harvard, the search was off to a fast start. Lucotte suggested that "Adam" was a pygmy who lived some 200,000 years ago and even pinpointed the location in what is now the Central African Republic. Most anthropologists, however, still held that the seat of humankind was somewhere along the East African Rift Valley.

The claim for a mitochondrial Eve living in Africa about 200,000 years ago was seriously challenged in 1991–92 from a variety of sectors. In responding to some methodological criticisms, the original researchers appeared late in 1991 to have firmly established Eve. However, David Maddison of Harvard University led an effort that suggested the original study was statistically flawed because of the nonrandom sampling used in that study. Allan Templeton of Washington University, St. Louis, Mo., provided an additional challenge to the Eve hypothesis when he found a better non-African tree. Blair Hedges and his colleagues at Pennsylvania State University, in a study of 50,000 trees using the David Swofford PAUP (parsimony-computing program), found that the variation was actually too great to be of any use. All of this led Templeton to suggest that it might never be possible to settle the question and Christopher Stringer to suggest that other evidence might have to be used to settle this debate.

Paleoanthropologist Curtis Runnels reported a discovery that could point the way to answering the question of who first moved out of Africa to settle Europe. Runnels found in Greece a hand ax that was about 200,000 years old. Greece is instrumental in settling the argument, as it lies on the route from Africa to other parts of Europe. Runnels' find was the oldest human artifact yet from Greece.

One of the most significant discoveries of 1991 was made in the Austrian Alps, where a prehistoric corpse about 4,000 years old was discovered. The corpse, quickly dubbed the "Ice Man," was released by a melting glacier in September and was immediately hailed as one of the most significant finds of the century. The tattooed body wore remnants of garments and was accompanied by tools characteristic of south-central Europe in the Bronze Age. Plans to recover genetic information from the body tissue were under way. Konrad Spindler of Austria began assembling an international and multidisciplinary team to study the mummified body and the cultural materials associated with it.

The relationship between anthropology and business continued to gain strength throughout 1991, highlighted by the move of significant numbers of individual entrepreneurs and groups of anthropologists into the business world. More companies than ever before were asking anthropologists for help in understanding other cultures. During the past year anthropologists studied why people from some cultures learn best by using one methodology while members of other cultures learn best from other methods, cultural barriers in implementing sophisticated computer systems, and the relationship between alcoholism and absenteeism in the workplace. IBM, Xerox, General Motors, Nissan, Arthur Anderson, and Boeing were among the large firms that were using anthropologists for such research projects. In these settings anthropologists focused on the work

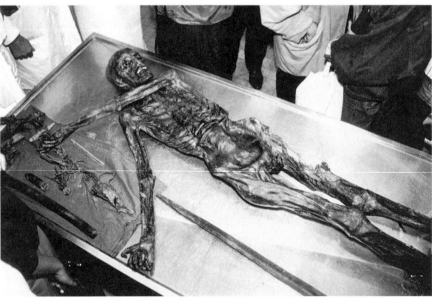

The mummified body of a man more than 4,000 years old lies with tools and other items found near him. The body was found in a melting glacier in the Austrian Alps.

group, business and production methods, and the design of user-friendly equipment. Studies to learn about how people behave while driving led to design changes in storage, use of space, steering-wheel feel, and other product developments at Nissan. With Xerox, anthropologists were studying workers and traffic at local airports to improve airline operations, while at Boeing they were focusing on the cross-cultural factors of airplane safety. General Motors was using anthropologists to study cultural adjustment by managers after their return to the U.S. from overseas and also to identify company inconsistencies. At the Nynex Corp. studies were being carried out to smooth the relationship between people and machines. In smaller settings anthropologists were studying alcoholism and absenteeism, interactions and work habits in the factory, and the relationships between middle and upper management.

—Larry L. Naylor

Archaeology

Archaeological advances during the past year included important finds of human remains in Utah, a handprint in a New Mexico cave, a vast Roman city under Florence, evidence of prehistoric horseback riding in Ukraine, and an ancient Egyptian city near the Sphinx. The human remains in Utah were of a nearly 5,000-year-old burial site along the shores of Utah Lake. These are some of the earliest human remains in the Great Basin and were expected to add to the understanding of Archaic cultures in the far west of North America. The handprint in clay on a New Mexico cave wall was radiocarbon dated to about 35,000 years ago, 23,000 years before the usually accepted dates for the settlement of North America.

Excavations under the Piazza della Signoria in Florence revealed a large portion of a 2,000-year-old Roman city. The find shows that Florence was a center of textile production and commerce long before the Renaissance. It also suggests that Florence itself was the Roman regional capital, questioning the previous belief that the distinction belonged to a smaller nearby city called Fiesole. In Ukraine, detailed study of bit marks found on ancient horse teeth revealed that the first riding horses were much older than previously thought. Transportation by horseback may have begun in Ukraine at least 6,000 years ago, well before the invention of the wheel.

In Nazlett El-Sammen, Egypt, workers recently began a project to bring modern water systems to the Giza region and help to remove underground wastewater from the area around the Sphinx. Excavations quickly revealed the presence of a large buried city belonging to the pyramid-building pharaohs of the Old Kingdom (about 2575 BC to about 2130 BC). Evidence for a widespread fire in the ruins supports ancient legends that tell of a city destroyed during a people's revolt against the pharaohs at the beginning of the First Intermediate Period, around 4,100 years ago.

People often ask, "Why is archaeology important?" The past fascinates many people, but many do not see that its study contributes to their daily lives. The

Remains of human habitation were discovered during the past year along the shores of Utah Lake (left). Among the findings at the almost 5,000-year-old burial site were fragments of a textile, examined by Joel Janetski of Brigham Young University, and other artifacts in the foreground (right).

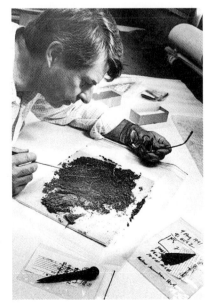

Gallery of the public baths (left) and small drains in a bathroom of the baths (right) were among the discoveries made by archaeologists when their excavations under the Piazza della Signoria in Florence revealed the remains of a large, 2,000-year-old Roman city.

problem continues because archaeologists usually do not clearly explain their projects and results to the interested public. This is changing, however, and many archaeologists are aware of the responsibility to distribute their research findings more widely. One way to do so is to show how archaeology sometimes contributes to the fields of medicine, biochemistry, and physics, among others. Usually the contributions are reciprocal, as archaeologists often employ techniques borrowed from other sciences. Such was the case with many recent archaeological projects.

Nuclear physics and Roman shipwrecks. An archaeological report of a sunken Roman sailing ship off the coast of Sardinia recently came to the attention of Ettore Fiorini, a physicist with the University of Milan. Fiorini worked at the Gran Sasso physics laboratory located a kilometer and a half below the surface of the Apennine Mountains in central Italy. He and his colleagues approached the archaeological authorities in Sardinia with a proposition to salvage the Roman ship, if the Gran Sasso laboratory could keep some of the cargo to use as equipment for their study of cosmic particles.

By the autumn of 1991, Sardinian and Italian archaeologists had carefully excavated and recovered the 2,000-year-old freighter and its cargo. The wooden ship had sunk in 30 m (100 ft) of water sometime between 70 and 50 BC while hauling back to Rome more than 1,000 33-kg (73-lb) lead ingots. Ancient Romans used lead for sealing terracotta water and sewer pipes, constructing buildings, and making utensils and household goods and in artistic projects. Much of the Roman lead was mined and refined in Sardinia and shipped to Rome and other cities.

Physicists at Gran Sasso, in their study of solar neutrinos, dark matter, and other cosmic particles, had been purchasing specially treated lead and copper to shield their detectors from background radiation. Newly refined lead used for the experimentation requires expensive techniques for reducing the amount of lead-210, a radioactive isotope that makes the lead unsuitable for use around sensitive detectors. However, time had almost entirely removed the contaminant from the Roman ingots; the old lead was as pure as or purer than decontaminated modern lead. Fiorini and Gran Sasso received 150 ingots for their part in the excavation, while the Sardinian archaeologists salvaged the ship and kept the inscribed top portion of each ingot for historical studies. The cost, about $250,000, for the salvage operation was about the same as for an equal amount of specially processed modern lead. For the money, Fiorini and the Gran Sasso laboratory not only obtained relatively pure lead for their experiments but also contributed to a greater understanding of Roman and Italian history.

Radioactivity and past diets. During the last several years increasingly sophisticated techniques have been devised for reconstructing the behavior of prehistoric humans. Among them have been studies of ancient human remains to determine past diets. One interesting project from 1991 suggested that *Homo sapiens neanderthalensis* (Neanderthal man) ate little except meat. André Mariotti of Marie Curie University in Paris analyzed carbon and nitrogen isotopes in bone collagen from a Neanderthal who lived at Maurillac, a cave north of Bordeaux, about 40,000 years ago. The remains were fossilized but contained enough organic material to show the source of food that provided amino acids for the protein collagen. Researchers in zoology and ecology have used the collagen technique to study the relative position of animals on the food chain. While scientists have used this technique to determine the diet of humans up to 10,000 years old, Mariotti's study was the first to apply it to Neanderthal fossils. The results showed that the diet of that Neanderthal man had been between that of the wolf, which is primarily a carnivore, and the fox, which gets some of its proteins from fruits and grains.

Collagen is a long-lasting protein, but some of its constituents break down over time. Mariotti and two colleagues from the University of Reims, France, refined a method of identifying collagen by means of its amino-acid spectrum. They then extracted it from fossilized bones of both the Neanderthal man and a range of animals—reindeer, fox, horse, marmot, wolf, auroch, and hyena specimens—from Maurillac. The levels of nitrogen-15 isotopes in these fossilized samples placed all the animals in their expected positions on the food chain. The results suggested that nitrogen isotope levels would provide similarly reliable dietary data on the Neanderthal specimen.

Nitrogen-15 is a key measure for carnivorous diets, and carbon-13 levels perform the same duty for measuring herbivorous diets. Comparing the two suggests the components of an overall diet and also can provide evidence of the environment in which an animal lived. For instance, the ratios of carbon-13 and nitrogen-15 in collagen can show whether a carnivore ate fish or meat from savannah or marsh environments. They can show that a herbivore was a grazer or a browser by indicating a diet of plants with certain photosynthetic pathways. Applying this method to the Neanderthal skeleton, Mariotti's team showed that the individual obtained most of his food from hunting or scavenging in the local area rather than traveling to the coast to eat fish.

Archaeology and fungal diseases. A disease called valley fever is common in the desert regions of southwestern North America. It sometimes afflicts archaeologists who excavate in the region, when they breathe or ingest from the dry soil fungal spores that cause the disease. Some 40 people die from the disease every year, and, although it has killed no archaeologists, it remains a concern to members of the field both as a danger and as a research target.

William Harrison, Charles Merbs, and Chester Leathers, all of Arizona State University, found that a skeleton excavated in 1981 from the Chavez Pass site in northern Arizona contained bone lesions resembling tuberculosis. The remains were of a 40–50-year-old individual from the Sinagua culture who died between 900 and 600 years ago. Recent study revealed that the skeletal lesions contained fossilized spores of *Coccidioides immitis,* the valley fever fungus. The disease may have killed this Sinaguan individual.

Because it attacks the bones in fewer than half the modern cases, valley fever is difficult to trace in skeletal remains. Spores are often found with human remains since the fungus has both a parasitic, disease-causing form and a saprophytic (obtaining nourishment osmotically from the products of organic decay) form that infects dead human and animal remains. The Chavez Pass find was the first sign of a fungal disease in pre-Columbian North America. Its presence in these ancient human remains suggests that the prevalence of the disease then was probably about the same as it is now. It apparently has never been virulent enough to cause humans to gain differential immunity to it, as ancient Native Americans seem to have had no more immunity to valley fever than did the first European visitors to the region.

Genetics, language, and human origins. Genetic evidence can be combined with data from archaeol-

Lead ingots (left and below) were salvaged from a 2,000-year-old Roman sailing ship that had sunk off the coast of Sardinia. They were later analyzed for the presence of the contaminating radioactive isotope lead-210 (see text).

(Left) Soprintendenza Archeologica di Cagliari e Oristano; (right) S. Parmeggiano

ogy and linguistics to provide a greater understanding of the origin and evolution of humans. A recent article by Luigi Cavalli-Sforza of Stanford University described the results of more than 12 years of work by several researchers on the origins and migrations of human populations.

Cavalli-Sforza and others studied a large body of genetic data gathered during the past 50 years. This included more than 100 genetic traits from 3,000 samples drawn from 1,800 populations around the world. They compared these data with a new set based on DNA (deoxyribonucleic acid) found in the nuclei of cells gathered during a seven-year collaborative project with researchers from Yale University. The results enhanced the understanding of human origins in three important ways.

First, the two sets of genetic data support the concept, based on archaeological and human physical evidence, of an African origin for the human species. Genetic distances—the amount of divergence between populations as measured by comparing the relative frequencies of specific genetic traits in those populations—are much greater between Africans and non-Africans than they are between any other human populations. The genetic difference between Africans and non-Africans is about twice that between native Australians and Asians, which is, in turn, more than twice that found between Europeans and Asians. This evidence suggests that the African separation was the first and oldest on the family tree. The projected rates of divergence are supported by fossil evidence that suggests that approximately 100,000 years separate Africans and Asians, about 50,000 years separate Asians and Australians, and about 35,000 to 40,000 years separate Asians and Europeans.

An independent research project conducted by Allan Wilson and his colleagues at the University of California at Berkeley, based on DNA found in the mitochondria of cells, further supports these data. An offspring inherits about equal amounts of nuclear DNA from the father and the mother. Mitochondrial DNA (mtDNA), on the other hand, passes to the offspring almost exclusively through the mother. This makes mtDNA convenient for the estimation of genetic distances. Wilson's team derived models of descent that showed that the human mtDNA had been evolving for the longest time in Africa and could be traced to a single African woman, who had lived about 150,000 to 200,000 years ago. This was striking news when the media reported it in 1989. It did not mean that a single woman, whom the press called "Eve," lived on the Earth. It merely meant that out of the many women who lived at the time, mtDNA from only one has managed to be preserved to the present. The other lineages became extinct through time.

In addition to finding genetic evidence for an African genesis, Cavalli-Sforza and his colleagues found that they could trace broad patterns of migrations out of Africa and across the world. They determined that human ancestors, possibly *Homo erectus*, moved out of Africa and into Asia about one million years ago. Their genetic studies corroborate archaeological data suggesting that archaic *Homo sapiens*, or possibly *Homo erectus*, moved into Europe between one million and 500,000 years ago. The team also found that anatomically modern humans migrated to Australia from Southeast Asia between 40,000 and 60,000 years ago and that the Americas may have been first settled as early as 35,000 years ago.

The situation in Europe is complex because of the many migratory waves over the millennia that passed between Europe and Africa and Asia. The earliest traceable anatomically modern human population in Europe appears to have been ancestral to the Basques of northern Spain and southwestern France. An independent analysis of genetic variation suggests that Basques are descended from some of the first European hunting and gathering populations. From these genetic studies, scientists have been able to construct a model of European settlement in which the Basques, located at the far end of the migratory path from the Middle East, were the last to come into contact with and mix their genes with the Neolithic farmers who slowly spread across Europe about 10,000 to 4,000 years ago.

The third important result of the genetic studies was the close correspondence found between distributions of genes and languages throughout the world. The Cavalli-Sforza team concluded that in certain cases languages and families of languages can serve to identify genetic populations. In addition, their models of descent show that genetic clustering in world populations closely matches that of languages. Higher levels of linguistic categories, called superfamilies, also show correspondence with the independent genetic data.

Why do languages and genes match so closely in their distributions? Genes do not control language, but circumstances of birth control the languages one speaks. Linguistic differences between human groups may generate genetic barriers, thus maintaining homogeneity through time. Although groups separate, move to other places, and evolve along independent paths, they continue to share certain genetic and linguistic characteristics with their parent populations, and these provide evidence for determining the date of each divergence. Unusual combinations of genes and elements of languages remain as unique links with even the most remote human ancestors.

—James D. Wilde

See also Feature Article: IN SEARCH OF THE FIRST AMERICANS.

Architecture and civil engineering

Many kinds of buildings are required for the complex and differing needs of people throughout the world. All must be conceived and built within the context of prevailing political, economical, and technical constraints. Sadly, the overwhelming majority are built without considerations of proportion, scale, texture, environment, mood, and all the other intangibles that are casually called "beauty." Collectively, they dominate the land while adding little joy to it.

Architecture remains unique among the arts. Buildings must stand up and function, as well as look handsome and stir emotions. Pure engineering forms—an unadorned bridge or transmission tower—often achieve a stark and lasting beauty derived from their purity of form rather than from some preconceived and passing social idea of shape or symbol. Architects respond to society in a variety of ways. Some seek to ascertain the particular taste and preference of their client and then strive to create that image. Others express their client's needs in the popular vernacular of a particular region or in a prevailing stylistic school. A few interpret the functional needs of their structures in individualistic ways, often creating their own followings or artistic schools. These divergent approaches to design, compounded by differences among followers within these schools, produce a wide range of structures.

Architecture. With the increasing internationalization of the world, airports are becoming more commonplace and are beginning to achieve the sta-tus and symbolism of the great train terminals of the last century. London's new Stansted Airport, designed by Foster Associates, is an excellent case in point. It boasts an elegant exposed structural system that organizes the entire process of airport use while making an aesthetic statement of its own. Passengers can glimpse the planes from the main concourse in much the manner that rail passengers once related to the trains within their huge sheds. Circulation from the roadways to the planes is straightforward, articulated by architecture rather than by signs. A structural system of four clustered delicate tubular steel members radiate out to support 18-m-square lattice-steel domes (1 m = 3.3 ft). Each dome contains a central skylight, and the entire ceiling is unencumbered by ducts, which are located in the floor. All the necessary subdivisions for food, tickets, shops, and lounges are carefully integrated into the structural module.

Another terminal that successfully exploits the drama of air transport is the main terminal of Japan's Kansai International Airport, being built on an artificial island in Osaka Bay. Designed by Renzio Piano, it is a high-tech building that features an asymmetrical undulating steel space-truss roof and a tree-filled arrival canyon that cuts through all three of the terminal's levels and contains the vertical circulation.

While many distinguished office buildings were constructed during the year, the most important, in terms of contribution to the evolution of what an office building can be in human as well as architectural aspects, was Herman Hertzberger's Ministry of Social Welfare in The Hague. It consists of three clusters of octagonal towers surrounding three multilevel

London's new Stansted Airport features a structural system in which four clustered tubular steel members radiate outward to support 18-square meter (194-square foot) lattice-steel domes.

Richard Davies—Foster Associates

The Netherlands' Ministry of Social Welfare in The Hague, designed by Herman Hertzberger, provides a maximum amount of perimeter office area to afford occupants both exterior and interior views.

The Capita Centre in Sydney, Australia, designed by Harry Siedler and Associates, features a central atrium that contains a vertical garden that changes shape as it rises 31 floors. Offices on all floors open onto the atrium.

glass-roofed spaces. These relatively low-rise buildings provide a maximum amount of perimeter office area, as occupants can look out on either internal or external views. Workers and visitors alike can sense the vitality of the building and the richness of its ever changing hierarchies of internal perspectives.

The Capita Centre in Sydney, Australia, designed by Harry Siedler and Associates, is one of the most dramatic new office buildings anywhere. The tower wraps around an atrium that contains a vertical garden that changes shape as it rises from the lobby to the 31st level. The building core (stairs, elevators, washrooms, duct shafts, and other mechanical spaces) is distributed around the exterior, permitting offices on all floors to open onto the central atrium. The exterior features powerful, fully exposed vertical trusses, which provide the wind-bracing function normally furnished by walls around a centrally located core.

Construction began on another controversial building in Paris. Dominique Perrault's design for France's national library places offices and books in four 20-story glass-clad, L-shaped towers located at the four corners of a huge low-rise rectangular mass that is partially below ground level. The rectangle contains reading rooms that surround a central sunken garden. When completed, the library will house 15 million books on its 385 km (240 mi) of shelves.

Expo '92, held in Seville, Spain, featured a number of exciting exhibition buildings. One of the most interesting was the Pavilion of the Future, designed by Bohigas, Martorell & Mackay. Approximately 280 m long, it was roofed with a series of 26 undulating S-shaped trusses. The most fascinating and, perhaps, most practical structure at the exposition was the double row of 30.5-m-high fabric funnels that provided air-conditioning for the open plaza. Raised above the plaza surface on four columns, the funnels contained spiral tubes that sprayed atomized water. The evaporating water removed heat from the air, which, being heavier when cooled, spilled out the funnel bottoms onto the plaza. The Soviet pavilion, designed by Latvian architect Juris Poga, featured a 3,000-sq m (32,300-sq ft) sloping roof covered with 1,705 pivoting cubes, each with individual sides colored red, green, white, and blue.

The most prestigious international awards for architecture are the Pritzker Architecture Prize and the Praemium Imperiale. Awarded for a lifetime portfolio of work, both carry the equivalent prestige of a Nobel Prize. The Pritzker in 1991 was awarded to U.S. architect Robert Venturi. His most recent works include the new Sainsbury Wing of the National Gallery of Art in London, the Seattle Art Museum, and the restoration of the University of Pennsylvania's Furness Library. Gae Aulenti of Italy was the recipient of the Praemium Imperiale. Best known for the rehabilitation of the Gare d'Orsay in Paris and Grassi Palace in Venice, she was also cited for her furniture and stage design. The American Institute of Architects selected Benjamin Thompson for its 1992 Gold Medal. Designer of "festival marketplaces" such as Boston's Faneuil Hall and Baltimore's Harborplace, he also is a distinguished educator.

Civil engineering. Were it not for the ongoing construction of the tunnel under the English Channel, the crossing of the Great Belt waterway (Store Strait) between Denmark's Funen and Zealand islands would be Europe's largest engineering undertaking. When completed, it will permit automobiles and trains from western Europe to roll across Jutland, the mainland half of Denmark, on to Copenhagen, the capital, located on Zealand. (The link between Jutland and Funen has already been completed.) The most dramatic element in this 18-km (11.2-mi) combination of tunnels, causeways, and bridges will be a 1,624-m suspension-cable automobile bridge over part of the east channel (trains will pass under the channel through twin 8-km [5-mi]-long tunnels). When completed, the bridge will be the first in the world to span more than a mile.

Swiss-trained Spanish engineer Santiago Calatrava has perhaps done more than any other current engineer to develop sophisticated new forms appropriate to today's technology. His Alamillo Bridge, built for Spain's Expo '92, is a striking cable-stayed structure supported by cables extending from a single, back-leaning pylon located on one side of the bridge and anchored to a series of points along a centrally lo-

cated steel box girder that runs the length of the bridge.

The cable-stayed bridge, a relatively recent structural innovation, has gained increasing popularity. The claim of being the world's longest-span cable-stayed bridge changed title several times during the past year. The 490-m Ikuchi Bridge in Japan surpassed British Columbia's Alex Fraser Bridge, at 465 m, to hold claim to the world record for only a matter of weeks before passing the title to the 530-m Skarnsundet Bridge, built near the Arctic Circle in Norway. Work was proceeding on still another record-long cable-stayed bridge, the Normandy, under construction over the Seine estuary in France. When completed, it will have an 861-m span.

The Georgia Dome, designed by Levy and Ouzoonian of Weidlinger Associates, is an exciting part of the pre-Olympic (1996 Summer Games) building boom in Atlanta, Ga. Covering 37,160 sq m (400,000 sq ft), the building's dramatic elliptical, cable-stayed dome supports a fabric roof. With a major axis of 225 m and a minor axis of 178 m, it is the largest roof of its kind.

After 18 years of construction and a cost of $18 billion, the 196-m-high Itaipú Dam project across the Paraná River (which flows between Brazil and Paraguay) was completed. Backing up 29 billion cu m (23.5 million ac-ft) of water, it has a generating capacity of 12,600 MW and became the world's largest hydroelectric project.

For sheer size of construction, a prosaic 15-level truck container storage building in Hong Kong, with a total floor area of more than 863,000 sq m (9.3 million sq ft), supplanted the Nizhny Tagil railroad car and tank plant in Russia as the largest building in the world. It can accommodate 2,600 container trucks.

Alamillo Bridge, designed by Santiago Calatrava for Spain's Expo '92 in Seville, is supported by cables extending from a single back-leaning pylon located on one side of the bridge and anchored to a series of points on a centrally located steel box girder that runs the length of the bridge.

Santiago Calatrava Valls SA

Georgia Dome, built for the 1996 Olympic Games in Atlanta, Georgia, has a cable-stayed dome that supports a fabric roof. Its major axis of 225 meters (743 feet) and minor axis of 178 meters (587 feet) make it the largest roof of its kind.

The American Society of Civil Engineers' annual Award of Merit went to the Portland, Ore., District of the U.S. Army Corps of Engineers for its 10-year-long series of recovery projects in response to the volcanic eruptions of Mt. St. Helens in southwestern Washington state. Work included opening shipping lanes on the Columbia River, stabilizing surrounding lake and river systems, and providing an outlet tunnel for Spirit Lake.

—David Guise

Astronomy

During the past year the least significant members of the solar system, asteroids, gained considerable attention. The Magellan spacecraft continued its extraordinary mapping of Venus. High-resolution radio observation led to new knowledge about both galactic and extragalactic objects. The superior resolution of the Hubble Space Telescope, despite its spherical aberration, permitted things to be seen that had long been hidden from view. Millimeter and submillimeter radiation observations gave new insights into the galactic center region and led to the discovery of the first true protostar.

Solar system. Two programs devoted to the search for Earth-approaching asteroids led to the discovery of two objects with very different orbital characteristics. On Jan. 18, 1991, James V. Scotti and David L. Rabinowitz of the University of Arizona found a faint streak on the output display of a charge-coupled device camera attached to the 0.9-m Spacewatch telescope at Kitt Peak (Arizona) National Observatory. Further observations during the next 4½ hours permitted the calculation of an orbit for the object. Labeled 1991 BA, it turned out to be a small asteroid on an orbit that carried it within 170,000 km (1 km = 0.62 mi) of the Earth, the closest approach of

any asteroid ever recorded. On the basis of its apparent brightness, Scotti and Rabinowitz estimated its diameter to be between 5 and 10 m (16.5 and 33 ft). Had it collided with the Earth, it would have released the energy of a 40-kiloton explosion.

A month later, on February 18, Robert McNaught, observing at the Siding Spring Observatory in Australia, discovered another faint object. This one, however, proved to be an asteroid measuring five kilometers in diameter traveling in a highly eccentric orbit that carries it 22.2 times farther than the Earth from the Sun. On its nearest approach it crosses just inside the orbit of Mars. Dubbed 1991 DA, it takes over from Chiron as the asteroid that travels farthest from the Sun.

The first image of the asteroid Gaspra was taken by the Galileo space probe in October 1991 from a distance of 16,200 kilometers (10,000 miles).

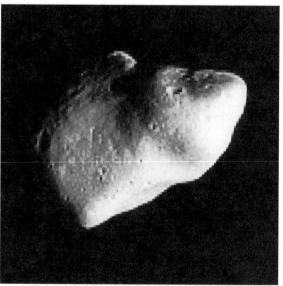

JPL/NASA

288

Not only were asteroids discovered but, for the first time, one was visited. During the year the Galileo spacecraft, scheduled to reach Jupiter in 1995, passed within 1,600 km of the asteroid Gaspra. The camera aboard Galileo took 150 pictures of the asteroid as the two traveled by one another at eight kilometers per second. Unfortunately, Galileo's high-gain antenna remained unfurled, and so data could be returned only through use of a smaller telemetry antenna at an extremely slow rate of 40 bits per second. A test transmission of 12 columns of pixels (a pixel is the smallest picture element size) was sent. When Gaspra was seen to be well centered in the field, a section 600 pixels wide was transmitted that contained the entire view of the asteroid. Because of the painfully slow transmission rate, it took some 20 hours to receive the image.

The image revealed Gaspra to have a cratered, irregular shape 12 × 16 km. It is believed to be more like 20 × 12 × 11 km in size, but it appeared smaller because only its sunlit surface could be imaged. Taken at a distance of 16,200 km, the image revealed features as small as 200 m (660 ft) in diameter. The remaining data stored aboard Galileo cannot be transmitted until the main antenna is successfully deployed or until the next time the spacecraft nears the Earth, in December 1992, for another slingshot acceleration on its way to Jupiter.

By early 1992 the Magellan spacecraft had logged more than a year of observing the surface of Venus. Its high-resolution, side-viewing radar continued to reveal the long-hidden features of the Venusian sur-face. Only about 850 craters had been seen, far fewer than on Mars or the Moon. Astronomers spec-ulated that the reasons for this are that objects that might have caused small craters disintegrated in Venus' dense atmosphere before striking the surface and that many larger craters have been obscured by ancient lava flows. As of early 1992 the radar imaging had not revealed evidence of plate tecton-ics, like that on Earth, but had shown features that are best explained by the upwelling and downwelling of material in the planet's interior. One particularly puzzling feature was a sinuous channel, christened Hildr Chasma, that is 2 km wide and traverses 6,800 km across the plains of the northern hemisphere of Venus. It is a bit longer than the Nile River on the Earth, thus making it the longest known channel in the solar system. It cannot be a riverbed because liquid water is impossible in the extreme tempera-ture of the planet's atmosphere. At the end of 1991 only a small percentage of the surface remained to be mapped, much of it having already been imaged twice.

The Sun put on a spectacular display of flares in mid-1991. On May 18 GOES-7, a satellite used by the U.S. National Oceanic and Atmospheric Ad-ministration (NOAA) to monitor the Sun, detected a huge increase in X-rays from a part of the solar surface that was just being carried out of sight by solar rotation. Two weeks later, as the region was to appear on the other limb of the Sun, a two-hour burst of X-rays was received that saturated the satellite's X-ray detector, exceeding any outburst

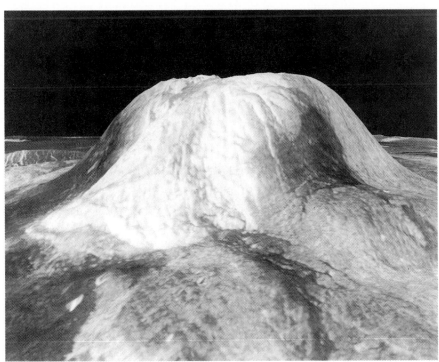

The volcano Gula Mons rises 3 kilometers (1.9 miles) above the surface of Venus in this computer-simulated image achieved by combining synthetic aperture radar data from the space probe Magellan with radar altimetry. Lava flows from the volcano extend for hundreds of kilometers across the surrounding plains.

JPL/NASA

Northern hemisphere of Venus is revealed by synthetic aperture radar mosaics from the Magellan space probe mapped onto a computer-simulated globe. The planet's north pole is at the center of the image.

studied since X-ray monitoring of the Sun began in 1974. Moments later the first of six huge visible-light flares that were seen from June 1 through June 15 appeared. Five of the flares were accompanied by X-ray outbursts that again saturated the detector. The Gamma Ray Observatory (GRO) that had been launched by the U.S. National Aeronautics and Space Administration (NASA) in April to survey the sky for high-energy radiation was a few weeks into its program at the time. The survey was interrupted, and the satellite was quickly turned toward the Sun. Bursts of gamma rays with energies exceeding 10 million electron volts were detected.

Flares are believed to occur when a localized region of the Sun's magnetic field is suddenly modified, releasing huge amounts of energy. The released energy hurls streams of charged particles from the region, some into space and some back down into the solar atmosphere. Collisions between the particles that are directed downward and atoms in the solar atmosphere excite atomic nuclei, causing them to emit gamma rays characteristic of the particular nuclei. In addition, the more energetic particles collide with enough force to rip some nuclei apart with a release of both very high-energy gamma rays and neutrons. One of the detectors aboard the GRO appeared to have detected neutrons. Particles released into space by the flare activity and intercepted by the Earth gave rise to enhanced aurora borealis displays seen as far south as Colorado. Radio communication disturbances were also noted.

Stars. Dale Frail at the U.S. National Radio Astronomy Observatory in Socorro, N.M., and Shrinivas R. Kulkarni at the California Institute of Technology (Caltech) used the Very Large Array (VLA) radio telescope system at Socorro to discover some unique properties of a pulsar. They obtained high-resolution radio maps of a galactic radio source known as G5.27–0.09. This source lies just to the west of and is related to another source, G5.4–1.2, a supernova remnant. They found that a pulsar, PSR1757–24, lies a few seconds of arc to the west of G5.27–0.09 and appears to be emerging from it. The pulsar has a very fast spin rate of eight rotations per second and is also spinning down at a fast rate. On the basis of its rate of spin and its spin-down rate, Frail and Kulkarni calculated the age of the pulsar to be 16,000 years. This is also the apparent age of the supernova remnant. They proposed that the pulsar was formed in the supernova but was vigorously ejected. To have reached its present location, it must be traveling across the sky at a speed of 2,300 km per second, the highest velocity for any known pulsar. This high speed allowed the pulsar to catch up with the supernova shell, which is being decelerated by surrounding interstellar matter. In passing through the shell, the pulsar energized the part of it that is seen as G5.27–0.09. If the two astronomers are correct, the pulsar should have a proper motion (angular speed across the sky) of 0.08 second of arc per year. They plan to continue to observe it during the next several years to measure its proper motion. If the angular speed is confirmed, Frail and Kulkarni will also have confirmed one possible suggestion for the frequent absence of pulsars in many supernova remnants, namely, asymmetrical explosions.

Gerard Gilmore of the University of Cambridge, Bengt Edvardsson of the Astronomical Observatory in Sweden, and P.E. Nissen of Århus (Den.) University used the Anglo-Australian Telescope in Coonabarabran, Australia, to observe the star known as HD 14023. HD 14023 was known to be a metal-poor star and, therefore, one that must have been born early in the life of the universe before heavy elements could be formed in supernovas. The star has an iron abundance only 0.05 that of the Sun, which implies that it is about 15 billion years old.

Gilmore, Edvardsson, and Nissen were successful in obtaining ultraviolet spectra of HD 14023 that permitted them to measure the amount of beryllium present in the star. According to the standard big bang model of the formation of the chemical elements, beryllium should be very rare. Most of the universe when the star formed consisted of hydrogen and helium with a smattering of lithium. The three researchers found the beryllium in HD 14023 to be 1,000 times the amount predicted by the homogeneous big bang model. Beryllium can also be made when energetic cosmic rays interact with carbon, nitrogen, or oxygen. But the amount of those elements in the early universe should have been so negligible that this process does not appear to be a reasonable source for the beryllium in HD 14023. However, if the very early universe was inhomogeneous, that is, had significant clumpiness, enough beryllium could have been formed to explain the abundance found in HD 14023. The observers consequently concluded that they had found a new tool to study the conditions in the early stages of the big bang.

The infrared source known as IRAS 4 in NGC 1333 was thought to be one of many young low-mass stars discovered in recent years. However, submillimeter photometry done by Goran Sandell, Colin Aspin, and William Duncan at the Joint Astronomy Center in Hawaii, by Adrian Russell at the Max Planck Institute for Radio Astronomy in Bonn, Germany, and by E. Ian Robson at Lancashire Polytechnic in the U.K. led them to propose that it is instead a protostar. (A protostar is an object in the earliest stages of star formation.) By combining their data with infrared measurements made earlier by the Infrared Astronomical Satellite, they determined the energy distribution of the source in the wavelength region from 50 micrometers (μm) to 2 mm. They also made high-resolution maps of the source at wavelengths of 0.45 mm and 0.8 mm. The maps showed it to be a double source connected by a bridge of faint emission. The researchers computed the temperature of IRAS 4A, the brighter compo-

nent, to be 37 K (−236° C [−393° F]) and that of IRAS 4B, the fainter component, to be 27 K (−246° C [−411° F]).

In analyzing the system, the astronomers concentrated on IRAS 4A because it is less affected by the surrounding faint emission. They found it to have an elongated structure measuring 3,200 AU in its longest dimension and 2,200 AU in its shortest. (One AU equals the distance of the Earth from the Sun, 150 million km.) They determined it to be a huge disk of dust, either a fat disk or a thin one seen in projection. From its size and the energy that it radiates, IRAS 4A has a mass about 9.2 times that of the Sun.

The researchers estimated that the smaller component, IRAS 4B, had a mass of 4 solar masses and that an additional 1.4 solar masses were contained in the material surrounding the binary system. No near-infrared source was associated with IRAS 4A, so if there is a starlike object in its deep interior, it must be less than two solar masses in size. IRAS 4A thus appears to be a true protostar, an object generating its energy of radiation primarily, if not only, from the gravitational energy released as it contracts in size.

Galactic astronomy. Paul T.P. Ho and Luis C. Ho of the Harvard-Smithsonian Center for Astrophysics, John C. Szczepanski and Alan H. Barrett of the Massachusetts Institute of Technology, James M. Jackson of Boston University, and J. Thomas Armstrong of the U.S. Naval Observatory concluded during the past year that they may have found the source of matter that supplies the ring of material circulating about the galactic center at a distance of 6.5 light-years. (One light-year equals 9,458,000,-000,000 km.) Using the VLA, they found that two giant molecular clouds, known as M-0.02-0.07 and M-0.13-0.08, lying 32 to 65 light-years from the ring, appear to be connected with it by a long, thin streamer of molecular gas. They suggested that the clouds are interacting with two nearby supernova remnants. This causes some matter from the clouds to be impelled inward toward the galactic center, where it is captured in the ring. Matter from the ring spiraling in toward a black hole at the galactic center had been proposed as the energy source for radiation from the center. The infall rate calculated along the streamer appears to be sufficient to replenish the ring for the matter that it loses to the central object.

For the past 20 years radiation at 511 KeV (thousand electron volts), associated with the annihilation of electrons by positrons, has been intermittently detected near the galactic center. Until recently none of the detectors measuring the radiation had sufficient spatial resolution to locate the source within a few degrees. Recently, however, a French detector aboard the Soviet satellite GRANAT observed a day-long burst of radiation peaking near 511 KeV with sufficient spatial resolution to locate it within 1.5 minutes of arc of the known X-ray source 1E1740.7-2942. This source was proposed as a possible place of origin of the positrons involved in the annihilation process. John Bally and Marvin Leventhal of AT&T Bell Laboratories, using millimeter-wavelength observations, found that this X-ray source lies on the line of sight to the 10,000-solar mass molecular cloud, designated G-0.86-0.08, near the galactic center. They presented arguments that 1E1740.7-2942 is produced by the chance encounter of a massive stellar-remnant black hole with this dense molecular cloud. The energy observed is supplied by matter from the cloud accreting onto the remnant. The accretion would be expected to be unsteady, in agreement with the observed variability of the gamma rays from the source.

Of all the globular clusters in our Galaxy, 47 Tucanae is the second brightest in the sky. At a distance of 15 light-years, half that to the next nearest globular cluster, it could be expected to be the Rosetta stone for understanding globular clusters. But even this cluster, when observed at optical wavelengths from the Earth, manages to hide its internal secrets in the overlapping images of its inner stars. That may have changed, however, because of recent observations by the Hubble Space Telescope and radio observations made in Australia.

Francesco Paresce of the Space Telescope Science Institute and 20 collaborators from France, Italy, Germany, The Netherlands, the U.K., and the U.S. obtained high-resolution images of the core of 47 Tucanae in the ultraviolet by using the faint object camera aboard the Hubble Space Telescope. The ability of the Hubble to resolve the inner stars of the cluster allowed the researchers to identify 21 so-called blue stragglers. These are hot blue stars that by all rights should not exist in a globular cluster. Globular clusters are old systems, of the order of 15 billion years. In that time any young hot stars should have long ago evolved into red giants; in addition, there is little or no free gas in globular clusters to form new stars.

The blue stragglers are thought to arise from collisions between stars in the cluster interior, where star densities 1,000 times greater than that in the Sun's vicinity would favor stellar collisions. The three most probable mechanisms for the invigorated output of the blue stragglers are coalescence after a direct collision, violent mixing induced in a star by a near miss, or capture into a close binary star with mass transfer from one component to the other supplying the needed energy. The high spatial density of the blue stragglers in the central regions is not mirrored in the outer regions of the cluster. The researchers concluded that the density gradient of the blue stragglers toward the cluster center indicates that they are more massive than the usual cluster stars and have in essence fallen inward to the central region. They believe that this supports the idea that these are massive binary systems and that the energy stored in them halts core contraction, allowing the globular clusters to have an extended life in their present form.

The radio observations by Richard Manchester of the Australia Telescope National Facility, M. Bailes, Andrew Lyne, and C. Robinson of the University of Manchester, England, N. D'Amico of the University of Palermo, Italy, and J. Lim of Macquarie University, North Ryde, Australia, supported similar

The globular cluster 47 Tucanae (right) is imaged by the European Southern Observatory's 2.2-meter telescope in Chile and a charge-coupled device at a resolution of 0.8 arc second. The core of the cluster (far right) is revealed by the faint object camera aboard the Hubble Space Telescope at a resolution of 0.1 arc second.

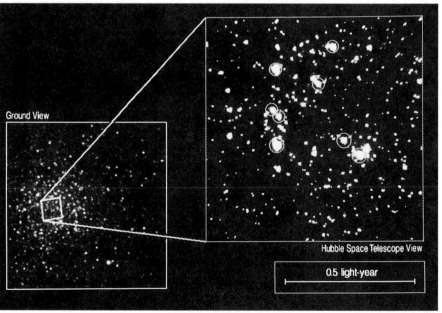

(Left) Meylan/ESO; (right) NASA/ESA

conclusions. Using the Parkes radio telescope, they identified 10 millisecond pulsars in 47 Tucanae, whereas only 13 in 12 different globular clusters had been previously known. They also found that more than half of the millisecond pulsars in 47 Tucanae show positive evidence of being binary systems. Millisecond pulsars are believed to be rotating neutron stars that have been caused to spin up by accreting matter from a more normal stellar companion. In addition, calculations by David Spergel of Princeton University indicate that winds at about the speed of light from millisecond pulsars could easily sweep gas lost in stellar evolution from globular clusters. If this is the case, the 10 pulsars found in 47 Tucanae could easily explain its gas-free condition.

Extragalactic astronomy. Jonathan Bland-Hawthorn of Rice University, Houston, Texas, Andrew Wilson of the University of Maryland, and R. Brent Tully of the University of Hawaii discovered what they believe may be the most massive black hole ever proposed. In mapping the velocity of hydrogen in NGC 6240, a pair of colliding galaxies some 300 million light-years distant, they found evidence of two disks of rotating matter. The first disk is centered on the optical image of the system and has a rotational velocity that might be expected of disks in normal spiral galaxies. The other disk is a different matter. It is centered on a point off to one side of the first disk and spins with nearly three times the speed. As yet there are no observations of a compact source in radio, millimeter, infrared, or X-ray radiation corresponding to the center of this disk. To account for the high velocities seen in the disk, they calculated that the disk must be centered on a compact mass containing as much matter as our entire Galaxy but in a volume 10,000 times smaller. They think that the object is a supermassive black hole, 10 to 100 times the mass of any yet proposed.

Most supernova remnants in our Galaxy have not been seen until a few hundred to tens of thousands of years after the event itself. During the past year, however, Norbert Bartel, Michael Rupen, and Irwin Shapiro of the Harvard-Smithsonian Center for Astrophysics, Robert Preston of Caltech, and A. Rius of the Facultad de Ciencias Matemáticas, Madrid, reported that they had detected a remnant only six years old; to do it, they had to observe it in a galaxy 40 million light-years away. The radio supernova 1986J, the most luminous ever seen, occurred in NGC 891, an edge-on spiral galaxy. Previously any attempt to see detail in such a distant object would have been doomed to failure. However, by using the technique of very long-baseline interferometry (VLBI) applied to eight radio telescopes in Germany, Sweden, Spain, and the U.S., the astronomers were able to achieve the resolution of a single telescope 8,000 km in diameter. Their radio image of the remnant reveals a shell of emission with jetlike protrusions. The two most prominent protrusions are about one-third of a light-year long and appear to be traveling outward at 18,000 km per second.

The researchers concluded that the energy from the shell comes from a shock front impinging on matter expelled from the star that exploded during its presupernova phase. The protrusions could be due to the expulsion of jets from the collapsing core or to the formation of giant loops of magnetic-field lines bulging out into the surrounding matter. They expected the remnant to remain bright enough for several more years, thereby permitting similar VLBI observations and thus providing a history of the development of a supernova remnant.

David Jauncey of the Australia Telescope National Facility and a team of 34 collaborators from Australia, India, South Africa, the U.K., and the U.S. observed the radio source PKS1830−211 by VLBI techniques and also with the British MERLIN radio array. They found that this source, which has been known for more than 25 years, is an Einstein ring. Albert Einstein in 1936 predicted that a distant object precisely aligned with one nearer to the Earth could be gravitationally imaged into an apparent ring of radiation. The third example of this phenomenon to be observed, PKS1830−211 was 100 times brighter than the others and the sixth brightest in the radio region of all known compact sources. The very-high-resolution maps that the astronomers obtained revealed two bright spots separated by one second of arc and a surrounding ring. They suggested that the object being imaged is a radio galaxy with a bright core and a luminous jet. The core is imaged into the two bright spots and the jet into the ring by an intervening massive body. A search of various catalogues and Schmidt plates of the region of PKS1830−211 revealed no obvious candidates for the intervening mass. The extreme brightness of the source was puzzling, and the research team suggested that it may result from the imaged source being an extraordinarily luminous object or from the alignment of the lensing object and the source being so precise that the imaging process greatly amplifies the energy received.

James Gunn of Princeton University, Maarten Schmidt of Caltech, and Donald Schneider of the Institute for Advanced Study, Princeton, N.J., announced the discovery of a new quasar, PC 1247 + 3406 in the constellation Canes Venatici. The discovery was noteworthy because PC 1247 + 3406 has the largest redshift, 4.897, of all known quasars, edging out the previous record holder by 0.164.

—W.M. Protheroe

See also Feature Articles: DEMYSTIFYING THE MISTY PLANET; JPL AND THE EXPLORATION OF SPACE.

Chemistry

The excitement that broke out in 1990 over confirmation of the existence of buckminsterfullerene continued in 1991 when scientists found the spherical, all-carbon molecule to be an electrical superconductor. Despite widespread skepticism, the case for cold fusion remained unsettled as a number of laboratories around the world worked to achieve reproducible positive results.

Inorganic chemistry

Inorganic chemistry in 1991 was the scene of intensive research on the fullerenes, a family of molecules representing a new form of elemental carbon. Several symposia on fullerenes were held, and many new observations on the novel molecules were reported, accompanied by much speculation in the popular press. The successes of previous years in the investigation of so-called high-temperature ceramic superconductors encouraged continued study of new materials in the quest for higher superconducting transition temperatures and for a better understanding of the underlying principles of superconductivity.

Fullerenes. Most of the fullerene research reported in the past year was devoted to studies of the synthesis and physical characterization of buckminsterfullerene and some of its larger relatives. Buckminsterfullerene, or C_{60}, is a molecule made solely of 60 carbon atoms arranged in a hollow,

Potassium atoms (small spheres) occupy distinct sites among molecules of buckminsterfullerene in a computer image of the crystalline lattice of potassium-doped C_{60}. The buckyball-based material was shown to be superconducting at 18 K.

Joseph W. Lauher and Peter W. Stephens, State University of New York, Stony Brook

closed-cage structure resembling a soccer ball. By the early 1990s, C_{60}—nicknamed "buckyball"—had become available in gram quantities, sufficient for research but inadequate for most applications. A structural study of an osmium derivative of C_{60}, determined by Joel Hawkins and colleagues at the University of California at Berkeley, proved that the buckyball structure comprises 12 regular pentagonal faces and 20 regular hexagonal faces, arranged so that all pentagonal faces are separated by hexagonal ones. Indeed, structural and spectroscopic evidence increasingly indicated that pentagonal faces do not share edges in any of the fullerenes.

Robert C. Haddon and colleagues at AT&T Bell Laboratories, Murray Hill, N.J., reported on the superconductivity of C_{60} that was mixed, or doped, with small amounts of potassium atoms and then crystallized. Upon cooling, the material reached its superconducting transition temperature, the temperature at which it loses all electrical resistance, at about 18 kelvins (K) at atmospheric pressure. (To convert kelvins to degrees Celsius, subtract 273; thus 18 K = −255° C. To convert Celsius to Fahrenheit, multiply by 1.8 and add 32.) According to Robert L. Whetten and co-workers of the University of California at Los Angeles (UCLA), the superconductivity of potassium-doped C_{60} is unusually pressure sensitive and decreases sharply at high pressures, falling to 8 K at 21 kilobars (21,000 atmospheres). In later work reported by other researchers, doping of C_{60} with such metals as rubidium, cesium, or thallium resulted in transition temperatures as high as 45 K.

The reaction chemistry of C_{60} and other fullerenes was explored by Paul Krusic of the Du Pont Co., Wilmington, Del., and by Keith F. Preston of the National Research Council of Canada, Ottawa, and their co-workers. The structure and composition of C_{60} require some delocalization of electrons throughout the cage; the only way all of the electrons can be accommodated is through some multiple bonding among the carbon atoms. But the high symmetry of the structure suggests that all its carbon-carbon bonds are similar and that the multiple bonding character must be distributed over all of the carbon atoms. The chemistry of the C_{60} cage, therefore, was expected to be similar to that of benzene and other aromatic molecules in which the multiple bonding is distributed over several carbon atoms.

The chemistry of carbon compounds having structures with delocalized electrons is dominated by electrophilic (electron-loving) substitution reactions. Thus, in reactions of benzene (C_6H_6) a reactant with some electron affinity, for example, a bromonium ion (Br^+), seeks the distributed electronic charge of the benzene ring and displaces one of the hydrogen atoms. In the product, as in the original benzene molecule, each carbon atom remains bonded to three atoms. On the other hand, reactions of compounds having discrete carbon-carbon double bonds are dominated by addition reactions, in which the multiple bond becomes a single bond and each carbon of the pair gains an atom attached by a single bond. In an addition reaction the number of atoms bonded to each carbon increases.

The reactions of buckminsterfullerene appear more similar to those of deactivated, or electron-poor, carbon-carbon multiple bonds. Since there are no hydrogen atoms to undergo substitution reactions, as in benzene, addition reactions are characteristic of the C_{60} cage. In common with other deactivated, multiple-bonded carbon compounds, the C_{60} cage is particularly susceptible to reactions with free radicals (molecules, molecular fragments, or ions with a lone nonbonded electron). Every addition reaction must be accompanied by a rearrangement of the C_{60} delocalized electronic structure, since an addition reaction increases the number of atoms bonded to the reactive site. One manifestation of the change in electronic structure is an increase in the chemical reactivity of the C_{60} cage.

In other C_{60} research Richard Smalley of Rice University, Houston, Texas, and co-workers captured lanthanum atoms within buckyball cage structures. Although sufficient quantities to allow full characterization had not yet been prepared, the encapsulation of metal atoms—which typically undergo facile electron transfer reactions and frequently participate in photochemical reactions—was expected to add another dimension to the chemistry of buckyballs. (See *Organic chemistry* and *Physical chemistry*, below.)

Metal atom clusters. During the past year Jack Lewis, Brian Johnson, and their co-workers at the University of Cambridge described a series of progressively larger clusters of osmium carbonyl. The structures are based on tetrahedral arrays of osmium atoms, with carbon monoxide (CO) ligands (attached groups) completing the coordination sphere of the osmium atom. The largest structure, $[Os_{20}(CO)_{40}]^{2-}$, is tetrahedral, with four osmium atoms on each edge and one in the center of each face (*see* 1). The apical osmium atoms are bonded to three CO molecules, the edge osmium atoms to two CO molecules, and the facial osmium atoms to one CO. It is interesting that the structure has triangular faces with an osmium atom at each apex; an equilateral triangle is the basic structural element of the famous geodesic domes of architect R. Buckminster Fuller, the inspiration for the naming of buckminsterfullerene.

The excitement generated by buckyballs is reminiscent of the announcement, in 1963, of the synthesis of a class of closed-cage, icosahedral, carbon-substituted boron hydrides first called carboranes and known now as carbaboranes. These compounds were so unusual that at their introduction in the

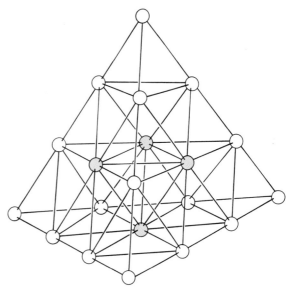

1   osmium atom core of $[Os_{20}(CO)_{40}]^{2-}$

Dec. 2, 1963, issue of *Inorganic Chemistry*, the journal devoted its lead article to a discussion of a systematic nomenclature for them.

Compounds made only of boron and hydrogen—analogues of the familiar hydrocarbons—had been studied by German chemist Alfred Stock and his students in the early 20th century. Most of those molecules, called boranes or boron hydrides, are electron deficient; boron has only three of the eight electrons required for completing a stable electronic configuration. When the three electrons are in-

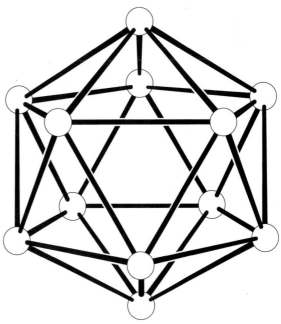

2   icosahedral structural element of crystalline boron

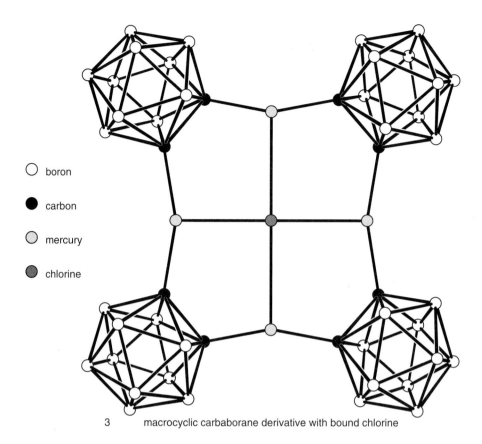

3   macrocyclic carbaborane derivative with bound chlorine

volved in chemical bonds, boron-centered molecules are still two electrons short of the stable octet. Most boron-centered compounds, therefore, react readily with oxygen, water, and other electron-rich molecules. Unlike the hydrocarbons, which are commonly found in petroleum in the form of chain and ring structures, boron hydrides tend to form cages in which the basic structural element is a triangle of boron atoms. Driven by the recognition that boron hydrides have a much higher energy content per unit weight than do hydrocarbons, researchers devoted significant effort to evaluating boron hydrides as rocket propellants. The by-product was a rich body of chemical knowledge.

Boron, like its family relative aluminum, is highly reactive and is never found in nature in the elemental state. From some of its compounds boron can be reduced to the element and crystallized in several different forms, or allotropes. The structural element common to all of the crystalline allotropes is an icosahedral cage having 12 vertices, which correspond to the positions of the boron atoms, and 20 equilateral triangular faces (*see* 2), with boron-boron distances averaging 177 picometers. (A picometer [pm] is a trillionth of a meter, or a hundredth of an angstrom.) The icosahedrons are bonded together with relatively weak boron-boron bonds, differing in arrangement among the allotropes.

Among the boron hydrides, the anion $[B_{12}H_{12}]^{2-}$ has the icosahedral cage structure of the crystalline element, except that one hydrogen atom is bonded to each vertex. In this electron-deficient structure each boron atom has four bonds—three to other borons and one to hydrogen. Unlike most smaller boron hydrides, the $[B_{12}H_{12}]^{2-}$ anion is extremely stable, resisting chemical attack even in boiling acid or alkali.

In 1963 chemists from Olin Mathieson Chemical Corp. and Thiokol Chemical Corp. independently reported the synthesis of a new class of compounds from $B_{10}H_{14}$ and alkynes (derivatives of acetylene, $HC{\equiv}CH$) in the presence of acetonitrile or other Lewis base (an electron-rich molecule or ion). In these compounds two carbon atoms replaced boron atoms in the icosahedral cage. If acetylene was used, the product was $B_{10}C_2H_{12}$, analogous to the $[B_{12}H_{12}]^{2-}$ anion but deriving two electrons from the carbon atoms. The structure is nearly indistinguishable from that of the $[B_{12}H_{12}]^{2-}$ anion. The carbon atoms are most easily identified by their chemical reactivity.

The chemistry of the carbaboranes is extensive. It is dominated by reactions at the carbon centers, since the icosahedral cage is comparatively chemically inert. Although there have been few commercially significant developments in carbaborane chemistry, the literature has continued to grow for almost 30 years. In 1991 M. Frederick Hawthorne and students of UCLA reported a novel carbaborane derivative in which four mercury atoms are bonded to the carbon atoms of four $B_{10}C_2$ cores to create a macrocyclic ring. The geometry of this macrocycle appears to be ideally suited for binding simple anions, such as chloride (*see* 3).

The strength of Mendeleyev's periodic table derived in part from its ability to predict the existence and some of the chemical and physical properties of elements that had not yet been discovered. Chemists have since used that predictive power as a tool for uncovering new classes of compounds with new properties. The columns in the periodic table contain elements that are expected to have similar chemistry. Thus, the existence of the boron hydrides, or boranes, suggests that there should be an analogous family of aluminum hydrides, or alanes. Some of these highly reactive species are known, but the chemical and structural diversity of the alanes is much more limited than that of the related boranes. In 1991 Werner Uhl and colleagues at the University of Tübingen, Germany, reported the structure of $K_2[Al_{12}(2\text{-butyl})_{12}]$, an aluminum compound having an icosahedral structure analogous to that of $[B_{12}H_{12}]^{2-}$. In the new structure an aluminum atom occupies each of the 12 vertices. Each aluminum atom is bonded to the second carbon of a four-carbon chain to form $CH_3CHAlCH_2CH_3$. It took more than 30 years to overcome the reactivity of aluminum compounds and the lack of apparent commercial value in this chemistry to prove, once again, the power of Mendeleyev's creation.

New binary compounds. In 1957 British chemists Ronald Gillespie and Ronald Nyholm devised an extension of American chemist G.N. Lewis' octet rule, which enables chemists to predict the structures of simple inorganic molecules and ions. Simply stated, the Gillespie-Nyholm rules relate structure to interelectron repulsion. Like charges tend to be separated by the largest possible distances. Limited to motion on the surface of a sphere, two electrons or two pairs of electrons will be diametrically opposed. Three pairs will be located at the apexes of an equilateral triangle; four will be found at the apexes of a tetrahedron; and six will be found at the apexes of an octahedron (which may be regarded as a trigonal antiprism, a triangular prism with the end triangular faces rotated 30° relative to one another). Since there are no regular Platonic solids with five or seven apexes, structures involving the maximum separation of five or seven like charges are derived from the equilateral triangle and octahedron, respectively. The regular Platonic solid affording the greatest separation of eight vertices is the Archimedean antiprism (square antiprism), a cube with two opposite faces rotated 45° relative to each other. Until Konrad Seppelt and Ali-Reza Mahjoub of the Free University

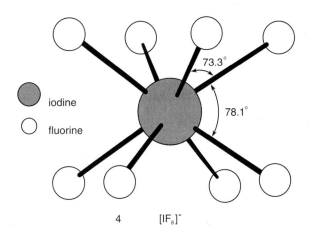

4    $[IF_8]^-$

of Berlin in 1991 reported the structure of $[IF_8]^-$, an anion of the halogen elements iodine (I) and fluorine (F), all known eight-coordinate structures were severely distorted cubo-octahedra. The $[IF_8]^-$ anion has a regular square antiprismatic geometry (*see* 4).

Applying Mendeleyev's principles, augmented by a knowledge of the relationship between electronic structure and the periodic table, chemists and students can predict the structures of large numbers of compounds. The interhalogen compounds, including IF_3, $[IF_4]^-$, IF_5, IF_7, and now $[IF_8]^-$, are among favorite examples in introductory chemistry courses.

Self-assembly of large molecules. Great interest exists in the processes whereby simple building blocks are assembled into large molecules, which often have properties strikingly different from those of their precursors. Some molecular assembly is controlled by the rate of formation of chemical bonds.

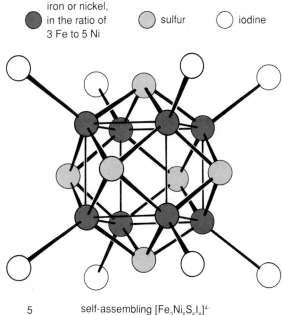

5   self-assembling $[Fe_3Ni_5S_6I_8]^{4-}$

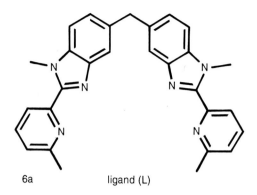

6a   ligand (L)

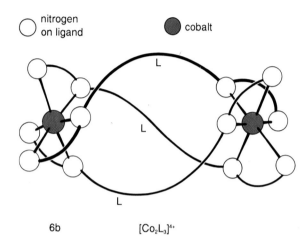

nitrogen on ligand   cobalt

6b   [Co₂L₃]⁴⁺

electrons in the system, suggests that the energy gained by delocalizing the electrons over all of these atoms is a significant contributor to the stability of the aggregate.

Alan Williams, Claude Piguet, and Gerald Bernardinelli of the University of Geneva reported the self-assembly of a more complex structure, albeit involving less intricate chemistry. A mixture of equimolar quantities (equal numbers of atoms, ions, or molecules) of a rigid ligand having bis[1-methyl-2,(6'-methyl-2'-pyridyl)benzimidazol-5-yl]methane (see 6a; abbreviated L), and cobalt(II) ions (Co^{2+}) in acetonitrile yielded a product with the composition $[Co_2L_3]^{4+}$ and the structure shown in 6b. The cobalt(II) ions are bound to nitrogen atoms near the ends of a triple helix formed by the ligands. The metal ions are about 830 pm apart, limiting intermetallic interactions to the constraining effects of the ligands; there is no metal-metal bond. The structure has a striking similarity to the well-known helical DNA and RNA structures first described by James Watson and Francis Crick.

—George R. Brubaker

Organic chemistry

The hottest topic of the past year in organic chemistry was the definitive characterization and subsequent chemical study of buckminsterfullerene, a new form of elemental carbon in which 60 carbon atoms form a spherical molecule resembling a soccer ball. Also reported were the laboratory syntheses of a variety of complex substances having unusual structures or properties. In addition, the hybrid field of bioorganic chemistry—the application of sophisticated organic chemical techniques to complex biological problems—continued to grow and to produce new insights in such important areas as cancer chemotherapy, immunology, and the search for new pharmaceuticals.

For example, the preparation of some synthetic polymers takes advantage of the different rates of reaction of the components to control the composition and properties of the products. The formation of other molecular assemblies appears to be controlled by an equilibrium among the components. The formation of crystalline salts may be driven by the crystal lattice energy, and the assembly of large biological molecules like proteins and nucleic acids may arise from the sum of many individually insignificant equilibrium steps. The practical and conceptual advances in molecular self-assembly were the subject of a symposium held at the April 1991 American Chemical Society meeting in Atlanta, Ga. Applications to molecular biochemistry, molecular electronic devices, and optical materials were among the topics discussed.

In related developments Wolfgang Saak and Siegfried Pohl of the University of Oldenburg, Germany, reported the self-assembly of $[Fe_3Ni_5S_6I_8]^{4-}$ (see 5), a cluster having a tube-shaped core of eight metal atoms, from the reaction of $[Fe_6S_6I_6]^{2-}$ with $[NiI_4]^{2-}$. In this reaction nickel displaces iron to produce a more electron-rich cluster; iron(III), with 25 electrons, is replaced by nickel(II), with 28 electrons. That nickel replaces iron, increasing the number of

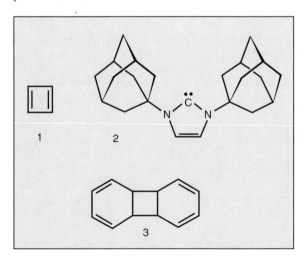

298

Fullerene chemistry. In 1991 the extraordinary structure of buckminsterfullerene, C_{60}, was proved unambiguously. First proposed in 1985 by Richard E. Smalley of Rice University, Houston, Texas, Harold W. Kroto of the University of Sussex, Brighton, England, and their collaborators, C_{60} became available in large amounts in late 1990 following development of a way to prepare it from graphite by Donald R. Huffman of the University of Arizona and Wolfgang Krätschmer of the Max Planck Institute for Nuclear Physics, Heidelberg, Germany (see *1992 Yearbook of Science and the Future* Year in Review: CHEMISTRY: *Organic chemistry*). The structural characterization of C_{60} and the first successful chemical reaction on the substance were carried out by Joel Hawkins and colleagues of the University of California at Berkeley. By first reacting C_{60} with osmium tetroxide, Hawkins was able to produce a C_{60}-osmium adduct whose atomic positions could be determined by X-ray crystallography. As had been predicted, he found that buckminsterfullerene is composed of 20 benzene-like, hexagonal rings and 12 pentagonal rings that form a pattern like that on the surface of a soccer ball. The distances between carbon atoms are in the range of 139–143 picometers (pm) as expected. (A picometer is a trillionth of a meter, or a hundredth of an angstrom.)

Among the many preliminary reports that appeared about the chemical properties of C_{60}, the most exciting was the finding that crystallized C_{60} containing metal-atom impurities behaves as an electrical superconductor, losing all resistance to current flow, at low temperature. Robert C. Haddon and his colleagues at AT&T Bell Laboratories, Murray Hill, N.J., discovered that combining C_{60} with three equivalents of potassium metal (K) leads to a stable K_3C_{60} complex that becomes superconducting when cooled below about 18 kelvins (K). (To convert kelvins to degrees Celsius, subtract 273; thus, 18 K = $-255°$ C. To convert Celsius to Fahrenheit, multiply by 1.8 and add 32.) The analogous rubidium complex behaves similarly, becoming a superconductor below 28 K. Even more impressively, Ray Baughman and Zafar Iqbal of Allied-Signal Inc., Morristown, N.J., prepared a rubidium/thallium-C_{60} that is superconducting below 45 K.

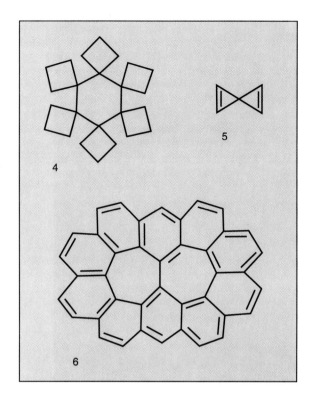

From the beginning of research on buckminsterfullerene, chemists have been intrigued by the possibility of trapping free atoms or small molecules within its spherical cage. Recently Smalley and his colleagues at Rice found that when C_{60} was prepared in the presence of lanthanum oxide at high temperature, small amounts of the product appeared to contain a lanthanum atom. Although the material had not yet been purified and fully characterized, evidence suggested that it is the hoped-for C_{60}-La inclusion complex. A related inclusion complex in which a helium atom is trapped in the C_{60} cage was reported by Helmut Schwartz and his colleagues at the Technical University of Berlin.

Although buckminsterfullerene itself was receiving most of the attention, Robert Whetten, François Diederich, and their students at the University of California at Los Angeles (UCLA) showed that other fullerenes—all-carbon molecules like C_{60} but with different numbers of atoms in their cage structures—

UV light

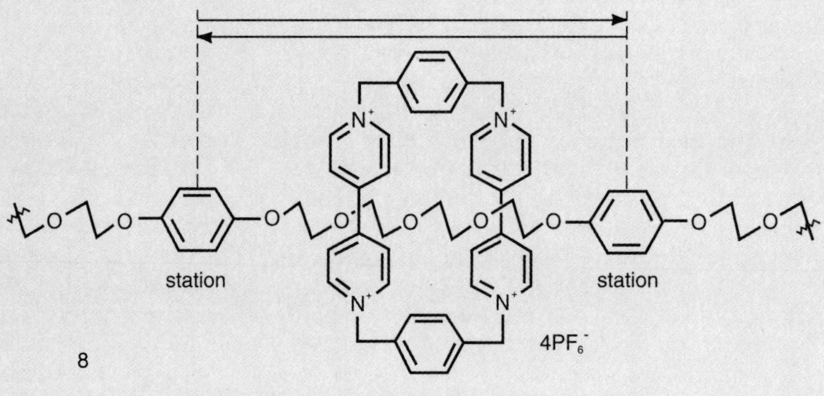

station   station

8 $4PF_6^-$

such as C_{70}, C_{76}, and C_{84} also can be prepared and purified. These larger molecules appeared not to be perfectly spherical but to have the elongated shape of a rugby ball. In addition, Sumio Iijima of NEC Fundamental Research Laboratories, Tsukuba, Japan, discovered a series of hollow microtubules of carbon with lengths as long as a micrometer (a millionth of a meter). Like the fullerenes, the microtubules appeared to consist of rings of carbon atoms but exclusively hexagonal ones. (See *Inorganic chemistry,* above, *Physical chemistry,* below, and PHYSICS: *Condensed-matter physics.*)

Unusual molecules. Cyclobutadiene (*see* 1, p. 298) is a small and simple molecule but one that has had a major role in the development of organic chemical theories. First prepared in 1965 after numerous attempts over a period of several decades, cyclobutadiene was found (as predicted) to be so reactive and unstable that it could not be isolated in pure form. In 1991, after an additional quarter century, UCLA chemist Donald Cram and collaborators reported that free cyclobutadiene molecules can be maintained inside the cavity of a large bowl-shaped molecular cage that they dubbed a hemicarcerand. The trapped cyclobutadiene molecules are unable to

9

escape their cages and thus undergo any reactions that might lead to their destruction.

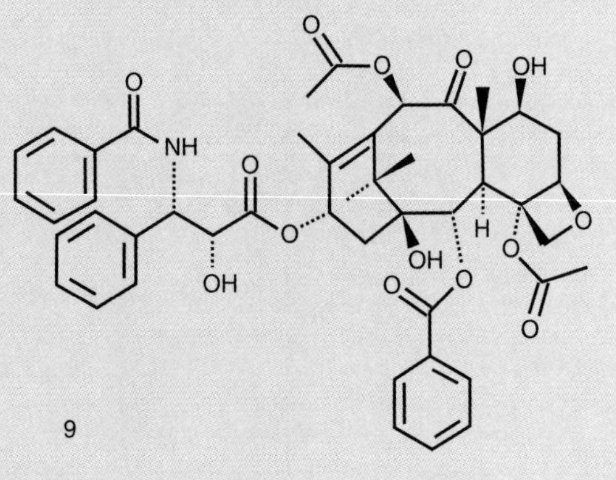

Carbenes, molecular structures that contain a carbon atom having only two bonds, are thought to be involved in many chemical transformations but are generally too reactive and unstable to be isolated. Anthony J. Arduengo III, Michael Kline, and Richard L. Harlow of the Du Pont Co., Wilmington, Del., found, however, that the carbene illustrated (*see* 2, p. 298) is so stable it can be crystallized and studied in detail (the two dots in the structure represent electrons that are not used for forming bonds).

Another surprise was the report by N. John Cooper, Robert Thompson, and Steven Geib of the University of Pittsburgh, Pa., that benzene (C_6H_6), one of the best studied organic compounds, can undergo a reaction previously thought impossible. On exposure to light in the presence of a manganese compound, benzene undergoes a process called cyclodimerization to yield the structure shown (*see* 3, p. 298).

Other unusual substances prepared in 1991 include 6.4-rotane (*see* 4), spiropentadiene (*see* 5), and [7.7]circulene (*see* 6, all three structures p. 299). Prepared by Lutz Fitjer and Mathias Noltemeyer of the University of Göttingen, Germany, 6.4-rotane is remarkable because its hexagonal ring of carbon atoms (a cyclohexane ring) is prevented by a record-high energy barrier from undergoing the kind of geometric inversion normally characteristic of compounds with cyclohexane rings. Spiropentadiene, a sensitive and highly reactive molecule synthesized by W. Edward Billups and Michael M. Haley at Rice University, is of interest to theorists because of its unusual geometry. Resembling a bow tie with one end twisted at right angles to the other, the structure requires the two double bonds to be held rigidly in a perpendicular relationship. [7.7]circulene, a saddle-shaped aromatic hydrocarbon prepared by Koji Yamamoto and his colleagues of the University of Osaka, Japan, is also of interest to theorists because of predicted unfavorable electronic interactions.

10

Molecular devices. As computers have grown ever more powerful and electronic devices ever smaller, the thoughts of some chemists have turned toward the ultimate level of miniaturization: the use of single molecules as switches or machines. In research carried out at the University of Groningen, Neth., Ben Feringa, Wolter Jager, Ben de Lange, and Egbert Meijer demonstrated one possible kind of molecular switching device that might find application in optical computing. The researchers prepared two compounds (*see* 7, p. 299) and found that they have different optical properties when they interact with circularly polarized light. Furthermore, since the compounds can be converted into each other by irradiation with ultraviolet (UV) light, the optical properties can be effectively switched back and forth.

Another kind of molecular device that might have potential application in information storage was reported by J. Fraser Stoddart and Neil Spencer of the University of Sheffield, England, in collaboration with Pier L. Anelli of the Center for Synthesis and Stereochemistry of Special Organic Systems, Milan, Italy. The chemists devised what they called a "molecular shuttle," in which a ring structure moves back and forth between two identical stations on a chain, much like a bead moving on a string (*see* 8). Measurements showed that the ring moves back and forth along the chain several hundred times a second. Although the movement was uncontrollable, future refinements of the idea would attempt to incorporate a method of driving the ring from one end of the chain to the other in a chemically controllable way.

Bioorganic chemistry. Taxol (*see* 9), a compound extracted from the bark of the Pacific yew tree (*Taxus brevifolia*), appears to be one of the most promising chemical agents yet discovered for the treatment of several kinds of cancer, including advanced ovarian and breast cancers. Unfortunately, clinical demand for the substance far exceeds the supply available from natural sources, prompting synthesis chemists

around the world to focus their efforts on developing methods for the laboratory preparation of taxol. Although work was not yet complete, Robert Holton of Florida State University reported a partial solution to the problem with his finding that taxol can be prepared by chemical manipulation of one of its more accessible relatives. At the same time, groups led by Andrew Greene of the University of Grenoble, France, Pierre Potier of the Institute for the Chemistry of Natural Substances, Gif-sur-Yvette, France, and Siegfried Blechert of the Technical University of Berlin prepared analogues of taxol that appeared to be even more potent than the natural substance in their anticancer activity.

Isolated in 1987 from the fermentation broth of the bacterium *Streptomyces tsukubaensis*, a compound code-named FK-506 (*see* 10) has proved to be one of the most powerful drugs known for suppressing the activity of the human immune system during organ transplantation. During the past year a collaborative effort between groups led by Stuart Schreiber of Harvard University and Jon Clardy of Cornell University, Ithaca, N.Y., uncovered key details of the way FK-506 works. Using X-ray crystallography, the investigators obtained the three-dimensional structure of the complex that forms when FK-506 binds to a receptor protein on the cell surface, and they also characterized that part of the structure of FK-506 responsible for binding to the receptor. Chemical synthesis of this binding domain was then carried out, and the synthetic material was found to bind tightly to the receptor. Ultimately, incorporation of the synthetic binding domain into other molecules may lead to new drugs useful for overcoming the body's rejection of transplanted organs.

Drug discovery is at present a slow, laborious process that involves the synthesis and testing of one new compound at a time. A group of chemists led by Stephen Fodor, J. Leighton Read, Lubert Stryer, Amy Tsai Lu, Dennis Solas, and Michael Pirrung of the Affymax Research Institute, Palo Alto, Calif., developed remarkable new technology that could dramatically accelerate the pace of drug discovery. Borrowing their idea from photolithography methods used in the computer industry to prepare integrated circuit chips, the Affymax researchers fixed a starting material to an insoluble polymer base and applied a mask to cover specific areas. When the coated polymer was exposed to light, only those uncovered regions on the polymer were activated for chemical reaction in a subsequent step. By then carrying out a series of repetitive masking-activation-reaction steps, they showed it was possible to prepare a checkerboard array of as many as 40,000 different compounds on a single polymer square measuring only one centimeter (less than a half inch) on a side.

—John E. McMurry

Physical chemistry

A Swiss physical chemist won the 1991 Nobel Prize for Chemistry for significant improvements in nuclear magnetic resonance spectroscopy, which has become an indispensable technique in chemical and biochemical analysis as well as an important medical diagnostic tool. Interest in buckminsterfullerene continued at a fever pitch, and attempts to control the course of chemical reactions by selectively breaking and making specific bonds in molecules came a little closer to achievement by means of new laser experiments. Powerful modern computers were playing an increasingly important role in helping scientists understand the behavior of materials at the atomic level. For example, a new computer study showed that aggregates of a small number of water molecules behave in some ways like water in bulk quantity.

Nobel for Ernst. The Royal Swedish Academy of Sciences awarded the 1991 Nobel Prize for Chemistry to physical chemist Richard R. Ernst (*see* SCIENTISTS OF THE YEAR) of the Federal Institute of Technology, Zürich, Switz. The award honored Ernst for two

major developments in the methodology of nuclear magnetic resonance (NMR) spectroscopy. This technique detects changes in the magnetic properties of certain atomic nuclei, particularly hydrogen and the carbon-13 isotope, under the combined effects of a magnetic field and radio-frequency radiation. The frequency at which a particular nucleus within a molecule absorbs the radio waves, or resonates, depends on its spatial relationship to the other atoms in the molecule. By analyzing the NMR signals emitted from different atoms, chemists can determine where each atom in the molecule is in relation to the others, providing a spotlight on the structure of the molecule.

Ernst improved the sensitivity of the technique by devising a new method of generating the NMR signal and applying a mathematical process, known as a Fourier transform, to convert the raw data to a conventional spectrum. Instead of slowly scanning the radio waves one frequency at a time as in conventional NMR, he beamed very short pulses of radio-frequency energy at the sample. Since a short pulse is equivalent to a mixture of all frequencies, he could observe the entire spectrum at once. Averaging the

Figure 1: A two-dimensional nuclear magnetic resonance (HETCOR) spectrum is shown for capreomycin IA, an antibiotic active against the bacillus that causes tuberculosis, along with an inset of the molecule's structure.

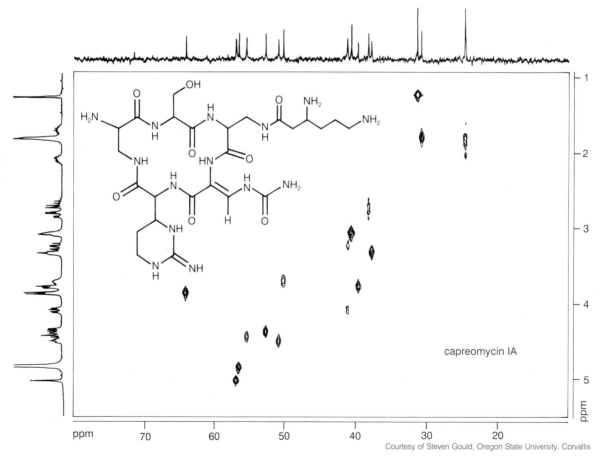

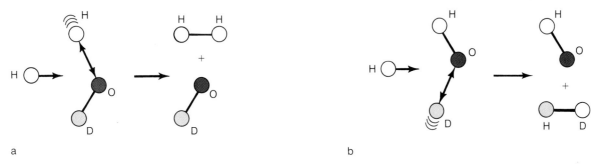

a   b

Figure 2: Depending on its tuning, an infrared laser causes either the O−H bond (a) or the O−D bond (b) of the water molecule HOD to vibrate such that reaction of the HOD with a beam of hydrogen atoms (H) results selectively in different products.

signal from many pulses to remove random noise dramatically increased the technique's sensitivity. However, because the radio-frequency energy was now supplied in pulses, the resonance signals from the nuclei in the sample decayed with time. Ernst realized that he could use a method developed by Jean-Baptiste-Joseph Fourier, a 19th-century French mathematician, to transform this time-dependent data into a conventional NMR frequency spectrum. Today, using Fourier-transform NMR, chemists can acquire spectra from minute amounts of material.

A normal NMR spectrum shows the response from one type of nucleus—a one-dimensional spectrum. The second advance for which Ernst was honored with the Nobel Prize was the development of two-dimensional NMR. In this technique the sample is bombarded with a sequence of radio-frequency pulses, separated by a certain time delay from a second set of pulses. During the delay the magnetic state of a nucleus in the sample changes, or relaxes, at a characteristic rate. Importantly, the relaxation rates for different atoms of the same type in the molecule are different owing to interactions with other atoms in the immediate vicinity. By applying Fourier-transform methods to data obtained from two experiments involving two different delay periods, chemists can obtain different types of NMR spectra.

Figure 1 shows an example of a particular type of two-dimensional NMR spectrum called a HETCOR (heteronuclear correlation) spectrum. It is for the molecule capreomycin IA, an antitubercular antibiotic. The spectrum shows the normal NMR spectrum from the hydrogen nuclei on the left axis and that from the carbon nuclei on the top axis. The location of the peaks in the middle of the plot indicate to which carbon atom a particular hydrogen atom is attached. By analyzing such peak patterns in spectra, one can build a model, atom by atom, of the structures of large, complex molecules involved in biological processes.

Bouncing, superconducting buckyballs. The excitement over buckminsterfullerene (C_{60}), or buckyballs, that erupted during 1990 (see *1992 Yearbook of Sci-*

ence and the Future Year in Review: CHEMISTRY: *Organic chemistry* and *Physical chemistry*) continued unabated during 1991. X-ray and electron diffraction experiments confirmed the hollow, soccer-ball structure of the 60-carbon-atom molecule in both the solid and gas phases. The buckminsterfullerene molecule proved to be less inert chemically than initially thought, and many research groups prepared a number of derivatives, including some in which metal atoms were trapped within the C_{60} cage or within expanded cages such as C_{82}. Robert L. Whetten and co-workers at the University of California at Los Angeles confirmed the physical stability of individual C_{60} molecules in a very direct manner. They found that a beam of high-speed C_{60} molecules bounces back from a silicon surface like a stream of rubber balls, whereas beams of other molecules are smashed apart by the collision. Interestingly, C_{60} molecules with metal atoms inside do not rebound as easily as do empty cages.

The most notable discovery in the physical chemistry of buckminsterfullerene in 1991 was that when C_{60} is crystallized with impurity atoms of such metals as potassium, rubidium, cesium, or thallium—alone or in certain combinations—the resulting solids exhibit superconducting properties, showing no resistance to the flow of electric current when cooled below a critical temperature (see *Inorganic chemistry* and *Organic chemistry*, above). The potential of such materials for no-loss power lines or high-efficiency transportation motors at economically realizable temperatures is exciting. Although the very low critical temperatures thus far obtained (no higher than about 45 K, or −228° C) require cooling with expensive liquid helium for superconductivity to be achieved, other results suggest that higher critical temperatures can be reached. If the critical temperature can be raised to 77 K (−196° C), then cooling with commonly available, and much less expensive, liquid nitrogen becomes possible. The discovery of superconductivity in these organic materials was a major surprise; the physical origin of their superconducting properties remains a mystery.

303

Chemical laser surgery. Using lasers as microscopic scalpels, chemists moved a few steps closer to controlling the chemical reaction pathways to desired products by selectively breaking certain chemical bonds in molecules. Richard Zare and co-workers at Stanford University, in collaboration with Betrand Girard from Paul Sabatier University, Toulouse, France, extended the work of F. Fleming Crim and co-workers of the University of Wisconsin (see *1992 Yearbook of Science and the Future* Year in Review: CHEMISTRY: *Physical chemistry*) on selectively cleaving the water molecule HOD, in which one hydrogen atom has been replaced by an atom of deuterium (D), a heavy isotope of hydrogen.

The Stanford team used tunable infrared lasers to cause either the $O-H$ or $O-D$ bond of the heavy water molecule to vibrate while leaving the other bond unaffected. They then allowed a beam of ordinary hydrogen atoms to collide with the HOD molecules. When they tuned the laser to cause the $O-H$ bond to vibrate, that bond stretched and weakened such that the HOD molecule released its hydrogen atom in a collision with the hydrogen-atom

Figure 3: Computer simulations of the interaction of microscopically small water droplets with a surface show the water molecules beading on a waxy surface (below) and spreading on a clean surface (bottom).

Photos courtesy of Michael L. Klein, University of Pennsylvania, Philadelphia

beam to form H_2 and OD (Figure 2a, p. 303). Conversely, when they tuned the laser to excite vibration of the $O-D$ bond, the HOD selectively reacted with the hydrogen-atom beam to produce OH and HD (Figure 2b). The work was unusual because of the use of low-energy infrared lasers, which caused just a small amount of bond stretching yet allowed a high degree of control over the reaction pathway. It was not yet clear, however, whether such bond-specific chemistry could be extended to other, more useful molecules and reactions.

Paul Brumer of the University of Toronto and Moshe Shapiro of the Weizmann Institute of Science, Rehovot, Israel, suggested a new approach to the problem of making chemicals with the correct handedness. Many important drugs exist in left- and right-handed mirror-image forms, but usually only the left-handed form is biologically active. Brumer and Shapiro proposed that carefully designed sequences of laser pulses could be used to break up a large molecule into smaller fragments that have a specific handedness.

Doing chemistry with computers. Powerful computers are becoming an increasingly important tool for theoretical chemists in investigations of the behavior of matter at the atomic level. Joseph Hautman and Michael L. Klein of the University of Pennsylvania provided a good example. From everyday experience one knows that water drops bead on a surface like a waxed table but spread and soak into untreated wood. Using a computer simulation, Hautman and Klein traced the interactions of extremely small droplets of water with waxy or clean surfaces. The model microdroplets contained fewer than 100 water molecules rather than the many billions in a visible droplet. The researchers' sophisticated computer software, which employed a procedure known as molecular dynamics, followed the way in which water molecules arrange themselves on the surface owing to interactions with the surface and among themselves. Interestingly, the simulation showed that, even in small numbers, water molecules bead or spread just like large drops (*see* Figure 3). The results suggest that it may become possible to understand the bulk properties of materials, involving the interactions of enormous numbers of molecules, from the behavior of just a few molecules "interacting" inside a computer.

—Philip R. Watson

Applied chemistry

During the past year research in applied chemistry led to developments in "cold" fusion, "hot" fusion, and fat and sugar substitutes. Another advance having broad potential applications, the discovery of superconductivity in doped forms of the all-carbon molecule buckminsterfullerene, is discussed in the first three sections of CHEMISTRY, above.

Cold fusion. In March 1989, at a press conference at the University of Utah, electrochemists B. Stanley Pons of the University of Utah and Martin Fleischmann of the University of Southampton, England, announced a process for producing room-temperature, or cold, nuclear fusion in which an electric current is passed through a platinum wire electrode coiled around an electrode of palladium in an electrolyte solution of alkaline heavy water. (Heavy water contains atoms of deuterium [hydrogen-2], a heavy isotope of hydrogen, in place of the common hydrogen atoms present in ordinary water.) Their highly controversial "discovery" was hailed by some as the greatest scientific event of recent decades. The media had a field day with the story, for in succeeding weeks scientists around the world obtained conflicting results in their own attempts to detect the heat, neutrons, and hydrogen isotope tritium (hydrogen-3) that Pons and Fleischmann cited as evidence that fusion was actually occurring.

No unanimity on the reality of cold fusion was reached by the end of 1989 or throughout 1990 (see *1992 Yearbook of Science and the Future* Year in Review: CHEMISTRY: *Physical chemistry* and *Applied chemistry*). Despite a number of dismissive articles in mainstream science journals, the controversy continued throughout 1991, although with less coverage as the media and many scientists began to lose interest in a case that showed no signs of being settled. Yet the quest for cold fusion failed to fade away, and the scientific community remained sharply polarized between the skeptical majority and a minority of cold fusion supporters.

In January 1991 Pons resigned his teaching position to devote more time to cold fusion research. Also in January, after communications between Pons and Fritz G. Will, director of the University of Utah's National Cold Fusion Institute (NCFI), had broken down over the question of sharing critical data with Will and institute scientists, Pons and Fleischmann were "divorced" from the NCFI. The NCFI itself ceased operation at the end of its fiscal year on June 30, when the last of the $5 million it had received from the state of Utah was spent.

Stephen E. Jones of Brigham Young University, Provo, Utah, whose cold fusion claims had been less flamboyant than those of Pons and Fleischmann, continued to carry out various types of experiments that yielded sporadic signs of fusion products. While most scientists dismissed Pons and Fleischmann's work as "wishful thinking overriding scientific judgment," they considered Jones's work "too irreproducible or too subtle to justify further time and money." Nevertheless, dozens of experiments to reproduce cold fusion continued in many countries.

In early 1991 Jones and Howard Menlove of the Los Alamos (N.M.) National Laboratory traveled to Japan to begin experiments with astrophysicist Yoji Totsuka of the University of Tokyo. Menlove previously had claimed to have consistently detected neutron bursts in a titanium-deuterium cold fusion apparatus. By seeking fusion products both with laboratory detectors and with the much more sensitive Kamiokande astrophysical particle detector (located underground in the Kamioka mine, where any neutrons detected could not have come from cosmic radiation), the three scientists intended to weed out possible instrumental errors from signs of actual nuclear reactions. Early results were negative, but detection of neutrons was announced in June.

In March physical chemist Melvin H. Miles, with postdoctoral research associate Gregory S. Ostrom of the U.S. Naval Weapons Center, China Lake, Calif., and Benjamin F. Bush, a postdoctoral research associate of Joseph J. Lagowski of the University of Texas at Austin, reported "the first definitive evidence for the formation of helium-4 [a possible cold fusion product] during the electrolysis of heavy water in a cold fusion cell." Also, dental films positioned near the apparatus were found, after developing, to be exposed—a possible indication of gamma-ray production. Will stated, "I would call this the most startling finding since that first announcement by Pons and Fleischmann. If this stands up, it will be revolutionary." On the other hand, metallurgist Nathan J. Hoffman of the U.S. Department of Energy's Energy Technology Engineering Center, Canoga Park, Calif., considered the results ambiguous, arguing that there are "many ways you can get spurious helium-4 results in the gas phase." Nuclear chemist John R. Huizenga of the University of Rochester, N.Y., declared that too much heat had been produced for the quantity of helium-4 generated and that "it just violates all that we know about nuclear physics." Some theoreticians, however, have suggested that cold fusion may not follow currently accepted fusion theory.

May 1991 brought the publication of two books summarizing the cold fusion controversy. As with research on the alleged phenomenon itself, the volumes were at odds with each other. In keeping with the unusual nature of the entire controversy, a highly critical book, *Too Hot to Handle: The Race for Cold Fusion,* by particle physicist Frank Close of the University of Tennessee, Oak Ridge (Tenn.) National Laboratory, and Rutherford Appleton Laboratory, Oxfordshire, England, was reviewed on the front page of the *New York Times* several weeks before publication. In the book Close warned, "If these events become regarded as a norm for science then public confidence would be threatened. It is important that the public see that the test-tube fusion story is *not* typical of normal science." By contrast, in his book with an opposing viewpoint, *Fire from Ice: Searching for the Truth Behind the Cold Fusion Furor,* Eugene F. Mallove, former chief science writer for the Massachusetts Institute of Technology News Office, concluded that "the evidence is *overwhelmingly* compelling that cold fusion is a real, new nuclear process capable of significant excess power generation. The evidence for significant power generation, however, cannot be said to be *conclusive. . . .* There is yet no *proved* nuclear explanation for the excess heat. That excess heat *exists* is amply proved."

In his review of both Close's and Mallove's books, Bruce V. Lewenstein, assistant professor of communication and of science and technology studies at Cornell University, Ithaca, N.Y., and director of the Cornell Cold Fusion Archive, disputed both authors' moral complaints that the cold fusion polemics do not constitute normal science. He wrote, "Media hype, competition, politics, patents, conflicting interpretations of data: each is absolutely normal, even integral to modern science. . . . By bringing together into a single case all of what is known about the social context of science, the incident is perhaps the best example we have of the fundamentally human character of science."

From June 29 to July 4, 1991, the second annual Cold Fusion Conference was held at the Alessandro Volta Center, Villa Olmo, Como, Italy, where roughly 200 researchers from around the world, including Pons, Fleischmann, Will, and members of the defunct NCFI, gathered to discuss their latest results. According to Carol White, editor in chief of the pro-cold-fusion magazine *21st Century Science & Technology*, the participants "have refused to capitulate to the tyranny of organizations like the American Physical Society, or institutions like *Nature* magazine, or scurrilous journalists who write for the popular press." She summarized the conference as "a celebration of this fact: Two years after the initial announcement by Martin Fleischmann and Stanley Pons, an international team of top scientists unequivocally confirmed their 1989 results, and their conclusions that what was occurring was a nuclear event—not merely electrochemical." Physicist Robert T. Bush of California State Polytechnic University stated, "The general message conveyed by the conference was that far from fading away, cold fusion research appears here to stay and is getting stronger." Indeed, 1992 began with the news that one scientist was killed and three were injured in a laboratory explosion at SRI International, Menlo Park, Calif., in the course of one of "a series of tests surrounding cold fusion."

Hot fusion. Unlike the case of cold fusion, which progressed like a soap opera or a media circus, research in hot fusion (so-called to differentiate it from room-temperature work) took place in a more conventional manner. The cluster-impact fusion research of chemists Robert Beuhler, Lewis Friedman, and Gerhart Friedlander of Brookhaven National Laboratory, Upton, N.Y., continued. In 1989 the researchers had reported detecting energy and nuclear fusion products from the bombardment of metal targets loaded with deuterium with tiny clusters of heavy water molecules (see *1991 Yearbook of Science and the Future* Year in Review: CHEMISTRY: *Applied chemistry*). After two years of further work, Friedlander said, "We have thousands of experiments now confirming that this is real." Experiments were being conducted not only at Brookhaven and other laboratories in the U.S. but also in France, The Netherlands, and possibly Japan. Theoreticians attempted to account for the results; skeptics criticized them; and the effect appeared to show promise as a new practical path to fusion.

Although commercial fusion power will probably not be accomplished for several decades, a major step forward was taken in November 1991 when about 200 scientists from 14 European countries successfully carried out a deuterium-tritium "burn" at the Joint European Torus (JET) nuclear research center at Abingdon, Oxfordshire, England. Fusion occurred for two seconds, and a record amount of power—about 1.7 MW (1.7 million w), about 20 times the power generated in previous deuterium-deuterium fusion experiments—was produced for nearly a second. According to JET director Paul-Henri Rebut, "This is the first time that a significant amount of power has been obtained from controlled nuclear fusion reactions." Nevertheless, the amount was still only about 10% of that required for heating the fuel, far short of the "break-even" point needed for a commercial reactor.

The fuel was heated to about 200 million° C (about 360 million° F), nearly 10 times the temperature of the interior of the Sun, in a torus- or doughnut-shaped device commonly called a tokamak, where magnetic fields and electric currents heat hydrogen nuclei to high temperatures while confining them together, thus causing the deuterium and tritium nuclei to fuse. Tritium had not previously been used because its natural radioactivity requires special handling and because it produces a high flux of neutrons, causing the reactor chamber itself to become radioactive. Only a small proportion of tritium was used for the 1991 experiment. In the future greater proportions will be employed; use of a 50:50 mixture of tritium and deuterium was planned for 1995–96.

Fat and sugar substitutes. As increasingly health-conscious people continue to demand reduced-fat foods and as government regulations hold food manufacturers to ever stricter definitions of such terms as *low-fat* and *97% fat-free*, companies have competed to develop low-calorie, low-cholesterol fat substitutes to supply a market that could be worth billions of dollars annually. In the late 1980s a no-calorie, no-cholesterol sucrose polyester (SPE) "fake" fat named olestra was announced by the Procter & Gamble Co., Cincinnati, Ohio (see *1989 Yearbook of Science and the Future* Year in Review: CHEMISTRY: *Applied chemistry*). Not long afterward a low-calorie, low-cholesterol fat substitute made from milk and egg-white proteins, trade named Simplesse, was announced by NutraSweet Co., a division of Monsanto Co., St. Louis, Mo. (see *1990 Yearbook of Science and the Future* Year in Review: CHEMISTRY: *Applied chemistry*). In June 1991 the A.E. Staley Manufacturing Co., Decatur, Ill., a division of Great Britain's Tate & Lyle Plc, announced a cornstarch-based fat substitute, trade named Stellar, which has a longer shelf life and broader range of uses than Simplesse, according to Staley spokesperson Mary Matiya.

In October Hercules, Inc., Wilmington, Del., introduced a fat substitute described as "a proprietary specialty pectin derived from citrus peel, standardized by the addition of sucrose [cane sugar]" and said to contain "virtually no calories." Pectins are purified carbohydrate hydrocolloids obtained commercially from the inner portion of the rind of citrus fruits or from apple pomace (pulpy residue obtained after crushing and pressing). Because pectin is a natural product long used in foods, the new "fake" fat, trade named Slendid, should encounter little difficulty in being approved by the U.S. Food and Drug Administration (FDA).

In its manufacture Slendid is extracted selectively to adapt it to replace emulsified fats and is unsuitable for other applications for pectin such as preparing jellies. Like other pectins, when mixed with water and a gelling agent such as calcium chloride, Slendid forms a gel that the company claims can replace as much as 100% of the fat in various processed foods. As the process of emulsification shears fat into small particles, so Slendid is emulsified to yield a gel that is more than 95% water yet contains small particles resembling emulsified fats in physical and sensory properties; *e.g.*, in being soft and deformable.

Artificial sweeteners, which can allow persons with diabetes or calorie-conscious dieters to satisfy their desire for sweetness without abandoning or compromising their diets, continued to be the focus of research by food chemists around the world despite the development of aspartame (NutraSweet) and other natural and synthetic sweeteners. In 1991 Coors Biotech, Inc., Westminster, Colo., announced its intention to utilize Japanese technology to produce in the U.S. a natural class of sugars called fructooligosaccharides, which were already used in Japan in about 50 different foods. According to Coors chemist Robert M. Speights, these natural sugar additives, which contain less than half the calories of sucrose, pass intact through the stomach and small intestine, where they are metabolized by beneficial bacteria (similar to those in yogurt) that make the intestinal tract less susceptible to *Salmonella* infections and possibly to carcinogens as well. Although they can be used as low-calorie sweeteners, the sugars will be marketed as a "healthful food additive."

A German and a U.S. company each developed a new bulking agent that can be used as a sugar substitute. According to chemist Hubert Schiweck of Südzücker AG, Grünstadt, even though the two products do not possess the intense sweetness of saccharin or aspartame, they look and behave so much like sucrose that they can replace it in frozen desserts and baked goods. Südzücker's product, trade named Isomalt, contains only half the calories of sucrose. According to chemist Manssur Yalpani of the NutraSweet Co., his company's product, a group of related compounds called sugar amides, passes intact through the human body and thus contains no calories. The two bulking agents, which have not yet been approved by the FDA, can reduce the caloric content of desserts by one-third to one-half when used along with artificial sweeteners.

Anniversaries. The year 1991 marked several important anniversaries. It was the 300th anniversary of the death of Robert Boyle (1627–91), the Irish chemist and physicist whose influential book *The Sceptical Chymist* (1661) did much to transform alchemy into chemistry. He made numerous contributions to the study of gases, and Boyle's Law—at constant temperature the volume of a gas is inversely proportional to the pressure that it sustains—is the basis for many pneumatic devices.

In 1991 numerous meetings and symposia were held to commemorate the 200th anniversary of the birth of English chemist and physicist Michael Faraday (1791–1867), whose laws of electrolysis put electrochemistry on a modern basis and whose discovery of benzene made possible today's extensive organic chemical industry. The son of a blacksmith, Faraday was self-taught. While apprenticed to a bookbinder, he worked his way through the electrical articles in the *Encyclopædia Britannica*.

German physical chemist and 1920 Nobel laureate Walther Nernst (1864–1941), the 50th anniversary of whose death was noted in 1991, discovered the third law of thermodynamics and made fundamental contributions to electrochemistry and photochemistry. The year 1991 also marked another golden anniversary: on Jan. 21, 1941, Dow Chemical Co. produced at Freeport, Texas, an ingot of magnesium—the first commercial ingot of any metal to be prepared from seawater.

—George B. Kauffman

Defense research

Many military analysts in 1991 saw the conflict in the Persian Gulf as a turning point in the history of warfare—and of defense research. Just as railroads, telegraph lines, rifled gun barrels, and the other technologies introduced during the American Civil War made possible the 20th-century strategy of massed forces seeking victory with superior firepower, the electronics-based technologies unveiled in the effort to oust the Iraqi invaders from Kuwait have begun to dictate a new strategy of smaller, more mobile, and better trained forces capable of swift, debilitating strikes.

"Brilliant weapons" and the Gulf war. The technological foundation of this revolution in warfare is the 1980s generation of microprocessor-controlled "brilliant weapons," successors to the "smart weapons" of the Vietnam era. They enabled the U.S.-led coalition forces in the Persian Gulf to use electronic warfare to neutralize opposing forces with pinpoint bombardment before committing ground troops.

Simply defined, electronic warfare (EW) consists of controlling the electromagnetic spectrum for any military purpose (command, control, communications, intelligence, battle management) while denying that use to an enemy. Any superiority of enemy weaponry is therefore negated by the enemy's inability to use it.

U.S. Rep. William L. Dickinson (Rep., Ala.), in a speech to a group of electronic warfare specialists in Washington in late 1991, described the contributions of EW to the allied success in the Gulf: "EW made over 85% of the Iraqi SAM missiles ineffective." He stressed the importance of "increasingly cost-effective force multipliers like electronic warfare systems."

Dickinson's term "cost-effective force multipliers" is the key to electronic warfare. U.S. military doctrine in Europe throughout the cold war assumed that the NATO defenders would be confronted by numerically superior Soviet and other Warsaw Pact forces. Therefore, a force multiplier was essential to achieve a more nearly even balance. It was pure serendipity that this doctrine, refined in Europe, provided the margin of victory in Iraq.

The critical factor in the superior performance of these new weapons was advanced digital electronics. In the past, radar and electro-optical images had to be processed by special-purpose computers as analog data. The new general-purpose computers processed the information digitally and merely required the loading of new software for each mission. This reduced costs as well as improving mission effectiveness.

Also, because the computers are modular, field forces could quickly replace failed modules rather than attempting to repair them under the trying conditions of warfare. Sophistication was built into the hardware in order to reduce the skills required of the military support personnel.

Fiber optics is another U.S.-pioneered technology that contributed to the military successes in the Gulf war. Optical fiber data networks are more efficient than conventional copper cables in tying together the electronic modules within a weapon system such as a tank or aircraft. They have much greater bandwidth (at least 100 million bits per second, as compared with one million bits per second for copper cables) and, because they transfer data as photons rather than electrons, they are virtually immune to enemy detection or electronic countermeasures.

Advanced electronics technologies also were employed in the military satellites that enabled U.S. forces to maintain unhampered surveillance of Iraq. The early-warning Defense Support Program (DSP) satellites observed Iraq's launches of its Scud missiles by detecting the infrared signatures of the rockets' exhaust and then relayed this information to the defenders in time for them to use their own radars to track the incoming missiles.

The Patriot air defense missiles, which were deployed against the Scuds, were originally developed

An ERIS Integrated Systems Test Vehicle missile is displayed in a launch silo. The missile was developed as part of a U.S. Strategic Defense Initiative program to destroy enemy missiles in space.

Lockheed Missiles & Space Company; photo, Ross Underwood

Photos, Arms Communications; (left) William B. Folsom; (right) Hans Halberstadt

A trainee works on a simulator for the U.S. Navy's Tomahawk cruise missile system (left), and a U.S. Army instructor wears night-vision goggles (above). Such technology gave the coalition forces a great advantage over Iraq in the Gulf war. The night-vision devices were particularly effective in the desert environment.

for battlefield use to protect U.S. troops and not for the defense of urban areas. Their use for that purpose stimulated another defense research project. The U.S. Department of Defense (DOD) began adapting technology derived from the Strategic Defense Initiative (SDI), which was intended to counter Soviet strategic nuclear missiles, to tactical, nonnuclear defenses. The U.S. Army Strategic Defense Command in 1991 accelerated its efforts to develop a more "leak-proof" tactical missile defense (TMD) system than the Patriot, which had been used to fulfill a role for which it had never been intended.

On the basis of U.S. Central Intelligence Agency estimates that 15 or more less developed nations may have tactical ballistic missiles—many of them potentially with chemical, and some with nuclear, warheads—by the year 2000, the Strategic Defense Command initiated a program to develop a new TMD system that in an emergency could be fielded as early as 1995. Known as Theater High-Altitude Area Defense (THAAD), the system was intended to serve as an overlay to the existing Patriot and other point defense systems that were under development. THAAD was envisioned as the long-range component of active TMD, one of four prongs in the overall TMD requirement. As established in 1982, the four consisted of attack operations (killing the enemy missile and its launcher on the ground prior to launch); active TMD (killing the missile in flight); passive TMD (hardening critical assets and preventing the enemy from determining the location of friendly units); and command, control, communications, and intelligence operations (detecting threatening missile launches and sending target data to the defenses).

THAAD was perceived as part of the proposed Global Protection Against Limited Strikes (GPALS) system being developed with SDI technology. As a subset of GPALS, it was designed to be capable of intercepting warheads up to 200 km (120 mi) downrange and up to 150 km (90 mi) in altitude. Supplementing THAAD in TMD would be an upgraded version of the Patriot and a new missile derived from SDI known as the Extended Range Intercept Technology (ERINT) missile.

Unlike Patriot, which detonates a warhead in the atmosphere to destroy incoming missiles, ERINT and THAAD are intended to be hit-to-kill weapons, guided all the way to their targets at hypersonic velocities (about Mach 7, or seven times faster than the speed of sound). During the Gulf war, Patriots flying at Mach 3 intercepted Scud missiles that were traveling at Mach 6 and destroyed more than half of their warheads. The maximum altitude achieved by the Patriots was approximately 10 km (6 mi), which was generally adequate to destroy the Iraqi conventional warheads. However, a weapon that strikes its targets beyond the Earth's atmosphere, such as ERINT or THAAD, would be needed to provide protection against nuclear or chemical warheads. Furthermore, such weapons would have to be easily transportable by air to hot spots around the world, a requirement that dictates microminiaturization of the electronic components.

Another TMD system, Arrow, was being jointly developed by the U.S. and Israel to attack incoming missiles at altitudes of about 40 km (25 mi). However, it was not intended to be a mobile system because Israel would not need to deploy it beyond its own borders.

309

The F-117 "stealth" fighter performed effectively for the coalition forces in the Gulf war. Computer-controlled simulation trainers were credited with having given the crews of the fighters thorough preparation for combat missions.

A challenge that faced those developing THAAD was what is known as a system architecture problem. To deal with this the SDI experience was again expected to be valuable. The basic idea was that any operational antimissile system must be compatible with existing sensors, such as the Airborne Warning and Control System (AWACS), which is a militarized Boeing 707 jet aircraft carrying advanced radar and communications equipment, and the DSP surveillance satellites, which were used successfully in the Gulf war. The system must also be compatible with such future sensors as the space-borne "Brilliant Eyes" being developed for SDI. Moreover, the system must be capable of "connectivity" with any air defense system of a host country seeking U.S. assistance against aggression, as was the case with Saudi Arabia in the Gulf war.

A further liability for Iraq in the Gulf war was the superiority of U.S. night-vision devices, which enabled the coalition air and ground forces to attack at will during the night and, to a lesser extent, in bad weather. These devices, using infrared and laser technologies, were particularly effective in a desert environment.

Still another category of advanced technology that was tested in the Gulf war was computer-controlled simulation for training military forces prior to combat. Advances in military training and simulation systems during the past decade, made possible primarily by the increasing availability of high-performance digital computer systems from the commercial marketplace, were of critical importance in the early phases of the war. Refinement of these technologies in anticipation of future military activities was being accelerated.

At least two facets of the Gulf war—the sophisticated electronic jamming that negated the Iraqi air defenses and the precision delivery of weapons that

destroyed high-value targets with minimal collateral damage to civilians—would have been impossible without the new levels of training realism, according to Gen. Robert H. Reed, executive director of the National Training Systems Association, Arlington, Va. Reed, a retired air force general, cited the example of the performance of the F-117 "stealth" fighters. "The trainers did an outstanding job of preparing the crews to do combat missions," he said, but he also noted the often-overlooked role of the maintenance trainers, which contributed to the reliability of these new aircraft. The trainers performed so well, he reported, that the Air Force was able to use them for troubleshooting of the F-117 fuel and hydraulic systems.

Other applications. Many of the same high-technology systems that helped fight the Iraqi forces were finding new uses in another struggle—the one to combat the influx of illegal drugs and other contraband into the United States. Government agencies, national laboratories, and private industry were cooperating to adapt military gear to counternarcotics operations and give law-enforcement officials new weapons in the war against international drug operations. Much needed to be done to accomplish this, according to Stan Morris, deputy director for supply reduction at the Office of National Drug Control Policy (ONDCP), the so-called Drug Czar office established to coordinate efforts among federal agencies to combat the drug scourge. Many of the highly publicized military systems that led to a quick end to the Gulf war could not immediately find practical use in operations to combat drug smugglers, according to Morris.

Part of the problem lay in the nature of the conflict. While the Gulf war was a classic confrontation between two armies, "our counter-drug efforts are closer to the Cold War," Morris noted, for which systems for surveillance, tracking, intelligence gathering, and communications are far more useful than are laser-guided bombs.

Another obstacle was the sheer size of much of the military high-tech hardware that could be employed. Ground-based satellite communications systems to provide worldwide communications and report precise locations could prove valuable to field agents but were too bulky for practical use.

Putting high technology to work in a new way did, however, produce some outstanding results in the drug war. In Hawaii, for instance, state law-enforcement officials had used small planes to fly over and identify suspected marijuana fields, after which they sent teams back to burn the plants. The program typically eliminated some 20–25% of the annual crop. DOD provided a high-level overflight of the islands, which were photographed and then marked into grids of suspect fields through a combination of military-style photo interpretation and advanced sensors. Because no advance warning was given to growers, as had occurred with the low-level flyovers, and since fields throughout the state could be identified all at once, the resulting raids destroyed an estimated 90% of Hawaiian marijuana production.

Another technology validated in the conflict in the Persian Gulf was being refined for future ground-combat vehicles. Known as vetronics, which is short for "vehicle electronics," it was derived from the avionics (aviation electronics) modules in such tactical aircraft as the U.S. Air Force's F-15 and F-16 and the U.S. Navy's F-14 and F/A-18, all of which were used extensively in the Gulf war.

Avionics and vetronics have one feature in common. They are basically packaging techniques that accelerate the insertion into vehicles of advanced electronics technologies, such as powerful new digital processors developed under the very high-speed integrated circuit (VHSIC) program.

The electronics industry was readying the avionics for the next generation of combat aircraft, which was scheduled to be operational during the early 21st century, and that technology should be available for vetronics. An example was the family of new applications-specific integrated circuits (ASICs), which were being fabricated by state-of-the-art semiconductor processes. ASICs, the 1990s equivalent of the VHSIC and MIMIC chips of the 1980s, promised greater flexibility for tailoring the vetronics systems of the future to respond to as-yet-undetermined threats. They made possible "fused" sensor systems that integrate threat data from many sources and present a coordinated picture to combat personnel. In combination with advanced automation techniques and expert systems, they were expected to change the nature of future warfare.

—John Rhea

Earth sciences

Global warming, ozone depletion, the events that took place at the boundary between the Cretaceous and Tertiary periods, the quality of stream water and groundwater, and oil spills in the ocean were among the subjects of investigation by Earth scientists during the past year. Mt. Pinatubo in the Philippines erupted explosively in June 1991, and an El Niño event in the Pacific Ocean affected weather throughout the world.

Atmospheric sciences

During the past year several issues in atmospheric science achieved worldwide attention. These included continued concern regarding the potential of global warming as a result of increased concentrations of "greenhouse" gases that trap heat in the Earth's atmosphere, the Kuwaiti oil-field fires and the influence of their smoke on weather, and the ejection of aerosols and gases into the stratosphere by the huge eruption of Mt. Pinatubo in June. Among the continuing rapid advances being made in other atmospheric science areas were improved monitoring systems and more capable computers for performing weather and climate simulations.

Global warming. Attention to the possibility of greenhouse gas warming was motivated by the current level in the atmosphere of carbon dioxide. At about 350 parts per million, it was higher than at any other time during the past 160,000 years. As of 1992 the rate of increase of carbon dioxide was about 0.5% per year. Also, methane, nitrogen oxides, and chlorofluorocarbons (CFCs), all added by human activities, have contributed to the concentration of gases that trap heat. Methane was increasing at a rate of about 0.9% per year, while CFC concentrations were about 4% greater each year.

Considerable uncertainty remained, however, concerning the effect of these enhanced concentrations of greenhouse gases on climate. Albert Arking of the U.S. National Aeronautics and Space Administration (NASA) concluded that the occurrence of 10% more cloudiness at night within the same overall average cloud cover would have a substantially greater effect on climate than a doubling of greenhouse gases. Cloud effects and their relationship to a greenhouse gas-enriched environment remained one of the major uncertainties in global circulation models. These models were the prime scientific tool used to investigate potential human-caused greenhouse gas warming.

There was conflicting observational evidence regarding climate change caused by an existing greenhouse effect. B.A. Bücher and Jean Dessens of the Observatoire Midi-Pyrénées in Toulouse, France, for

The Upper Atmosphere Research Satellite, designed to study ozone depletion in the upper atmosphere, is ready to be deployed from the remote manipulator system of the space shuttle Discovery *in September 1991.*

example, documented an annual increase of 0.83° C (1.5° F) between 1882 and 1970 at a site 2,862 m (9,387 ft) above sea level in France, a result consistent with the influence of greenhouse-gas global warming. This warming occurred at night (+2.11° C [+3.8° F]), with −0.45° C (−0.81° F) average cooling during the daylight. Cloud coverage during the same period increased by 15% at this location.

The direct effect of carbon dioxide enrichment could be positive, as suggested by the research of Bert Drake of the Smithsonian Environmental Research Center, Edgewater, Md., and separately by Robert Balling of Arizona State University. Drake found that with a doubling of carbon dioxide concentrations, water demand would decrease between 17 and 27%, depending on species, and plant growth would increase by as much as 84%.

The intervention of man to mitigate and deliberately alter climate change, referred to as "global environmental engineering," was discussed at a December 1991 meeting of the American Geophysical Union in San Francisco and in a 1991 U.S. National Academy of Sciences report entitled "Policy Implications of Greenhouse Warming." One of the suggestions was to place 50,000 mirrors, each measuring 100 sq km (39 sq mi) into Earth orbit to reflect incoming sunlight. Many atmospheric scientists, however, believed that there was a need to better understand previous climate change and natural variability in global climate before undertaking such a major project.

Ozone depletion. The depletion of ozone in the stratosphere in polar regions continued to provoke considerable scientific interest. This reduction in ozone levels, due to chemical reactions in the stratosphere during the late winter and spring, permits damaging high-energy ultraviolet radiation to reach the surface in regions under the ozone hole. CFCs, used extensively in refrigeration and as foam-blowing agents, have been implicated as a human-caused reason for this depletion. The reduction of ozone between 17 and 21 km (10 and 13 mi) over Antarctica began about a week earlier in 1991 than it had in previous years. In the region between latitudes 30° and 64° N, an ozone decrease of 3–5% was measured between 1969 and 1988. The U.S. Environmental Protection Agency (EPA) proposed that all U.S. production and importation of CFCs and other depleters of stratospheric ozone be halted by the year 2000. However, in February 1992, in response to new evidence of ozone depletion over the U.S., Pres. George Bush ordered a ban on CFC production effective Dec. 31, 1995.

A joint U.S.-Soviet agreement on cooperation in the exploration and use of outer space for peaceful purposes resulted in the launching of the Total Ozone Mapping Spectrometer (TOMS) by a Soviet rocket in August 1991. This launch, which took place prior to the 1991 period of ozone depletion in the south polar region, provided daily mapping of global ozone with high spatial resolution. A second satellite to monitor the Earth's upper atmosphere, including the Antarctic ozone hole, called the Upper Atmosphere Research Satellite (UARS), was launched on September 12 from the space shuttle *Discovery.* A polar-orbiting satellite launched on May 14, 1991, had the capability to monitor cloud cover and surface temperature.

Atmospheric-measurement systems. Problems with atmospheric-measurement systems also occurred during the year. The GOES (Geostationary Operational Environment Satellite) 7, which had provided weather coverage from space, was expected to lose its capability to provide data and might even fail by late 1992. The replacement satellite, GOES-NEXT, was more than two years behind schedule and $500 million over budget. To provide weather coverage until the GOES-NEXT was launched, the U.S. planned to borrow the European Meteorological Satellite Consortium Meteosat-3 satellite and perhaps move it to a position at longitude 90° W in order to view weather systems over North America.

The measurement of atmospheric structure by surface-based platforms continued to develop rapidly during the year. The application of over-the-horizon (OTH) defense radars—each costing more than $100 million—to the monitoring of winds and ocean waves to distances exceeding 2,000 km (1,200 mi) from the coast was reported. The U.S. Federal Aviation Administration and the National Weather

Service were installing Terminal Doppler Weather Radar, developed by Raytheon Corp., at 45 major airports to alert air traffic controllers and airline pilots of such hazards as microburst wind shears and clear-air turbulence. The installation of remote-sensing wind profilers continued during the year, with eight sites becoming operational. The profilers, to be established at 20 sites in the central U.S., were designed to provide continuous monitoring of winds at heights of up to about 20 km (12.5 mi).

Over ocean areas a new international marine weather dissemination system that uses geostationary communications satellites was inaugurated in February 1992 and was scheduled to be completed by 1999. Part of the Global Maritime Distress and Safety System, it was designed to transmit weather forecasts and warnings to ships at sea regardless of their locations. The availability of this system could perhaps have minimized the considerable damage to shipping caused by Typhoon Mireille along the coast of Japan in late September 1991.

Pinatubo. The eruption of the Mt. Pinatubo volcano in the Philippines on June 12–16, 1991, spewed aerosol particles and gases as high as 30 km (18.5 mi) with an areal coverage 10 days after the initial eruption in a nearly continuous band that extended 11,000 km (6,800 mi) from Indonesia to central Africa. Brilliant red sunsets and sunrises in the tropics and, by fall, in the mid-latitudes in the Northern Hemisphere resulted from sunlight passing through the ejected material high in the atmosphere. Three weeks after the eruption the stratospheric aerosol formed a semicontinuous band between latitudes 20° N and 20° S.

The amount of material ejected into the stratosphere might have been the greatest since Katmai in 1912 and was at least double that of the El Chichón eruption in 1982. The elevated aerosols act to reflect sunlight back into space and to absorb sunlight, which cools the lower atmosphere. Moreover, because vertical air currents are weak in the stratosphere, where much of this aerosol material resides, the influence on climate can persist for several years. The worldwide depression of temperature during this period due to the volcano was expected to be about 0.5° C (0.9° F). (See *Geophysics*, below.)

Kuwait oil well fires. The massive oil well fires in Kuwait, ignited early in 1991 by Iraqi troops occupying that country, prompted immediate concern over the potential global effect on the weather. More than 500 oil wells were left burning, producing a smoke plume that was tens of thousands of square kilometres in extent. The fires each day accounted for about 5% of the oil burned throughout the world and for about 2% of the global carbon dioxide emissions. The World Meteorological Organization estimated that at the fires' peak 5 million bbl of oil and 70 million cu

Gaseous cloud of sulfur dioxide (white area) caused by the eruption of Mt. Pinatubo in the Philippines is imaged by the Nimbus 7 spacecraft in June 1991. The cloud could chill the Earth slightly during the next few years.

m (2,470,000,000 cu ft) of gas were burned each day. As a result of the obscuration of the Sun by the smoke, Bahrain experienced its coldest May in 35 years, with temperatures more than 3° C (5.4° F) below average.

An expedition sponsored by the U.S. National Science Foundation studied the smoke plumes in May and June 1991, however, and concluded that while the influence of the smoke on the local weather was significant, its influence on global climate was likely to be undetectable. The smoke only occasionally rose above 6.5 km (4 mi), was generally between 300 and 3,000 m (1,000 and 10,000 ft), and consisted of aerosols that served as cloud-condensation nuclei and thus could be scavenged efficiently from the atmosphere by rainfall. In November 1991 the last of the fires was extinguished. (*See also* Feature Article: EARTH: THE GULF WAR'S SILENT VICTIM.)

Other developments. Other air-quality concerns remained prominent during the year. The U.S. and Canada signed an agreement to reduce the transborder transport of air pollution. The U.S. agreed to reduce sulfur dioxide emissions to 10 million tons below 1980 levels by the year 2000, while Canada accepted a limit of 2.3 million tons by 1994. In France air-quality regulations appeared to be having clearly defined effects. In Paris lichens, which are susceptible to sulfur dioxide damage and were eliminated from the city in the mid-1800s owing to dirty air, recently began to reappear as coal-burning stoves that use sulfur-rich coal were being phased out.

In the U.S. the Navajo Generating Station in Page, Ariz., was required to reduce its emissions by 90% by 1999 at a cost of more than $2 billion in order to improve the visibility in Grand Canyon National Park and other vistas in the region. This was the first time that such extensive controls had been required in order to protect a visual resource.

The ability of atmospheric scientists to simulate weather and climate depends on computer capabilities. New supercomputers were purchased for this research, including CRAY Y-MPs by the National Center for Atmospheric Research in Boulder, Colo., for climate research and other atmospheric science studies and by the Naval Oceanographic Office at the Stennis Space Center in Mississippi for oceanographic prediction. Recently, high-performance workstations with capabilities for individual researchers on the order of the supercomputers became available. These included the IBM RISC 6000 series and the HP 9000 series. The availability of these computers was expected to revolutionize the ability to simulate accurately such atmospheric studies as global climate change, air-pollution dispersion and chemical transformation, and weather prediction.

Storage devices were also developed to archive the voluminous amounts of weather data. For example, the U.S. National Oceanic and Atmospheric Administration and NASA planned to transfer four trillion bytes of 14-year satellite data, which currently are stored on 31,000 magnetic tapes, to approximately 600 30.5-cm (12-in) optical discs. The easier access to these data was expected to facilitate research.

—Roger A. Pielke

Geologic sciences

Geology and geochemistry. The principle that emphasizes the gradual action of familiar processes throughout the history of the Earth appeared during the past year to be in retreat on all geologic fronts. Ever since Luis Alvarez suggested in 1981 that a mass extinction at the end of the Cretaceous Period 65 million years ago was caused by an impact of an asteroid, cataclysmic events have figured more prominently in geologic explanations.

Cretaceous-Tertiary boundary events. The suggestion by Alan Hildebrand of the University of Arizona and his colleagues that a large impact structure might be found in the Caribbean region received further confirmation. The structure has no surface expression, being buried beneath a thick blanket of carbonate sediments of Cretaceous age on the Yucatán Peninsula. Magnetic and gravitational anomalies, however, reveal a circular structure about 180 km (110 mi) in diameter. Quartz grains recovered from oil wells drilled within the boundaries of the crater have a structure characteristic of material that has been subjected to the extremely high shock pressures that could be expected to result from the impact of a large extraterrestrial object. (For additional information, *see* Feature Article: THE SEARCH FOR THE KT CRATER.)

After a decade of searching for the site of the impact that produced such havoc at the end of the Cretaceous, geologists may now be facing an embarrassment of riches. Alan Deino of the Institute of Human Origins in Berkeley, Calif., reported that a single rock sample from the 105-km (65-mi)-diameter Popigai crater in Siberia had yielded a date of 65 million years before the present. The age of the crater had previously been estimated to be between 30 million and 40 million years. A 35-km (22-mi)-diameter crater in Iowa was also dated at 65 million years. It is improbable that three asteroids large enough to have caused craters of this size would, by chance, have struck the Earth in a geologic "instant"; thus, some event that provides a single cause for them all, such as the disintegration of a comet passing close to the Sun, may have been responsible.

Early climate. The ability of geologists, geochemists, and paleontologists to infer climatic conditions during remote periods in the Earth's history has increased dramatically during the past three or four decades. An example was provided by the work of three geologists, A. Sarkar and S.K. Bhattacharya of the Physical Research Laboratory in Ahmedabad, India, and D.M. Mohabey of the Geological Survey of India, who took advantage of a remarkable paleontological discovery to infer climatic conditions of west central India during late Cretaceous time. Well-preserved clutches of sauropod dinosaur eggs were recovered from the Upper Cretaceous Lameta limestones of the Kheda district. Experimental studies have demonstrated that there is a strong correlation between the relative concentration of the stable oxygen isotope ^{18}O in the water ingested by reptiles and birds and the relative concentration of this isotope in the carbonates of their eggshells. Studies have also revealed a relationship between the concentration of the stable carbon isotope ^{13}C in the carbonates of eggshells and in the food eaten by the reptiles and birds. In a paper published in the November issue of *Geology*, the authors concluded that the dinosaurs who laid these eggs drank from rivers and pools and fed on shrubs and conifers in a semiarid climate.

Roger Larson of the University of Rhode Island advanced the idea that a period of intense volcanism in which millions of cubic kilometers of gas-laden lava were spread over the floor of the Pacific Ocean may have been responsible for a period of global warming beginning in mid-Cretaceous time about 120 million years ago. The release of carbon dioxide from those lavas would sharply increase the concentration of the gas in seawater and, ultimately, in the atmosphere, where it would enhance the greenhouse effect. Some geologists questioned Larson's conclusion, contending that the limited number of samples available did not support so great an area of mid-Cretaceous basalt in the Pacific Basin. Continued exploration was expected to eventually settle this issue. The cause of such extensive and intense volcanism was, according to Larson, initiated by a plume of hot, buoyant material rising from deep in the Earth's mantle.

Scientists at the University of Rhode Island and Pennsylvania State University encountered some difficulties in attempting to determine the concentration of carbon dioxide in the atmosphere during this period of mid-Cretaceous warming. Michael Arthur of Penn State reported that although the ratio of stable carbon isotopes to one another in the organic compounds of phytoplankton reflects the concentration of carbon dioxide in seawater and, consequently, in the atmosphere, experiments have shown that different species of these microscopic marine plants produce different ratios in response to the same concentration of carbon dioxide. Despite this difficulty, a preliminary study suggested that between 120 million and 70 million years ago carbon dioxide levels in the atmosphere were between 6 and 10 times higher than they are today, more than enough to produce a dramatic warming of the atmosphere.

One of the dreaded consequences of global warming is the melting of polar ice and the consequent inundation of the most populous regions of the Earth. A recent study indicated, however, that under some circumstances, global warming might lead to a net increase of ice. Radiocarbon dating of sediments from the continental shelf off the east coast of Antarctica revealed that biogenic, open marine sediments accumulated during the past 4,000 years, while sediments containing rocks derived from the Antarctic continent and deposited on the edge of melting glaciers accumulated during a period between 7,000 and 4,000 years ago. This distribution of sediments suggests that glaciers were expanding during the earlier period, which corresponds to the Hypsithermal, regarded on independent evidence to have been the warmest period since the end of the Pleistocene Epoch about 10,000 years ago. Eugene Domack of Hamilton College, Clinton, N.Y., A. J. Timothy Jull of the University of Arizona, and Seizo Nakao of the Geological Survey of Japan concluded that in a cold polar climate, warming would increase precipitation in the form of snow, which would contribute to glacial expansion. They cited theoretical calculations that indicate that a temperature increase of more than 5° C (9° F) would be needed to induce glacial retreat, a figure well above the estimated rise of 2° C (3.6° F) during the Hypsithermal.

Mantle plumes. Mantle plumes, invoked by Larson to explain the mid-Cretaceous warming, were receiving increased attention as their significance became more evident. These plumes consist of bodies of hot rock that rise to the Earth's crust from somewhere in the mantle at a rate of 10–20 cm (4–8 in) per year.

The mantle is that portion of the Earth's interior extending from a boundary with the Earth's core, at a depth of 2,900 km (1,800 mi), to immediately beneath the relatively thin crust. Geologists disagree sharply as to whether the plumes originate deep in the mantle, near the core, or entirely within the 670-km (415-mi)-thick outer mantle.

This disagreement was thoroughly aired in May at a meeting held at the California Institute of Technology. Questions concerning heat loss from the Earth's interior were a focal point of discussions. Geoffrey Davis of the Australian National University at Canberra argued that if plumes cannot cross the boundary between the lower and upper mantle, then 70% of the heat loss from the core and lower mantle must be by way of plumes originating at the bottom of the upper mantle. He concluded that a rise of the ocean floor above major plumes of only about one kilometer (0.62 mi) indicates that the plumes are not carrying much heat. Donald Turcotte of Cornell University, Ithaca, N.Y., countered this argument by claiming that slabs of ocean crustal plate pushed into the mantle at ocean trenches would absorb some of the heat rising from the lower mantle. Yashio Fukao and his colleagues from Nagoya (Japan) University obtained seismic data that indicate that pieces of oceanic crust may indeed sink into the mantle and, in some cases, even penetrate the boundary between the upper and lower mantle and descend to depths of as much as 1,200 km (750 mi). Although the hypothesis that at least some of the plumes originate in the lower mantle was gaining adherents, the controversy promised to continue.

Paleontology and tectonics. The role of paleontology in evolutionary and paleoecological studies is fully recognized. What may not be evident, however, is the contribution of this discipline to the solution of problems in such seemingly unrelated fields as tectonics. Brian Atwater of the U.S. Geological Survey and David Yamaguchi of the Mountain Research Station and Institute of Arctic and Alpine Research at the University of Colorado concluded that a general rise in sea level of several meters per century, a rate suggested by evidence from Hudson Bay and the North Sea, is insufficient to account for the sudden burial of forests in coastal Washington in the recent past. Tree-ring analyses and radiocarbon dating of red cedar and Sitka spruce found standing in their growth position are consistent in yielding a date of 300 years ago for the death of the trees. The tree rings reveal, furthermore, that the growth of the trees remained normal until shortly before their death. The preservation of stems and leaves suggests that burial was so sudden as to outpace decomposition, which in modern salt marshes occurs within a few years. Coarse, thick, sand deposits located to the seaward of the lowland forest deposits were apparently produced by a landward surge such as might be produced by a tsunami (a giant sea wave often produced by the movement of crustal plates beneath the ocean).

Buried forests along the coast of Washington bear evidence to other episodes of sudden rises in sea level, roughly 1,700 and 3,100 years ago. The authors concluded that the evidence from fossil plants accords well with independent evidence of magnitude 8 or 9 earthquakes generated along the Cascadian subduction zone at the boundary between the North American and Juan de Fuca plates.

Environmental problems. Political as well as scientific and technological difficulties continued to stand in the way of solutions to some pressing environmental problems. As waste continued to accumulate in what were intended to be temporary storage facilities at reactor sites, controversy over the suitability of the proposed Yucca Mountain area in Nevada as a location for the disposal of high-level radioactive waste continued unabated. Concern was being expressed that because of the potential for volcanic activity and earthquakes in the region and because of the possible intrusion of groundwater into the facility, the geological isolation of the repository during the prescribed 10,000 to 100,000 years could not be guaranteed.

Mike Goldstein of the technology and policy program at the Massachusetts Institute of Technology suggested that the requirement of absolute certainty of isolation during the prescribed period might be impossible to meet and that the detailed regulations and specifications designed by the U.S. Department of Energy to meet this requirement might better be abandoned in favor of the design-as-you-go approach suited to taking into account experience and data as it accumulates. The proposed completion date of the repository was extended to 2010.

Nirex, Great Britain's radioactive waste agency, encountered similar opposition to its proposal to establish a repository for low- and intermediate-level radioactive waste in caverns excavated from bedrock beneath the Sellafield nuclear complex in northwestern England. In July *New Scientist* magazine reported that a senior member of the Waste Management Advisory Committee believed that the agency had not carried out enough investigations to assure the public that a suitable site had been chosen. Phil Richardson, who has completed a study for Greenpeace, argued that because the Borrowdale Volcanic Series in which the caverns would be excavated has been subject to extensive deformation, the movement of groundwater in which escaping radioactive material might become dissolved will be "extremely complicated and totally unpredictable." Nirex officials defended their choice on the grounds that the rock is very impermeable.

Geothermal energy. The prospect of abundant, inexpensive geothermal energy was diminished somewhat by continuing bad news from the largest geothermal generating field in the U.S. The Geysers, a series of geothermal generating plants in the Mayacamas Mountains 115 km (70 mi) north of San Francisco, supplied 6% of California's electrical power and represented 75% of the developed geothermal energy capacity of the U.S. in 1991. Groundwater, heated by an underlying magnetic body to produce steam in shallow reservoir rock, is delivered directly to generating plants through wells drilled from the surface. During the last several years, however, steam pressure has been declining at such a precipitous rate that by the late 1990s power output may have declined to half what it was in the mid-1980s. The cause of the diminished pressure is not a lack of heat, which is virtually inexhaustible, but the depletion of groundwater. Geologists generally agreed that the resource had been overdeveloped, with far too many wells being drilled in an attempt to meet the increasing demand for inexpensive electric power. Some success in arresting, and even reversing, the decline of steam pressure was achieved by injecting water condensed from used steam back into the reservoir rock. A program of injection of water condensed from geothermally generated steam was also undertaken in Mexico's Cerro Prieto field in the hope of slowing the decline of steam pressure.

—David B. Kitts

See also Feature Article: THE DINOSAUR RENAISSANCE.

Geophysics. Several years into the International Decade for Natural Disaster Reduction, earthquakes and volcanoes continued to take their toll of lives and property. The most important geophysical event of 1991 was the cataclysmic eruption of Mt. Pinatubo in the Philippines. One of the largest volcanic eruptions of the 20th century, it caused hundreds of deaths and extensive property damage. The casualties would have been higher, however, if mass evacuations had not taken place. The warnings of an impending eruption that led to these evacuations were made possible by recent advances in electronics and instrumentation. This is but one example of many new data-acquisition systems that will have a profound impact on geophysics in the next decade.

Mt. Pinatubo. A dormant volcano that last erupted 600 years ago, Mt. Pinatubo on the island of Luzon in the Philippines was of little concern to the many people living near it (including those at the U.S.'s Clark Air Base) until a series of small hydrothermal explosions occurred near the volcano's summit on April 2, 1991. Volcanologists from the Philippine Institute of Volcanology and Seismology performed aerial reconnaissance and installed portable seismographs near Pinatubo. These seismographs registered many

Mudflow on a mountain in the Philippine province of Pampanga passes a riverbank covered with hardened mud from the eruption of Mt. Pinatubo. The mudflows were created when heavy rains carried ash from Pinatubo down mountain slopes, causing considerable damage to farms and towns.

small (magnitude 0.5 to 3) earthquakes at a depth of about five kilometers (three miles) and a distance of about five kilometers from the vents from which the hydrothermal explosions issued. Although it was not known whether these events were of tectonic (motion of the Earth's crustal plates), hydrothermal, or magmatic (from molten material within the Earth) origin, the possibility of a large eruption prompted the Philippine scientists to request assistance from the U.S. Geological Survey. The USGS sent a team of Earth scientists.

The Philippine and U.S. teams worked closely together and proceeded to make a wide variety of observations in the vicinity of the volcano. Mapping and age dating of deposits from previous eruptions showed that the volcano had experienced large eruptions about every 600 to 2,000 years. The signals from the portable seismometers installed around Pinatubo were relayed to a command center on Clark Air Base. The record of the evolution of seismic activity that this network provided was the primary tool used in forecasting the eruption. Visual observations and the measurement of sulfur dioxide emissions were also key parts of the forecasting effort.

The sulfur dioxide emissions indicated that the volcanic unrest was almost certainly due to magma moving beneath the mountain. The emissions increased in late May, and during the first part of June the seismic activity moved closer to the summit of the volcano and became shallower, signs that the magma was migrating toward the surface. A lava dome of solid material was extruded into the summit area of the volcano and doubled in size within a week. All of these signs warned of an eruption, and people around the volcano were evacuated. Eruptions became more frequent, culminating in the explosive eruption on June 15 that removed at least 200 m (660 ft) from the mountaintop and produced a caldera 2 km (1.2 mi) in diameter. This eruption

took place about midday, but the large amount of ash in the air prevented it from being visually observed. The cloud of ash turned day into night and, together with heavy rains from a typhoon, the series of magnitude-5 earthquakes that accompanied the large eruptions, and the sounds of the continuing explosions, created a harrowing experience for the scientists who were monitoring the volcano from a bunker on Clark Air Base. The scientists knew that something was happening, but without visual information they did not know the extent or the direction of movement of the main plume that was produced by the eruption.

Because of the forecasts of the eruption, mass evacuations (more than 58,000 people) were undertaken; therefore, the loss of life was very small for an eruption of that magnitude. The effects of the eruption, however, reached far beyond the short time of the eruptions themselves. The volume of ash and shattered rock deposited around the volcano was estimated at 10 billion cu m (13 billion cu yd), making it one of the three largest volcanic eruptions of the century. The torrential rains common in that part of the world turned these loose, unconsolidated deposits into a slurry (termed "lahar") that moved downhill under the influence of gravity, clogging river channels, destroying bridges, and burying villages. A monitoring and radio communications system was installed to warn of lahars. Little could be done about them other than to evacuate people in their path. By early 1992 almost every bridge within a radius of 30 km (18.5 mi) of Mt. Pinatubo had been destroyed, and several towns had been buried.

The low loss of life could be attributed to a number of factors: more than two months went by between the first signs of activity and the climactic eruption; the technology was available to monitor the activity adequately; and the evacuations were successfully carried out. Crucial to successful evacuations are adequate communications and the ability to convince local officials and residents that the threat is real. These factors were not in place for several previous eruptions, including that of Nevado del Ruíz in Colombia, which left 22,000 people dead in spite of clear warnings about the volcano's hazard.

Of particular importance for the Mt. Pinatubo evacuations was a video of volcanic hazards by Maurice and Katia Krafft, two French volcanologists known for their educational books and videos on volcanology. This video dramatically portrayed to local officials and military authorities the possible consequences of an eruption. Ironically, at about the same time that their video was being used to help in the evacuation around Mt. Pinatubo, the Kraffts were killed by an eruption of Mt. Unzen in Japan on June 3.

Other volcanoes. Volcanic activity is common (particularly around the rim of the Pacific Ocean), although it is not usually newsworthy unless it directly affects humans (as did Mt. Pinatubo). For example, on Aug. 12, 1991, Hudson Volcano in southern Chile erupted explosively, sending rock fragments to a height of 16–18 km (10–11.2 mi), depositing more than one billion cubic meters of volcanic debris in

Mt. Unzen in southern Japan spews forth hot gas, ash, and molten rock during a major eruption in June 1991. An explosion several days earlier killed more than 30 people, including three volcanologists.

AP/Wide World

Argentina, and dropping material 1,000 km (620 mi) away on the Falkland Islands/Islas Malvinas. But because few humans were affected, it received little mention in the world press.

Receiving more mention was the eruption of Mt. Unzen, which killed the Kraffts, a U.S. volcanologist, and 34 others. The previous eruption of Unzen had been in 1792, when landslides and tidal waves killed 15,000 people—the worst volcano disaster in Japan's history. The current eruption forced more than 10,000 people from their homes. Although both the Mt. Unzen and Mt. Pinatubo eruptions occurred in June, there was no obvious connection between them.

Kilauea, on the island of Hawaii, had been erupting intermittently for almost 10 years and had increased the land area of the island of Hawaii by more than one square kilometer (0.39 sq mi). It had covered 75 sq km (29 sq mi) of the surface with lava up to a thickness of 25 m (82.5 ft). The eruptions were well studied and, as a result, the onset of an eruption could often be predicted by observations of ground deformation and the occurrence of earthquakes.

Earthquakes. Twenty-one earthquakes killed more than 2,800 people in 1991, some 2,000 of them during a magnitude 7.1 earthquake that struck India on October 19. In addition, tens of thousands of residences were damaged, and more than 100,000 people were left homeless. The largest earthquake (magnitude 7.6) was in Costa Rica on April 22 and killed 82 people. Most of the casualties due to earthquakes in 1991 could be ascribed to poorly constructed buildings. Unlike damaging earthquakes in developed countries during previous years, the earthquakes in 1991 were of interest more for their geologic characteristics than for their significance to modern engineered structures.

The Costa Rican earthquake occurred beneath the Caribbean coast of the nation, near the city of Limón. It was the strongest earthquake in Costa Rica since 1950 and the largest event ever recorded in the vicinity of Limón. Most earthquakes in Costa Rica are produced by the northeastward subduction of the Cocos plate beneath the Pacific coast. The recent earthquake was unusual in that it resulted from plate motion in the opposite direction, involving subduction of the Caribbean plate beneath Costa Rica in a southwestward direction. Teams of seismologists from a number of countries were studying the records from this earthquake to better understand the processes of back-arc subduction, a process not often considered in estimates of seismic hazards.

A few days after the Costa Rican earthquake, a magnitude 7 earthquake struck the western Caucasus Mountains near South Ossetia, Georgia. Aftershocks of this event were recorded on portable instruments installed by a joint team of U.S. and Soviet seismologists. Their analysis of the main shock and aftershock

Workers dig through the ruins of the International Hotel in Limón, Costa Rica, in April 1991. An earthquake registering 7.6 on the Richter scale destroyed the hotel and killed more than 80 people.

data suggests that the rupture during the main shock took place on a shallowly dipping fault plane. This is of interest for understanding mountain building in regions of convergence between crustal plates. Geologic mapping in such regions often points to large amounts of slip occurring on low-angle faults, but earthquake fault planes often dip more steeply. This inconsistency could be interpreted to mean either that slip on the shallow planes occurs aseismically—without generating earthquakes—or that the earthquakes on the shallow planes are infrequent but large. The recent earthquake in Georgia lends support to the latter interpretation.

Advances in data acquisition. A major revolution was under way in the quantity and quality of data available to seismologists for understanding earthquake faulting and the structure of the Earth and in their ease of access to those data. Seismometers had been developed that could record a very wide range of signal frequencies over a broad range of signal amplitudes. Coupled with advances in digital electronics (including microcomputers) and global communications, these signals could be made available in a short time to researchers throughout the world. Consortia of research institutions involving different countries were formed to deploy and operate the data-gathering stations and to distribute the data to interested researchers.

Many countries maintained networks of these new instruments, and these networks banded together under the umbrella of the Federation of Digital Broadband Seismographic Networks (FDSN) to ensure that, among other things, data formats were compatible and coverage of the Earth would take place with little duplication.

In the U.S. the organizations primarily responsible for the new data acquisition were the Incorporated Research Institutions for Seismology (IRIS) and the U.S. Geological Survey (USGS). IRIS and the USGS were cooperating on the installation of broadband instruments throughout the world. Their goal was a network of 128 matched instruments spread uniformly around the Earth; by early 1992 more than 27 of the instruments had been installed.

The distribution pattern of land over the globe had left large regions uncovered in the absence of development and deployment of ocean-bottom seismometers. IRIS was developing such stations and was taking advantage of the abandonment of submarine cables by telecommunications companies. A cable from Japan to Guam was recently donated to IRIS and the Earthquake Research Institute of the University of Tokyo by the commercial owners. This cable was to be used to transmit data from a number of seafloor geophysical observatories to central recording sites on land.

In addition to the global array, the IRIS consortium developed a new generation of high-quality, robust, and relatively inexpensive portable seismometers. These instruments and the support facilities provided by IRIS were intended to be used in specific experiments of limited duration. During the last few years more than 30 institutions had used these instruments in cooperative projects ranging from deployments in Tibet in order to better understand the structure of the Tibetan Plateau to studies of aftershocks from the 1989 Loma Prieta earthquake in California.

Another large region of the Earth that until recently would have been difficult to instrument adequately was the former Soviet Union. In 1987 several temporary stations were installed there as part of a cooperative program to monitor nuclear explosions. This and the continuing thaw in U.S.-Soviet relations provided an opportunity to greatly expand high-quality instrumentation in the former U.S.S.R. A number of the broadband stations mentioned above were installed, as were the portable instruments. Although the primary motivation was to monitor the nuclear test-ban treaties, the scientific payoff was expected to be much larger. In addition, specialized networks and small arrays were installed in regions of high seismic hazard. The impact of the disintegration of the Soviet Union on the cooperative program remained to be seen, but early indications were that the cooperation would strengthen.

The impact of the revolution on geophysical data acquisition was already being felt. At every research conference many papers were presented that used these data to investigate Earth structure and earthquake source processes with unprecedented detail. In the past, geophysicists often had had to rely on laborious investigations of very few data (in some cases, papers published using only one recording from an earthquake), with much uncertainty in the final result being the inevitable consequence. Although the Earth would never submit to the controlled experiments possible in some of the sciences, the envelope of uncertainty surrounding Earth structure and earthquake source processes was sure to shrink drastically in the next few decades.

—David M. Boore

Hydrologic sciences

Hydrology. Early in 1991 the U.S. National Research Council (NRC) released a report entitled *Opportunities in the Hydrologic Sciences*. This book, prepared by a commission of the NRC chaired by Peter S. Eagleson of the Massachusetts Institute of Technology, should be an important milestone in the development of hydrology. The commission's premise was that hydrologic science has a natural place as a geoscience alongside the atmospheric, oceanic, and solid-earth sciences but that the scientific infrastructure to support basic research and educational programs does not exist and must be put in place. The commission argued that hydrologic science should be viewed as a discipline interactive on a wide range of space and time scales with the oceanic, atmospheric, and geologic sciences as well as with plant and animal sciences. Hydrologic science involves issues related to the circulation of water through the atmosphere, over and through the land, and to the ocean; it is also concerned with issues of changing water quality and the ways human activity such as deforestation, urbanization, and pollution affect the global water cycle.

To transmit the excitement and significance of research initiatives in hydrologic science, the NRC commission outlined its views on scientific priorities in critical and emerging areas of the field. These areas are: (1) chemical and biological components of the hydrologic cycle, including solute transformations, biogeochemical functioning, and interactions between ecosystems and the hydrologic cycle; (2) the formulation of a basis for developing models or predictions at larger or smaller scales from hydrologic processes observed at one scale; (3) the investigation of reciprocal influences between land-surface processes and weather and climate; (4) coordinated global-scale observation of water reservoirs and the fluxes of water and energy so that scientists can better understand the state and variability of the global water balance; and (5) the hydrologic effects of human activity.

Progress in many of the topic areas listed above was limited by a lack of observational data. High-quality data are essential to the testing of existing and new models of hydrologic processes. The NRC commission highlighted the need to maintain continuous, long-term data sets; the need to improve information management, especially in light of increasing amounts of satellite and ground-based remote-sensing data; and the desire to distribute to the scientific community the data from large-scale coordinated experiments.

As of 1992 there were only a few programs within the North American university system that provided a coordinated education in the hydrologic sciences. Most students entered the hydrologic sciences as a specialization within either geology, geography, or engineering departments. The NRC commission members concluded that a new educational model was needed to advance the health and stature of hydrologic sciences. They promoted the establishment of multidisciplinary graduate education programs in hydrologic sciences as departmental units or programs. Only in this way would graduates view themselves first as hydrologists rather than as geologists, geographers, or engineers who knew something of hydrology.

The commission also emphasized the importance of providing students with experience in modern observational equipment and field-based experimental approaches. The report, published by the National Academy Press, is recommended reading for anyone wanting an overview of research opportunities in the hydrologic sciences or for students thinking of pursuing a career in the field.

Issues related to water quality were prominent during the past year. A research team at the University of Washington, led by Dennis Lettenmaier, reported in the journal *Water Resources Research* (March 1991) on trends in stream-water quality in the continental United States for the period 1978–

87. They noted that since the passage of the Federal Clean Water Act of 1972, more than $100 billion of government funds had been spent on municipal wastewater-treatment plants; comparable private funds had been spent to reduce industrial discharges; and there had been large expenditures to protect surface waters from "nonpoint source pollution" (for example, urban stormwater) and from changes in land-use practices (mining and forestry). Their analysis provided a snapshot of the changing quality of surface water across the U.S.

The research team analyzed data from 403 stations in the National Stream Quality Accounting Network, which was operated by the United States Geological Survey. This network provided measurements of common ions, trace metals, nutrients, and other chemical indicators sampled on a quarterly or bimonthly basis. Identification of trends in water quality is a difficult task. Problems arise because of short data records, the considerable natural variability in water-quality characteristics, missing data, changes in sampling frequencies over time, changes in detection limits due to improvements in instrumentation, high proportions of nondetectable values for some chemicals, and correlations between concentration values and the magnitude of stream flow. Trends, therefore, must be described in terms of probabilities.

Trends in water quality were detected for only a minority of the stations examined in the network. Of those stations exhibiting a trend, the chemical groups accounting for the greatest percentage of the trends were common ions (mostly upward; greater concentrations in the stream water) and nutrients (mostly upward for total nitrogen and mostly downward for total phosphorous). Most of the downtrends were

recorded at sampling stations located in the major population areas of the eastern and midwestern U.S. The authors concluded that the most noteworthy result of their analysis was the large proportion of uptrends in the alkalinity of the stream waters and the large proportion of downtrends in dissolved arsenic, cadmium, and lead (Figure 1). A reduction in atmospheric deposition due to controls on emissions from major sources was suggested as the explanation for these findings. In the case of lead the downward trend may be due to reduced use of leaded fuels in automobiles. In the case of most chemicals, however, no simple explanation was apparent.

Groundwater quality continued to be a major focus of research in hydrology. Few well-planned, large-scale field experiments had been carried out to examine how contaminants dissolved in groundwater spread through the subsurface. The degree to which a plume (a region of contaminated groundwater) spreads through the subsurface determines such factors as the arrival time of a contaminant at a downstream well or surface body of water and the concentration levels of contaminants within the plume. In recent years a number of models had been proposed that attempted to relate the rate at which a contaminant plume grows in size to the geologic properties of the soils or rocks through which the groundwater flows. These models must be tested in controlled field experiments. The experimental procedure involved injecting a tracer into the subsurface and then monitoring its movement by using an extensive network of wells. The latest experiment to be reported, published in *Water Resources Research* (May 1991), was for a site in Massachusetts. Over a three-year period, Denis LeBlanc and his co-workers of the U.S. Geological Survey documented the

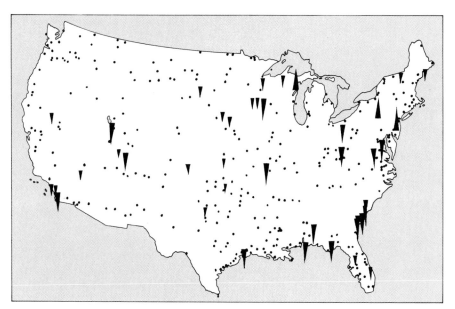

Figure 1. Map reveals the geographic distribution of trends in dissolved lead in surface waters of the United States during 1978–87. The direction of the arrows indicates uptrends (increased amounts of lead) or downtrends, and the larger the arrow is, the more likely it is that the trend is real and not due to chance. The dots indicate no trend.

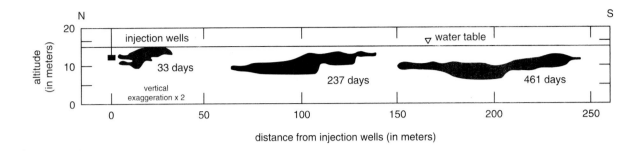

Figure 2. Migration of a tracer plume through an aquifer reveals the geometry of the plume and its rate of growth as it is carried farther from the source area. For additional information, see text.

movement of a tracer in a sand and gravel aquifer over a distance of nearly 300 m (950 ft). Several different tracers were used; one was bromide, which is chemically inert, while others reacted with the mineral grains that make up the geologic deposits.

The tracer plume spread mainly in the direction of groundwater flow, with relatively little mixing occurring in the vertical direction (Figure 2). This experiment is important because it supports theories that predict that the rate at which a contaminant plume will grow becomes constant after an initial start-up period. There are important implications of this result in the development of methods of assessing potential impacts on groundwater quality of land-based waste-disposal operations.

David Rudolph and co-workers at the University of Waterloo, Ont., published the results of their hydrogeologic investigations in the basin of Mexico. Mexico City is located within this groundwater basin. The regional aquifer there provides approximately 70% of the water supply for the nearly 20 million people living in the region. This is the largest urban population in the world that relies on groundwater to meet its water-supply needs. The aquifer is overlain by a sequence of clay deposits, which supply water to the aquifer by downward leakage of water contained in the clays. The clays are also thought to provide some protection for the aquifer from the numerous sources of pollution that occur on the ground surface. These sources of contamination include unlined sewage canals and landfills that had few or no design features to reduce the downward infiltration of contaminants.

The conventional belief was that because of the fine-grained nature of the clay deposits, the rate of downward groundwater flow was very slow. Rudolph and his group, however, analyzed chemical patterns of major ions and environmental isotopes from water samples collected within the clays and on this basis concluded that the downward infiltration of water

is occurring at a rate that can be explained only if the clay deposits contain vertical fractures that penetrate to significant depths. Fractures can lead to substantial increases in the rates of groundwater flow in fine-grained sediments. The conclusion that could be drawn from this study was that the rate at which contaminants are moving downward through the clays toward the main aquifer (from which fresh water is withdrawn) may be greater than previously thought. Consequently, if vertical fractures in the clays are common in the basin of Mexico, the water supply in Mexico City is susceptible to potential contamination from poor waste-management practices on the ground surface.

—Leslie Smith

Oceanography. For oceanographers, 1991 started with a sound heard around the world from a low-frequency source that emanated signals near Heard Island in the southern Indian Ocean for a six-day period in late January. The experiment involved scientists, ships, and listening stations from several countries; major support was provided by the U.S. Navy. Results showed that the attempt was successful; the sound was heard clearly at listening stations in the Indian, Atlantic, and Pacific oceans. Since the speed of sound in water is a sensitive function of temperature, changes in travel time as the sound traverses ocean basins can be linked to changes in the average temperature of the water in the basin. It appeared from the success of this pilot study that this technique might be used to detect changes in the average temperature of the large ocean basins—in particular, the slow changes that could be associated with the greenhouse warming effect in the atmosphere.

Planning was under way for a more comprehensive program with sound sources in several locations around the world for several years. The only negative note was struck by marine mammal experts, who raised concerns about whether the experiment might disrupt feeding behavior and communications of whales, porpoises, seals, and other sea mammals. Representative sets of such mammals were closely monitored before, during, and after the pilot study, and no significant short-term effects were detected. Studies about possible effects of a longer program would continue.

Oil spills. On the same side of the world as Heard Island, and also in January, millions of barrels of oil were released by Iraqi troops into the Persian Gulf. This was one of the largest oil spills in history and affected a significant fraction of the coast of Saudi Arabia. The spill was of lightweight crude oil, and thus much of it evaporated in the first week. The remainder, however, made up of heavier chemical fractions, could take years to flush out of the relatively closed gulf. At the time, it was not feasible to collect or remove most of the spilled oil. As a consequence, scientists were not able to predict the spill's long-term effects on local ecosystems. Satellite data were used to document the movement of the oil and its source directly after the spill. To study the effects further, the Intergovernmental Oceanographic Commission, an agency of the United Nations, held an emergency meeting to design a cleanup response and to study the impacts of the oil spill. The U.S. National Oceanic and Atmospheric Administration (NOAA) agreed to provide a ship for the first study, which was scheduled to take place in early 1992. For additional information, *see* Feature Article: EARTH—THE GULF WAR'S SILENT VICTIM.

The massive oil spill from the *Exxon Valdez* in Prince William Sound, Alaska, in 1989 continued in the news as unexpected lessons were learned about cleanup techniques. NOAA announced in April that the process of washing the oil off about 650 km (400 mi) of beach with powerful streams of hot seawater appeared to be more destructive than just leaving the oil in place would have been. Studies showed that small plants and animals, including clams, snails, and barnacles, were killed both by the heat and by being smothered when the streams moved the mud around. Some of the oil ended up in tidal pools, where it caused more damage. NOAA reported that untreated beaches were currently actually in better shape than the treated ones.

Algae, coral, and plankton. On a subject perhaps related to pollution, marine scientists announced during the year that the world's oceans were experiencing an explosion of noxious algal blooms, such as toxic red tides. It appeared that the outbreaks were more than the localized, episodic nuisances typical of past years. For example, researchers found that large sections of reefs (coral and otherwise) and sea grass beds were overgrown with massive blooms of benthic (deep-ocean) algae. At an international meeting held in Newport, R.I., in October, researchers reported

that a high percentage of previously benign algal blooms had become toxic. The cause of the shift was not understood; some believed that it might be part of a long-term natural oscillation of the biological system, that it might be enhanced by human wastes in the sea, or that it might be related to global climate change. The meeting called for urgent attention to the problem by the world's governments. In a related development, the Norwegian Institute of Marine Research reported that effects of the poison algae on aquaculture had already been devastating, killing large percentages of young fish being grown for market.

The health of coral reefs continued to deteriorate, with one important indicator being the degree of coral bleaching. In recent years scientists had suggested that global climate change—in particular, warming—was responsible for the bleaching. The process, which occurs when corals expel the algae that reside in their cells, had been observed globally. For example, the massive bleaching episode in the Pacific in the early 1980s was closely linked to warmer waters caused by the 1982–83 El Niño episode. (See *El Niño*, below.) During 1991 a meeting of scientists from several disciplines was convened in Miami, Fla., to examine the proposed links between bleaching and warming. The meeting concluded that current knowledge made it impossible to claim that coral bleaching was an early indicator of the global greenhouse effect. Noting the continuing deterioration of coral reefs, meeting participants endorsed an international program of long-term monitoring of the physical and biological factors that affect reef health. Some experts suggested that the biggest threat to reef health worldwide was the cumulative effect of local perturbations from population growth, land use, and resource exploitation; these together could be more important than global climate change.

Marine scientists continued to debate the role of plankton growth in the global carbon cycle—in particular, whether the rate of addition of carbon dioxide to the atmosphere might be slowed if increased photosynthesis (the process by which plants use carbon dioxide) in the ocean could be achieved. A proposal had been made in previous years that iron was a limiting element in the growth cycle of plankton in the Antarctic Ocean. The logical conclusion was that by adding a few million tons of iron compounds to that ocean, massive growth of plankton would occur in the nutrient-rich but iron-poor waters there. During the year the hypothesis received much critical examination. Models including the effects of ocean currents as well as biological processes showed that the rate of carbon dioxide uptake by Antarctic waters is critically dependent on the rate at which surface waters mix with deep waters. To achieve a significant reduction of the atmospheric carbon dioxide,

Staghorn coral reef, normally yellowish brown, is one of many that in recent years have been bleached. This happens when the colorful symbiotic algae of the coral animals have been expelled, and it can result in the death of the reef. Scientists agreed to undertake long-term monitoring of the reefs to try to determine why the expulsions were taking place.

the surface waters of the Antarctic Ocean must be replaced frequently from below by mixing processes. It appeared, though, that the actual rate of mixing is too slow to create a significant decrease in the atmospheric carbon dioxide.

Other studies suggested that the availability of trace metals does not limit the growth of plankton. Additional studies were clearly required. The debate over the role of iron in regulating productivity stimulated plans for further study and for small-scale iron-fertilization experiments in the Pacific Ocean that were to take place in 1993; also, there were calls for better measurements of the rates of both deep- and intermediate-water formation.

El Niño. Late in the year the winds and ocean currents in the Pacific Ocean began to exhibit the combined climate fluctuation known as El Niño. The tropical winds in the western Pacific became weaker, and the equatorial surface waters warmed. The onset of this El Niño had been correctly predicted by two different computer-based models of the system.

At the beginning this El Niño seemed to be weaker than normal, but as the year ended, all the characteristics for an intense global effect were in place. El Niño was expected to bring warm water to the South American coast by the spring of 1992, causing losses to the anchovy industry along the shore of Peru and bringing heavier-than-normal rainfall to that region. The 1991–92 El Niño was expected, like previous manifestations of the phenomenon, to produce droughts and floods throughout the world. It could mean more rain for the southeastern coast of the United States and the Gulf of Mexico, eastern and central Africa, and southern Brazil. In India and the western Pacific, droughts were possible. Weather was expected to be abnormally warm in the midwestern and northwestern U.S., western Canada, and Alaska. The hurricane season was expected to be mild.

The oceanographers and meteorologists who were studying the phenomenon were also pleased to see that their models had correctly predicted that there would not be an El Niño the previous year, even as the non-model-based forecasts showed that warming was imminent. The long-term support of research into El Niño and related phenomena and the application of new observing systems and computer modeling were beginning to provide the necessary understanding for developing successful climate predictions.

Ocean drilling. Climate studies were one major focus of the international Ocean Drilling Program, which continued in operation in the Pacific Ocean during the past year. Because of the importance of understanding the crucial role played by the oceans in regulating global environmental change, long-term records of past climate and fluctuations of biological systems are essential. These data can come from cores from the seafloor, which consist of sediments with a record of physical and biological changes. Up to the present, however, only a few high-quality sediment cores recovered from conventional ships from the top few meters of the seafloor existed. The climate and biological record in those cores represented only the past few hundred thousand years. Much longer cores, representing a look back in time of several million years, were needed for a more complete understanding of the ocean-climate system to be achieved. During an ocean-drilling expedition to the eastern equatorial Pacific in 1991, more than 5,000 m (16,400 ft) of core were recovered, a major achievement. The new cores provided a nearly continuous record for more than 12 million years and a resolution in space and time that was much more detailed than previous information.

Initial studies of the cores revealed climate fluctuations consistent with the changes that would be induced by variations in the Earth's orbit around the Sun. It also appeared that the new detailed records could be correlated with other data, thousands of kilometers away, to give records typical of broad areas. The new data were expected to keep paleoceanographers busy for a long time.

Results from a study of data collected from Antarctic waters during previous years of ocean drilling were presented during the year to show that about 57 million years ago an abrupt influx of warm, oxygen-poor water at the seafloor seemed to have triggered a major biological extinction. Although the extinction was known from previous data, the cores, collected by a device that does not disturb the sediments, showed that the extinction occurred over a much shorter time, about 2,000 years, than the previously estimated 2 million years. A change in water temperature at that time was also observed. The timing of the extinction and the water-temperature change are closely correlated, suggesting that at that time a major reversal in ocean circulation flooded the ocean with warm water that contained less oxygen.

The events recorded in the sediments occurred at the same time as major changes in land plants and fossil mammal teeth in Wyoming are observed in the continental record. It was clear that the more these high-resolution records were studied, the more brief, dramatic events would be discovered that could have profound effects on the understanding of ancient changes in global climate and ecosystems.

In related ocean-drilling events, a hole was drilled about 250 km (155 mi) southwest of Hawaii in March for the future emplacement of an ocean-bottom seismometer. The seismometer was to be part of a global network for monitoring earthquakes and other changes in Earth structure. Also during the year the Ocean Drilling Program extended the deepest hole already drilled to more than 2 km (1.25 mi) below the seafloor in the quest for achievement of a complete record of oceanic crust. There appeared to be no technical difficulties in extending this hole to significantly greater depths.

Coastal Transition Zone program. A major study involving physical and biological systems with a focus on the waters off the northern coast of California presented its results during the year. The Coastal Transition Zone program was aimed at understanding the physics of the filamentary structure so common to eastern boundaries of oceans (west coasts of continents). The filaments, first observed by satellite-borne instruments, are long, narrow, and transient. They are typically accompanied by high concentrations of chlorophyll and, therefore, are of key importance to biology.

The Coastal Transition Zone experiment was aimed at understanding how the filaments are caused by and interact with winds and currents and their biological effects. Biological, physical, and chemical techniques were used to characterize the filaments during the period of the study. The results showed that the summertime period is characterized by meandering jets and eddies, which produce the filaments. High nutrients are observed within and inshore of the filaments. During the winter the circulation is very different; there are no filaments, and as of early 1992 the process was not understood.

Satellite studies. Two new ocean-related satellite missions began in 1991, and another was scheduled for mid-1992. The European Space Agency's ERS-1, launched in April 1991, carried instruments for measuring sea-surface temperature, sea-surface height, waves and winds, and the concentration and extent of ice. The instruments used visible and infrared as well as microwave radar techniques. Most of the instruments worked as planned, and the initial data appeared to be good. The Almaz satellite, launched by the Soviet Union, also had a radar system for ice measurements. ERS-1 and Almaz were expected to be the precursors of a series of ocean-related missions for the 1990s.

In mid-1992 a precision altimeter mission, TOPEX/Poseidon, was to be flown jointly by the U.S. and France. The mission was designed to measure the height of the sea surface to an accuracy of a few centimeters, thus accurately providing estimates of global ocean currents. It was designed for a lifetime of five years. A U.S. ocean color mission was planned for 1993 to provide data on concentrations of global and coastal plankton.

Roger Revelle. In July a sad note was struck for oceanographers and Earth scientists in general. Roger Revelle, trained as an oceanographer but scientifically active in many areas, died in San Diego, Calif. Revelle was perhaps most famous for his work with Hans Suess that showed that increased populations and an increasingly mechanized world must be leading to an increase in carbon dioxide in the atmosphere. He supported the establishment of a monitoring program for carbon dioxide, which revealed the now well-known result of rapid increase of that and other greenhouse gases. Revelle's interest spanned all of Earth science; he and his colleagues were the first to measure heat flow through the seafloor. They discovered "subduction," a process by which the seafloor slowly slides under the continental crust at the ocean margin, later explained by the theory of plate tectonics.

In his work Revelle emphasized the interactive nature of the biology, chemistry, geology, and physics of the Earth and how they affect and are affected by people. Contemporary interdisciplinary Earth science was largely due to his influence. (*See* SCIENTISTS OF THE YEAR: *Obituaries*).

—D. James Baker

Electronics and information sciences

Ranging from laser-guided "smart" weapons to a variety of sophisticated electronic information systems, the products of the recent technological advances in electronics and the information sciences demonstrated their value in often spectacular ways during the Gulf war. In other developments, new workstations achieved the computational power of large mainframes, and the future of the space program of the Soviet Union was uncertain after that country's dissolution.

Communications systems

What was new in communications systems? Nothing was new and everything was new. The three transmission media of the industry—copper, fiber, radio—had all been in use for many years. Copper was the first to be employed, and the current-carrying capacity of a copper wire was no less or more in 1992 than it had been 100 years earlier. Wireless (radio) was used in vehicles long before the invention of the transistor. Fiber, the newest of the three, was itself more than a dozen years old. So, really, nothing was new.

But everything was new. Copper wires could do more than had ever been thought possible. Fiber optics (and its associated electronics) was improving rapidly. In fact, the capacity of fiber had doubled each year and a half. And radio was just starting to show its true capability.

Transmission technologies. Integrated Services Digital Network (ISDN), a copper-based technology, was found to be capable of transmitting digital information at megabit rates—not across the U.S., to be sure, but certainly from a corporate campus to a telephone switching office. With ISDN two twisted pairs of copper wire could transmit many voice and data channels simultaneously.

Fiber optics, however, was becoming the medium of choice. The realization that light is simply an extension of the electromagnetic spectrum made it possible to extend the speed of transmission to previously unheard-of limits. In the U.S. a technology called Synchronous Optical Network (Sonet) was being developed. As much as it was a network, Sonet was also a set of standards that defined all the protocols and speeds that fiber optics made possible. As an example, OC-1 (Optical Carrier, level one) operated at a speed of 51,840,000 bits. This was not outstanding; copper-based transmission systems had operated at those speeds for years. OC-48, however, permitted operation at 2.488 gigabits—2,488,000,000 bits—per second. In the European Communities, Sonet was not the standard; rather, the Synchronous Digital Hierarchy was used. Fortunately, the differences between the two were not insurmountable.

It should be made clear that the term "bits per second" (or gigabits per second) identifies the transmission as being digital in nature. All the information being transmitted—be it computer data or the human voice—is encoded into a series of 1s and 0s. Digital transmission is at the heart of all present-day telecommunications systems.

Fiber-optic systems were being used extensively in the long-distance telephone network in the U.S. Furthermore, fiber was quite common in the links between a telephone switching office and the "feeder plant," a place near an office complex or group of homes. What was left to do was to apply fiber to "the last kilometer"—the distribution network, or the local loop between the feeder plant and the home or office. This was an immense job and, although Japan promised to accomplish this by the year 2005, significant deployment of the fiber in the local loop in the U.S. was expected to take longer.

Many countries and continents were connected with undersea fiber-optic cables, and the number of those cables increased each year. By 1992 the network was extensive enough to provide an alternate route if one cable failed or became overloaded.

The third transmission medium is radio. Cellular radio was becoming increasingly popular, and a number of eastern European countries were intending to rely heavily on it for their telecommunications needs in the near future owing to the relative ease of setting up a system. In the U.S. cellular service was enjoying double-digit expansion.

Even cellular radio was experiencing technological challenges. Present-day systems employed analog techniques; the system used in the U.S. was called Advanced Mobile Phone Service, and the modulation technique was frequency division multiple access (FDMA). The shortcoming of FDMA was capacity; cellular radio was becoming so popular that the capacity of the cell-site equipment was being strained in a number of cities.

As was often the case in the communications industry, the solution seemed to be to move to digital techniques. This was being done, and the industry adopted a standardized digital scheme called time division multiple access (TDMA). Its capacity was approximately three times that of FDMA. However, cellular telephones themselves would have to be able to operate with both analog and digital signals because the cellular systems now in operation throughout the U.S. are totally analog and adding digital capability to all of them would be expensive.

To make the situation even more challenging, yet a third scheme was proposed. Based on the spread-spectrum technologies often used by the military, it was called code division multiple access (CDMA). The capacity of a system based on CDMA would be 20 times greater than for FDMA.

Tests were also taking place on an entirely different kind of wireless system called personal communications service (PCS). This service assumed that there was a need for a cellular-type phone system for mobile, but not vehicular, users. Such users would not be traveling at high rates of speed and, consequently, cells could be smaller (handing off a call as a user went from one cell to another was complex). With smaller cells, the phones could be equipped with smaller batteries and would, therefore, be small themselves; some industry experts speculated that such phones would fit in a shirt pocket. PCS would be valuable in an office environment; more calls would be completed because a person would no longer be away from his or her desk.

Applications. Technology for the sake of technology is of little value. Applications for the technology are required. For example, data were being transmitted at tremendous speeds between office complexes, thus reducing the problems associated with distance. Several technologies were competing to provide this service; among them were frame relay, cell relay, switched multimegabit data service, and fiber distributed data interface. All employed packet switching, a technique whereby bundles or "packets" of bits were sent in a burst over a transmission path at tremendous speeds, after which that transmission path was made available to other unrelated data exchanges. As speeds increased, the term "fast packet" was applied. An ultimate goal of packet switching was to assemble the bits associated with a voice conversation into the same kinds of packets as are used for data, transmit them over high-speed channels, and reassemble them at the receiving end to re-create the voice.

The use of these high-speed data-transmission techniques was also expected to make it possible to "move" the well-known 800 numbers from one long-distance carrier to another and also from one answering station to another. For instance, a call to a particular 800 number might be automatically directed to one location during the daytime hours but to a different location at night.

At a seemingly less sophisticated level (but only seemingly) was a service called Caller ID. If a particular switching system was properly equipped and if a telephone subscriber owned a small specialized electronic device, the called party would see the caller's telephone number displayed on a small screen after the ringing had started but before the phone had been answered. The service was described as an electronic peephole. There were legal problems with Caller ID, however, and some civil libertarians claimed that such a service was an invasion of pri-

Videophone 2500, a picture phone priced at $1,500, was scheduled to be marketed by AT&T in May 1992. It can be plugged into a typical wall jack and use existing telephone lines.

vacy. To counter this charge, many telephone companies were providing blocking along with the Caller ID service. By pushing a button, a calling party could block his or her number from being displayed on the called party's device.

Videoconferencing is another service that was being developed. Prices of equipment were dropping, and it seemed likely that some business travel would be replaced by videoconferencing.

Education was expected to benefit from the new technologies. No longer would students in a small rural community be denied advanced classes for want of a teacher. Electronic networks would bring a teacher to each and every classroom as a result of advanced transmission techniques, the ability to compress the data representing the video, and the availability of fiber-optic transmission links. Known as distance learning, it was being implemented during the past year.

Industry developments. It was not only technology that changed. Significant changes were taking place in the communications industry. For example, as a result of its merger with Contel, GTE became the largest telephone company in the U.S. During the year a Southwestern Bell/France Telecom consortium purchased controlling interest in Telmex, the Mexican telephone system. Ameritech, in partnership with Bell Atlantic, purchased the New Zealand telephone system. And a consortium led by GTE late in 1991 was awarded the contract for the purchase of a 40% stake in the Venezuela telephone system.

These large telephone companies claimed that the reason they had to look to offshore opportunities was the restrictions that they faced in the U.S. They cited three restrictions in particular: (1) the Bell operating companies could not design or manufacture equipment; (2) the Bell operating companies could not participate in information processing; (3) the large telephone companies were forbidden to provide cable TV systems in their own franchised territories. During the year item 2 was relaxed by court order. Item 1 was being argued in the U.S. Congress, and item 3 was likewise being vigorously argued—in Congress and in the public forum.

Along with all these advances were associated problems. The equipment used was so intricate, and the software programs driving the equipment were so complex, that occasional serious problems seemed inevitable. Late in 1991 such a problem surfaced; most of the long-distance telephone service in the New York City area—including air traffic control—was halted. The cause was an error in the software. As it turned out, three data bits out of one million had been typed incorrectly. In spite of problems such as this, the telecommunications industry continued forward at a headlong pace, entering—and creating—the information age.

—Robert E. Stoffels

Computers and computer science

Early in 1990 IBM Corp. announced a new line of scientific workstations that provided significantly more computational power than competitors' machines. The new IBM machines surprised the industry and spurred competition among other vendors. During the past year many workstation manufacturers delivered new products that offered even more powerful performances than the models from IBM. That development illustrated the fact that the computer industry had managed to sustain exponential growth.

Computer and software companies began to form joint ventures designed to make hardware and software more standard across the industry. Several new groups appeared during the year, each one trying to define standards that would give it a position of leadership. Most notably, IBM and Apple Computer Inc., once bitter rivals, agreed to merge their personal computer technologies to create a new system that would perform better than current machines from either company.

Also, during the year the U.S. government passed new legislation that spurred additional research in high-performance computing. The legislation provided government funding for research and develop-

IBM president Jack Kuehler (left) and Apple Computer president John Sculley display a document in which the two firms have agreed to work together to create a new generation of personal computers.

ment of high-performance processing and network communication hardware, for software that used the new high-performance hardware, and for computer networking.

Scientific workstations. A scientific workstation is a computer used by an individual scientist or engineer. Although workstations offer general-purpose computing facilities, they are used most often to perform mathematical computations. The chief advantage of a workstation is its flexibility; workstations resemble personal computers in that they allow individuals to control computational resources. Although a workstation has the ability to handle many users and many computations concurrently, workstations are designed to be used and controlled by individuals. A user can choose which programs to run on a workstation at any time. If there is an important problem to solve, the user can choose to devote the workstation's entire computational facility to that problem. If there are several problems to solve, the user can run many programs at the same time.

Most workstations contain only a single central processing unit (CPU). Because this limits the amount of processing power, processing must be allocated among all the programs being run at any given time. Consequently, when a workstation has several programs to execute, a given individual program will not be completed as quickly as it would be when the workstation had nothing else to run. Thus, when a user chooses which programs to run, the choice affects how long each program will take to complete; the choice becomes a question of how to allocate the CPU resource among the problems at hand.

Physically, most workstations are as small as personal computers; a workstation can fit on a desktop. In addition to the workstation itself, each workstation system includes a monitor used to display text and graphics, a keyboard used to enter text, and a mouse used to select or manipulate items. Furthermore, because a workstation is quiet and uses standard 110-v power, the system can be used in a conventional office.

Computationally, however, workstations are not small. Compared with the processors used in personal computers, processors used in workstations are significantly more powerful. Also, a scientific workstation contains special-purpose hardware (usually a single chip) that performs "floating-point" computations at extremely high speeds. Unlike computations of integers, used in many applications, floating-point computations handle fractional numbers. Because scientists and engineers use fractional numbers to represent measured quantities, most of the mathematical computations they perform rely on floating-point arithmetic.

Besides faster computational speed, workstations usually provide much larger memories than do personal computers. For example, while personal computers can operate easily with between one and three megabytes of memory, most workstations need memories with at least eight megabytes. (One megabyte equals 1,048,576 bytes; one byte equals eight bits.) High-speed workstations often need 16 megabytes or more, using the additional memory to run larger, more powerful operating systems and to store more information. Allocating additional space for data helps increase processing speed because it keeps copies of data in main memory so that the processor can access them without having to use slow secondary storage devices such as disks.

The sequence of advances in workstation technology during the past decade has been incredible. Early workstations resembled personal computers; they had slow processors and small memories. A typical workstation from a decade ago could execute at most one million instructions per second and had a one-megabyte memory. The computational power available in workstations increased rapidly, often doubling in a single year. In short, workstations grew in giant steps from the power of a personal computer to that of a large mainframe.

During the year Hewlett-Packard Inc. (HP) took the lead in defining new workstation technology. HP delivered a new set of scientific workstations with processor speeds almost double those available in the previous year. Known as the Precision Architecture-Reduced Instruction Set Computing (PA-RISC) 9000 series, the new models included processors that ranged in speed from 29 million through 76 million instructions per second (MIPS). The new

Sophisticated computer workstations are used to design and electronically preassemble entire Boeing 777 airplanes. Designers create and manipulate full-color images that represent airplane sections and systems.

hardware was especially impressive because its performance exceeded by a considerable margin the fastest machines announced during the previous year and established a new record against which the performance of workstations offered by other vendors would have to be measured.

To achieve the best performance possible, the new HP machines require large memories. For example, the fastest HP machines can be configured as file servers that provide file access for many other workstations. Such servers require between 32 and 512 megabytes of memory.

Despite the race among vendors to create ever faster workstations, speed does not always guarantee market share. While Hewlett-Packard, which offered the fastest machines, captured only 20% of the workstation market, Sun Microsystems Inc., which offered slower and less expensive machines, held nearly 38%.

Large-capacity disk drives. For a computer system to exhibit faster overall performance, all components must work faster. The new high-speed workstations cannot deliver their best performances without high-speed versions of input and output devices such as hard disks. Advances in disk technology during the year resulted in faster disks. Fujitsu America, a leading producer of magnetic-disk hardware, introduced a new line of disk drives that offered massive amounts of disk storage in a small package. Physically, the new units fit a 13.3-cm (5.25-in) slot, replacing much larger units.

The CM-5 supercomputer, developed by Thinking Machines Corp., achieves its power by using hundreds or thousands of individual computers working in parallel (simultaneously computing different parts of a problem).

Despite their small physical size, the new disk drives offered much more storage capacity than was previously available. A single 13.3-cm Fujitsu unit could store as many as 2 gigabytes (1,073,741,824 bytes) of data (1.62 gigabytes after the disk had been formatted into standard 512-byte blocks). An increase in disk capacity usually requires an increase in the physical size of the disk. Because disks use electromechanical mechanisms to access data, an increase in physical size requires that the disk heads move farther in order to access data. Thus, high-capacity disks usually have slow access times. The new Fujitsu disks, however, had some of the lowest data-access times in the industry. To achieve this, Fujitsu used a higher density of magnetic material than had been employed in previous models, allowing the disks to store more data in the same space. As a result, it became possible to seek to the desired location in an average of only 11 milliseconds. Furthermore, because the disks rotated at 5,400 rpm, the rotation delayed access by an average of only 5.6 milliseconds. These access times made the new disks compatible with new high-speed workstations.

Parallel computer systems. Thinking Machines Corp. introduced a new massively parallel machine in 1991. Named the CM-5, the new machine achieved high performance by using hundreds or thousands of individual computers all working in parallel (simultaneously computing different parts of a problem). In 1992 the aggregate computing power available from the largest CM-5 exceeded that of all other computers. In fact, each of the individual computing

elements in the CM-5 had computational power approximately equal to that of a scientific workstation. However, because the new machine used computers working in parallel, programs had to be rewritten before they could take advantage of the machine's power. Despite the effort required for writing programs, Thinking Machines received orders for several of the new machines.

Cooperation and competition among vendors. Throughout its history the computer industry has been criticized for its diversity and lack of uniform hardware and software standards. The standardization that did exist often resulted from unplanned events instead of from foresight. For example, after its introduction, the IBM PC became a de facto standard for the personal computer market. Hardware vendors began to design and sell peripheral devices that plugged into the IBM PC directly, and software firms began to design and sell software than ran on it. Other vendors produced competing designs, however, so customers were faced with problems of incompatibility.

During the year many computer vendors decided to cooperate directly in the creation of new standards. They formed several groups, each of which would attempt to define standard hardware or software systems. One group was led by Digital Equipment Corp., Mips Computer Systems Inc., and Microsoft Corp. Called Advanced Computing Environment (ACE), the consortium made a commitment to the development of a new desktop system standard. It hoped to produce a design that achieved two goals: allow vendors to manufacture machines inexpensively, making it possible to replace current personal computers and low-end workstations; and lay the foundation for future growth by providing a design that could expand as memory sizes and processor speeds increased. ACE announced that its new computer standard would specify either a processor designed by Mips or one designed by Intel Corp., with the details to be announced after more work had been done to define the system. By 1992 ACE included 60 companies and had committed itself to following the Open Software Foundation's (OSF's) choice of a computer operating system.

OSF represented another group of vendors that had joined together in an attempt to define a standard operating system for desktop systems. The OSF standard made the powerful UNIX® operating system available for a wide range of computers, including small PCs and large high-speed workstations.

Perhaps the most surprising cooperation arose between vendors of personal computers. Two giants in the PC business, IBM and Apple, joined forces to define a standard desktop system. Once bitter rivals, the two companies announced that they intended to work together on products that would benefit both

330

of them. They sought to develop a new hardware architecture and a standard software system that could be used on a variety of models, ranging from small, entry-level personal computers to large, powerful workstations.

Both participants brought expertise to the union. IBM planned to use its experience in building high-speed Reduced Instruction Set Computer (RISC) processors to help Motorola Corp. design a new high-speed CPU chip that could be used in Macintosh systems. Apple would benefit because it needed access to better processor technology. Meanwhile, Apple would use its experience with user-interface software (derived from its popular Macintosh personal computer) to provide a user-friendly software environment. IBM would benefit because its personal computer lacked a friendly graphical interface. Both companies were expected to combine their experience in networking to define standards for network hardware and software that would allow the new machines to connect with large IBM mainframes or other personal computers.

It was expected to be several years before the new Apple-IBM cooperation resulted in products. Nevertheless, the industry reacted positively to the announcement. Users anticipated that each company would benefit from the other's strengths and that a uniform standard would make it easier to purchase hardware and software.

Government support. During the year the U.S. government passed legislation designed to stimulate computer and communications research. The High-Performance Computing and Communications (HPCC) Act of 1991 recognized the importance of maintaining U.S. leadership in computer and communications technologies. Partly in response to government funding in Japan and other countries, the bill allocated nearly $600 million for high-performance computing research over a five-year period.

The HPCC act endorsed a plan to construct a national research and education network (NREN) that would provide high-speed computer communication among the nation's researchers and educational institutions, a plan for research networking analogous to the interstate highway system. As of 1992 the National Science Foundation (NSF) was operating a primitive version of an NREN called NSFNET. NSFNET interconnected hundreds of universities as well as government and private research laboratories. Researchers and students at institutions that connected to NSFNET had access to remote data bases and could exchange documents, data files, and computer programs. They communicated with colleagues instantly by means of electronic mail.

The NSFNET network hardware consisted of computers called packet switches that were interconnected by transmission lines leased from common carriers. The transmission lines operated at a speed of 45 million bits per second. While considered adequate for current uses, NSFNET was growing so quickly that the technology was expected to become obsolete in only a few years.

Like the existing NSFNET, the NREN would be designed to provide data communication by using packet-switching technology. This technology divided data into small units called packets for transmission; each packet was transported across the network independently. Packet switching made it possible to share the underlying transmission lines among multiple pairs of communicating machines, allowing many communications to proceed concurrently.

To allow the NREN to connect more sites than the NSFNET and to handle new types of traffic, it would be designed to operate at a much higher speed than the existing network. For example, although most experts agreed that storage and transmission of video would play an important role in future computing systems, the NSFNET did not have sufficient capacity to transfer real-time video images between sites. Furthermore, no packet-switching technology available in 1992 could provide the needed capacity.

Fingernail-sized silicon chip, developed by IBM Corp., can store 16 million bits of data, the equivalent of about 1,600 pages of double-spaced typewritten text. This is four times the capacity of the previously most advanced chips.

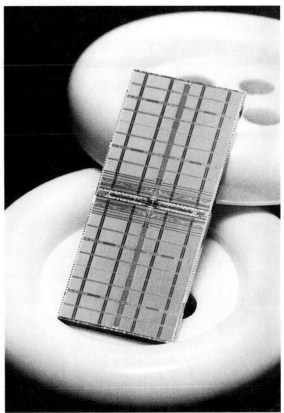

IBM

New research would explore and develop the technologies needed to scale the existing NSFNET up to transmission speeds of one gigabit per second by 1996.

In addition to stimulating research on high-speed networks, the HPCC legislation provided funding for new research on high-performance computing systems. Since the mid-1980s the United States had gradually lost its leadership role in building the fastest computers (called supercomputers). While private industry had funded supercomputer research in the U.S., the Japanese government had provided significant funding for such research in Japan. As a result, by 1992 Japanese industry had taken the lead in producing fast computers. The HPCC bill recognized that U.S. industry would not be able to regain its lead without government support and therefore provided funding for research into high-performance computer hardware.

The HPCC bill also provided funding for research into new software systems. Without such software, new high-speed hardware would not be as useful, nor would it perform competitively.

—Douglas E. Comer

Electronics

The economic signals for the U.S. electronics industry remained mixed during the past year. Depending on one's perspective, one could, by a judicious selection of facts, make a case for or against a recession of the industry. The optimists pointed out that indicators that define a recession, such as a 5% drop in manufacturing output, a 1% drop in real gross national product, and a 2% rise in unemployment, did not apply to the electronics industry during the year. Also, this group maintained that the decline of the dollar would make U.S. goods more attractive overseas. Those who took a more pessimistic view noted that the U.S. economy was becoming less competitive in the international marketplace. For them neither Congress nor the president seemed to be either willing or able to effect some action in regard to the staggering deficit that was hamstringing the economy.

Beyond these particular positions, a cautious optimism about the state of the economy in general and the electronics industry in particular seemed to manifest itself slowly in early 1992. For the electronics industry, inventory productivity was increasing, especially in aerospace, communications equipment, computers, and electronic and electrical equipment. The bad news was that orders were at a lower level than expected, especially for computers. While prices for them had been lowered, lack of new software that utilized the existing computing power had slowed the growth of the hardware market.

European manufacturers were outpacing their U.S. counterparts in selling computers to the newly opened markets of eastern Europe. Paris-based Bull SA concluded a contract with the Finance Ministry of Czechoslovakia and a similar one with the government of Poland. Siemens AG of Germany, not surprisingly, was dominating the computer market in the former East Germany. ICL Ltd. of London succeeded in negotiating a sales contract for computers with the Hungarian government.

Despite their newly found unity in the European Communities (EC), Europeans began to adopt fundamentally different attitudes as to how to meet the Japanese challenge. France, Italy, and Belgium favored protectionism. The French government made it quite clear that in its opinion the European electronics industry could be saved only when both production and marketing were regulated with a primary focus on the well-being of the EC.

Taking an opposite stand was the German government. It maintained that Europe's competitive edge should rest on free enterprise and the concomitant market forces. The Germans deemed it best that all governments work together to create an environment that would be favorable to the industry. Thus, they opposed protectionism but did call for increased research-and-development efforts, better technology transfer, and greater cooperation between the European nations.

In Germany, unification added millions of consumers to the market. Many of the former East Germans were only too eager to buy audio and video equipment if at all possible. Apparently there was enough money in the hands of these newcomers to generate a 7% growth rate in the electronics consumer market of a united Germany. While the East Germans in general earned less than their brethren in the West, they had more savings in the bank: $8,387 per capita versus $5,161 for their western counterparts. Coupled with these savings by the former East Germans was their long-standing desire to purchase electronic goods made in the West. In consequence, the electronics market experienced a strong growth rate. This growth was expected to increase as the salary levels of the former East Germans rose.

French manufacturers lowered their prices by as much as 20% to stimulate sales and to compete with Far Eastern products in the domestic marketplace. A 6% rise for the year was expected, which should bring the level of spending on electronic consumer goods to about $4.5 billion. While the French tried to minimize the importing of electronic goods from the Far East, at the same time they exported about 35% of their manufactured television sets to Germany. The French domestic market expanded, especially in sales of videocassette recorders (VCRs).

The rise in oil prices in Italy slowed the growth of the electronics consumer section there. The final tally for its growth rate was expected to be about 6% for the year, rising to a level of about $3.3 billion. In early 1992 color TVs were replacing the black-and-white sets, and VCRs were achieving a low level of market penetration.

The United Kingdom experienced a growth rate of 1% during the past year. The primary reason was the general economic climate prevailing in Britain. Sales of small and medium-sized television sets, of the kind most popular with young homemakers, fell sharply as the disposable incomes of that age group shrank steadily. Those over 59 seemed to have more disposable income, some of which was invested in equipment to capture the sound and sight of their grandchildren. Consequently, the market for VCRs and camcorders was predicted to grow by almost 50% during the year.

Some Asian manufacturers expected to reap the benefits of an expanding European market. For instance, the South Korean firm of Daewoo reported that 60% of its industrial output went to eastern Germany and eastern Europe. However, the generally gloomy economic picture in much of the world seemed likely to result in a flat year for the Asian manufacturers.

Testing of a digital radio system was being conducted by the Popov Institute in Leningrad (now St. Petersburg), Russia's premier organization for developments in radio and television. The participation of Russia should advance the drive toward a worldwide acceptance and standard for digital audio broadcasting.

Chips. During the year concerns were raised that the U.S. was losing not only its market share for semiconductors but also the needed plant facilities for manufacturing them in the future. A state-of-the-art fabrication facility for the manufacture of semiconductor wafers was estimated in 1992 to cost $300 million. For most U.S. companies, raising the needed capital to start production was difficult at best. Added to this were high interest rates compounded by a tax structure that did not favor the making of the needed investments. This situation was especially difficult for small companies. Also, many in the industry believed that the government was indifferent to the link between high technology and the economic well-being of the nation. Consequently, there was a shift of wafer manufacture to both Japan and the Pacific Rim nations. This shift caused a loss of jobs and of manufacturing expertise in the U.S.

A direct result of the high cost of building new fabrication facilities was the emergence of "fabless" companies. They developed and marketed products but contracted the manufacturing of the chips to companies with a "fab" capability. Another variation was the joining of various companies in alliances and partnerships designed to share the cost and risk of chip manufacture.

Military applications. Nothing demonstrated the importance of electronics as dramatically during the year as the swift victory of the UN coalition forces over those of Iraq. It was the enormous variety and sophistication of the coalition's radar systems, infrared sensing devices, laser-guided "smart" weapons, and a host of sophisticated electronic information systems that ensured its quick and decisive victory on land, on sea, and in the air. While no Iraqi soldier could escape the electronic surveillance of the coalition, an entire coalition corps could be moved without the Iraqi military command's gaining any detailed information about it.

The complexity of the electronic systems used was truly staggering. Radar and electro-optic sensors, borne by both aircraft and satellites, covered the entire combat zone. They provided the coalition forces with instant intelligence concerning the movement of men and matériel of the enemy. An elaborate structure consisting of at least four different types of surveillance satellites together with numerous planes filled with sophisticated electronic equipment and data links relayed information instantly to command centers located behind the front lines. Even individual coalition soldiers were equipped with handheld computers that relayed information about Iraqi positions to satellites. Within minutes and sometimes even seconds, orders and information were relayed to the fighting units. At the same time, the coalition's electronic countermeasures spread an electronic fog over the combat area that gagged and blindfolded the Iraqi military. It was a war in which the coalition forces could see and hear and the Iraqis could not.

A prominent component of the air superiority enjoyed by the coalition was the F-14 fighter jet. In a fortuitous move, a new data link installed in those fighters just before the outbreak of the Gulf war allowed tactical data to be linked between F-14 fighter jets without the need for a central command. Each F-14 had on board a visual display that showed the location of other F-14s in the area and their radar targets. According to pilots who used the system, this electronic fighter-to-fighter link provided "fantastic situational awareness." By knowing where both the enemy and the friendly airplanes were at any given instant, the F-14s were able to devise on-the-spot tactics without having to await instructions from a central command post.

Consumer electronics. The WideCom Corp. of Ontario introduced a widebody fax machine that could transmit a document 0.6 m (2 ft) wide and up to 60 m (200 ft) in length. It also could reduce oversize documents.

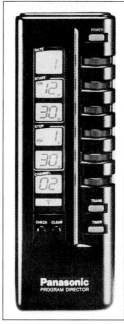

A handheld program director, Panasonic's PV-PG100 LCD, is designed to make it easier to program VCRs. The unit displays the date, the start and stop times of the desired program, and the channel. The user enters the desired data into the device by rotating the knobs on the right.

Both the Franklin Electronics Publishers and the SelecTronics Inc. marketed electronic encyclopaedias that allowed one to search through massive volumes of data simply by entering a word, a phrase, or even just a clue. The data base for the Franklin device was the 1989 *Concise Columbia Encyclopedia,* while the SelecTronics machine managed to squeeze the 1990 new and revised edition of the *Random House Encyclopedia* into its electronic confines.

For those who found it difficult to use and program their VCRs, Panasonic introduced a handheld director, the PV-PG100 LCD, which was designed to take the mystery and the frustration out of operating a VCR. The unit, which was wireless, displayed the date, the start and stop times of the desired programming, and the channel. The user would simply enter the desired data into the device by means of rotating knobs. Associated with each knob was a display that indicated to the user whether the desired data had been entered correctly.

Automotive applications. The Audi Corp. of Germany during the year introduced a sunroof into which 28 photovoltaic cells were embedded. These cells could deliver a total of about 20 w of electrical power, which would be used to ventilate a parked car in the summer by means of exhaust fans. In cooler weather the solar-derived power would be used to help recharge the car's battery. The Mazda Corp. introduced a similar active sunroof on its Sentia model.

Thanks to a cooperative effort between the General Motors Corp., the American Automobile Association, the Federal Highway Administration, and the Florida Department of Transportation and the city

of Orlando, travelers during the year could rent an Oldsmobile Toronado equipped with TravTek to find their way around Orlando. TravTek consisted of an onboard computer system that by voice and display provided navigation assistance, real-time traffic information, and the best alternatives for travel in case of congestion or accidents on selected roads. The data were collected from TravTek cars, traffic-signal monitors, highway-surveillance systems, and police and construction reports.

TravTek's internal navigation tracked a vehicle by means of wheel sensors and a built-in magnetic compass. It continually matched the obtained road information with the geographic information that was stored in a map data base in the computer. The vehicle's position was then continuously displayed on a computer screen. The computer also had a menu system that allowed drivers to choose popular destinations from an item list. Given a particular request for such a location, the computer would proceed to calculate the best route quickly.

Environmental issues. Each year approximately 167 million used batteries are tossed into landfills and incinerators in the U.S. Of that number only about 1% are of the nickel-cadmium (NiCad) variety yet, despite their relative small number, their negative impact on the environment is far from negligible. The reason for this disproportionate effect on the environment is that cadmium, a by-product of zinc mining, is highly toxic. It is carcinogenic when inhaled and causes kidney damage when ingested; for example, by eating contaminated fish.

To counter the negative impact of these batteries, manufacturers began to look for alternatives. One of the candidates was a battery based on the element lithium. As of 1992, efforts were under way to

Automobile sunroof introduced by the Audi Corp. contains 28 photovoltaic cells. They can deliver about 20 watts of electrical power, which could be used to run exhaust fans or to help recharge a car's battery.

take advantage of the extremely long shelf life of a lithium-based battery while at the same time minimizing its tendency to explode when exposed to water. Another choice was to make a better lead battery. Lead, however, also has a negative impact on the environment, and the batteries are relatively short-lived. The most promising alternative as of 1992 was the nickel-metal-hybrid battery, which seemed to pose less of an environmental risk. The Ovonic Battery Co. licensed the manufacturing of batteries to five battery manufacturers throughout the world. An independent environmental study claimed that this battery did not constitute an environmental hazard and could safely be mixed with other refuse. Another plus for the manufacturers was that the new batteries could replace the existing NiCad batteries without the need for any major circuit modifications.

—Franz J. Monssen

Information systems and services

New technologies are changing the ways in which information can be created, stored, and disseminated. However, this does not mean that information stored in books and journals in libraries throughout the world is obsolete and can be discarded. Libraries large and small, old and new, are still where people prefer to get information and literature for recreation and relaxation. Unfortunately, nearly 80 million books in North American research libraries are deteriorating because they were printed on acidic paper. Approximately 25% of the book collection at the Library of Congress is already brittle, and more than 75,000 more volumes become brittle each year. To combat this problem, the Library of Congress developed a process that removed acid from paper by exposing the books to DEZ (diethylzinc) gas in a controlled environment; however, the procedure was expensive. If the paper in a document had deteriorated beyond the possibility of strengthening, the document could be microfilmed, but this too was expensive. The best and most cost-effective long-term solution to prevent the deterioration of the books would be to print publications on acid-free permanent paper.

Not only were books deteriorating; entire libraries had also been destroyed, and restoration efforts were needed. The library in Alexandria, Egypt, was founded in 284 BC by Ptolemy I Soter, a king of Egypt. Parts of the library were destroyed during Julius Caesar's campaign in Egypt in 48 BC and, according to tradition, the library had been completely destroyed by the 6th century AD. During its heyday the library was one of the glories of the ancient world, with an estimated collection of some 30,000 books and 700,000 manuscripts on papyrus rolls collected from all over the world.

Through an international effort sponsored by Unesco and supported by the Egyptian government, a project was under way to create a modern public research library and museum complex at the site of the ancient library and to rebuild Alexandria as an intellectual center of learning in science, art, and culture. The new Bibliotheca Alexandrina was to start operations with some 200,000 new volumes and 1,500 journal titles and would eventually include some four million volumes plus a museum, a planetarium, and an international school for information studies. Modern technology would be used to provide access to this information, store it, and preserve ancient documents. The cost of the library was estimated at $160 million.

Unfortunately, this was not the only library that needed help. For the last half century Romanian libraries were barred from almost all contact with Western libraries and universities. To make matters worse, the main building of the Central University Library in Bucharest was destroyed during the December 1989 revolution, and approximately 500,000 books were lost. University Microfilms International (UMI) and the American Library Association (ALA) were among a number of organizations that helped rebuild Romanian libraries. UMI donated $50,000 worth of microfilm and microfiche products to the Library of the Romanian Academy and to the Central Library in Bucharest. The donation consisted of journal titles selected by a Romanian committee. In addition, the Disaster Relief Committee of the ALA initiated a book-donation drive for Romania that resulted in shipments totaling $4.5 million worth of books, journals, and computers.

U.S. information systems. The development of on-line information systems and services allowed users of the smallest and least developed countries of the world to have the same level of access to the world's on-line data bases as did the largest and richest nations, provided that the former had an adequate telecommunications infrastructure. Many less developed countries with poor telecommunications systems were unable to share in the information available in on-line products. Data bases on CD-ROM (compact disc-read only memory) helped overcome this problem because they were portable data bases that could be purchased and used locally. CD-ROM data bases available in 1992 covered the literature of science, technology, medicine, social science, art, law, government, computers, and general-interest information. Although expensive, they allowed unlimited access with no telecommunication charges; when that was taken into account, the cost might be considered reasonable. CD-ROM data bases provided users throughout the world with another choice among a growing number of technologies used for retrieving information.

The Cuadra/Gale Directory of Portable Databases provided comprehensive descriptions of the world's publicly available data bases. This CD-ROM covered more than 4,700 on-line data bases and more than 1,500 "portable" data bases that were available on CD-ROM, diskette, and magnetic tape. Each entry recorded the data base name, producer, vendor, coverage, frequency of updating, and conditions of access or price.

Countries of the World, a multimedia CD-ROM produced by the Bureau of Electronic Publishing, recorded the full text of all 106 U.S. Army Country Series handbooks, plus maps, flags in color, and national anthems. Topics covered for each country included the historical setting, environment, economy, government, politics, and national security. Also included were high-resolution color maps of the world, along with information on political and geographic boundaries, population, climate, agriculture, mining, and land use. The search program made it easy to browse through this large collection of handbooks; to search by article, word, event, or picture; and to print the retrieved information.

The Smithsonian Institution's National Portrait Gallery of more than 3,000 portraits was reproduced on a CD-ROM. These high-resolution color images represented artwork that dated from the early 17th century to the present. The disk also contained textual information about each portrait. A special feature of the disk provided users with the capability to zoom closer to the displayed images in order to see enlarged views of any portrait in the collection.

MUSE (MUsic SEarch) a CD-ROM data base, was produced by the National Information Service Corp. and the International Repertory of Music Literature at the City University of New York. This data base provided access, for general readers and scholars, to all significant music literature published in books, journals, newsletters, conference proceedings, and elsewhere. It was updated annually and was the world's most complete bibliography of music literature.

MAXX (Maximum Access to Diagnosis and Therapy) was produced by the publisher Little, Brown & Co. The single compact disc contained more than 10,000 pages of medical information, including full text, tables, and illustrations. This integrated medical data base was the equivalent of a small clinical library, with access to current diagnostic, therapeutic, laboratory, and drug information. The MAXX retrieval software included a comprehensive index and links from the text to tables, references, and illustrations.

International information systems. The European Commission was guided by the principle that the more the countries of Europe understood each other, the easier it would be to find common solutions to European problems. In order to encourage communication and understanding between the residents of the different countries, the commission developed multilingual intelligent interfaces to interconnected systems and hosts across Europe and used a computer-aided translation system, called Systran, to provide multilingual access to printed information. The program was acquired in 1976 and was expanded and improved so that during the past year 16 language pairs could be translated by machine.

The number of data bases in the Nordic countries increased over the years and by 1992 numbered more than 500. Using the MINITEL system in France as a model, the Finnish Ministry of Transport and Communication initiated the TELMO project, which

Architect's model shows the Bibliotheca Alexandrina, a library to be built in Alexandria, Egypt. Among its many features will be an international school for information studies.

pulled together existing and newly developed services under a single umbrella agency. The services included electronic mail, a nationwide electronic telephone directory, an electronic marketplace, banking, travel information, and reservations.

The Danish data base Weather Information produced precipitation maps showing snow and rain areas in real time. Data were collected from radar stations in Karup (Jutland) and Kastrup (Zeeland) by the Meteorological Institute, and the data were updated every 10 minutes. Weather forecasts and five-day prognoses were also provided by the service.

Remote sensing, a technology used in Earth observation from aircraft and spacecraft, was of critical importance for environmental monitoring, natural resource assessment, mapping, and military surveillance. A bibliographic data base devoted to remote sensing, called RESORS, was developed by the Canada Centre of Remote Sensing. It contained about 80,000 references and was growing at the rate of 5,000 per year.

The Planning Exchange was an on-line information service based in Glasgow, Scotland. It processed and distributed information on local economic conditions and employment initiatives and case histories recounting lessons that could be learned from those initiatives.

The 1981 British census was made available by Chadwyck-Healey on three CD-ROM discs. Included were the complete Small Area Statistics (SAS) data base at both ward and enumeration district level and all vector boundary maps covering basic demographic characteristics, housing, and economic activity. The tables contained information on age, sex, marital status, employment status, country of birth, migrations, car ownership, household amenities, and much more. These data provided a socioeconomic profile of the U.K.

Research. A cooperative U.S.-China research project was organized between Xü Meiling (Hsü Meiling) of the University of Minnesota and Chen Shupeng (Ch'en Shu-p'eng) of the Institute of Geography, Chinese Academy of Sciences, Beijing (Peking). The project investigators established a geographic information system for urban China and conducted research on the characteristics and functions of Chinese urban places, the process of urbanization, and the evolution of the Chinese urban system.

The Andrew W. Mellon Foundation awarded a grant to the Association of Research Libraries (ARL) for development of a national strategy for ensuring the continued strength of U.S. research library collections of foreign material. The study was important because as the value of the U.S. dollar declined against other major currencies, the acquisition of foreign materials decreased by 40–50% among U.S. research libraries.

The U.S. National Endowment for the Humanities (NEH) awarded a grant to the AMIGOS Bibliographic Council to document the preservation needs of libraries and archives in the Southwest and to assist in planning affordable programs to meet those needs. This was one of a number of grants awarded by the NEH for helping preserve knowledge in deteriorating library and archival materials.

Researchers at the School of Information Studies at Syracuse (N.Y.) University received a grant from the Defense Advanced Research Projects Agency (DARPA) for development of an improved information retrieval system utilizing linguistic knowledge to modify the way documents could be located and retrieved from electronic data bases. The research project was titled Document Retrieval Using Linguistic Knowledge, or DR-LINK.

The Brandeis University (Waltham, Mass.) libraries received grants of computer equipment from Digital Equipment Corp. and of software from Geac Computers, Inc., to support research into the personal information management needs of academic scholars. Called the Gesher (Hebrew for "bridge") project, the study focused on achieving a better understanding of how faculty and other research professionals collect and organize the data with which they work and also explored new software tools for the personal use of information. The project team investigated patterns of information use across a spectrum of disciplines and asked selected faculty to participate in the design and testing of software for organizing their personal information files.

—Harold Borko

Satellite systems

Earth applications satellites consist of three general classes: communications, Earth observation, and navigation. These automated satellites are designed, built, launched, and operated by individual nations, groups of nations, and commercial firms.

The past year marked major changes in the development, use, and control of Earth-orbiting satellites. For the first time, satellite systems were integrated into modern warfare, resulting in great advantage to their users. During the Gulf war to liberate Kuwait in early 1991, instrumented space vehicles directly supported United Nations military forces in campaign-level and tactical combat operations. Military surveillance satellites provided missile warning, environmental, weather, and intelligence information to the coalition forces. Communications satellites relayed these and other data between the national command authorities of the UN nations participating in the conflict and commanders in the battlefield. Navstar (Navigation Satellite Tracking and Ranging) Global Positioning System (GPS) satellites furnished navigation information for ground, sea, and air force operations and made possible—or greatly enhanced—precision bombing and artillery fire support, the precise positioning of maneuvering troop formations, and certain special-force operations in a featureless terrain.

The Soviet space program approached a crisis at the end of 1991 with the dissolution of the Soviet Union and emergence of the Commonwealth of Independent States. Still mounting the world's largest military and civil space programs, the Soviets launched fewer satellites in 1991 than in 1990. A faltering economy, a breakdown in transportation and distribution, the conversion of military communications satellites to civilian use, and contention over which of the newly independent republics owned which part of those programs portended possible chaos in future months.

The Russian Republic controlled most of the former Soviet space program infrastructure, including the launch complexes at Plesetsk and Kapustin Yar, which launched almost all military and civil instrumented satellites. Kazakhstan controlled the Baikonur Cosmodrome used to launch all Soviet manned spacecraft. Important rocket- and spacecraft-manufacturing facilities were within Ukraine. Some analysts concluded that there might be as many as five national space agencies created to manage what was once a single Soviet space program.

Communications satellites. This largest class of satellites continued to grow in size, complexity, and performance. In a year marked by many innovations, it was clear that the satellite communications industry was in a state of ferment and transition. Deregulation was opening the door to competitive enterprise. Perhaps most striking was the fact that there were at least 10 new proposals for mobile satellite communications systems (see below).

The commercial cooperative International Telecommunications Satellite Organization (Intelsat) dominated international traffic. By 1992 Intelsat was providing a wide range of international telecommunications services to nearly 180 countries and territories around the world as well as domestic long-distance service to nearly 40 countries. These services included telephone, data, FAX, telex, videoconferencing, electronic mail, file transfer, radio, audio, television services, and specialized business services. Intelsat in 1992 operated 17 satellites in geosynchronous orbit. Such satellites were positioned at an orbital altitude of exactly 35,870 km (22,289 mi). They traveled at the same angular velocity as the Earth and thus appeared to remain stationary over the same point on the Earth's equator.

By the end of 1991, Intelsat's full-time traffic exceeded the equivalent of 124,000 duplex telephone circuits (allowing communication in opposite direc-

tions simultaneously) plus more than two dozen full-time TV channels. There were approximately 750 international Earth stations in the Intelsat system and a comparable number for domestic long-distance service.

During the Gulf war the public watched daily broadcasts from Riyadh (Saudi Arabia), Israel, Jordan, and even Baghdad (Iraq). Ted Turner's Atlanta, Ga.-based network, CNN, provided 24-hour coverage. Equally intense coverage was given the coup attempt in the Soviet Union and the subsequent dissolution of the U.S.S.R. In 1991 almost total global coverage was achieved. This increase was the result of the Soviet Union's finally joining Intelsat as its 121st member some months before the breakup of the nation. By early 1992 it seemed likely that the Intersputnik system, previously sponsored by the Soviet Union, would become inactive and that Intelsat would serve as the primary provider of global communications.

With the addition of Iceland, London-based Inmarsat, an international cooperative providing worldwide mobile satellite communications for maritime, air, and land mobile users, had 64 member countries. During the year the number of international commercial aircraft with satellite telephone installations increased to 50. Twenty corporate aircraft were being outfitted similarly. In September Inmarsat announced plans for a new global communications satellite system, known as Project 21. This system would employ 21 satellites at low to medium orbital altitude, providing mobile and personal communications to small hand-held receivers.

A much larger communications system would be Iridium, proposed by the Motorola Co. This impressive concept would, at a cost of $3 billion, place 77 satellites in a 600–800 km (360–500 mi) orbit. As conceived, there would be seven groups of 11 satellites. Full capability would provide a total of 283,272 full duplex (simultaneous two-way) voice channels. Iridium would need replacement satellites launched at four-week intervals.

In Europe and Japan the use of direct satellite-to-home broadcasting continued to increase. By the end of the year British Sky Broadcasting (BSkyB) reportedly had two million small satellite receiver dishes in place.

Earth-observation satellites. This category includes meteorologic (weather), Earth resources, and military reconnaissance/surveillance.

Weather satellites. Continuous global weather observations were obtained from U.S., European Space Agency (ESA), and Japanese weather satellites in geostationary orbits. In polar or near-polar orbits at lower altitudes, global weather observations were supplied by U.S., Commonwealth of Independent States, and Chinese satellites.

To maintain complete national and global weather coverage, the U.S. Department of Commerce's National Oceanic and Atmospheric Administration (NOAA) operated two meteorologic Geostationary Operational Environmental Satellites (GOES) in high-altitude geostationary orbits above the east and west coasts of the U.S. At least two operational NOAA weather satellites were in low-altitude polar orbits. One of two aging GOES satellites was failing. The replacement, GOES-NEXT, was not expected to be complete until 1993. Meanwhile, NOAA planned to lease the ESA Meteosat 3, which would be moved west to cover the east coast of the U.S. and Caribbean. GOES 7, presently in that position, would be moved west to cover Pacific weather. Two other geostationary ESA Meteosats, -4 and -5, served the European Communities.

NOAA 12 was launched in May to join NOAA 11. NOAA 9 and 10 remained in orbit, although failure of some of their instruments degraded their performance.

The U.S. Defense Meteorological Satellite Program (DMSP) maintained two low-altitude polar orbiting satellites. On Dec. 1, 1990, during the military buildup prior to the Gulf war, a third DMSP was launched. Such weather data were important for tracking sandstorms, planning aircraft sorties, and deciding when to use laser-guided missiles.

Earth-resources satellites. This class of remote-sensing satellites by transmission of multispectral imagery provided a powerful tool for the study of the size and health of regional crops, water supply, location of oil and mineral deposits, and demographic change. The U.S. Department of Commerce funded and managed the Landsat program, while the Earth Observation Satellite Co. (EOSAT) operated the system. During the year Landsats 4 and 5 continued to function in Earth orbit, supplying wide-area multispectral imagery to coalition forces in the Gulf war for maps, charts, traffic and terrain analyses, and the detection of Iraqi attempts at battlefield concealment. At the war's end Landsat imagery aided fire fighters in setting priorities for the extinguishing of more than 500 burning oil wells. Spectral imagery identified the hottest fires, those wells contaminated by underground water, and wells with accumulated pools of oil.

Landsat 6 was scheduled for launch in mid-1992. At that time the Department of Commerce planned to cease management of the Landsat system, and future responsibilities were to be assumed by the Department of Defense and the National Aeronautics and Space Administration. EOSAT would continue to market Landsat images commercially.

In Europe, France's Centre National d'Études Spatiales continued to fund and manage the SPOT 2 satellite, equipped with a multispectral scanner as its primary instrument. The SPOT system (Satellite pour Observation de la Terre) was operated by a commercial firm, SPOT Image Corp., which marketed the data. ESA launched its first Earth resources satellite, ERS 1, in July. Its primary instrument, a synthetic aperture radar (SAR), provided images of the Earth regardless of weather conditions.

In July 1991 the Soviet Union launched an Earth resources satellite, Almaz. Equipped with an SAR, it was an all-weather satellite with a resolution of 15 m (49.5 ft). Almaz data were to be marketed commercially by the state space program. Japan's National Space Development Agency planned to launch the first Japanese Earth resources satellite, JERS 1, in 1992. To be launched by an H-1 rocket, it would carry shortwave, infrared optical sensors that would provide high resolution and deliver stereoscopic images. It would also have an SAR. The Japanese Ministry of International Trade and Industry planned to distribute imaging data to foreign users.

Military reconnaissance/surveillance satellites. Reconnaissance satellites provide optical and radar images of the Earth and monitor electronic emissions of terrestrial and airborne communication and radar systems. "Early warning" surveillance satellites are equipped with infrared sensors to detect missile launches (from the heat emission of rocket exhaust plumes) within minutes on land or sea and also to record nuclear explosions on the ground or in space. Reconnaissance/surveillance satellites normally operate in low-altitude polar or near-polar orbits, highly elliptical Molniya (Northern Hemisphere-loitering) orbits, and geostationary orbits.

The Soviet Union operated all forms of reconnaissance and surveillance in its Cosmos series. The Cosmos satellites were believed to be equipped with an electrooptical device that transmitted images to Earth as digital data; they also provided radar imaging, primarily for tracking maritime movements, and electronic eavesdropping. A constellation of nine Soviet surveillance satellites operated in Molniya orbits to furnish early warning of ballistic missile launches. A large proportion of the 56 Cosmos launches during the year were devoted to such missions. Launch activity was especially heavy from Plesetsk and Kapustin Yar during the Gulf war.

The U.S. also operated all forms of reconnaissance and surveillance satellites. They unquestionably played a vital role during the Gulf war, furnishing images for identifying targets, tracking troop movements, assessing bomb damage, and eavesdropping on Iraqi electronic communications. The constellation of advanced American Defense Support Program (DSP) surveillance satellites operated in geostationary orbits and provided advance warning of Iraqi short-range Scud ballistic missiles launched against Saudi Arabia and Israel. Information on time of launch, bearing, and probable point of impact was relayed to troops manning the U.S. Patriot antimissile launchers. With few exceptions this provided an early warning to the public as well as an opportunity to launch Patriot missiles to intercept the Scuds.

The French Defense Ministry accelerated and expanded its reconnaissance/surveillance satellite program during the past year, announcing plans to fund development of a radar-imaging satellite, an advanced electrooptical imaging satellite, and a DSP-type early-warning satellite. All judged vital to France's national defense, they were scheduled for launch after the turn of the century. The French Helios 1 and 2 reconnaissance satellites were under construction and scheduled for launch in 1994 and 1995, respectively.

Navigation satellites. Both the U.S. and the Soviet Union and its successor commonwealth continued to operate navigation satellites to provide those equipped with receivers geographic coordinates and velocity with a high degree of accuracy. The Soviets had both military and civil programs. The low-altitude Cosmos constellation consisted of six satellites in orbits at 1,000 km (620 mi) to provide users (primarily the Navy and Merchant Marine) with geographic coordinates with an accuracy of 80–100 m (264–330 ft). The civilian counterpart system, Tsikada, maintained four satellites in virtually identical orbits but positioned in the hemisphere opposite that of the military network. The Soviet high-altitude

Global Navigation Satellite System (GLONASS) was virtually a duplicate of the U.S. counterpart, GPS. When completed in 1995, GLONASS would consist of 21 satellites, separated in circular orbits inclined 65° to the equator. Twelve of those satellites were in operation at the end of the year. Northwest Airlines experimented in 1991 with GLONASS receivers.

The U.S. continued to operate its military navigation satellite network, Navstar GPS. This network, composed in early 1992 of 16 satellites in high-altitude orbits at 20,200 km (10,900 naut mi), would consist of 21 satellites and 3 spares in Earth orbit when completed in 1993. The Air Force launched a Block II GPS satellite in July to replace a Block I that failed in March. In early 1992 the network consisted of 5 Block I and 11 Block II GPS satellites. All carried secondary nuclear-detection payloads similar to those on DSP surveillance satellites.

The 10th anniversary of the international cooperative, humanitarian program Cospas/Sarsat took place in 1992. By means of small portable beacons, emergency distress signals could be sent to Russian and U.S. navigational satellites. These signals could be relayed to line-of-sight user terminals, providing both an emergency alert and position data for rescue operations.

—F.C. Durant III; R. Cargill Hall
See also Feature Articles: LIFE AS WE DON'T KNOW IT; THE FRUSTRATIONS OF A PUSH-BUTTON WORLD; THE MANY WORLDS OF VIRTUAL REALITY.

Imagery achieved by France's SPOT (Satellite pour Observation de la Terre) 2 aided the coalition nations in the Gulf war against Iraq. At the left is a fuel depot south of Basra, Iraq, and at the right is the depot on fire as a result of coalition bombing.

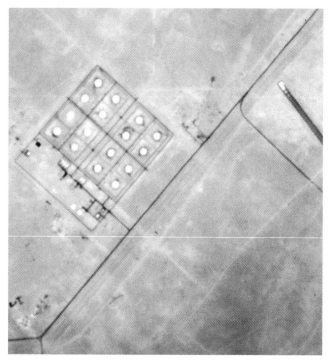 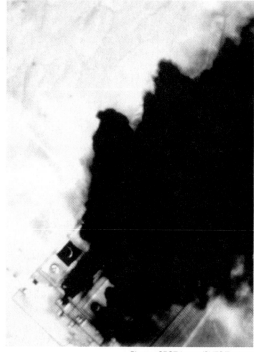

Energy

Unexpected change remained the rule in energy. The most important political events of the past year had major energy implications. The collapse, first of Soviet dominance over eastern Europe and then of the Soviet Union itself, initiated a process of profound alterations that were expected to change the world economy greatly. In addition, the occurrence of yet another Middle Eastern oil crisis also significantly altered the development of world energy conditions.

Crisis in the Middle East. The nonmilitary governmental responses to the Iraqi conquest of Kuwait in August 1990 were, if anything, harmful. The crisis proved manageable despite the failure of the leading consuming countries to use any of the programs designed to offset the disruption of their oil supplies. For example, the U.S. government did little to utilize the stockpiles established for such crises. U.S. politicians from both parties also joined in urging the oil industry not to raise prices.

The crisis further discredited cherished beliefs of the U.S. Department of State. The State Department had long contended that good political relations with oil suppliers were critical to crisis prevention. Thus, extensive cooperation with Iraq prevailed before the attack on Kuwait, tempered by concern over the threat posed by Iraq's aggressive armament program. Exactly what the U.S. government did or did not do when the Iraqi threats began remained a matter of dispute. Some in Congress charged that the U.S. made too ambiguous a response when the threats to Kuwait arose. Others suggested that the U.S. was unduly soothed by optimistic reports from other Arab leaders. It was also believed possible that Iraqi leader Saddam Hussein thought the U.S. was bluffing. In

any case, the result was the Gulf war between Iraq and a U.S.-led coalition.

The energy consequences of the Gulf war were far more clear-cut than those of the demise of Communism. The invasion of Kuwait and its reversal began changes in energy policy that were expected to persist for many decades. The immediate response demonstrated the substantial short-term flexibility of world oil supplies. The crisis removed the combined production of Kuwait and Iraq (about 3.5 million bbl per day) from the world total of about 60 million bbl per day. To make up for the shortage, OPEC increased its output in December 1990 to nearly match the preinvasion output of July; total world production in December was above that of July.

Saudi Arabia was a major contributor to this increase. At the time of the conquest of Kuwait, the Saudis were producing at rates below the peaks reached in the early 1980s. After the attack, output was raised substantially, though not to prior peaks. Just before the Iraqi invasion of Kuwait, Saudi output was about 5.5 million bbl per day. By the end of 1990, output was above 8.5 million bbl. During its peak period, from late 1980 to the summer of 1981, Saudi output averaged 10.2 million bbl per day. Production increases from other countries covered the rest of the 1990 loss.

After the war Kuwait recovered faster than many observers expected. All the oil-well fires set by the Iraqis were extinguished before the end of 1991, and oil flows resumed. (*See* Feature Article: EARTH—THE GULF WAR'S SILENT VICTIM.) However, the postwar situation was marked by a severe weakening of the already fragile ability of members of OPEC to cooperate. Throughout the 1980s OPEC was strained by discords over how to share the burden of reduced output. The price collapse of 1985 arose from the

Saudi tanker docks at an oil refinery in Ras-Tanura, Saudi Arabia, during the Gulf war. The Saudis increased their oil production substantially during the war to compensate for the lost output from Iraq and Kuwait.

Table I. Oil Production from July 1990 to June 1991
(000 bbl per day)

Date	Saudi Arabia	Persian Gulf	OPEC	World
7/90	5,450	16,211	24,300	60,125
8/90	5,850	12,342	20,820	56,622
9/90	7,740	14,282	23,060	59,191
10/90	7,810	14,088	23,090	59,530
11/90	8,310	14,827	23,855	60,350
12/90	8,570	15,232	24,330	60,575
1/91	8,140	14,532	23,770	60,301
2/91	8,200	14,455	23,700	59,934
3/91	8,000	14,383	23,575	60,299
4/91	7,400	13,881	23,025	58,968
5/91	7,400	13,831	22,955	58,775
6/91	8,150	14,681	23,755	59,017

Source: U.S. Energy Information Administration, data disk version of the September 1991 *Monthly Energy Review*.

need of Saudi Arabia to show how it would react to efforts to reduce its market share. The subsequent truce incompletely reduced the conflicts. OPEC discussions centered on working out short-lived accords to adjust output and national shares in order to lessen downward pressures on price.

As of 1992 Iraq and Kuwait each had reduced output, while other nations had raised their production. The result was increased animosities, which were expected to further undermine OPEC cooperation. Kuwait sought to restore its preconflict output. Other OPEC countries realized that accommodations had to be made but seemed likely to resist agreeing fully to Kuwaiti demands. Iraq was unlikely to be well

Table II. Oil Prices
(Average cost in dollars per barrel f.o.b. supplier to U.S. of oil from Arab OPEC)

January 1990	$18.03
February 1990	$16.64
March 1990	$14.98
April 1990	$13.24
May 1990	$12.82
June 1990	$14.63
July 1990	$20.27
August 1990	$28.34
September 1990	$27.46
October 1990	$29.85
November 1990	$25.51
December 1990	$16.17
January 1991	$16.04
February 1991	$14.56
March 1991	$15.21
April 1991	$16.01
May 1991	$15.64
June 1991	$15.54
July 1991	$15.52
August 1991	$16.33
September 1991	$17.00

Source: U.S. Energy Information Administration, data disk version of the September 1991 *Monthly Energy Review*.

treated by the OPEC members. If the governments of consuming countries did not return to protectionist policies (a possibly overly optimistic assumption), downward pressures on world energy prices should result.

Collapse of Communism. The collapse of Communism provided instructive reminders of the fallibility of knowledge. At least until signs of decay emerged in the 1980s, many historians, political scientists, journalists, and politicians at least implicitly expected Communism to persist. Given this history, any statements about what would happen next would have to be made gingerly. A political and economic restructuring of this scale had never been attempted; no one seemed sure as to the best way to effect reform, how close reality would approximate that best way, and what would eventually emerge.

A key aspect of the difficulty facing the former Communist nations was their lack of properly skilled people. In particular, they lacked experienced independent managers. The primary problem of replacing Communism with a market economy, thus, was ensuring that an officialdom unfamiliar with market economies made the right decisions. Liberation of firms might be mishandled. Actions might be dilatory and fail to break up industry complexes into a large enough number of firms. The leaders might succumb to the common free-market error of intervening when a powerful group suffered.

The evidence suggested that a successful efficient restructuring would greatly increase world supplies of at least oil and gas. Export of extraction equipment and expertise from the West to the former Communist nations could become substantial. The basis of the output prediction was that generally those countries had large endowments of energy minerals, management systems that raised production and distribution costs, and pricing systems that overstimulated consumption.

Given the natural resources in much of the former Soviet Union, considerable opportunities were expected to arise for increasing exports of a wide variety of minerals. The Soviet Union in 1990, before its breakup, was the largest producer of oil and natural gas and the third largest producer of coal.

The desirability of Western firms' helping the former Communist countries to improve the development and operation of the oil and gas fields, their distribution networks, and their refineries was clear. The major problems would be to provide the incentives for this Western participation. If all difficulties were overcome, the prospects were for considerable increases in oil and gas production in the former Soviet Union. A notorious problem of Communist economies was that they threw masses of inputs at problems. In particular, they used large amounts of energy. As these economies became market-oriented, it seemed certain that they would use inputs more efficiently. Rising output and falling use could occur only if some other users emerged—that is, exports had to rise.

The exact dimensions of these changes could not yet be determined. A crude idea of the potential for decreased fuel use could be gleaned from a comparison between the former Soviet Union and the U.S. In 1990 Soviet fuel use was about 68% of that in the U.S. Estimates of the size of the Soviet economy were difficult to obtain. For decades U.S. analysts sought to generate lower, more realistic figures than the Soviet government provided. A feature of the debate over the breakup of the Soviet Union was that various sources argued that even U.S.-made estimates were too high. Since the debate could be resolved only if the successor to the Soviet Union, the Commonwealth of Independent States, established a satisfactory statistical system, it would be best to use a range of estimates. On this basis the Soviet economy might be considered to have been 25–40% the size of the U.S. economy.

Differences in geography, economic structure, and fuel supply caused the optimal ratio of energy use to gross domestic product (GDP) to be different for different economies. The Commonwealth of Independent States might have a somewhat higher optimal ratio of energy use to GDP because its area was larger than that of the U.S. and because it had a higher proportion of production sectors that used energy heavily. However, this should be offset in the future with the drastic shrinking of the Commonwealth's military. Thus, a move to a ratio closer to that of the U.S. seemed likely. This could result in energy use 40–60% of the 1990 levels.

The future of coal was less clear because the coalfields in European Russia might have reached levels of depletion comparable to those in Western Europe. The cost of resorting to Siberian coal might prove prohibitive. A long-standing problem in the Soviet Union was that its inefficiencies prevented the development of either alternative for moving the coal energy—better coal-transportation networks or long-distance electricity-transmission networks.

In regard to nuclear power, Western specialists in uranium markets pointed out that demilitarization released large supplies of enriched uranium that was usable in reactors. Given the previous disasters of Soviet efforts to develop nuclear power, one course for the members of the Commonwealth and the old Eastern bloc would be to follow Japan, France, and the United Kingdom in licensing U.S. light-water-reactor technology. Should this happen, U.S. vendors would be competing vigorously with their licensees elsewhere.

These prognoses added up to potentially large benefits to consumers throughout the world and to those firms that could provide the best technology and short- and long-term management assistance. However, the existence of energy producers elsewhere seemed certain to be challenged. These changes in the former Communist world were expected to occur simultaneously with efforts of the OPEC countries to expand their outputs. If this should happen, downward pressures would be placed on world energy prices. These pressures were expected to persist for at least a half century.

Policy issues. Industrial countries continued to struggle with energy policy issues. The U.S. government presented an energy strategy of "continuing the successful policy of market reliance. Whenever possible, markets should be allowed to determine prices, quantities, and technological choices. In specific instances where markets cannot or do not work efficiently, government action should be aimed at removing or overcoming barriers to efficient market operation."

As was necessarily true of any effort to maximize policy goals, this statement could justify almost all possible concepts of energy policy. Its proposed implementation contained many elements objectionable to those strongly devoted to free markets. In particular, the plan advocated federal promotion of automobiles powered by fuels other than gasoline, continuation of programs by electric utilities to assist customers in reducing consumption, and the expansion of programs to set efficiency standards for energy use.

Conversely, the initiatives to deregulate in some areas and expand oil drilling in protected areas were unacceptable to those more skeptical of market forces. Indeed, the effort by the U.S. Congress to pass a 1991 energy bill failed because of a bitter dispute over oil and gas drilling in the Arctic National Wildlife Refuge. This issue became the test case of the proper way to reconcile energy and environmental goals. Advocates of drilling pointed to a long history of drilling in wildlife refuges that caused no disruptions; examples were given of environmental groups leasing rights to their own refuges. Opponents feared that increased leasing could not be so well controlled. The opposition was so successful that Congress decided that 1992 efforts at energy legislation would exclude consideration of drilling in this Alaskan refuge.

Another emerging development was an effort to restructure the conduct of the electric-power- and gas-distribution markets. Traditionally, most electric power was generated, transmitted from plant to market area, and distributed to customers by a single company serving a particular area. Natural gas was purchased from producers by pipeline companies. The pipeline companies in turn arranged for sales to both local companies and large industrial customers.

Efforts were under way, however, to allow for alternative arrangements. In regard to electric power, the first step would be to increase the generation of electricity by companies independent of the established local utilities. Such independent producers could sell both to different utilities and directly to large customers. Similarly, natural gas distributors and large users would seek suppliers other than the pipelines. For both electricity and natural gas, a primary issue would be access to the long-distance distribution network.

The proposals proved divisive. For electric power one group of companies supported increased power production by independent companies; another group denounced such changes. The proponents included companies frustrated in their ability to build new production capacity profitably and seeing independent producers as the best available alternative. In addition, several companies with underutilized abilities to design and build power plants hoped that building plants for other companies would enable profitable use of their unused capacity.

The opponents saw increased independent generation as continuing what they considered the practice of state regulators of forcing the adoption of energy alternatives more expensive than the utilities would have chosen. They believed that the independent producers might be treated too favorably when regulators considered expansion options for utilities. Rate structures might also intensify the competition for industrial business. Typically, rates for utilities had been designed so that residential customers were undercharged and industrial customers were overcharged. Consequently, utilities would be vulnerable to competition in industrial markets from independent producers. Even some of the proponents of independent generation shared the opponents' concern that legislated rules for establishing common-carrier status would set rates for the independents that were too low.

Elsewhere in the world, progress continued after more than three decades of agonizing over uneconomic coal industries in Western Europe and Japan. A recurrent theme in appraising this situation was that World War I was a force for evil from which the world was still recovering. Among the problems that it generated was a disruption of European coal industries that on balance worsened during the great depression of the 1930s and World War II. After World War II it was widely believed that coal was a mismanaged industry that could thrive if given the right direction. This faith and the election of socialist governments in Britain and France led to nationalization of the industry. The Dutch also developed their coal industry as a nationalized venture, while the Germans and the Belgians did not.

Everywhere but Belgium it was believed that a vigorous rebuilding program would restore the coal industry to its former might. The Belgians recognized that the many small old mines in the southern part of their country were beyond saving but had to be protected for political reasons.

The situation was complicated by French statesman Jean Monnet's idea that coal and steel were so central to the Western European economy that cooperation on these two sectors was the best way to initiate a process of European unification. Thus, he persuaded the French government to propose a European Coal and Steel Community (ECSC) in order to create what was generally too literally translated into English as a "common market." The term "integrated market" better conveyed the goal.

The idea proved a bad guess, and its execution was flawed from the start. Nevertheless, six European countries (France, West Germany, Italy, Belgium, The Netherlands, and Luxembourg) agreed to join. The treaty establishing the ECSC was full of hedges. The ECSC had an option to act as a promoter of either competition or cartelization, and the member states retained considerable veto power. Although it

A new natural gas pipeline, operated by the Iroquois Gas Transmission System, extends 595 kilometers (370 miles) from Canada to Long Island, New York. Newly completed, it will provide the largest new source of energy to the New York City area since the 1950s.

Michael Shavel—The New York Times

was eventually discovered that this faith in coal and steel was misplaced, the ECSC was able to create confidence in broader cooperation through a European Economic Community (EEC).

In its early days (from its start in 1951 to 1958), the ECSC saw West Germany and France as managing a desirable expansion program but grappled with helping Belgium achieve its coal adjustments within the community framework. The aftermath of the 1956 Suez Canal crisis buried these beliefs forever. The surge of postcrisis oil supplies made it clear to coal producers that competition from oil was more formidable than previously recognized. It became apparent that oil would be capable of underselling coal for many decades.

Severe national differences of opinion caused each of the coal-producing countries among both the six original and six newer members of the ECSC and EEC to adopt largely independent policies. These had important differences in both goals and programs. The impact of the differences among countries could be most clearly seen in a comparison of production trends. The two extreme cases were The Netherlands and Germany. The Dutch managed to find a gas field that could, among other things, displace coal for domestic consumption and produce enough for export. The Dutch were the first to get out of the coal industry. The Germans, by contrast, erected an elaborate structure of defenses for their industry and were (at least in relative terms) the most reluctant to contract it. The French and the Belgians moved toward substantial contraction. Belgium, whose efforts to streamline the industry began more than a decade before those elsewhere, announced that its coal industry would shut down by Jan. 1, 1993. The British preserved a large proportion of their total production capacity; however, British output declined more than that of the Germans, so the industries in the two countries became more similar in size than they had been when the coal crisis began.

Differences also arose in the ways each country carried out its program. The Dutch were the simplest case. When the coal mines were closed, the coal mining company was made a participant in the gas production. The Belgians developed an explicit gradual extermination plan for their southern mines. The seven large low-cost mines in the northern Dutch-speaking region were put under a single company. Over time the government became the dominant stockholder in the northern mines through conversions of its loans into stockholdings. The fate of these mines became entwined in the peculiarities of Belgian politics and particularly the cultural clash between its French and Dutch-speaking communities. To lessen tensions, the government decided that each community would receive its own budget to spend as it wished. Following predictions made before the plan went into effect, the Dutch-speaking community quickly recognized better uses than subsidizing coal. This inspired the shutdown plan.

The French approach involved a high-tech solution. France became convinced that nuclear power was the answer to its energy problems and moved ahead with an extensive nuclear program. Coal was cast aside, though at a leisurely pace. The preservation program was largely one of direct subsidies to coal mines.

In all cases except that of Germany, the relationships between electric utilities and coal producers were difficult to evaluate. The extent to which the utilities were forced to take domestic coal at prices above those of imported energy was well documented only for Germany. A further complication was that France maintained a national buying organization, influenced by the government, that purchased all coal from non-EEC sources.

The two leading British political parties were less ideological in practice than their rhetoric suggested. The leaders of the Labour Party adopted moderate views, while, on the other hand, the Conservative Party commitment to free markets was highly qualified. Thus, between them the two parties fostered a policy that resulted in unduly slow contraction of the industry.

The Germans maintained the most complex and intractable of the systems. Support for the national industry came from three directions—funds from general federal and state revenues, funds from a special tax on electricity consumers, and revenues from consumers forced to pay more than market prices. Government aid was similarly dispensed in several forms: a scattering of subsidies for various current activities of the coal industry; assumptions of some of the cost burdens—mostly pensions for miners—from past mining; and programs to promote the use of German hard coal in coking and electricity generation. The subsidy of more than $80 a metric ton contrasted with prices delivered in Europe of about $50 a ton for coal for power plants and less than $60 a ton for coal used to make coke that met steel-producing requirements.

Pressures to rethink these national policies were emerging from many directions. Among the most important were: (1) the impact of the emerging changes discussed above on OPEC; (2) the multiple consequences of the collapse of Communism; and (3) the imperatives of ever really reaching by even the year 2000 the goals of the Europe 1992 program for full economic integration. Britain also had to deal with the consequences of past and future privatizations. The dismantling of Communism was also expected to add to the downward pressures on world energy prices. Among additional influences that were likely to be significant were the impacts of German

A plant engineer assesses the damage caused by a fire that destroyed the roof area of the hall housing the power turbines at the Chernobyl nuclear power plant near Kiev, Ukraine, in October 1991. The plant had experienced a serious nuclear accident in 1986, and there was considerable public pressure to shut it down permanently.

unification and a probable massive restructuring of Russian and eastern European steelmaking.

Future prospects. Given these changes, attitudes about energy had to be rethought. For at least most of the 20th century, political concerns exerted considerable influence on energy in general and crude oil in particular. For many years oil specialists debated whether the industry required unified direction by a government or a private-company cartel. Some insisted that this was essential, while others saw such regulation as dubious in principle and horrible in execution.

Recent experience was more supportive of the antiregulation case. Politicization appeared to have caused, rather than solved, problems in regard to energy. Government policies should be directed at relentlessly reducing its scope of influence and promoting competition and a commercial approach to the industries. The often-used security-of-supply argument for coordinated intervention reversed the truth. If many firms were struggling for business, none could afford to interfere with the flow of commerce. With sufficiently vigorous competition, no one producer mattered enough for its disruption to affect markets.

Of course, disruptions would arise from natural and man-made disasters. In a competitive, flexible, unfettered world, such disturbances were likely to have small impacts in both size and duration. Efforts to restore supplies rapidly would be made by those that had been disrupted and their rivals. The speed with which the lost output of Kuwait and Iraq was replaced in 1990 illustrated this point.

Moreover, as long as the threat of intervention did not interfere, prudence caused potential victims to prepare to offset crises. One clear illustration was the U.S. coal market. Strikes had been a regular feature of this industry for decades, but the disruption

they caused was not harmful because users stocked up in anticipation of the crisis.

Where competition was weak, disruption could promote further weakening. The oil shocks of the 1970s showed that the market could at least temporarily bear prices far above what even the most avaricious producers believed possible. OPEC countries quietly maintained supply restrictions to perpetuate the high prices. These actions were more successful than price-rigging efforts in other industries (and earlier ones in oil), though 1990 prices exceeded those of 1974 by less than the rise in the world price levels.

This situation arose because consuming countries pursued policies that encouraged collusion among the OPEC countries. Public policy in the U.S. and other countries systematically thwarted competition and encouraged politicization. Dismantling the policies that produced this outcome was by far the most effective way to increase competition and alleviate crises.

—Richard L. Gordon

Environment

During the past year there were many environmental disasters throughout the world. In the discussion of several of these, below, common features among them were being sought. A second important development during the year was the search for an appropriate conceptual model for the environmental sciences. What mix of disciplines is necessary and sufficient to explain, predict, and prevent environmental problems? Another highly visible development was interest in space as a unifying concept. This was demonstrated in studies on geographic information systems (GIS) and landscape ecology. In addition to these general themes, there were events of unusual significance.

AIDS. Scientists during the year were gaining a more certain understanding of the epidemiology of AIDS. The cumulative number of AIDS cases diagnosed by a particular year is dependent on the infection rate in each prior year and the incubation period. This period is the elapsed number of years from the year of infection with HIV, the human immunodeficiency virus that gives rise to AIDS, to the year of AIDS diagnosis. The mathematical relationship between (1) number of AIDS cases, (2) incubation period, and (3) prior time and rate of infection with HIV implies that one could work backward from (1) and (2) to (3). Ron Brookmeyer of Johns Hopkins University, Baltimore, Md., accomplished this by reconstructing the dynamics of the AIDS epidemic in the United States and predicting its future trend. The infection rate for homosexual and bisexual men increased rapidly to 1982, peaked in 1984, and declined rapidly thereafter. The infection rate among drug users peaked between 1984 and 1986 and declined afterward. It was projected that the heterosexual rate would continue growing until at least 1995. Brookmeyer pointed out that his results did not preclude a "second wave" epidemic in some groups. Though findings had to be interpreted with caution, they did suggest that the HIV infection rate may have peaked for all groups except heterosexuals.

A major area of uncertainty concerning AIDS worldwide was the ultimate scale of the pandemic in Third World countries and the possibility that AIDS there would recharge the epidemic in the developed countries by means of the return of HIV in the blood of tourists. There was considerable publicity during the past year about AIDS in Asia, particularly Thailand, and in Africa. To illustrate the size of the pandemic, by late November 1991, the World Health Organization had announced that 9 million to 11 million people were HIV positive, including those with full-blown AIDS. Of these, more than seven million were African. It was estimated that by the year 2000 more than 14 million African adults and 4 million children would be infected.

Birthrates and the cost of living. It is clear that as the cost of living increases, the human reproductive rate decreases. To illustrate, in late November, Japan released new census figures showing that the birthrate had dropped to 9.9 babies per 1,000 people per year by 1990, lower than any of the other industrialized countries. In an absolutely zero-growth population, if people lived exactly 75 years, $1/75$ of the population would die each year, and one child per 75 people would have to be born to maintain population stability. This implies an annual birthrate per 1,000 people of 1,000/75, or 13.3.

Shielded against the intense heat, Canadian fire fighters spray water on areas surrounding a burning oil well in Kuwait in November 1991. The retreating Iraqi Army set fire to some 650 Kuwaiti oil wells.

On the basis of these figures, Japan had a birthrate that would lead to population decline, a pattern that seemed likely to appear soon in many developed countries. An accompanying news release noted that the cost of rearing a child in Japan was high.

Disasters. The past year was unusual for the number and severity of environmental disasters. Probably the worst were the oil-well fires and crude-oil spills started at the end of the invasion of Kuwait by Iraq. In late February 1991 the retreating Iraqi Army blew up a large number of oil wells, which caught on fire. As with most large-scale disasters, there was difficulty in making a precise estimate of the magnitude; estimates of the exact number of oil-well fires ranged from 600 to 720. Using C-130 aircraft of the U.K. Meteorological Office Research Flight, D.W. Johnson and his colleagues studied the effects of the fires. Roughly 3.9 million bbl of crude oil were burned per day. In order for an air-pollutant source to be of global rather than just regional significance, the ash must rise into the stratosphere, which begins at about 15 km (1 km = 0.62 mi). The tops of the smoke plumes in Kuwait reached about 4.5 km, and so, despite their startling regional

347

A buoy that normally would float on the surface of Lake Oroville, about 6 to 9 meters (20 to 30 feet) above the lake bed, rests on dry ground in February 1991 as California entered its fifth year of drought.

appearance and health effects, the fires were not important on a worldwide scale. To put the fires into global perspective, Johnson and his colleagues reported that the associated carbon dioxide emissions were only 3% of normal total annual global fossil-fuel emissions. (For additional information on the oil-well fires, *see* Feature Article: EARTH—THE GULF WAR'S SILENT VICTIM.)

On June 15, 1991, Mt. Pinatubo in the Philippines erupted, ejecting 10 times more ash than Mt. St. Helens did in 1980. Though it was regarded as perhaps the most serious volcanic eruption in the 20th century, its total global impact on climate appeared to be considerably less than that of the two major 19th-century eruptions, Tambora and Cosequina. Pinatubo's eruption did, however, have major regional environmental effects. It destroyed 41,000 homes and damaged 67,000 others. The volcanic ash at the top of the mountain was washed off in rainstorms, generating tidal wave floods of mud 4.5 m (15 ft) high.

The volcano also had surprising aftereffects. A.J. Prata and his colleagues reported 14 incidents in which Pinatubo volcanic ash clouds were hazards to aircraft. Glass and silicate-bearing minerals from high-altitude volcanic ash particles melt under the high operating temperatures of jet engines and fuse onto internal surfaces. This can limit the rate of air flow through and in the most extreme cases can cause engine stalling.

The drought in California for the past several years was a common cause of three different types of local catastrophes. Droughts increase the danger of fire, increase the likelihood of severe dust storms, and decrease the availability of fresh water to dilute contaminants accidentally spilled into such water.

On July 14 a freight train derailed on a sharp curve over the Sacramento River, about eight kilometers north of Dunsmuir, spilling from 51,100 to 73,900 liters (13,500 to 19,500 gal) of metam sodium liquid, used on farms to kill weeds, insects, and fungi. Hundreds of thousands of fish and a great many plankton, insects, algae, and other plants were destroyed over a 17.5-km stretch of the river. There also appeared to have been a major population decline in such wildlife as otters, mink, heron, and egrets that have a diet that includes the river organisms.

Precise estimates of the public health consequences of the spill were scheduled to begin in February 1992. From those who lived near the spill, there were complaints of miscarriages, skin rashes, nosebleeds, breathing problems, deteriorating vision, headaches, and chest and back pains. Four months after the spill, at least 200 local residents continued to complain of mysterious medical problems. For example, one nine-year-old girl had 200 nosebleeds in four months. A 12-year-old girl suddenly found large discolorations on her chest and stomach.

One reason that documenting health effects is a problem is that local physicians who linked those conditions to the spill could find themselves embroiled in a time-consuming and potentially dangerous legal web. The accident should not have come as a great surprise; one report stated that there had been 30 derailments in the region between Mt. Shasta and Shasta Lake in the period 1972 to 1976.

Ironically, almost exactly at the end of the official fire season, on October 20, a fire storm in the hills of Oakland, Calif., spread very suddenly, destroying 2,500 homes. This fire storm was produced by a low-probability combination of conditions, including hot, dry winds coming from an unusual direction; an accumulation of dry, highly combustible vegetation adjacent to buildings; and highly combustible roofing material. Subsequent investigations raised a variety of questions about communication problems at the time the fire was burning most rapidly. After the fact it was clear that the ultimate impact of the fire would have been much less if it had been possible to mobilize all fire equipment of all branches and levels of government within 160 km on an emergency basis. For this to have happened, however, an extraordinary degree of coordination between local, state, and federal governments and an extremely ingenious communications network designed to exclude use for noncritical messages would have been necessary.

Then on November 29 a dust storm on the main north-south freeway in California blinded drivers suddenly. Seventeen people were killed, 150 were injured, and 11 large trucks and 93 cars were damaged or destroyed.

These incidents had several features in common. They developed suddenly and unexpectedly and initiated chain reactions. Environmental disasters initiate "chain reactions" in two senses: at each step of the chain, one cause may trigger multiple effects so that the scale of the incident increases rapidly, often explosively; also, each cause may produce effects of an entirely different nature from the cause. For example, a malfunction in a nuclear or chemical plant creates completely unexpected levels of demand for hospital services.

Given the frequency and severity of such incidents, they have attracted the attention of scholars, who call them low-probability–high-consequence accidents. In the interest of developing a generalized framework for analyzing and dealing with such incidents, B. Bowonder, S.S. Arvind, and T. Miyake undertook an exhaustive analysis of the Bhopal accident in India. On the evening of Dec. 2–3, 1984, a plant near Bhopal accidentally released methyl isocyanate. This is a highly reactive and toxic substance that reacts violently with water, alkali, acids, and alcohols. This incident also illustrates the problem of obtaining information about the exact extent of the

damage. Even now there are different estimates of the number of people killed in this incident, ranging from 2,083 to 8,000. The low estimate was from the government; the high estimate was the top end of the range of estimates obtained from detailed door-to-door surveys.

There appear to be three root causes for low-probability–high-consequence accidents. The most fundamental is the absence of a prior overview of the threat. Because this has not been done, there is no conceptual model of the incident against which the appropriateness of equipment, procedures, or institutional design and functioning can be evaluated. The authors noted that organizations view disasters as a threat and, therefore, attempt to suppress information. The arena for discussion is "tilted" so that optimism is perceived as realism and realism is perceived as doomsaying. Pessimism is made a taboo topic for discussion. Since none of the potentially affected individuals or institutions is allowed to talk about "worst-case scenarios," there is no thought given to the types of designs, decisions, procedures, or practices that should be avoided or the types of information that would be useful warning indicators of an impending disaster.

The consequences of such policies can be truly mind-boggling. Investigators of the Bhopal incident identified 21 equipment-failure errors, 12 operator errors, 65 management errors, and 28 regulatory

A fire storm in the hills of Oakland, California, in October 1991 killed at least 24 people and destroyed more than 2,000 houses and apartment buildings.

P.F. Bentley—Time Magazine

errors. The authors define an error as an incorrect belief or an incorrect action, with one often leading to the other. This pattern of numerous independent errors seems to allow only one explanation: there was such a firm belief that a worst-case scenario was impossible that a large number of independent decisions unwittingly increased its probability of occurrence. Also, early indications of impending disaster are overlooked because there is no existing conceptual model allowing them to be interpreted appropriately.

The second root cause of these incidents is inadequate coordination within and between the affected institutions and organizations. A characteristic of many high-consequence environmental incidents is the propagation of a chain of causes and effects through subsystems of many different types. To illustrate, an equipment malfunction releases a toxic substance into the environment, which then produces a medical effect. In such a case engineers, environmental scientists, toxicologists, and family physicians must all be able to talk to each other intelligibly and urgently. There must be a coordinated response by several different types of organizations, each of which corresponds to one of the affected subsystems (the equipment that malfunctioned, the toxic substance, and the medical effect). A system of information transfer that communicates necessary emergency information to all responsible parties in

Crews work to clear a section of the Interstate 5 freeway near Coalinga, California, on Nov. 29, 1991, after a sudden dust storm blinded drivers and caused more than 100 collisions and 17 deaths.

a language that has the maximum possible utility to them must be in place. Though this seems so self-evident as to be unworthy of mention, it is the opposite of the procedure that has characterized many high-consequence incidents. In the Bhopal case, for example, there was severe confusion about the nature of the gas that leaked; details had not been disclosed. There was controversy concerning the appropriate medical treatment. One senior medical official said that the people who died showed symptoms of cyanide poisoning; another disagreed. A telex from Union Carbide Corp. headquarters advised that if symptoms of cyanide poisoning persisted, patients should be injected with sodium thiosulphate and amyl nitrate; the contents of this telex were not disclosed. Consequently, the private physicians treating patients were not informed about the correct line of treatment and simply dealt with specific symptoms they saw.

The third root cause for high-consequence incidents is the inability of most organizations to respond fast enough to match the speed of development of the threat. High-consequence accidents cannot be dealt with in the customary time allowed for making decisions. All responses must be instantaneous, automatic, and triggered by signals routinely collected by monitoring equipment. The speed of response of the affected people and institutions must be developed to the highest degree by training and drilling of the type used for quick-response police, military, or fire-fighting units. The authors offered a long list of advice, which includes analysis of emergency response behavior and continuous risk assessment and upgrading of response systems.

A conceptual model. Environmental issues pose difficult decisions for modern civilization. It often appears that one is faced with a choice between jobs or environment, population control or right to life, preservation of tropical forests or the fostering of economic growth of tropical nations. It is clear that environmental controversies include scientific, economic, and ethical components. What is needed is some new means of making decisions that considers such decisions from all relevant perspectives. Recognizing this need, F. Herbert Bormann and Stephen R. Kellert of Yale University brought together a group of scholars to seek a new, more comprehensive approach to making societal decisions. It would have a scientific foundation, mindful of the long-term consequences of a deteriorating environment, and a moral component, seeking more equitable living standards of rich and poor people.

The book that resulted from their efforts provides an answer to the question, "Are science, economics, and ethics sufficient to understand and prevent environmental problems?" Or, to put that question differently, do pollution and environmental degradation occur because of inherent deficiencies or defects in one or all of science, ethics, or economics? The answer one gleans from the report on this workshop is a resounding no. Environmental problems have important political and cultural components, and even if science, economics, and ethics, separately or in combination, were comprehensive and perfect, that would not be sufficient for understanding or solution. The book makes clear that environmental problems may occur for reasons that make no sense at all in terms of science, any economic theory, or ethics. Rather, environmental problems arise because a group seeks to use political power and influence to improve its power relative to other groups, even when the action taken does not make economic sense to the group seeking power. In addition, traditional cultural values do not teach people that it is important to either design institutions or take action to prevent this concentration of power.

The argument that environmental destruction cannot be explained in terms of defective economic theory was made most convincingly by Malcolm Gillis, vice-provost at Duke University, Durham, N.C. He makes his case by considering a set of examples of water, rangeland, and forest management in various countries. For example, grazing fees charged for cattle on government-owned lands in the U.S. were set at 20 to 25% of fair-market value. In the Soviet Union near-zero prices were charged for irrigation water taken from the Aral Sea. In Brazil 72% of all the forest alterations detected by the Landsat satellite were accounted for by conversion to cattle pasture. The typical large Amazonian cattle ranch would have lost $2.8 million annually, but it received tax and credit subsidies of $5.6 million. In all these cases, intrinsically uneconomic operations are rendered profitable because of actions by government.

The problem is not purely political. In the complete discussion by Gillis, it is clear that neither government nor the electorate has a realistic view as to the real source of value in natural resources. For example, the value of nonwood relative to wood resources has been consistently underestimated. In addition to wood, tropical forests produce nuts, oils, fibers, meat, cosmetic compounds, dyes, fruits, latex, ornamental plants, spices, and pharmaceutical substances. All of these can be produced in perpetuity if the forest is not cut down. This is a problem of perception and inappropriate cultural values rather than one of science, economics, ethics, or politics.

Space and environmental studies. A cluster of interrelated themes including space, landscape, and the region recently became an active research area, for three reasons. The first is the rapid evolution of computer hardware and software systems; great memory capacity and processing speed are widely available at prices many organizations can afford.

The second is the rapid evolution of several separate fields of research that can benefit one another and the gradual coming together of those fields. GIS from geography; landscape ecology from ecology; artificial intelligence, computer science, linguistics, and percolation theory from physics; the geometry of fractals from mathematics; and the processing and interpretation of satellite images from photogrammetry are all coalescing. The third reason may be most important of all. The environmental movement of the last quarter century has made many people concerned about the wise management of the planet. However, no agency has the authority or, probably, skill to manage the planet or even large and middle-sized nations. Landscapes within regions are the actual management units entrusted to such agencies.

An important advantage of a regional-scale focus for wise environmental management is that, since regions are small, there are many of them. If any one is managed unwisely, the others can learn from those mistakes. If strategies applied to one work out beyond anyone's best expectations, the lessons will be applied to all regions. In short, regions compete with one another, and the rate of evolution of regional-scale management strategies is increased by this competition.

The two fields making the largest contributions to this cluster of research themes are GIS and landscape ecology. The status of each is described in new and comprehensive treatises by John C. Antenucci, Kay Brown, Peter L. Croswell, Michael J. Kevany, and Hugh Archer on the former and a work edited by Monica G. Turner and Robert H. Gardner on the latter.

The first is intended as a comprehensive guide to GIS, which can be defined as a computer system that combines map data with a structured data base of related information. Maps generated by this technology combine information on aboveground features, such as subdivision parcel boundaries and proximity to fire hydrants of child-care centers, with underground features, such as the relative suitability of soils for septic fields and the position of utility wires or pipes. An astonishingly diverse array of institutions and agencies are prospective clients for GIS: petroleum-exploration crews, market analysts, engineers planning airport expansion, and city politicians analyzing the compatibility of various land uses in terms of their proximity to adult entertainment enterprises.

GIS seems certain to evolve rapidly because of rapid improvements in computer hardware and software, optical disc storage, and new hardware-software systems for data communications and networking. A key to the rapid evolution of GIS will be networking of hardware systems from multiple vendors and improvements in computer operating systems and data communication standards.

The focus on landscape is leading to a new, more all-encompassing concept of natural resource management. Robert Coulson and his colleagues refer to natural resource management as the orchestrated modification of landscape components and the rate of alteration of the ecological mosaic over time.

To illustrate the application of these abstract notions, one might consider the example of a forester charged with evaluating the impact of a proposed timber harvest on a resident population of elk. It is necessary for the forester to understand that elk will starve if their food resources are depleted below a critical level, that they will die of exposure if the size of their refuge area falls below a critical level, and that they will be exposed to hunters if they have to travel across the site where timber has been harvested to move from their feeding area to their refuge area. If asphalt or cement roads are near the site where timber is harvested, this will increase the access of hunters to the area. GIS provides quantitative data allowing precise assessment of the elk mortality rate. When integrated with an artificial intelligence system, GIS would collate in the form of a set of rules the expert opinions of wildlife biologists and foresters.

In effect, what has been described above is a knowledge-representation scheme built on different sets of rules. These rules are of three types. Rules from data bases deal with relationships such as those between the age of trees and the characteristics of a forest stand. Map rules evaluate information associated with a map: how are values assigned to variables in a map? The third type of rules, heuristic rules, evaluate the knowledge of experts. An important basic idea in this study of the dynamics of landscape is that the forces causing change can be separated into two groups: those that operate globally, producing certain changes everywhere at the same period in history, and those that operate locally.

The key to the computer modeling of landscape dynamics is a large map of a region, represented in the computer's memory as rows and columns of squares, each one corresponding to an actual square parcel of land. To produce change in landscape, a smaller square—of, say, five rows and columns of squares—"floats" over this "model landscape," one square at a time. The small square describes the probability that some type of movement, such as human population migration, will take place from the 24 surrounding squares to a central square. These probabilities are applied to density gradients between origin and destination squares on the large map. By appropriate design of the small square, and the computer-simulation program, any type of scientific principle describing motion of people or other entities over landscape may be simulated. The computer may simulate totally or partially uninhabitable

sections of landscape ("deserts"), forces that direct change over landscape (rivers, shoreline of lakes), transportation corridors, "leapfrog" development, inhibition of growth one place by growth someplace else, or agglomeration effects, as when commuting to downtown Houston, Texas, or Los Angeles converts a circle around downtown into parking lots.

When such a computer-simulation program is run repeatedly, to mimic the real-time equivalent of 50 or 100 years, it mimics the changing pattern of land use actually observed around metropolitan regions or in national parks or wilderness areas. The parameters in the computer can be "tuned" or "fitted" to actual historical data sets as depicted in historical sequences of maps in order to produce a simulation model that mimics actual history with very high accuracy. Such a model can then be used as a public policy research tool, to play "What if we managed this region using policy X for the next half century?"

Highly realistic models are available for forecasting economic and demographic change. They incorporate new insights into capital investment and economic-demographic forces operating through history. These models have been tuned to long-run historical data sets, which they mimic with high accuracy. They can then be linked to spatial models in order to supply the global component of the system of forces producing change in landscape.

—Kenneth E.F. Watt

See also Feature Article: THE SALVATION ISLANDS.

Food and agriculture

Production worldwide dropped for most crops in 1991–92, owing to unfavorable weather conditions in several major producing countries, while production of animal products set new records. World commodity demand increased slightly. Fundamental differences between the European Communities (EC), the U.S., and the Cairns Group of 14 agricultural exporting nations threatened to scuttle trade accords. Controversy over the use of genetically engineered growth hormones to increase milk production in dairy cows began anew, but the overall outlook for agriculture research to improve daily life was bright.

Agriculture

Unfavorable weather conditions in Australia, the United States, and the former Soviet Union reduced output for these major producers. At the same time, output of animal products reached record levels as poultry supplies and red meat, particularly U.S. pork production, rose. World commodity demand increased slightly in response to real economic growth and population increases. However, reduced avail-

Thousands of farmers march through Paris in September 1991 to protest declining prices for their products and to express their fears of competition from farmers in other European countries.

ability and higher prices dampened consumption of grains, particularly in the former Soviet Union, where political and economic woes brought major upheavals. Political restructuring there was a dominant factor in world grain markets. Grain crops in the former Soviet republics were down sharply from the near-record 1990 levels, and government procurement fell precipitously. Soviet grain imports increased in 1991 but not enough to offset the decline in production. U.S. exports, particularly corn and cotton, were hurt by expanding supplies from competing countries and reduced demand from major customers.

Trade. The outlook was not bright for trade agreements being negotiated by the U.S. and its trading partners in the Uruguay round of talks under the General Agreement on Tariffs and Trade (GATT). As 108 countries gathered for talks in mid-January 1992, there was a good news-bad news feeling to the discussions. The group had agreed unanimously to use a package of 26 trade deals drafted late in 1991 as the basis for a final decision by Easter 1992, about the latest date possible if the round's final results were to be ratified by the participating countries' legislative bodies in time for implementation in January 1993. However, the EC's objections to the agriculture deal assembled by Arthur Dunkel, the director general of the talks, still threatened to break up the entire package.

Dunkel offered his draft plan after the U.S. and the EC failed to agree on cutting farm subsidies that appear to hamper trade. The U.S. and most of the Cairns Group would have liked him to go further, but Japan, South Korea, Switzerland, and Canada, which opposed plans to replace import controls by high tariffs, wanted less. The outlook for agreement

would have been brighter if the EC had not given early notice that it would offer amendments providing "substantial improvements" to the draft plan.

EC objections focused on the "green box," a category of farm subsidies that do not influence production or price decisions. These would not have to be reduced because they do not distort trade. However, the EC said that Dunkel had stipulated such strict criteria for the green box that proposed payments to compensate farmers for price and production cuts resulting from reform of the EC common agricultural policy (CAP) would be excluded. Ray MacSharry, the EC's farm commissioner, said that unless the payments qualified for the green box, CAP reform and the subsidy cuts required under the GATT agreement could not be accomplished.

As Easter approached, the U.S. and the Cairns Group did not seem inclined to accept further compromises. U.S. officials had expressed strong sentiments about what appeared to be unwillingness on the part of the EC to reach agreement. The Cairns Group said putting the EC's proposed compensation payments into the green box would strongly interfere with the subsidy-reduction deal. Further complicating the successful completion of the GATT negotiations was the U.S. election-year climate. Farm groups, textile groups, and others were clamoring for congressional attention to the possible negative effect of a trade agreement on U.S. industry.

U.S. Secretary of Agriculture Edward Madigan said that failure to reach agreement would mean the U.S. would spend an additional $1 billion on the Export Enhancement Program, which would trigger marketing loans on wheat and feed grains as dictated by the 1990 Farm Bill. Marketing loans would permit farmers to repay their Commodity Credit Corporation loans at the loan rate plus interest or at an adjusted world price or alternative loan-repayment rate, whichever was lower. Current prices for wheat and feed grains were much higher than the loan rate, so marketing loans would have no significance except to alert world competitors that the U.S. was unlikely to hold wheat and feed grains off the market if, at some future time, world prices deteriorated.

There had been seven previous GATT negotiating rounds, beginning in 1947. The Uruguay round began in 1986 and focused largely on agriculture, although questions regarding services, intellectual property, and investments were also debated.

Hormones. The controversy over a genetically engineered hormone that boosts milk production in cows stirred again in 1991 as the European Commission extended its ban on the use of bovine somatotropin (BST) until the end of 1993. The EC agriculture ministers were expected to approve the ban, which was imposed to allow time for study of the possible health and trade risks of BST. The ban had generated concern among the EC's trading partners.

In the U.S. the controversy, which had quieted down, flared up again as a California-based consumer- and animal-protection organization launched a national advertising campaign against the product. The group placed ads in national magazines protesting the presence of genetically engineered hormones in milk and calling for a consumer boycott of milk from cows injected with the BST. The group also objected to the procedure for the sake of the animals. Some farm groups also opposed use of the hormone for fear it might result in overproduction of milk and force them out of business.

In 1985 the U.S. Food and Drug Administration (FDA) declared that milk and meat from cows treated with BST was safe for human consumption, but it had not approved the hormone for commercial use on dairy farms. Other government groups, as well as peer-reviewed articles in major science and medical journals, seemed to agree with the FDA position that milk and meat from cows injected with the hormone are safe.

Green gold. The real treasure Christopher Columbus loaded in his ships almost 500 years ago was not gold or silver but baskets of "green gold"—New World wonders that would feed millions, spawn industries, cure disease, satisfy the palate, and serve as the seed for wealth and creativity throughout the world. Chief among these is corn, which has been the dietary staple of millions. Now it promises to do more than feed people and livestock. It can power cars, deice roads, and be used in baby diapers. Some researchers were working on ways to make degradable plastics using cornstarch as a prime ingredient.

While much of the research is still in the beginning stages, there have been some important break-

throughs. A new study by the independent Oak Ridge (Tenn.) National Laboratory showed that ethanol, which is refined from fermented corn, generates at least 20% more usable energy than is required for producing it. The study predicted that ethanol production costs would continue to decrease during the next three years, reducing reliance on traditional fuel resources. Research aimed at improving the corn fermentation process and raising ethanol processing yields would help reduce costs. The U.S. Clean Air Act standards, which were to take effect in November 1992, were expected to boost the demand for ethanol further.

In addition to being used as a gasoline additive, ethanol helps remove sulfur from coal with a high sulfur content. The sulfur and some of the ethanol can be recaptured and used in other processes. One by-product of the procedure, acetic acid, can be made into calcium magnesium acetate, which can be used as a deicer. While higher in cost than salt, the corn-based deicer is not corrosive, is much safer to use, and is more environmentally compatible. Research was now focusing on the coal-desulfurization process, which, if successful, could help reduce costs and environmental pollution associated with the burning of coal.

Crop protection. Some members of the U.S. Congress were attempting to block federally funded research on genetically engineered plants with a higher resistance to herbicides. Opponents of genetic engineering say such research encourages greater use of chemicals when the focus should be on better growing techniques. Many farm groups think a program of integrated pest management (IPM) is the best idea. The idea behind IPM is to use pesticides, cultural practices, resistant crop varieties, and biological insect control (good bugs destroying bad bugs) together to produce commercially acceptable crops. The approach reduces the use of pesticides. Farm groups said that the use of pesticides was decreasing as environmental concerns grew and programs like IPM were adopted, but that pesticides may always have a place in a farmer's overall crop-protection plan because unique growing conditions may require their use in a given area.

In the quest for ways to handle crop protection, Du Pont and Crop Genetics International Corp. joined forces to develop a virus-based insecticide that would give crop-eating pests a "fatal flu." The original insecticidal virus products were developed at a seven-person company in Columbia, Md., called Espro, Inc., that was later acquired by Crop Genetics. The virus infects Lepidoptera, the family of insects that grow from caterpillars to butterflies and moths. These creatures can ravage lettuce, tomatoes, and other fruits and vegetables. The virus is sprayed on the crops, and caterpillars that munch on the crops catch the virus and develop the fatal flu. The idea is to wipe out insects biologically by using a species-specific virus.

The virus is costly to manufacture. Scientists use caterpillars as living factories to produce the virus in quantities. Insects are grown until they reach the caterpillar stage. The caterpillars are sprayed with the virus, which multiplies inside the insect and kills it. The virus is then extracted. Researchers were looking for a cheaper method.

Some environmental groups took issue with Crop Genetics' claim that the viral insecticides pose no risk to humans or animals. They argued that viral insecticides have not been widely used, and it is impossible to predict the effects heavy use might have. However, an ecologist with the National Coalition Against the Misuse of Pesticides conceded that naturally occurring organisms in viral insecticides do appear to be safer than chemical or genetically engineered alternatives; it is possible that the viruses might travel from insects to people, but it is unlikely.

Researchers at Iowa State University were believed to have discovered what could be the first "natural" weed killer and fertilizer: corn gluten meal. The product, a protein substance extracted from corn during processing, interferes with germination in crabgrass and other annual weeds. At the same time, its 10% nitrogen content acts as a fertilizer. The corn by-product, as developed so far, was less effective and more expensive than synthetic weed killers, but it would offer consumers a good alternative to standard herbicides.

Health benefits. The quest for healthier hogs could lead to healthier pregnant diabetic women. The mysterious role of insulin in reproduction was the subject of current research. Mississippi State University scientists were searching for the key to how hormones that respond to diet, such as insulin, affect animal fertility. The most notable discovery the team had made thus far concerned the role of insulin-like growth factor-I (IGF-I). Present in all mammals and manufactured in many body tissues, IGF-I is important to normal functioning of the follicles in the ovary. However, the amount present in the follicles of diabetics is very low. The pituitary hormone, growth hormone or somatotropin, is thought to control IGF-I. In diabetic pigs the level of growth hormone was found to be abnormally high while the IGF-I level was low. Researchers believe growth hormone is responsible for some of the problems associated with human diabetes. Other effects of insulin deficiency include decreased estrogen production and an increased number of degenerating cells in the ovary.

At Ohio State University researchers were looking for ways to improve the taste of soybeans so they would be more acceptable to the American palate.

Alan Decker—The New York Times

Jerry Caulder, president and chief executive of the Mycogen Corp., shows one of the laboratories where research was taking place to develop new pesticides. The company's genetically engineered pesticides, delivered in dead bacteria, became the first to win approval from the U.S. Environmental Protection Agency.

When soybeans are crushed in processing, enzymes are released. These enzymes link with fatty acids within the beans and react with oxygen to create an unpleasant flavor. Other compounds that affect flavor may be produced by heating or processing treatments. To find the distasteful culprits, scientists put a few beans in a small container and analyze the gases. Then they use a gas chromatograph to separate and identify the undesirable compounds that form as the enzymes react during processing. Once the compounds are known, processors can work to develop new handling methods that will eliminate the bad taste.

In 1991 researchers reported the results of a study in Singapore indicating that soybean protein may lower the risk of breast cancer in premenopausal women by 60%. The Singapore study focused on phytoestrogens found in proteins that are present in soy sauce, tofu, and soybeans. Researchers from England, Singapore, and France speculated that these plant forms of the hormone estrogen might block the activity of human estrogens and reduce the incidence of breast cancer. However, other scientists believed that more research was needed. A number of other health benefits from soybeans have been documented. Soybean oil is low in the saturated fats believed to contribute to heart disease. It is popular in cooking and food processing. However, the taste has prevented soybeans from gaining wide acceptance among Western consumers, and as a result, food manufacturers have not rushed to substitute soybeans for other food ingredients.

New products. A new process to convert the fatty acids in vegetable oil for use in industrial products could open new markets for those oils. The new process subjects the fatty acids to high temperature and pressure to form estolides, which can be used as is or split to form hydroxy fatty acids. Estolides have potential applications in lubricants or cosmetics. Hydroxy fatty acids, now obtained from imported castor oil, are used in lubricants, plasticizers, and cosmetics. The yield of estolides from the new process was now less than 20%, but U.S. Department of Agriculture researchers were working to boost production to economically feasible levels.

—John Patrick Jordan and Patricia Brazeel Lewis

Nutrition

Many people consider dietary supplements to be essential for a healthy life. The term *dietary supplement* refers to any substance that is defined not as a drug or medicine but as a supplement to the customary food intake of a person. Such supplements are usually food products of plant origin that are not classed as drugs or medication but are distinct from commonly eaten foods. People take them because they feel uncertain about the adequacy of their diets and want to ensure that they are obtaining everything that they need to maintain health and reduce the risk of illness. This attitude is especially prevalent among older people who live apart from their children and are independent of institutional supervision.

The promotion and sale of aids to health and long life to middle-aged and older adults has proved to be a profitable business. The FDA has been trying to regulate these substances, as to both quantity recommended and safety for the people targeted as consumers. The American Dietetic Association has proposed that a dietary supplement be defined as "a substance for which scientific proof of a nutrient-like action has been documented as one that is required for the nutrition of human beings." These substances either cannot be synthesized by the body at all or are not produced in sufficient amounts to maintain health. The American Institute of Nutrition, the American Society for Clinical Nutrition, and the National Council Against Health Fraud endorse this definition. Substances that meet the definition of dietary supplement should be "packaged and distributed in a manner and amount that is compatible with physiologic tolerance." This differs from the regulations for substances classified as food. To regulate "potentially hazardous" substances as diet supplements is a major undertaking for any regulatory agency. The classification of "safe" does not imply that the supplement is essential or necessary for health.

Dietary counseling and guidance. According to Sharon Denny, program administrator for the National Center for Nutrition and Dietetics in Chicago (sponsored by the American Dietetic Association), the most common questions received by the center have been those concerning cholesterol, fat, the feeding of children, specific nutrients, and diabetes-related problems. Most callers wanted to know how to obtain individual counseling from a registered dietitian and were grateful for help.

Numerous food guides to adequate nutrition have been presented to the American public over the years, with the aim of informing people of all ages that they need to eat an assortment of food from specified categories or food groups. Initially, the emphasis was on "protective foods," which were often missing from the standard bread-meat-potato diet. Supplements to this meager fare were seasonal native fresh plants and fruits available in a given area. In winter and early spring, when local fresh plant products were scarce, diseases such as scurvy were prevalent among less affluent families, especially in women and young children.

Historically, Battle Creek, Mich., "the cereal-food capital of the world," was the home of the ready-to-eat cereal products that changed the North American diet. John Harvey Kellogg and W.K. Kellogg, founders of what became the Kellogg Co., capitalized on ideas promoted by Sylvester Graham, a diet reformer whose name survives in the graham cracker. Graham was a temperance advocate who proposed that cereals be used as food for people instead of being made into intoxicating drinks. Another developer of cereal products, C.W. Post, introduced Postum, a popular no-caffeine drink made from grain that is still available today. The Kelloggs and Post were dedicated promoters of cereal products made from whole grain, which required no enrichment or fortification.

The concept of "enriching" refined cereals and flour was unheard of. Cereals and flours made from whole wheat, barley, and other whole grains are nutritionally superior to refined and processed products. Before the development of modern transportation, they were the major component of most people's diets, supplemented with seasonally available wild game, fruits, and vegetables.

Today nutrition guidance stresses inclusion of all the basic food groups. The American Dietetic Association, at its 1991 annual meeting, launched "A Health Start—Food to Grow on," an informational and educational campaign promoting food choices and eating habits that will contribute to a healthful life-style. "A Man's Guide to Nutrition," introduced June 4, 1991, at a news conference in New York City, received widespread attention in most major newspapers and on television and radio. Such information, and exposure to various foods and products, help the consumer to make appropriate food choices.

Obesity: excessive caloric intake. From the beginning of nutrition awareness, it has been acknowledged that people have a choice of food, that food is both a pleasure and a necessity, and that certain kinds of foods are essential for health and well-being. On the other hand, "enough of a good thing is enough," and this especially is true of caloric intake. Obesity continues to afflict the U.S. population, even though people spend billions of dollars on low-calorie foods and exercise devices. G.K. Goodrich and J.P. Foregt of the Nutrition Research Clinic at Baylor College of Medicine in Houston, Texas, have pointed out that no long-lasting treatment for obesity has been found. Obesity results from a combination of excessive caloric intake and insufficient physical activity. Reversing this pattern requires exceptional self-control in improving eating and activity behaviors.

Only about 5 to 10% of those who try to take in fewer calories and burn up more through exercise are successful in achieving their "ideal weight." Dieting too often results in a seesaw pattern of weight change. Negative moods and emotional stress may lead to a breakdown of an individual's self-control. The obvious reason for weight gain after a reducing regimen is the return to former eating and exercise habits. Also, metabolic factors may make it easier to regain weight after a period of calorie deficit.

Awards. Nevin Scrimshaw, professor emeritus and former head of the department of nutrition and food science at the Massachusetts Institute of Technology, was presented with the 1991 World Food Prize. This prize is the foremost international award recognizing achievement in improving the quality, quantity, or availability of food in the world. It was conceived by Norman E. Borlaug, a Nobel laureate in 1970 and founding sponsor of the General Food Fund in 1986. Scrimshaw's major interest for 20 years was the study of various food proteins and the

FDA Commissioner David Kessler (right) announces in November 1991 proposals for extensive changes in food labeling, affecting such terms as fresh *and* light. *Joining him is Health and Human Services Secretary Louis Sullivan.*

human requirement for protein and amino acids. He first described the synergistic relationship between nutrition and infection. He was a founding director of the Institute of Nutrition of Central America and Panama in 1949.

During the year *Nutrition News* from the National Institutes of Health reported that the National Cancer Institute was inviting submission of applications from persons holding a Ph.D., M.D., or similar professional degree for career development awards in cancer prevention. Subject areas appropriate for awards under this program included cancer-related aspects of human genetics, human nutrition, behavioral and social sciences, biochemical and genetic epidemiology, prevention clinical trials, health education and promotion, nursing, and public health. Awards would be provided through the existing Preventive Oncology Academic Award grant mechanism. Each award would be made for a project period of three to five years.

—Mina W. Lamb

"I love you, too, but with my high cholesterol and your high triglycerides we could never have children."

Life sciences

Determination of the three-dimensional structure of the cholera toxin molecule, exploration of recently discovered processes in which RNA molecules are "edited" before their translation into protein, and the discoveries of cold-bloodedness in a mammal and the skull of an enormous fossil crocodilian were among highlights of the past year's activity in the life sciences. Scientists also reported what appeared to be a homeobox gene, a master gene controlling the expression of other genes, in maize—the first such gene known in plants.

Botany

Progress in botany during the past year explored intriguing relationships and concerns in such topics as genetics, reproduction and development, food plants, global warming, and the welfare of forests.

Genetics. An exciting report in plant developmental genetics came from the work of Sarah Hake and associates of the U.S. Department of Agriculture (USDA) Plant Gene Expression Center, Albany, Calif., and the University of California at Berkeley. In their studies of maize (corn), the researchers appeared to have confirmed the existence of homeobox genes in plants. Homeobox genes control aspects of the early development of organisms when differentiation of certain organismic features is being established. The genes have some DNA base sequences in common (the homeobox) and produce proteins that have some common structure and that are instrumental in controlling the expression of other genes. Thus, homeobox genes affect the activity of other genes that are involved in guiding the differentiation of whole groups of cells during development.

Homeobox genes had been known for some time from work on animals like the fruit fly (*Drosophila melanogaster*) and on fungi like yeast but never before from plants. Hake's group identified a segment of maize DNA, called the *Knotted-1* (*Kn1*) locus, that may be mutated by the insertion of a transposon (transposable genetic element) or the duplication of a portion of the locus. The resulting corn plants form outpockets or knots on their leaves because of the failure of some groups of leaf cells to differentiate properly (presumably due to the disrupted activity of the mutated gene).

The actual sequence of the *Kn1* gene was identified, and the protein for which it codes was predicted. When compared with protein products of homeobox genes from other organisms, the protein of the *Kn1* gene showed enough similarities to allow the conclusion that *Kn1* is in fact a homeobox gene. The research group continued to locate more homeoboxes in maize, tomatoes, and rice.

Sarah Hake, USDA Plant Gene Expression Center, Albany, Calif.

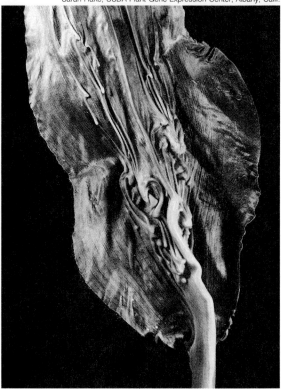

In maize (corn) expressing the Knotted-1 mutation, some groups of leaf cells fail to differentiate properly, resulting in leaves with outpockets or knots. The gene whose activity is disrupted by the mutation is thought to be a homeobox gene, the first such found in plants.

A group of German workers reported on the discovery of a number of genes that influence early development in the primary parts of plant embryos. Gerd Jurgens and associates of the University of Munich studied the development of *Arabidopsis thaliana* (common wall cress), a small, quick-growing species that has become a popular experimental subject for plant genetic studies. Normal embryos of flowering plants have four primary regions—shoot, cotyledon, hypocotyl, and root. Jurgens' team discovered mutated versions of four genes that may modify the shape of these primary structures or even cause the lack of one. While avoiding the term *homeobox,* the investigators pointed out some of the similarities of their findings to those in studies conducted with *Drosophila* in which a small proportion of the fly's genes were shown to contribute very specifically to its developmental pattern.

In the first decade of the 20th century German botanist Carl Correns observed that inheritance patterns of certain traits in plants differed from the patterns usually observed. Scientists now know that Correns had observed traits influenced by genes that are carried in the chloroplasts of plant cells rather

358

than in cell nuclei, where most genes reside. Since chloroplasts appear ordinarily to be transmitted to offspring entirely by the female parent, the genetic endowment (genome) of chloroplasts has become the focus of considerable attention for a number of reasons. One is that chloroplast genomes may be a particularly reliable data base to study evolutionary relationships and hence to refine classification systems. In 1991 gene mapping of chloroplast DNA (cpDNA) was proceeding on more than 200 species of higher plants as well as many algae.

The usual technique for studying cpDNA is to fragment it with enzymes called restriction endonucleases, which cleave it at specific base sequences. By means of the laboratory technique of chromatography, the fragments are then sorted into different lengths and the sorted groups visualized. Mutations in the restriction sites are detected when fragments that are different from those of "normal" lengths appear in chromatograms.

Attention being given to the utility of cpDNA in plant classification was reflected in the increasing number of reports appearing in journals. The four examples listed below were published in the *American Journal of Botany* in 1991; each employed the restriction-site mapping technique and concluded by recommending modifications in the phylogeny (evolutionary relationships) of plant groups. Birgitta Bremer of the University of Stockholm and Robert K. Jansen of the University of Connecticut proposed modifications in the classification of the subfamilies of the family Rubiaceae (madder family). Jansen and associates of the University of Connecticut and Oregon State University arrived at new relationships among a subgroup of the family Asteraceae (composite, or aster, family). Douglas E. Soltis and associates of Washington State University recommended taxonomic changes in the family Saxifragaceae (saxifrage family). David M. Spooner and associates of the University of Wisconsin at Madison suggested improvements in understanding the origins and migration of sections of the genus *Solanum* within the family Solanaceae (nightshade, or potato, family).

Reproduction and development. Figs (genus *Ficus*) are a very large, widely dispersed group of plants. They have a syconium, a distinctive multiple "fruit" formed when tissues of the receptacle enlarge, grow up around the flower parts, and thus enclose the true fruits. Each individual fruit is actually a drupelet containing a seed covered with a hard endocarp (detected as crunchiness when a commercial fig is eaten). Some fig species also have a fleshy exocarp layer on each fruit. Each species of fig produces its own characteristic syconium. In some cases this highly specialized structure makes it possible for the species to exploit two different kinds of animals to disperse the seeds.

Sandra Kaufmann and associates, working out of the University of Miami, Fla., demonstrated how dispersal works for one species, *Ficus microcarpa*. Birds are the initial dispersers, being attracted to the fleshy, whole multiple fruit. The outer portions are digested by passage through the birds' digestive tract, while the drupelets are voided. Ants subsequently are attracted by the fleshy exocarp of each individual drupelet and serve to scatter the enclosed seeds even farther. The researchers suggested that such a dispersal pattern by two vectors may be important to the success of this species where it is spreading rapidly after being naturalized.

Martha R. Weiss of the University of California at Berkeley reported that insect pollinators of flowers in at least 74 angiosperm (flowering plant) families are able to recognize color differences in flowers of the same plants. Weiss experimented with the flowers of *Lantana camara* and two species of butterflies. She found that the newly opening flowers of *L. camara* were yellow and turned orange and then red on subsequent days. The butterflies, normal pollinators of the plant, were seen to choose the yellow flowers, which also happen to be more likely to have nectar. The behavior seems to be learned, according to Weiss's work; newly emerged butterflies visit *L. camara* flowers of all colors but choose the yellow flowers later on. The colors of the older flowers serve a function, however, for butterflies are attracted to large masses of color even when the orange and red flowers are included. The pollinators discriminate among the colors after they arrive.

Food plants. For a number of years researchers have actively investigated the potential for crop plants that can grow in salty soil. Such interest is promoted by the desire to expand cropland, to reclaim land made salty by irrigation, and to use seawater for irrigation. Much attention has been given to genetically improved salt tolerance in known crop plants. An alternative approach is to recruit new crop plants from among species already known to be salt tolerant. A group of investigators of the Environmental Research Laboratory, Tucson, Ariz., and the University of Arizona worked with *Salicornia bigelovii*, a naturally salt-tolerant plant. Edward P. Glenn and associates raised the plant with direct seawater irrigation for six years and found that it is a candidate oilseed crop. The seed contains 26–33% oil and 31% protein. The oil is high in linoleic acid (73–75%), making it a valuable polyunsaturated oil for human consumption. The researchers suggested that the seed meal could be used in chicken diets.

How many species of plants serve as the main food supply in various countries of the world? Estimates made by a number of organizations and authors have varied from 7 to 30 depending on how food categories have been constructed and on the thorough-

Martha R. Weiss, University of California, Berkeley

Flowers of Lantana camara *change from yellow (light) to red (dark) as they age. Researchers showed that the plant's normal butterfly pollinators recognize the color differences and choose newer flowers, which are more likely to have nectar.*

ness of surveys. Robert and Christine Prescott-Allen, two Canadian reviewers of data of the UN Food and Agriculture Organization (FAO), concluded that there are no fewer than 103 species that are important somewhere in the world. Their report included production or supply figures for 300 plant and animal food commodities in 146 countries; the figures covered 94% of the population of the less developed countries, 100% of the population of the developed countries, and 95% of the world's population. The reviewers found that plant species vary in the importance of their contribution to total commodity weight, calories, protein, and fat. Accounting for more than 5% of commodities by weight alone are wheat (116 countries), sugarcane (104), rice (66), potato (51), banana and plantain (48), maize (43), cassava (35), tomato (19), orange (18), and coconut (16). On the basis of importance of calories, the top species are wheat (124 countries), sugarcane (117), rice (78), maize (58), potato (27), cassava (26), coconut (19), and soybean (19). While the remainder of species seem to be favored in fewer countries, they are important nevertheless and provide additional reason for concern about species diversity, in terms of both number of species and genetic variability.

Effects of global warming. The imminent possibility of climatic changes associated with global warming via an enhanced greenhouse effect has sharpened interest in biogeography, the search for evidence of how plants and animals responded to similar changes in the past. With respect to populations of seed plants, the most productive approach has been the study of pollen found in cores taken from peat bogs, where the pollen has been preserved from the times that it fell on the bogs as the peat was forming. Two English researchers found that pollen records are not always reliable. Annabel Gear and Brian Huntley of the University of Durham reported finding fossil stumps of Scots pine (*Pinus sylvestris*) in far northern Scotland where pollen evidence is lacking. They used radiocarbon dating, ring studies, and pollen data from nearby regions to conclude that a 70–80-km (43–50-mi) advance of the pines occurred so rapidly that the pollen record is poor. Moreover, their study of tree rings in the stumps enabled them to correlate this advance with climatic change and to reflect on the rate of advance. Their calculated rate of 375–800 m (1,230–2,620 ft) per year agreed with pollen records of postglacial migrations of certain plant species. The researchers made the point that these rates are slower than would be required for maintenance of species-environment equilibrium if the global-warming projections now being made are realized.

Essentially the same conclusion was drawn by three global-warming computer modelers who attempted to predict changes that will occur in the vegetation of eastern North America. Jonathan T. Overpeck of the National Oceanic and Atmospheric Administration, Boulder, Colo., Patrick J. Bartlein of the University of Oregon, and Thompson Webb III of Brown University, Providence, R.I., used known data about pollen distribution of certain plant species and climatic factors from the period following the last glaciation of North America. They calculated how rapidly the vegetation changed during that period in the face of the climatic change. They then compared that rate with the rate of vegetation change that would correspond to the predicted temperature and rainfall if certain global-warming levels were to be experienced in the future. They concluded that the rate of vegetation change caused by global warming would be much greater than that following the retreat of glaciers, resulting in a period of disequilibrium until change slowed. The result made more specific predictions of future change very difficult.

Forest welfare. A century ago the U.S. Congress passed the Forest Reserve Act, which empowered the president to designate forest "reserves." Later the areas became national forests, and they now comprise more than 77 million ha (191 million ac) of forests and grasslands. They do not include all of the forests of the U.S., since many others exist under other federal, state, or local jurisdiction; however, the national forests serve as the focus for large forest-related problems of today. A major concern has been for their "health." This concern relates not only to the nature of the forest itself but also to the growing conflict among economic and environmental interests. As such, it serves as a global paradigm of conflict over forest welfare.

Forest health is difficult to measure, having been judged traditionally by a given forest's general appearance to professionals or in the extremely practical terms of timber and pulpwood yield. There is no established baseline of characteristics by which to judge a particular forest and predict its future. By the early 1990s national forest programs were in motion to establish and develop computer analyses for the needed data bases in New England, Delaware, Maryland, New Jersey, Virginia, Georgia, and Alabama. The intention is to include all the forests of the contiguous 48 states under the National Forest Health Monitoring Program. Characteristics of forests will be studied systematically and will include such tree features as species, sizes, and crown densities. Soil properties are also important since they register effects of disturbances like acid rain.

Another approach is to designate and study indicator species. These organisms are plants and animals that are particularly dependent on continued normal conditions of certain forests and in which changes may indicate the presence of certain risk factors for forest health. The indicator species approach is included in what has been called the decade's biggest controversy in U.S. forestry—the competition for old-growth forests, particularly in the Northwest. The forest products industry has continued to argue that old-growth trees must be cut for the economic health of the regions in which they are found, if not the whole nation. Environmentalists have argued that old-growth forests must be maintained for reasons of heritage, aesthetics, environmental stability, and biodiversity. Complicating the debate is the need for a definition of old-growth, which continues to be disputed by people with different interests. Cited as an indicator species by environmentalists, the northern spotted owl appears to depend on old-growth forests of the Northwest. Thus, old-growth is reasoned necessary to the survival of the owl. That logic has led to the designation of the northern spotted owl as a threatened species and to the argument that the old-growth forest must be protected.

An example of a case in which protection of native forests may provide unexpected and important benefits has surfaced in the form of a small tree. In the 1980s clinical trials of a natural product called taxol sparked excitement among cancer researchers when the compound demonstrated significant potential for treating patients with advanced ovarian cancer. Taxol is found in the bark of the Pacific yew (*Taxus brevifolia*), a small understory tree of the forests of the U.S. Northwest. As of early 1992 one small firm, working under agreements made between the drug company Bristol-Myers Squibb and the USDA and the Department of the Interior, was selectively cutting the tree before tract logging to harvest the bark for extraction of taxol. Because of the comparatively

small number of trees and the demand for taxol for cancer research, researchers and environmentalists petitioned for declaration of the tree as an endangered species.

Miscellaneous. A number of plants have the ability to trap and digest insects as a source of nitrogen. Such plants often live in otherwise nitrogen-poor environments. The most studied example is Venus's-flytrap (*Dionaea muscipula*), an object of attention of Charles Darwin more than a century ago. The leaf traps of the flytrap consist of two hinged halves that are open at rest but spring together when trigger hairs are stimulated by a prey organism. The closed halves confine the prey and press it tightly as digestion and absorption take place.

Beginning with Darwin, there have been conflicting explanations of the way in which the action of the trap is effected. One of the latest reports came in 1991 from Wayne R. Fagerberg and Dawn Allain of the University of New Hampshire. Fagerberg and Allain interpreted trap closure in terms of three distinct stages: capture, appression, and sealing. Capture, the only phase in which rapid movement of the trap parts takes place, is initiated by stimulation of the trigger hairs and facilitated by rapid closure of the trap halves and the presence of coarse pronglike projections at the trap margins. Appression, or close pressing, is accomplished by close contact of the trap margins, completed in 30 minutes from stimulation. Sealing involves the formation of a tight digestive sac around the prey within one hour of stimulation. The investigators were able to detect tissue changes in various parts of the trap as the closure process progressed. Fifteen minutes after stimulation and capture, activity in tissues near the hinge (movement) and near the margins of the trap (tissue enlargement) causes tight closure of the trap margins to begin. After 30 minutes the body of the trap halves becomes active to provide appression. Movements were shown to be due to differential expansion of the various layers of cells in the trap walls.

What makes blue fruits blue? The answer is anthocyanins, a group of pigments that can be extracted from plant tissues with water. Whereas this answer is true for most fruits—for example, blue grapes—David Lee of Florida International University and the Fairchild Tropical Garden, Miami, found an exception. *Elaeocarpus* is a genus of trees native to tropical areas of Asia and Australia. Although most of its 60 species have blue fruits, at least one, *E. angustifolius*, does not have blue pigment. Lee used light measurements and microscopy to determine that the blue color was due to special structures composed of layers of strands of polysaccharides (complex sugars) arranged in the outer parts of the epidermal cells. The structures, which Lee named iridosomes, have the capacity to reflect blue light (at a peak wavelength of 439 nanometers) by means of a wave interference effect called iridescence while transmitting other parts of the light spectrum to lower levels of fruit tissue. It was found that this arrangement allows ripening and mature fruits to remain active in photosynthesis even in the shade.

—Albert J. Smith

Microbiology

During the past year exciting advances took place in a number of different areas of microbiology. These included environmental microbiology, microbial biotechnology, medical microbiology, and microbial evolution.

Environmental microbiology. The release of coal and oil by-products into the environment is a serious problem that threatens both wildlife and water quality. However, not all organisms are poisoned by these compounds. Many microorganisms utilize these organic molecules as carbon and energy sources, eventually degrading them to less toxic molecules such as carbon dioxide.

Biodegradation of many different toxic compounds has been observed under laboratory conditions, but proof of degradation by native populations of microorganisms in the natural environment is more difficult to obtain because one must demonstrate that the mass of the pollutants has decreased and that microorganisms are the causative agents. William C. Ghiorse and his associates at Cornell University, Ithaca, N.Y., provided indirect evidence that bacteria degrade toxic waste under natural conditions when they examined the chemical and microbial composition of an aquifer contaminated by buried coal tar. The groundwater current distributed the coal tar components in a plume (an elongated column), and samples were taken from boreholes in downstream and pristine (uncontaminated) areas. The contaminated areas contained naphthalene and phenanthrene, while the pristine borehole was free of these compounds. The contaminated areas also contained a population of organisms that rapidly degraded these compounds to carbon dioxide in liquid cultures. While microorganisms in the pristine area were also able to degrade these compounds, they did so at a greatly reduced rate, suggesting that the population contained fewer of the degrading bacteria.

One might expect that the bacteria in the polluted areas would grow more rapidly owing to the utilization of the coal tar components as a carbon source. Although the total bacterial population in the contaminated areas was not substantially larger than that of the pristine area, the protozoan population was much higher. Protozoa typically graze on bacteria, suggesting a food chain in which the bacteria grow on the coal tar products and the protozoa prey

on the excess bacteria. These results suggest that microorganisms that live in contaminated areas help degrade the toxic waste.

On March 24, 1989, approximately 41.5 million liters (11 million gal) of crude oil spilled into the waters of Prince William Sound, eventually contaminating nearly 1,600 km (1,000 mi) of Alaskan shoreline. This ecological disaster served as the focal point for a number of studies on the biodegradation of oil by microorganisms. During any effort to degrade pollutants, the toxicity of the pollutant may increase if nontoxic components are converted to toxic species by the microbial population. One criterion that is used to measure toxicity is the ability of the substance to cause mutations in the bacterium *Salmonella*. Both the Prudhoe Bay crude oil and the weathered oil collected from the water caused such mutations, unlike samples treated with fertilizers that were used by the U.S. Environmental Protection Agency in an effort to accelerate the rate of biodegradation. Apparently the mutagenic components of the oil were depleted in the fertilizer-treated sample faster than the organic material. While these results are encouraging, one must remember that each oil spill is a unique disaster; similar studies must be performed on many oil spills before it can be determined whether all oil spills follow the same pattern of remediation.

Microbial biotechnology. It may one day be possible to put biological molecules to work in simple electronic and optical devices. Bacteriorhodopsin, which is produced by the photosynthetic halobacteria, is part of a pathway that converts light energy into chemical energy. It is a protein that undergoes a conformational change in the presence of light that ultimately leads to the synthesis of the nucleoside ATP (adenosine triphosphate) by the cell. The conformational change in the protein is accompanied by a change in color from purple to yellow.

Robert Birge and his colleagues at Syracuse (N.Y.) University embedded bacteriorhodopsin within cubes of plastic to create a data-storage medium. By using laser beams, they hoped to read and record data encoded in the color of the rhodopsin molecules. A cube measuring 2.5 cm (1 in) on an edge could conceivably hold several billion bits of data, enough to store an entire library.

Medical microbiology. Cholera, a serious and often fatal disease caused by the bacterium *Vibrio cholerae*, has swept through the world in several major pandemics during the 20th century. *V. cholerae* is transmitted by the consumption of water contaminated with fecal material from diseased individuals. Unfortunately, the incidence of cholera is on the rise again in many Third World countries. While the *V. cholerae* infection is usually mild and self-limiting, the major consequence of the illness, the loss of up to 34 l (9 gal) of water a day as diarrhea, is caused by an extracellular toxin. The crystal structure of this toxin molecule was recently revealed by researchers at Yale University, Boston University, and Argonne (Ill.) National Laboratory. Cholera toxin contains two protein subunits, A and B. The B subunit is a doughnut-shaped molecule that binds to the intestinal wall and facilitates the entry of the A subunit into the intestinal epithelial cells. The A subunit chemically modifies the structure of a membrane protein and in doing so stimulates the synthesis of the nucleic acid cyclic AMP, which initiates a chain of events that leads to water secretion instead of water absorption.

Cholera toxin has a structure and mode of action similar to that of the *Escherichia coli* LT toxin, which causes a milder form of intestinal distress sometimes referred to as traveler's diarrhea. The crystal structure of the LT toxin was also revealed during the year by workers at the University of Groningen, Neth. The cholera toxin stimulates far more cyclic AMP production than the LT toxin and consequently much more water loss. The remarkable properties of these toxins that enable them to gain entry to the intestinal cells could one day be harnessed to treat other diseases. Disarmed toxin molecules could conceivably be used to inject beneficial drugs into cells.

The human immunodeficiency viruses HIV-1 and HIV-2, the causative agents of AIDS, continue to spread in spite of increased public awareness of the manner in which the virus is transmitted—contact with infected blood or other bodily fluids. While the rate of growth of the epidemic was decreasing among male homosexuals in developed countries, there was a continued rapid spread among intravenous drug users. There was also a slow but steady rise in the infection rate among heterosexuals in South America, parts of Asia, and certain developed countries. The most severely affected continent was Africa. The two most common means of transmission in many African countries occurred between heterosexual adults and from an infected mother to her infant. It was estimated that in some urban centers 20–30% of the general population may already be infected, and estimates of the doubling time of the African HIV-1 epidemic ranged from one to three years in the general populations of those regions.

There have been continued efforts to identify novel compounds produced by bacteria that are beneficial to man. Research groups in Braunschweig and Göttingen, Germany, combined their efforts to purify a compound known as phenoxan from species of the myxobacterium *Polyangium*. This compound, which inhibits the replication of the HIV-1 virus in a simple cell growth assay, is part of a larger family of compounds referred to as gamma-pyrones. All the compounds in this group have a pyrone residue coupled to a five-membered heterocyclic ring with carbon chains of varying lengths.

The mechanism of the antiviral activity of phenoxan is not yet known, but the most likely possibility is that it inhibits the enzyme reverse transcriptase, which is essential for virus replication. Reverse transcriptase synthesizes a single-stranded DNA molecule from the single-stranded viral RNA template. Aureothin, another gamma-pyrone, which is produced by *Streptomyces luteus*, inhibits Rauscher leukemia virus reverse transcriptase. Spectinabilin, which is isolated from *Streptomyces spectabilis*, inhibits HIV reverse transcriptase.

These results suggest that this family of compounds acts as specific inhibitors of reverse transcriptase, and scientists are expected to examine them more carefully for their clinical usefulness. Only a small percentage of compounds identified in this manner are nontoxic enough to be useful in therapy. Nevertheless, the identification of these and other naturally occurring compounds provides continued hope for the treatment of AIDS and other fatal diseases.

Some bacterial pathogens multiply within a living host cell. Following attachment to the surface of the host cell, the bacterium gains entry to the host and reproduces inside the cell. The question of how this select group of bacteria enters the host cell has received considerable attention. In the case of the bacterium *Yersinia pseudotuberculosis*, the entry process is facilitated by a cell surface protein called invasin. This protein mediates both the attachment and engulfment processes. In fact, latex beads coated with invasin are internalized by (incorporated into) cultured mammalian cells. Invasin appears to bind to a mammalian surface protein known as integrin, which is normally involved in interactions between mammalian cells. Internalization appears to be a reflexive action on the part of the mammalian host cell that is triggered in response to any molecule that binds integrin with high affinity. For example, particles coated with anti-integrin antibodies were also efficiently internalized by mammalian cells. This reaction may some day be exploited to inject drugs or even genes into mammalian cells.

Microbial evolution. On the basis of his studies of nucleic acid sequences, Carl R. Woese of the University of Illinois concluded that a primitive progenitor cell gave rise to the three kingdoms of organisms that exist today: archaebacteria, eubacteria, and eukaryotes, which, unlike the other two, are cells with membrane-bound nuclei. The discovery that all cells have a common ancestor spawned a debate on the physical and chemical structure of the progenitor cell.

One aspect of this debate focused on the organization of the genes. In most eukaryotes, genes are interrupted by introns, noncoding regions that are transcribed into ribonucleic acid (RNA) along with the coding regions but then are removed by an RNA splicing event prior to translation. (Translation is the process by which the linear sequence of nucleotides in a molecule of messenger RNA directs the synthesis of a specific linear sequence of amino acids.) One school of thought argues that introns were present in the progenitor cell. Thomas R. Cech of the University of Colorado discovered that some self-splicing introns remove themselves from the RNA molecule in the absence of a protein catalyst. Pieces of RNA that both encode essential genetic information and act as chemical catalysts could have played a critical role in the evolution of the early cell. The other school of thought proposes that introns appeared late in evolution and arose in eukaryotic cells.

One way to begin to distinguish between these possibilities is to examine the structure of genes in organisms that took different evolutionary courses. Many hundreds of millions of years ago, a cyanobacterium (a photosynthetic microorganism) was engulfed by a eukaryotic cell and, through the process of endosymbiosis (living within the host), became the plant chloroplast (the cell organelle that contains chlorophyll pigments and functions in photosynthesis). The search for introns in chloroplasts and present-day cyanobacteria has focused on the leucine transfer RNA, which incorporates the amino acid leucine into protein. David Shub at the State University of New York at Albany and Jeffrey Palmer of Indiana University discovered that chloroplasts as well as seven distinct cyanobacteria species contain self-splicing introns in their leucine transfer RNA gene. These results suggest that the ancestral intron was already widespread prior to the endosymbiotic event that led to formation of the chloroplast and that self-splicing introns predate emergence of the present-day plant cell. While these results suggest that some introns are very old, they still do not answer the question of whether the progenitor cells contained introns, since the progenitor cell predated the chloroplast by two billion to three billion years.

—Lawrence J. Shimkets

Molecular biology

The general rules by which genetic information is used to create the structures that make up living cells have been understood for the past 30 years. The genes carry information in the sequence of nucleotides (abbreviated A, G, C, and T for their constituent bases adenine, guanine, cytosine, and thymine) in DNA. The gene sequences are correctly transcribed into sequences of nucleotides (A, G, C, and U [for the base uracil]) in RNA molecules, which carry that information to molecular workbenches called ribosomes, where the sequence information in RNA is translated into sequence information in protein. The genetic code, which was thought to be the same in all organisms, relates nucleotide sequences in groups of three (nucleotide triplets, or codons) to each of the 20 amino-acid building blocks of proteins. Individual proteins, which can vary in length from less than a hundred to more than a thousand amino acids, differ in function from one another by virtue of their different three-dimensional structures. The way proteins fold into their final structures is determined by the sequence of amino acids. Thus, the final structure, and therefore the function, of each protein is specified by the sequence of nucleotides in the gene encoding that protein.

This framework, generally speaking, is correct. It permits research to be done on simple, experimentally flexible organisms like bacteria and viruses, with the results applicable even to human beings. In recent years, however, exceptions to these rules have been discovered. In some cases the exceptions shed light on more widespread and conventional processes; in others they reveal how oversimplified scientists' earlier ideas were.

The most dramatic exception to the rule that information flows uniquely from DNA to RNA to protein came with the discovery of the enzyme called reverse transcriptase, which transcribes nucleotide sequences in RNA into nucleotide sequences in DNA. Such enzymes are part of the replication machinery of RNA tumor viruses, whose genes consist of RNA sequences. But even though reverse transcriptase changes the direction of information flow, the process is still conventional in the sense that the RNA nucleotide sequence in viral genes is strictly in the same linear order as the corresponding, final amino-acid sequence in the viral proteins. In recent years, however, a process called RNA editing has been discovered, in which nucleotides are added to an RNA molecule after its transcription from DNA has been completed or nucleotides are changed in the mature RNA molecule before it is translated into protein. In such cases it is impossible to relate the nucleotide sequence of the gene to the amino-acid sequence of the finished protein encoded by that gene. Several examples of such editing are described below.

It also turns out that the genetic code is not quite universal. It is the same for the handful of organisms most studied by molecular biologists, but as more organisms and particularly more organelles (specifically, mitochondria and chloroplasts, which contain their own DNA) are investigated, more exceptions are found. Indeed, it is fortunate that the bacterium *Escherichia coli*, yeast, fruit flies, and vertebrates were studied first. Otherwise, the nature of the code would have been confusing and debated for a long time.

Finally, the notion that only the amino-acid sequence of a protein is needed to determine its structure, a notion that had been ingrained by a dramatic experiment on the refolding of the enzyme ribonuclease, has had to be modified. For many proteins, other proteins called chaperones are required for proper folding of the linear amino-acid chain, for proper delivery to the appropriate cellular compartment, or for both. Some very recent work on the operation of molecular chaperones in bacteria is described below.

RNA editing. Changes after transcription in the nucleotide sequence of messenger (protein-encoding) RNA (mRNA) have been described in many systems: C is changed to U, and U is changed to C in some plant mitochondrial RNAs; C is changed to U in at least one chloroplast RNA; A is changed to G, converting a single codon for glutamine into a codon for arginine in mammalian neural glutamate-gated ion-channel protein; and C is changed to U at a single position in the 14,000-nucleotide RNA that encodes human apolipoprotein B (apo B). The last change converts a codon for glutamine to nonsense (UAA), which causes further assembly of the amino-acid chain to terminate, resulting in a second, truncated form of apo B roughly half the size of the full molecule. All of these editing changes are conservative with respect to the number of nucleotides in the RNA. In certain parasitic protozoans, however, more radical editing has been observed. These organisms (species of *Trypanosoma, Leishmania,* and *Crithidia*) have organelles called kinetoplasts that are modified mitochondria. Kinetoplast DNA contains up to 10,000 small DNA circles, each 1,000 base pairs long and interlinked. In addition, there are 25–50 larger circles, each 15,000–16,000 base pairs long. The "maxicircles" contain gene sequences, while the "minicircles" contain some of the information used for editing. The editing is insertional rather than conservative; up to 90% of the final RNA sequence can consist of U's added to the original RNA transcript.

Consider first the (perhaps) simpler case of the editing of apo B mRNA. Many laboratories have contributed to its study, but a particularly illuminating series of publications are due to the work of James Scott and colleagues of the MRC Clinical Research Centre, Harrow, England. The chemistry of apo B editing consists of converting an amino (NH_2) group of cytidine into a carbonyl ($C=O$) group of uridine. (Cytidine and uridine are the nucleosides [base-sugar combinations] containing cytosine and uracil, respectively.) This is a well-known reaction catalyzed by an enzyme called cytidine deaminase. However, that enzyme does not normally attack RNA; if it did, no cell could survive the extensive mutations that would result. Consequently, there must be something

unique about the C at codon 2153 in apo B mRNA. The special feature of that C is the nucleotide sequence of its neighbors. By specifically changing the sequence of each nucleotide surrounding the special C, Scott and colleagues found that the sequence immediately around the C was not very important, but any changes in the nucleotides between 5 and 15 nucleotides downstream (*i.e.,* toward the 3′ end of the RNA) destroyed the ability of the C to be deaminated. The target for this editing process can thus be described as . . . **C**NNNNUGAUCAGUAUA . . ., in which **C** is the special C and N can be any nucleotide.

At present it appears that the molecular agent responsible for the editing consists purely of protein, without an RNA cofactor. The agent behaves during purification like a rather large protein, probably comprising multiple subunits. It is presumed that part of the protein recognizes the nucleotide sequence shown above, and another part provides the deaminase activity (Figure 1 p. 366). There seems to be a little flexibility in the deaminase protein; if a nucleotide next to the unique C is changed to C, it too will be deaminated.

What purpose the editing serves remains to be clarified. In the human liver slightly more than half the apo B is the truncated form, while in the intestine nearly all the apo B is truncated. Both forms of apo B transport fat in the form of triglyceride complexes from the liver or intestine to the rest of the body. The full-length form contains, in its second half, sequences that are bound by the low-density lipoprotein receptor present on cell surfaces, so it has the additional function of delivering cholesterol to other tissues as well. The action of the editing deaminase protein is clearly regulated at the tissue level, since the proportion of edited RNA (and truncated apo B) varies in different tissues.

The editing observed in the mRNA of kinetoplasts in trypanosomes and other parasites is quite different from that of apo B mRNA in terms of extent and mechanism. Again, many laboratories have been involved in this work, but much of what follows is based on results obtained by Larry Simpson and his colleagues at the University of California at Los Angeles in studying the organism *Leishmania*. As mentioned above, the gene sequences in kinetoplasts are located on circular DNA molecules 15,000–16,000 base pairs long. Most of the sequences, however, actually contain many fewer nucleotides than are required for encoding their corresponding proteins. The missing nucleotides, all of them U, are present in mature mRNA. How are the missing U's added to the pre-mRNA transcribed from the gene sequences?

Essentially every aspect of molecular genetics discovered to date involves the complementary base-pairing rule described by James Watson and Francis Crick in 1953: A pairs with T or U, and G pairs with

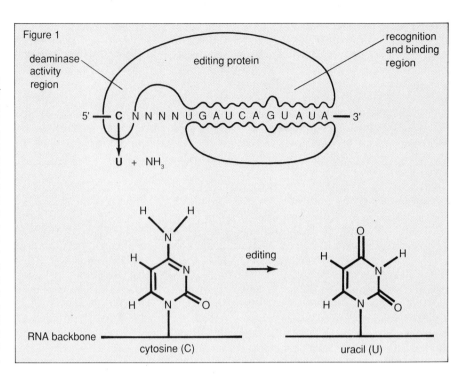

Figure 1

deaminase activity region

editing protein

recognition and binding region

5' — C N N N N U G A U C A G U A U A — 3'

U + NH₃

editing

RNA backbone

cytosine (C)   uracil (U)

Diagram shows a generalized conception of the configuration of the deaminase protein believed to be responsible for editing the RNA that encodes human apolipoprotein B. Part of the protein recognizes and binds to a specific nucleotide sequence lying 5 to 15 nucleotides downstream from the particular cytidine (cytosine-sugar combination) to be changed. The other part of the protein provides the deaminase activity, in which the amino (NH₂) group of the cytosine is converted to a carbonyl (C = O) group of uracil, thus changing the cytidine to a uridine.

C. An outstanding exception to the general rule is the pairing observed in the translation of the genetic code from mRNA to protein in which the triplets in mRNA pair with complementary triplets (anticodons) in amino acyl transfer RNA (tRNA) on the surface of the ribosome. (Transfer RNA functions by adding free amino acids to the protein chain being assembled on the ribosome, matching its own anticodon to the complementary codon on the mRNA in order to ensure proper amino-acid placement in the chain.) Although the first two positions of each codon and anticodon triplet pair up strictly according to the Watson-Crick rules, the third (called the "wobble" position) allows for some relaxation—permitting G to pair with U, for example. The G-U pair is weaker than the G-C pair, but it can be formed if the neighboring bases are paired.

For a base-pairing mechanism to be used for the editing of the pre-mRNA, there has to be a template, a nucleic acid molecule whose sequence can be used to direct the insertion of the missing nucleotides. Kinetoplast DNA was examined for such a sequence, but none was found. Instead, a large variety of small RNA molecules, most of which are encoded in the 1,000-base-pair minicircles, were discovered. Parts of the sequences of these RNAs are complementary to short regions of the pre-mRNA, but the remainder of their sequences are not complementary to either the pre-mRNA or the mature, edited mRNA. The role of the small RNAs, which average 30 nucleotides in length, was a mystery until it was realized that they could serve perfectly as templates for the editing

process if G in the small RNA was allowed to pair up imperfectly with U in the edited RNA. This insight and others derived from the nucleotide sequences of partially edited RNA molecules allowed a reasonable model for the editing process to be constructed.

The small RNAs function as guides for the editing process; indeed, they have been named guide RNAs (gRNAs). Editing starts at the 3' end of the pre-mRNA with the association of a gRNA by perfect base pairing of a short stretch (about six nucleotides) at the 5' end of the gRNA. Imagine that the paired molecules then attempt to zip up to form a double helix (Figure 2a). However, the gRNA has a G in its next position, the pre-mRNA an A. It is not possible for G to pair with A. Instead, the pre-mRNA is cut apart, or cleaved, at that point, and a U is added to its newly created 3' end. In fact, U's continue to be added until a U is reached in the gRNA (Figure 2b). At that point a perfect pairing of A in the pre-mRNA and U in the guide halts the insertion of U's. Pairing of pre-mRNA and guide continue until, again, an unpairable match occurs (Figure 2c). Addition of U's resumes, and the process is repeated until the end of the guide RNA is reached. Since the guide is only 30 nucleotides long, the edited stretch of pre-mRNA is rather short. The guide and pre-mRNA would be firmly bound to one another but for the fact that the edited stretch is now full of G-U base pairs, which are less stable than G-C base pairs. This allows the gRNA that has just finished its job to be replaced by a new guide, whose 5' end can base-pair perfectly for a few nucleotides with the just-edited sequence of

366

the pre-mRNA. Repetition of this procedure results in the eventual editing of the entire pre-mRNA.

Researchers do not know the chemical mechanism of cleavage of the pre-mRNA, followed by addition of U's, and then by ligation of the last U to the 5′ end of the just-cleaved pre-mRNA. One possibility is that an enzyme complex associates with the pre-mRNA/gRNA structure and successively catalyzes cleavage, U addition, and ligation. An alternative is similar to the mechanism discovered for certain RNA molecules that can cut and splice themselves (see *1989 Yearbook of Science and the Future* Year in Review: LIFE SCIENCES: *Molecular biology*), with the guide RNA forming a loop around the target sequence and using its 3′ end to initiate a series of reactions that result in U insertion.

Molecular chaperones. Another tenet of the general beliefs formulated in the early 1960s is that the information provided by the sequence of amino acids in proteins is sufficient for the protein to fold into its correct three-dimensional structure. Early on, it was understood that there were difficulties with this proposition. Proteins contain many amino acids that are capable of forming weak bonds with each other. If every possible thermodynamically stable structure were to be tried out in the folding process, it would take literally forever for each protein to achieve its

final form. Yet a simple experiment performed at that time showed that the tenet was supportable. The enzyme ribonuclease was completely unfolded experimentally by denaturing agents, and then the agents were removed and the enzyme allowed to refold. In a reasonable time, it refolded and regained its enzymatic activity. Since nothing was present but the protein itself, the information for correct folding had to be present in the amino-acid sequence.

It turns out that this example is rather special. Some proteins indeed can fold correctly without assistance, but many need help. The help is provided by a remarkable set of proteins called chaperones. These proteins were discovered first in bacteria and then in chloroplasts; by the early 1990s they were known to be nearly everywhere. Many years ago, mutants of *E. coli* were isolated that did not allow the growth of the virus called lambda. The virus was able to attach to the mutant *E. coli,* injecting its DNA and carrying out nearly all the functions needed for successful infection. Where it failed was in the proper assembly of the protein constituting its "head" capsule, leading to its inability to carry out another round of infection. The bacterial mutants were termed Gro because they did not allow the virus to grow. Eventually the bacterial genes involved were identified by Costa Georgopoulos of the University of

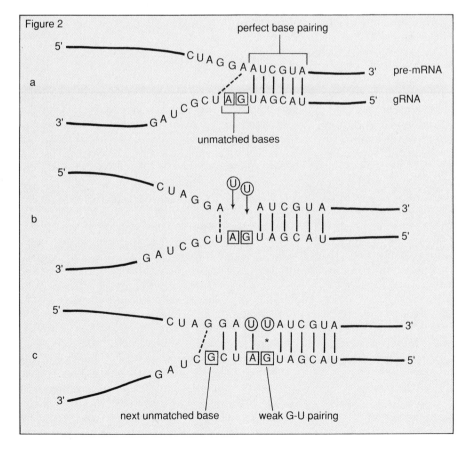

The process by which guide RNA (gRNA) molecules have been found to serve as templates for editing messenger RNA (mRNA) molecules in certain parasitic protozoans is shown in a hypothetical example and discussed in text on the facing page. The net result of the editing process is the insertion of additional uracils (U's) into newly transcribed mRNA, converting the molecule to its mature form.

Utah Medical School and were found to encode two proteins, called GroEL and GroES. The former is found as a complex of 14 identical subunits arranged as a cylinder composed of two disks, each having seven subunits. The GroES protein has seven identical subunits, each much smaller than the GroEL subunit. Significant advances in understanding the role that these proteins play in the folding of other proteins were made during the past year.

Hints of the Gro function came from the discovery of related proteins in other organisms. The major protein in chloroplasts is the enzyme called ribulose bisphosphate carboxylase/oxygenase (RuBisCO), which is responsible for the first step in the fixation of atmospheric carbon dioxide by green plants and photosynthetic microorganisms. This enzyme itself is complex, containing eight large and eight small subunits. Its assembly was known to be complicated because the large subunit is encoded in chloroplast DNA while the small subunit is encoded in the nucleus. The small subunit is actually synthesized in the cell cytoplasm and then transported into the chloroplast, where it must find the large subunit or a subassembly of large subunits. R. John Ellis of the University of Warwick, Coventry, England, found that the subassembly of large subunits is complexed with another protein, which maintains it in a soluble, unaggregated form until the small subunits arrive. The second protein in the complex was purified and found to be related in its amino-acid sequence to GroEL. Ellis applied the term *molecular chaperone* to the chloroplast protein, a name that has come to refer to the entire family of Gro-related proteins.

Another member of the family is induced in a wide variety of cells, including yeast and mammalian cells, by mild heat shock. A brief pulse of elevated temperature induces the synthesis of a number of proteins in all cells, from bacteria to human beings. These so-called heat-shock proteins provide some protection against a subsequent heat treatment. The heat-shock proteins are diverse and include some that affect transcription of genes, but one of them, hsp60, is a member of the GroEL family. Its function is to interact with other proteins that have unfolded as a consequence of the elevated temperature, to protect those proteins from aggregation, and then to promote their proper refolding when the thermal stress is relieved.

The heat-shock proteins are required for normal growth as well as in the response to heat shock. Their role under normal conditions is to bind the unfolded parts of those proteins that are made in the cytoplasm and are then transported into mitochondria or chloroplasts. Such organelle-destined proteins, of which the small subunit of RuBisCO mentioned above is a good example, contain an amino-acid sequence at one end that functions as a signal for transport into the correct organelle. This signal sequence is "unfolded" and recognized as such by the heat-shock protein, which binds to it, protects it, and delivers it to the transport machinery embedded in the membrane that surrounds the organelle.

The detailed mechanism by which GroEL and GroES promote the refolding or, by extension, the original folding of several proteins has been illuminated by studies in the laboratory of F.-Ulrich Hartl, first in Munich and later at the Sloan-Kettering Institute, New York City. When an unfolded protein is mixed with GroEL, one 14-subunit complex of GroEL binds to each unfolded molecule. The next step is hard to describe: the unfolded protein starts to refold; the energy-providing molecule ATP is hydrolyzed (broken apart) into ADP and phosphate; and one small doughnut of the seven-subunit GroES is bound to the complex of target protein and GroEL. The situation is dynamic, with the target protein binding, folding, releasing, and then rebinding to GroEL, all the time hydrolyzing ATP and binding GroES. When the target protein is completely folded, it no longer binds to GroEL, ATP hydrolysis stops, and GroES is separated from GroEL, until the next unfolded molecule is seized. In this way the molecular chaperones prevent improper interactions between potentially complementary surfaces, which could lead to protein aggregation and precipitation inside the cell, as originally pointed out by Ellis.

—Robert Haselkorn

Zoology

Considerable activity took place in zoology during the past year. New discoveries in paleobiology included a huge fossil crocodile, an earlier origin for tetrapods, controversy on the origin of birds, and information on an early venomous reptile. Ecological concerns involved extinction of Hawaiian birds, a population explosion of zebra mussels, and high mortality of the black sea urchin. The variety of zoological interests included the origin of bats, advancement in potential control of African sleeping sickness, social behavior of dominant male fish, a new species of whale, and the discovery of a cold-blooded mammal. Embryology witnessed some fascinating discoveries, including the advantage of low sperm production in a nematode, sperm chemotaxis in humans, and the way in which the frog embryonic axis is formed.

Largest crocodile. What may be the largest terrestrial carnivore ever known, even rivaling the dinosaur *Tyrannosaurus rex* in size, was the giant crocodilian *Purussaurus brasiliensis,* which lived in the Amazon River basin more than eight million years ago. A skull of this creature was excavated in 1986 on the border between Peru and Brazil and was examined by Carl D. Frailey of the Johnson County Community College, Overland Park, Kan., and Kenneth E. Campbell of the Natural History Museum of Los Angeles county. A cast of the skull and lower jaws of this giant was first presented to the annual meeting of the Society of Vertebrate Paleontology in San Diego, Calif., in October 1991. These researchers believe that the skull belonged to a crocodilian measuring 12 m (40 ft) in length and 2.5 m (8.2 ft) in height and weighing 10,000 to 12,000 kg (22,000 to 26,500 lb).

This probably is not the largest individual of the species ever described. A Brazilian museum has a jawbone measuring 30 cm (12 in) longer than the one presented by Frailey and Campbell. This crocodile would measure to a length of 14 m (46 ft).

Tetrapod origin. The time of vertebrate transition from water to land or fish to tetrapod (possessing four legs) is one of the most intriguing questions in evolution. In addition, another beguiling question is whether vertebrate legs developed first for use in an aquatic environment or developed specifically for the transition to land. New evidence has now placed the origin of such a creature approximately seven

million years earlier than the previous estimate. This conclusion was based on work by P.E. Ahlberg of the University of Oxford, who obtained data from examination of a previously unrecognized tibia, a humerus, and jaw parts of fossil bones collected during the 19th century from the Upper Frasnian (Late Devonian, about 370 million years old) site of Scat Craig, near Elgin, Scotland. On the basis of the characteristics of the tibia and humerus, Ahlberg described the animal as a tetrapod existing in an aquatic environment, supporting the hypothesis that the development of legs occurred before the transition to land.

This hypothesis was also supported by Michael I. Coates and Jennifer A. Clack of the University Museum of Zoology, Cambridge, England. In their study on *Acanthostega gunnari*, from the Upper Devonian (360 million years old) of eastern Greenland, which has legs with digits, they described fishlike gills, implying that *Acanthostega* not only was a tetrapod but also was dependent on an aquatic environment. Coates and Clack thus concluded that this creature, like Ahlberg's tetrapod, evolved legs first for use in water.

Michael Stokes (left) and Kenneth Campbell (right), both of the Natural History Museum of Los Angeles county, display a cast of the skull and lower jaws of the giant crocodilian Purussaurus brasiliensis, *which lived in the Amazon River basin more than eight million years ago. On the basis of the size of the skull, the animal may be the largest terrestrial carnivore ever known, measuring 12 meters (40 feet) in length and 2.5 meters (8.2 feet) in height and weighing 10,000 to 12,000 kilograms (22,000 to 26,500 pounds).*

The Natural History Museum of Los Angeles county; photo, Richard Meier

Origin of birds. Considerable attention by bird paleobiologists focused on a specimen that may be the earliest known fossil bird. Sankar Chatterjee of Texas Tech University made such a claim from specimens found in western Texas mudstones (Late Triassic Epoch, 225 million years ago). This specimen, if accepted, predates the famous pheasant-size *Archaeopteryx* fossil bird discovered in 1861 at Solnhofen, Germany, by 75 million years.

Chatterjee named his specimen *Protoavis texenis,* and in a paper published in 1991 he described its skull. Unlike the *Archaeopteryx,* imprints of feathers were not found with *Protoavis,* but Chatterjee explained that the fossil has a birdlike anatomy based on enormous eyes and a well-developed brain and such anatomical features as limb modification for flying and a keeled sternum for flight muscle attachment. Chatterjee's claim also suggests that the origin of birds may be a nondinosaur reptile with ancestral relationships to crocodiles, whereas the hypothesis using *Archaeopteryx* as the earliest bird supports bird origin from a later dinosaur group of reptiles, the therapods.

Among opponents of Chatterjee's claim, Storrs L. Olson of the National Museum of Natural History, Smithsonian Institution, Washington, D.C., concluded that the *Protoavis* specimen may be a mixture of bones from several animals and questioned the procedures by which the fossil was reconstructed. In support of the claim, Larry D. Martin of the University of Kansas determined that the avian features of *Protoavis* indicate a birdlike reptile; he also supported the hypothesis of an earlier origin of birds. In any case, *Protoavis* stimulated interest again in the origin of birds.

Early venomous reptile. A new species of Late Triassic (230 million–208 million years ago) reptile was described by Hans-Dieter Sues of the National Museum of Natural History. It represents the earliest record by 100 million years of the use of oral venoms among squamate reptiles (lizards and snakes). The species is described as a carnivorous reptile and is named *Uatchitodon.* Fossils were found in Chesterfield county, Va. Although *Uatchitodon* is a tetrapod, not enough of the skeleton was obtained for an exact placement of the animal in the phylogenetic tree. However, of particular interest was a *Uatchitodon* tooth, which appeared to be about 7 mm (0.28 in) long. Serrated on both cutting edges, it has a deep groove on each side that gives the appearance of tubes running from the base of the tooth to the tip. Presumably, oral toxins were conducted through these grooves to the oral cavity.

Sues speculated that this creature used oral toxins as a means to immobilize prey before eating or to aid digestion. Defensive purposes of oral toxins are believed to have developed at a later time.

Extinction of Hawaiian birds. Somewhat surprisingly, the extinction of many Hawaiian birds predated the invasion of the islands by Europeans, which began with Capt. James Cook's visit to Hawaii in 1778. Storrs Olson and Helen F. James of the National Museum of Natural History identified 32 species of Hawaiian birds that became extinct between the time the Polynesians arrived, about AD 400, and Captain Cook's arrival. These species, plus three others previously described and another suspected 22 species, led to the conclusion that more than 50 species became extinct during this period as opposed to about 12 after the Europeans arrived.

Olson and James obtained subfossils from five of the main Hawaiian Islands—Kauai, Oahu, Molokai, Maui, and Hawaii—and from a variety of sites—sand dunes, limestone sinkholes, lava tubes, a crater lake bed, and archaeological sites. (Subfossils are remains of less than fossil age but partially fossilized.) The subfossils and sites were dated by means of radiocarbon techniques, and the specimens were painstakingly examined, assembled, and cataloged. Among the extinctions were large numbers of flightless birds, including two ibises, nine rails, and four gooselike ducks. Raptorial birds (hawks, owls, and an eagle) that preyed on these species also disappeared. The flightless gooselike ducks were the most unusual, having tiny wings, massive hind limbs, and strange beaks. These anatomic features suggest that they were terrestrial and herbivorous and may have served ecological roles similar to the tortoises on the Galapagos Islands. In summary, Olson and James attributed this large number of extinctions to predation, diseases, and environmental degradation (agriculture and forest destruction) caused by Polynesians and their introduced predators (pigs, chickens, and dogs).

In reference to bird evolution and the safety of isolated islands, Olson and James concluded that the repeated and rapid evolution of flightlessness of nonpasserine birds on islands reveals that there is strong selective advantage in being flightless. (Passerine birds are the typical songbirds with perching habits.) Unfortunately, as also demonstrated by their studies, such birds are very vulnerable to the invasions and activities of humans.

Bat evolution. There are two major groups of bats, the Microchiroptera (microbats) and the Megachiroptera (megabats or flying foxes). The microbats are small nocturnal insectivores and use echolocation for flight and capturing insects. (Echolocation is a process for locating distant or invisible objects by means of sound waves reflected back to the emitter.) The megabats are larger and fly primarily by vision. An interesting debate among bat scientists concerns the origin of bats, whether they are monophyletic or diphyletic; that is, whether they have one origin or

The zebra mussel, Dreissena polymorpha *(below), arrived in North America from its native Caspian Sea in 1986. Since then this tiny mollusk has proliferated rapidly throughout the Great Lakes and nearby waters. Adult zebra mussels cluster together in concentrations of up to 700,000 per square meter and can clog intake pipes for municipal and industrial water supplies (left).*

two distinct origins. A single origin is traditionally supported, but a recent study by John D. Pettigrew of the University of Queensland, Australia, advocates the diphyletic hypothesis. Pettigrew based his conclusion on the uniqueness of the visual neural pathways in the brains of the megabats and primates. He supports the idea that megabats evolved from primitive flying lemurs (primates), while microbats evolved from nocturnal insectivores. These separate origins could be as much as 30 million years apart. The fact that both groups have similar wings for power flight is attributed by Pettigrew to convergent evolution that occurred once in the primitive primates and once in the insectivores. Among opponents are Robert J. Baker of Texas Tech University and Michael J. Novacek and Nancy B. Simmons of the American Museum of Natural History, New York City, who support the monophyletic hypothesis. They argue that the strong similarity of wings between the two bat groups indicates the same origin and that the brain similarity among the megabats and primates is convergent evolution.

Pettigrew's hypothesis was supported with studies by J.R. Speakman and P.A. Racey of the University of Aberdeen, Scotland. These researchers studied the energy involved in echolocation for microbats in flight and at rest. Finding that echolocation is energy-efficient and requires no more energy than that used by nonecholocating megabats, they deduced that evolution of the complicated echolocation occurred over a long period of time to facilitate nocturnal flight and capturing insects while megabats evolved a complicated visual system for the same purpose. According to Speakman and Racey, the early bats would not give up one complicated system for an-

other one. They therefore suggest that a primate ancestry for megabats is consistent since both have well-developed vision systems.

All participants in this controversy agreed that more research is needed, not only with anatomic and physiological features but also with molecular techniques such as serum protein immunologic data and gene sequencing.

Invertebrate evolution. Some of the most extraordinary invertebrate fossils have been obtained recently from the Burgess Shale of British Columbia and from Chengjiang in southern China. These magnificent fossil beds represent the Late and Middle Cambrian epochs, dating 540 million–505 million years ago. This was also the time of the Cambrian explosion, when most of the animal groups represented today first evolved. These two sources of invertebrates are unique because they contain fossilization of soft tissues of organisms; in most fossil beds only hard parts are preserved. For example, more than 3,000 remarkably preserved soft-bodied specimens were collected from the Chinese deposits. However, many of the creatures described were so unusual that it was difficult to fit them into a modern scheme of classification. Thus, some scientists suggested that these fossils should be examined in an unbiased manner and allowed to fit into a different scheme of classification.

Two specimens from the areas, *Hallucigenia* and *Microdictyon,* are such enigmas. In a Chinese-Swedish project, Lars Ramskold of the Swedish Museum of Natural History, Stockholm, and Hou Xianguang of the Nanjing Institute of Geology and Palaeontology described a well-preserved specimen from the Chinese deposits that looks like a compressed caterpillar-like animal. Their specimen shows similarities not only to *Hallucigenia* and *Microdictyon* but also to the present phylum Onychophora, an uncommon group of animals that look like fat centipedes and live among damp leaves and rotting wood in the Southern Hemisphere. Thus, on the basis of their and other investigators' observations, Ramskold and Hou now believe that onychophorans were present and quite common in the marine environment during the Cambrian Period.

Social behavior. The African cichlid fish has become important in research laboratories mainly because of its ease of culturing, rapid growth, large size, and high level of fecundity. Also, as reported by Russell D. Fernald and colleagues of the University of Oregon, one species, *Haplochromis burtoni,* in this group (more than 190 species) demonstrates interesting social behavior. In studies initiated at Lake Tanganyika in South Africa, Fernald observed that 10% of the *H. burtoni* males dominated the breeding territories of the population. These males were very aggressive, bright in color, and large. The rest of the males and the females were nonaggressive, duller in color, and smaller. If an aggressive male was killed or removed, previously nonaggressive males would become dominant and develop aggressive habits.

Fernald, a neurophysiologist, found that the changes in aggressiveness coincided with changes in the hypothalamus, an area of the brain affecting hormonal balance. In fact, the neurons in the hypothalamus of a dominant male were six to eight times larger than equivalent cells in the nonaggressive males. Also, the testes would enlarge and the animal became sexually active. Interestingly, Fernald discovered that this condition could be reversed. If a larger, more aggressive male was introduced, a previously aggressive, but smaller, male would become passive and duller in color, a process also reflected in the reduction of neuron size in the hypothalamus.

New species of whale. Many animal species are identified every year, and millions more remain to be discovered. Still, it is somewhat surprising to find a new species of whale, a group that one would expect, because of commercial and popular interest, to be completely identified. Nevertheless, the first new whale species in 28 years and only the fifth since 1937 was found during the past year. The latest member of the order Cetacea is a small beaked whale from the little-known family Ziphiidae. In contrast to the well-known baleen whales, in which the last of 10 species was described in 1878, 7 of 11 species described since 1900 have been beaked whales and the other 4 have been porpoises or dolphins.

The new species, *Mesoplodon peruvianus,* was described by Julio C. Reyes and K.V. Van Waerebeek of Grupo Cetáceos-ECCO in Lima, Peru. This whale lives along the Peruvian coast and is the smallest of the beaked whales, with a maximum known length of 372 cm (12 ft). The major characteristic of beaked whales is the presence of only two functional teeth, which are on the lower jaw. In *M. peruvianus* each tooth is nearly perpendicular to the long axis of the jaw, a characteristic peculiar to this species. Only 10 specimens have been examined by Reyes and Van Waerebeek, and these were inadvertently obtained from gillnets for sharks or were washed ashore. Because of the scarcity of these whales, little is known about their biology or habits.

Ecology. A population explosion often happens when a foreign species is introduced into an area with optimal environmental conditions and few, if any, predators. The zebra mussel, *Dreissena polymorpha,* native to the Caspian Sea, is a good recent example. This species arrived in North America as a stowaway around 1986 in ballast water of a freighter and was flushed into Lake St. Clair, which lies between Lakes Huron and Erie. From this site the species rapidly reproduced and spread into the Great Lakes and now is invading other waters, including inland lakes in Minnesota, the Mississippi River, and the inland canals of New York state.

This small striped mollusk, no larger than a fingernail, can rapidly reach sexual maturity at optimal water temperatures. A single female can produce 30,-000 to 50,000 planktonic larvae during the normal breeding season, May to October. The larvae attach with powerful adhesive strands to any hard surface. Both larvae and adults feed voraciously on phytoplankton (algae). When phytoplankton is blooming, adult zebra mussels can reach concentrations up to 700,000 per square meter (585,000 per square

The naked mole rat (Heterocephalus glaber) *is the only mammal known to be cold-blooded. It cannot regulate its body temperature when the temperature of the surrounding air is less than 29° C (84° F).*

yard). They clog intake pipes for water-treatment and nuclear plants and foul piers, boats, and the water intakes of marine engines. As a result, biologists try to develop means to control the population of this species without destroying native mollusks.

In an innovative approach, Jeffrey L. Ram of Wayne State University, Detroit, Mich., and David W. Garton of Ohio State University tried to trick the animals into spawning at a time when the larvae would starve to death. This involves initiating spawning at an inopportune time, such as out of season or when phytoplankton are not available. Susan W. Fisher, also of Ohio State University, discovered that potassium ions prevent the attachment of zebra mussels to hard surfaces. Since high concentrations of potassium ions are detrimental to other bivalves, Fisher began testing a system in which small amounts of potassium ion are continually released, aiming for the prevention of larval settlements in confined areas such as water intakes. On the other hand, the zebra mussel may have some benefits. As stated by Fisher, the organism filters algae, and large populations of zebra mussels have cleared parts of Lake Erie.

In contrast to the zebra mussel, the populations of the black sea urchin, *Diadema antillarum,* of the Florida Keys, Puerto Rico, and various portions of the Caribbean were being decimated. In a letter of concern to the public in the Aug. 1, 1991, issue of *Nature,* Ernest H. Williams, Jr., of the Caribbean Aquatic Animal Health Project at the University of Puerto Rico expressed concern about the mass mortalities of this species that have occurred during the last decade.

This large sea urchin has a body up to 10 cm (4 in) in diameter and numerous pointed spines that are 20 cm (8 in) or more in length. Visitors to the Florida Keys have marveled over these splendid creatures for decades. Williams examined several dying populations and concluded that the sea urchins are infected with a bacterial pathogen that causes the spines to drop off and the animal tissue to deteriorate, all within a week. In 1983–84 from 95 to 99% of all black sea urchins died throughout the western Atlantic. In 1990 mass mortalities of this species occurred in the Caribbean Sea near Jamaica, the Cayman Islands, and Belize. Williams hoped that cooperative efforts would identify the disease and prevent future disturbances.

Parasitism. African sleeping sickness is a disease caused by a flagellated protozoan, *Trypanosoma brucei,* that lives and reproduces in the bloodstream and nervous system of wild game, livestock, and humans. The organism is transmitted from one host to another by the biting tsetse fly, *Glossina.* For decades the parasite has wreaked havoc on the human and cattle populations of tropical East and West Africa. An estimated 10,000 people are infected annually, most of whom die within months.

The human immune system is incapable of developing sustained responses to the many changes made in the protein coat of the organism. As antibodies are produced for one coat protein, the *T. brucei* forms a new coat protein and continues to survive. A recent development may, however, be able to resolve this problem. One group of investigators, Josiane Eid and Barbara Sollner-Webb of the Johns Hopkins University School of Medicine, Baltimore, Md., developed techniques to manipulate and replace the genes of *T. brucei.* They experienced 100% success in inserting into the organism a mutant gene that interferes with calcium uptake. They speculated that other mutant genes can be developed that will affect the mechanism for changing the proteins in the surface coat of the protozoan. Perhaps African sleeping sickness can eventually be controlled either through development of a noninfective strain for the production of vaccines or by a drug that specifically interferes with the mechanism for the coat formation.

Physiology. The naked mole rat, *Heterocephalus glaber,* lives in subterranean burrows in the tropical semiarid portions of northeastern Africa and rarely in its lifetime is exposed to temperatures below 28° C (82° F). A small mammal averaging 35 g (1.3 oz), it lives in colonies of up to 300 individuals, has a life span of 16 years or more, and is effectively naked, possessing a loosely folded skin that has no sweat glands and is very permeable to water. Researchers have determined that the mammal may physiologically be cold-blooded, unable to control its body temperature.

To examine this question, Rochelle Buffenstein and Shlomo Yahav of the University of the Witwatersrand, Johannesburg, South Africa, collected 17 of the animals from northern Kenya and measured their body temperatures as the animals were exposed to varying temperature changes ranging from 12° to 37° C (53° to 99° F). The results showed that *H. glaber* could not control its body temperature below 29° C (84° F) and stayed within 0.5° C (0.9° F) of the experimental temperature. However, above 29° C the animal could control its body temperature. Thus, *H. glaber* is a poikilotherm (cold-blooded animal) since it is unable to regulate its body temperature in cooler temperatures, a phenomenon previously not observed in mammals except under conditions of hibernation. The naked mole rat is unique as the only mammal that has this behavior.

Embryology. *Caenorhabditis elegans* is a soil nematode that has attracted much attention in the field of molecular and developmental biology, rivaling the contributions of other genetic stalwarts such as the fruit fly, *Drosophila melanogaster,* the African clawed frog, *Xenopus laevis,* and various species of sea urchins. One odd characteristic of *C. elegans* is its reproductive strategy. The nematode is almost exclusively hermaphroditic, practicing self-fertilization. In this process it first produces about 300 spermatozoa and then produces a much larger number of eggs, of which only 300 can be fertilized. The question arises as to why the nematode does not produce more spermatozoa and thus more offspring.

In answer to this question, Jonathan Hodgkin and Thomas M. Barnes of the Medical Research Council Laboratory of Molecular Biology, Cambridge, found a mutant *C. elegans* that produced more spermatozoa and thus more offspring. However, the production of eggs and the birth of the new brood were delayed. These results showed that the natural sperm production was optimal. By changing the sperm production and increasing the fecundity, the animal was placed at a disadvantage since it took too long to produce a brood.

A problem pursued in sperm-egg interactions of animals is whether the sperm is chemically attracted to the vicinity of the egg, a process called sperm chemotaxis. Such a phenomenon is common in aquatic plants but is quite rare in animals, previously being described only in some coelenterates and in sea urchins but never in any vertebrate. Thus, with some surprise, several investigators demonstrated sperm chemotaxis in humans. Dina Ralt of the Weizmann Institute of Science, Rehovot, Israel, and a host of other scientists in Israel and the U.S. demonstrated the attraction of spermatozoa to follicular fluids obtained from the ovarian follicles of 40 females. Interestingly, not all follicular fluids but only those in which the eggs could be fertilized attracted spermatozoa. The authors concluded that these findings suggest that the attraction is a key and specific event and may provide a mechanism for early sperm-egg communication. The blockage of such an event by genetic manipulation could lead to the development of an alternative contraceptive.

During the 1920s the German embryologist Hans Spemann and his students demonstrated in a series of experiments on amphibian embryos that a specific small piece of tissue was responsible for inducing the formation of the actual embryonic axis (the head, trunk, and tail); they showed that if this tissue was transplanted to the proper place in another embryo at the appropriate time, two embryonic axes would develop, the normal one and an induced one. This tissue was called the primary, or Spemann, organizer, and in its absence the embryonic axis could not form. Spemann's findings stimulated considerable interest in embryology, and researchers spent the next 70 years trying to determine the nature of the mechanism located in the Spemann organizer.

Although many studies have been published, none explained the phenomenon until this past year. In a study published in *Cell* magazine on Nov. 15, 1991, the organizer in *X. laevis* was investigated. Sergei Sokol and Douglas Melton of Harvard University and Jan L. Christian and Randall T. Moon of the University of Washington School of Medicine carried out experiments that demonstrated the formation of the embryonic axis. The investigators irradiated *Xenopus* embryos in such a manner that the embryonic axis would not form. Then they injected a specific synthetic messenger ribonucleic acid (mRNA) into the treated frog embryos. Small proteins (peptides) were formed from the specific mRNA and induced the formation of the embryonic axis. Sokol and his colleagues concluded that these peptides are the long-sought Spemann organizer.

—George G. Brown

See also Feature Articles: The Biology and Culture of Human Odor; The Dinosaur Renaissance; Earth—The Gulf War's Silent Victim; Gene Therapy: A New Frontier in Medicine; Life As We Don't Know It; The Salvation Islands; The Search for the KT Crater.

Materials sciences

Reinforcing ceramics for structural applications and developing metal alloys for new military and civilian aircraft were among the major achievements of materials scientists during the past year.

Ceramics

Several developments during recent months help signal the increasing use of ceramics for a range of structural applications. Of special note were the creation of fine-scale multiphase materials (those consisting of more than one homogeneous solid physical species) with dramatically enhanced mechanical properties and the commercialization of a new technique for making a variety of ceramic composites of complex shape without the need for extensive machining.

Nanocomposites. Researchers at Osaka (Japan) University reported impressive behavior for two-phase materials containing fine silicon carbide (SiC) particulate dispersions in alumina, magnesia, and silicon nitride matrices. Dubbed nanocomposites, owing to the nanometer (10^{-9} m)-size scale of the SiC particles in the final structure, these materials exhibit significantly improved strength and toughness compared with the unreinforced matrices. The composites are fabricated by applications of heat—1,600°–1,900° C (2,912°–3,452° F)—and pressure (30–35 megapascals [MPa]) to powder mixtures of the constituents. The result is a dispersion of SiC particles, typically 20 to 200 nanometers in size, located within the matrix grains and in some cases also along the matrix grain boundaries. (The matrix grains are individual crystallites of the matrix material and are 10 to 100 times larger than the dispersed SiC particles.) Properties vary with the volume percentage of SiC present, but in the best cases the load required for fracturing the material is doubled while the toughness is tripled. For alumina (Al_2O_3) having a volume percentage of 5% SiC, annealing at 1,300° C (2,372° F) for two hours in air or in argon improved the strength from 1,000 MPa to a remarkable 1,540 MPa. (The strength of the Al_2O_3 without SiC was 350 MPa.)

Strength enhancement may be due to grain size and structure refinement, while toughness increases are likely the result of favorable interactions between cracks and the SiC particles. High-temperature properties of the nanocomposites are also excellent, with significant property retention to at least 1,400° C (2,552° F).

Of special note, researchers at the Tokyo Institute of Technology reported creep rates two orders of magnitude lower for MgO (magnesia)/SiC than for unreinforced MgO. (Creep is permanent dimensional change in a body while subjected to a constant mechanical load.) Though not fully understood, these improvements in creep behavior are believed to be due to beneficial effects of the residual stresses in the composites and/or interactions between the particles and the defects whose motion through the material causes deformation.

Since these nanocomposites can be processed to complex shapes by traditional fabrication methodologies, there is considerable interest in a variety of applications currently filled by the respective unreinforced matrix materials. Continued research is anticipated to assess the ultimate commercial utility of these composites.

Fibers. By far the most significant improvements in toughness are afforded by reinforcement of a ceramic with a continuous fiber (a long strand of manufactured fiber). Energy is expended as (1) cracks are deflected along the length of the fiber, (2) the fiber debonds (separates) from the matrix, and (3) the fiber pulls out of the matrix on fracture. These events produce considerable toughening of an otherwise brittle ceramic and the ability to tolerate damage without failing catastrophically. However, high-temperature capabilities of composite materials with matrices such as those mentioned above depend on fibers that can retain their strength and oxidative stability (resistance to chemical reactions that form oxygen-containing species) at elevated temperatures. Unfortunately, commercially available fibers do not retain such properties much above 1,100° C (2,012° F). During the past year, however, researchers developed an improved fiber that might significantly expand this temperature limit. Referred to as oxygen-free Nicalon, it is a more thermally stable version of the Nicalon fiber produced in Japan by Nippon Carbon Co. Nicalon is made by converting an organosilicon precursor polymer to the ceramic fiber. This is accomplished by melting the polymer, forcing it through a spinneret (a plate with a series of small holes) to form the fiber shape, curing the fiber by polymer cross-linking (connecting parallel chains) to retain the spun shape, and pyrolyzing the fiber (subjecting it to high-temperature heat treatment) to drive off volatile constituents and convert it to a ceramic composition and structure.

The chemistry of the final product is determined by the chemistry of the precursor polymer and the chemical changes that occur during each of the processing steps. Commercially available Nicalon fiber resembles SiC, but it contains appreciable excess carbon and oxygen. As a result, it is subject to degradation reactions above 1,100° C, whereas stoichiometric SiC (no excess carbon or oxygen) is stable to nearly 1,650° C (3,002° F). Much of the oxygen is incorporated into Nicalon during an oxidative curing step in which oxygen atoms link the polymer chains.

Nippon Carbon's research, in collaboration with the University of Osaka Prefecture and the Japan Atomic Energy Research Institute, sought ways to accommodate cross-linking without introducing oxygen. A successful result was achieved by electron beam irradiation. The oxygen content was reduced to as low as 0.4% weight (compared with 10–14% weight in the standard product). The fiber continued to contain excess carbon, but its high-temperature properties were substantially improved. For example, the fiber with a low weight percentage of oxygen showed little weight change after 10 hours of exposure in argon at 1,500° C (2,732° F), whereas the standard fiber lost 26.3% of its original weight. Impressively, the radiation-cured fiber kept its fibrous form and was flexible after inert atmosphere exposure at 2,000° C (3,632° F), while the fiber cured by oxidation experienced extreme grain growth and turned to powder. The tensile strength (maximum stress that a material subjected to a stretching load can withstand without breaking) and stiffness of the new fiber were excellent to temperatures as high as 1,500° C. Strength ranged from 2,800 MPa at room temperature to 1,400 MPa at 1,500° C, while the stiffness ranged from 270 GPa (gigapascals) to 150 GPa at those points. Oxidation rates were superior to the standard fiber.

This new fiber appeared to hold great promise for effective, stable ceramic composite reinforcement to very high temperatures. Small quantities for evaluation were available from the manufacturer, with full production expected in a few years.

Processing. Cost-affordable complex shape processing is required if fiber-reinforced ceramic composites are to gain widespread application. A leading methodology for providing such composites is the recently commercialized directed metal oxidation (DIMOX™) process developed by the Lanxide Corp. in the U.S. The process was based on the observation that accelerated oxidation of aluminum alloys, typically considered a problem in the aluminum industry, could be turned into an advantage for rapidly growing a ceramic matrix through a composite reinforcement preform. The preform can be made of ceramic particulates, whiskers (microscopic rods), or fibers and is shaped to conform to the geometry of the part to be fabricated. In practice, the preform and metal are heated to the growth temperature (above the parent alloy's melting temperature). The molten alloy contacts the shaped preform but does not react with it; rather, the alloy reacts with the gaseous environment in the growth furnace. Gas species present in the furnace, such as air for alumina growth, are selected by virtue of the desired matrix composition. The reaction product, most often an oxide or nitride, grows through the open channels in the preform, encapsulating the reinforcement without disturbing its geometry. The reaction is maintained at the growth interface because the liquid metal is transported through the reaction product by capillary action along narrow interconnected channels. This behavior is tailored by the use of appropriate dopants to the liquid metal composition.

The reaction proceeds through the preform until it contacts a gas-permeable barrier layer that stops the reaction in order to achieve control of the shape of the composite. The small percentage (about 7–10% weight) of residual metal remaining in the ma-

Fiber-reinforced ceramic composite wear parts were made by the directed metal oxidation process developed by the Lanxide Corp. (see text). The largest wear ring pictured measures 114 centimeters (45 inches) in diameter.

Exhaust nozzle of the SNECMA M-88 engine (left) has flaps made of silicon carbide reinforced with carbon fibers by a process called chemical vapor infiltration (see text). The engine was to be used in France's new Rafale fighter jet, a prototype of which flew with the nozzle flaps at the 1991 Paris Air Show (above).

trix provides desirable toughness for low-temperature applications. The metal can be mostly removed for high-temperature applications, leaving some porosity, or treated to prevent melting or further oxidation during service.

This process is especially attractive, as it uses commodity-grade matrix starting materials, can produce a range of matrix chemistries (aluminum nitride and silicon nitride as recent examples) through the choices of molten metal and vapor phase reactants, operates at low temperature (about 1,000° C [1,832° F]), and can yield large, complex shapes of varying wall thickness. Lanxide's first products were alumina reinforced with SiC particulates for a variety of wear-resistant applications. Examples include pump housings, liners, and rings for resistance to erosion by abrasive slurries. More recently, lightweight ceramic composite armor tiles were supplied to the U.S. Army. Heat exchanger and radiant furnace burner tubes were successfully tested to 1,530° C (2,786° F), and significant progress was made with alumina reinforced with particulates or with continuous fibers for a range of prototype gas turbine engine components. Particularly encouraging results were obtained with Nicalon fiber that is coated before the growth process to tailor the fiber-matrix interface for tough behavior.

Aerospace applications. Ceramic composite gas turbine engine exhaust nozzle flaps went into production in France during the past year. Made by the Société Européenne de Propulsion (SEP), the parts were to be used in the SNECMA M-88 engine. This engine was to power the new French Rafale fighter jet, which flew with the full complement of ceramic composite flaps at the 1991 Paris Air Show. Termed

outer flaps because of their position at the extreme rear of the nozzle, they are made of SiC reinforced with carbon fibers by a process called chemical vapor infiltration. This method involves deposition of the matrix from the gas phase directly onto the fiber preform in a reaction vessel. The nozzle parts were reported to have operated at 510° C (950° F) during the cruise cycle and 704°–760° C (1,300°–1,400° F) during the afterburner cycle.

The benefits of these ceramic composite components are reduced engine weight and increased resistance to acoustic fatigue (by sound-pressure waves during engine operation). This undertaking is a significant demonstration of the applicability and readiness of ceramic composites to fulfill an important aerospace need.

—Allan P. Katz

Metallurgy

The design goals established for planned military and civilian aircraft over the next decades require materials that will perform reliably under more severe conditions than those experienced by materials currently in use. The nickel-based alloys described as superalloys—complex materials that often contain cobalt, tungsten, chromium, and aluminum in addition to nickel—were extended into performance ranges near 1,000° C (1,800° F), but most of those alloys melt at temperatures only a few hundred degrees higher. The high melting temperature (better than 2,000° C), excellent resistance to oxidation at high temperatures, and high stiffness of molybdenum disilicide ($MoSi_2$) and similar silicides have spawned many research efforts during the last few years. Proposed applications of those materials include the hottest areas within the next generation of jet engines—turbine airfoils, augmentor liners, seals, and turbine nozzles.

The rapid increase in research efforts to develop these materials led in late 1991 to the first workshop on silicides for structural applications (sponsored by the U.S. Office of Naval Research). At this workshop more than 25 research groups from universities, government laboratories, and industry presented results on chemistry, mechanical properties, production, oxidation, and performance of $MoSi_2$ and similar materials.

History of $MoSi_2$. The synthesis of $MoSi_2$ was apparently first reported in Germany in 1907, but it was not proposed for use as a structural material until 1949. The most widespread use has been as resistance heating elements for very-high-temperature furnaces. The resistance to oxidation and high electrical resistivity of $MoSi_2$ at elevated temperatures permitted operation of furnaces up to 1,800° C (3,300° F) in open-air environments (patented by the Kanthal Co. of Sweden in 1956). Most laboratory furnaces that operate at temperatures between 1,500° C (2,700° F) and 1,800° C use $MoSi_2$ as the heat source.

Although these $MoSi_2$ heating elements revolutionized the temperature capabilities of open-air furnaces, the structural capabilities of this material at high temperature and its brittleness at low temperatures prevented its use in more demanding structural applications. In the mid-1980s Frank D. Gac and John J. Petrovic of the Los Alamos (N.M.) National Laboratory reported the results of a feasibility study on composites of $MoSi_2$ and whisker (short-fiber) reinforcements of silicon carbide (SiC). Their initial room-temperature results demonstrated that the addition of the SiC reinforcement could double the bending strength and increase the toughness (a measure of the resistance to fracture) of $MoSi_2$ by more than 50%. These results, and subsequent research at higher temperatures, led to the current increased interest in composites having matrices made from $MoSi_2$ and other silicides for structural applications.

The combination of strength and good oxidation resistance at high temperatures attracted substantial interest. However, as discussed below, the lower temperature toughness and oxidation resistance of $MoSi_2$ at low temperatures are potential liabilities for the application of these materials.

Structure and properties of $MoSi_2$. The crystal structure of $MoSi_2$ is somewhat more complex than the cubic alloys of aluminum and steel with which most people are familiar. The crystal structure of $MoSi_2$ and the most closely related material, tungsten disilicide (WSi_2), is called body-centered-tetrag-

onal and consists of two silicon atoms for every molybdenum atom. As in all materials, the bonding between the atoms determines the structure and the properties. In the case of $MoSi_2$, the bonding characteristics fall somewhere between those observed in metals and those observed in ceramics. The electrical resistivity of $MoSi_2$ is reasonably high at room temperature, very close to that of steel, and, like many metals, the resistivity increases with increasing temperature. Because of recent successes in manufacturing individual crystals of $MoSi_2$ and WSi_2, scientists in both Japan and Canada recently were able to carry out fundamental measurements of the physical properties of those silicides. Strong anisotropy (having different values when measured along axes in different directions) of properties was demonstrated in single crystals of $MoSi_2$ and WSi_2. At room temperature the electrical resistivity of these materials differs by as much as 40% depending on the direction that voltage is applied in the crystals.

The value of the elastic stiffness (Young's modulus) at room temperature is often employed as an indication of the bond strength of a material. The Young's modulus of $MoSi_2$ and WSi_2 is very high and substantially anisotropic. The room-temperature Young's modulus for $MoSi_2$ is approximately 430 gigapascals (GPa), twice that of steel and six times that of aluminum. Because of anisotropy, the Young's modulus of $MoSi_2$ can be more than 30% lower in some directions than in others.

The mechanical properties of $MoSi_2$ at room temperature are similar to those of many ceramics in that $MoSi_2$ is more likely to fracture than deform plastically. As mentioned above, a material's resistance to fracture is called toughness. The room-temperature fracture toughness of pure $MoSi_2$ is approximately five megapascals-root-meter (MPa $\sqrt{m}$). This is a higher value than that for common window glass, which has a fracture toughness of less than one megapascal-root-meter, but is quite close to that of aluminum oxide (Al_2O_3) or silicon nitride (Si_3N_4), two common ceramics used for structural applications.

Most metals used in industrial applications have fracture toughnesses much greater than 30 MPa $\sqrt{m}$. On the other hand, the tendency to deform plastically and the fracture toughness of $MoSi_2$ increase substantially at temperatures greater than about 900° C (1,650° F). This transition from brittleness to deformability is quite rapid. By 1,200° to 1,300° C (2,200° to 2,400° F) $MoSi_2$ is too deformable for many structural applications. By adding ceramic reinforcements to $MoSi_2$, some investigators boosted the fracture toughness by 60%. With relatively small additions of ceramic reinforcements, the oxidation resistance of the composite material is not significantly degraded.

Another approach designed to provide enhanced low-temperature toughness was the use of metal fibers as reinforcements. Unfortunately, most attempts to enhance the room-temperature toughness by this method met with little success because of the concurrent degradation of the resistances to high-temperature creep (time-dependent strain caused by stress) and oxidation. Efforts to improve the high-temperature performance of $MoSi_2$ also included attempts to reduce the amount of SiO_2 (silicon dioxide) present at the grain boundaries, the surfaces between individual grains in metals. Recent work revealed that significant increases in hardness and toughness could be achieved with the use of carbon additions that reduced the amount of SiO_2 at grain boundaries.

The resistance of $MoSi_2$ to oxidation is unusual in that the material is more susceptible to oxidation at intermediate temperatures than at very high temperatures. The high-temperature resistance of $MoSi_2$ to oxidation is derived from the formation of a protective SiO_2 layer at temperatures greater than 800° C (1,500° F). This SiO_2 layer grows to a finite thickness, which prevents significant oxidation unless fresh $MoSi_2$ surface is exposed to air by damage to the protective oxide layer.

At lower temperatures—550° C (1,000° F)—molybdenum disilicide does not produce a protective oxide layer but demonstrates a susceptibility to a phenomenon called "pesting." Without a protective SiO_2 layer, the volatile oxidation of molybdenum to form MoO_3 results in a severe intergranular attack that can literally disintegrate the $MoSi_2$. Even though the SiO_2 layer that forms at high temperatures can protect $MoSi_2$, any cracking or other defect that damages the protective layer results in catastrophic damage. Several investigators attempted to modify the oxidation characteristics of $MoSi_2$, although no approach was very successful.

Future prospects. The accomplishments of the past year in research on $MoSi_2$ and related silicides demonstrated the substantial lack of knowledge of the chemistry and properties of $MoSi_2$. With an increased number of metallurgy and ceramics researchers investigating the structure, processing, properties, and performance of silicide materials, methods to deal with the liabilities that could prevent future applications of these materials may be developed.

Besides additional research on composites of these materials, metallurgists investigated the potential for producing silicide materials by the traditional method of solidification processing—changing a fluid into a solid. By using the metallurgist's understanding of alloy design, researchers may realize the potential for silicides with unique microstructures. Researchers at the University of Michigan demonstrated that a very

fine structure of silicide materials, called a eutectic microstructure, can resemble that found in many existing engineering materials by changing the ratio of molybdenum and silicon. This type of alloy design provides $MoSi_2$-Mo_5Si_3 composites that could have important properties for engineering applications.

—Keith J. Bowman

Mathematics

The major news in mathematics during the past year was the spread of research and applications involving wavelets. Other announced developments included determining the "kissing number" for spheres, extending the period of random number generators, and new facts about the boundary of the Mandelbrot set fractal. There was progress toward breaking the U.S.-government-sponsored code for commercial communications, while the government proposed a controversial new standard to guarantee the authenticity of digital signatures. There were mixed results in initial trials of the Turing test, an attempt to decide if computers can think. A computer was used to solve a long-standing chess problem; and a new record was established for the number of computed digits of pi.

Wavelets. Wavelets provide a way to compress and decompress data quickly, particularly pictures and sound, without sacrificing detail or requiring great amounts of storage. Wavelets are similar in principle to the sine and cosine curves used in decomposing a sound frequency curve into an additive series of its constituent frequencies. For example, the sound produced by striking a single piano key can be decomposed into the tonic frequency and, with increasingly smaller coefficients, its successive overtones. This approach, known as Fourier analysis, was discovered two centuries ago and is used regularly in analyzing analog data (numbers representing directly measurable quantities).

In the 1970s Fourier analysis was adapted to digital computers and was named the fast Fourier transform. Sines and cosines, however, are not totally suitable for all purposes because they work best for phenomena that repeat exactly at regular intervals. They do not handle well the "transient" parts of signals or signals that are irregular. Also, the information in the Fourier transform is built from all parts of the original curve, so that any local variation in the curve is "smeared" over—and distorts—the entire Fourier approximation.

Wavelets, on the other hand, offer what engineers call simultaneous localization in the time and frequency domains. For example, a minor disturbance, such as a cough during a musical performance, affects only a few wavelets in the decomposition.

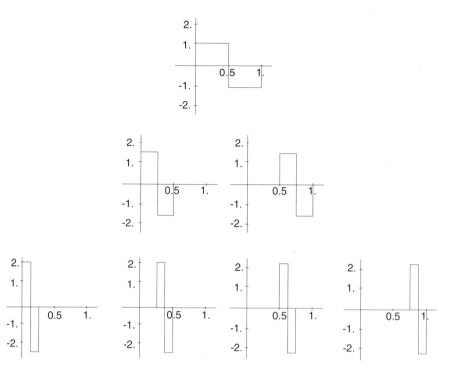

Figure 1. In a family of wavelets the "mother" wavelet (top) is shrunk, stretched, or moved to form the other family members (bottom).

A family of wavelets consists of a "mother" wavelet together with other wavelets that are constructed by shrinking, stretching, or moving the mother wavelet (Figure 1). The mother wavelet is a mathematical function mainly concentrated on an interval, perhaps with exponential decay to the sides. Its progeny consist of functions that are similar in shape but a power of two times as spread out (for shrinking: 1/2, 1/4, . . . ; for stretching: 1, 2, 4, . . .) and moved an integral number of units to the left or right. Different mother wavelets lead to different families; the choice of wavelet family needs to be tailored to the application.

Any function can be represented in a unique way by a sum of wavelets from a family, each multiplied by the appropriate coefficient. For example, the musical tone produced by striking a piano key for a full note could be represented as a sum of the base note (tonic) together with multiples of the half note at the first overtone (twice the frequency of the tonic), the quarter note at the second overtone (four times the frequency), and so forth. The particular multiples used in the wavelet decomposition depend on the characteristics of the individual piano.

Wavelets were invented by Jean Morlet, a French geophysicist, in the early 1980s. The mathematics on which they are based, however, was developed in the early 20th century in the field of harmonic analysis. In 1985 Yves Meyer of the Université de Paris—Dauphine recognized the connections between this work and what Morlet was doing, and Meyer found the first orthogonal family of wavelets. For an or-

thogonal family, any two wavelets have net overlap of zero, and therefore it is easy to determine the decomposition of a signal into wavelets. Research on wavelets intensified in the past two years, including publication in 1990 of a simple family of orthogonal wavelets on intervals, a family shown to be the most efficient, by Ingrid Daubechies of AT&T Bell Laboratories (Figure 2).

Decomposition of a signal into wavelets can be done quickly. The speed of the decomposition algorithm is proportional to the number of sample points on the signal, whereas the amount of computation for the fast Fourier transform on n sample points is proportional to $n \log n$. Also, wavelet decompositions offer data-compression ratios of 40 to 1 or better.

Figure 2. The "mother" Daubechies wavelet was discovered by Ingrid Daubechies and first published in 1990.

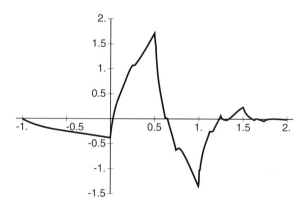

Wavelet compression, for which there is already a wavelet computer chip, can thus compete with commercial fractal-compression techniques.

Morlet invented wavelets to help analyze seismograms. Potential applications include compact storage in digital form of fingerprints, X-rays, and weather satellite data. High-definition television, digital videotape, computer vision, and digital speech also require the data compression that wavelets provide. Perhaps the first products featuring wavelet compression will be computer modems, used for transmitting data over telephone lines.

Kissing number. In 1990 Wu-Yi Hsiang of the University of California at Berkeley announced a proof that one specific way of packing ordinary same-size spheres is the densest. Known as face-centered cubic packing, the method is familiar to fruit buyers throughout the world as the standard way to stack oranges; in the 17th century Sir Isaac Newton had conjectured its optimality. By the end of 1991, however, mathematicians still had not been able to verify Hsiang's proof, since he had not yet written down all the hundreds of pages of details. The careful enumeration of configurations that must be considered does not lend itself easily to computer checking, and Hsiang used only a calculator in his work.

In the packing in question, every sphere is touched by 12 others. This is the greatest number of same-size spheres that can be fitted in to touch another, a result that had also been conjectured by Newton and proved in the 19th century. The problem of determining such a maximum, the kissing number, can be considered in other dimensions. For example, in a plane, the analogue of a sphere is a circle; no more than six circles can surround and touch a seventh, as experiments with pennies suggest (Figure 3). Similarly, in one dimension (a line), a "sphere" is a line segment, and a single segment can be tangent to ("kissed" by) only two others. Curiously, the only other dimensions in which mathematicians had been able to determine the kissing number were 8 and 24, where the numbers are, respectively, 240 and 196,560. Dimension 24 has been the subject of intensive study in recent years because of its connection with the 1980 enumeration of all "simple" groups and other important open questions.

In 1991 Hsiang announced a proof that the kissing number in four dimensions is 24; it had been known that it must be either 24 or 25. Mathematicians were awaiting the publication of Hsiang's proofs for this and the packing result, hoping that his arguments would stand up to close scrutiny and finally settle those conjectures.

Improved random-number generators. As the speed of computers increases, scientists performing simulations reach the limits of conventional random-number generators. No algorithmic procedure can

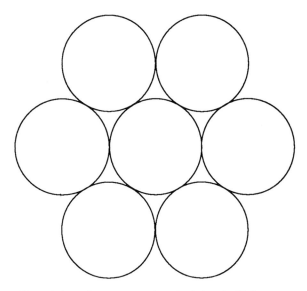

Figure 3. In a plane no more than six circles, the kissing number, can surround and touch a seventh.

provide truly random numbers, but good computer random-number generators supply pseudorandom numbers that imitate randomness in most testable respects except one: each can generate only a finite number of pseudorandom numbers. After a few days of computation, a conventional random-number generator will arrive back at the starting number and cycle through all the same numbers again, in the same order. The number of different random numbers in the cycle is the period of the generator, which depends in part on the starting number.

George Marsaglia and Arif Zaman of Florida State University found ways to take a conventional random-number generator and greatly extend its period, without much additional computation. One of their methods, called "add-with-carry," extends the period of an ordinary random-number generator found on personal computers from 10^9 to 10^{250}. The proof is based on simple aspects of prime numbers that have been known for hundreds of years. Marsaglia refers to the techniques as "randomness amplifiers" (Figure 4).

Mandelbrot set. The Mandelbrot set is the best-known fractal; its boundary is immensely intricate, repeating a structure of protrusions and bays at arbitrarily small scales. During the past year Mitsuhiro Shishikura of the Tokyo Institute of Technology demonstrated that the boundary achieves the ultimate degree of convolution that can be attained by a planar curve: It has fractal (Hausdorff) dimension 2. In other words, the boundary appears in some respects to be a two-dimensional object. Not yet determined were whether the area of the boundary is zero and whether the boundary is what mathematicians call locally connected.

The Fibonacci sequence, generated by

$$x_0 = 1, \quad x_1 = 1, \quad x_n = x_{n-1} + x_{n-2},$$

consists of the numbers

1, 1, 2, 3, 5, 8, 13, 21, 34, 55, 89, 144, 233, 377, 610, 987, 1597, . . . ,

which have final digits

1, 1, 2, 3, 5, 8, 3, 1, 4, 5, 9, 4, 3, 7, 0, 7, 7, ...

At the 61st term, the sequence starts over again with 1, 1, ...

In the Marsaglia-Zaman procedure, if there was a "carry" (from the ones place to the tens place) in the addition to get x_n, then an extra 1 is added in arriving at x_{n+1}—the carry is "lagged" (and added to the units place). We get

1, 1, 2, 3, 5, 8, 13, 22, 36, 58, 94, 153, 248, 401, 700, 1102, 1802, . . . ,

with final digits

1, 1, 2, 3, 5, 8, 3, 2, 6, 8, 4, 3, 8, 1, 0, 2, 2, ...

This sequence, too, will repeat but with a longer period, $10^2 + 10^1 - 2 = 108$.

Figure 4. The "add-with-carry" method, shown at the right in a simplified case, extends the period of an ordinary random-number generator found on personal computers from 10^9 to 10^{250}.

Data Encryption Standard. The Data Encryption Standard (DES) is a code endorsed by the U.S. Department of Commerce for commercial and non-classified government use; banks use it routinely in transferring billions of dollars each day. The DES uses a 56-bit key selected by the user. Adi Shamir of the Weizmann Institute in Israel, one of the world's leading cryptographers, and Eli Biham, a student at the Technion in Israel, announced in late 1991 that they could greatly reduce the effort needed to break this code, provided they had access to the coded version of a message of their choice. Such a circumstance would be unlikely in practice, but Shamir and Biham's success signaled a weakness in DES that indicated its "aging."

Their achievement also confirmed the initial skepticism of some experts when DES was promulgated by the U.S. National Bureau of Standards in 1977, as well as more recent doubts on the part of the U.S. National Security Agency (NSA), which in 1988 considered not recertifying DES as a federal standard. The skeptics believed that the length of the key, which had been reduced from 128 bits to 56 at the recommendation of the NSA, was dangerously short—short enough that the NSA could break the code at will. By 1988 the NSA itself contended that DES was being used in extremely sensitive applications, which made it too much—and perhaps too weak—a target for sustained efforts to break it.

Digital signatures. For thousands of years the authenticity of a document's authorship has depended on a signature. But how can one "sign" a document, such as a contract, that is transmitted in electronic form? And how can the recipient of an electronic document prove later that it was "signed" by the originator? Along with progress in cryptography during the past decade came a variety of schemes to provide such authentication—electronic "signatures." In 1991 the National Institute of Standards and Technology (NIST) proposed a standard protocol for such signatures, the Digital Signature Standard (DSS), which would allow the recipient of a message to verify both the identity of the sender and the integrity of the document.

The underlying mathematical algorithm relies on trapdoor public-key cryptography. Two keys are used: one to encrypt (encode) the document and a second to decrypt it; the second (the "trapdoor") cannot be deduced easily from the first. The first key is kept secret, but the second is made public. Using the second key, anyone can decrypt a document in order to verify it; however, no one can forge a document without discovering the first key.

The DSS would use the ElGamal scheme, which relies on a key about 150 digits long that is known to be prime (has no factors other than itself and 1). Encryption consists of raising another particular integer (the base) to large powers, dividing the result by the key, and transmitting to the intended recipient the remainder of the division. The security of the DSS depends on the difficulty of calculating "discrete logarithms," that is, given the remainder, to determine the power to which the (known) base was raised.

The DSS was criticized by Ronald Rivest of the Massachusetts Institute of Technology, who claimed that such a standard should not specify key length and that in any case the key length specified in the proposal was too short. Rivest recommended instead a standard based on the encryption method known as "RSA" (for Rivest-Shamir-Adleman) as offering greater security. RSA uses two very large (approximately 100 digits) prime numbers and their product. The message's author keeps secret the two prime numbers, which are used to encrypt the message (also by exponentiation, as in the DSS), but divulges their product, which anyone can use to decrypt the message. The security of this technique depends on the difficulty of factoring large integers. With current algorithms and the fastest conceivable computers, the practical limit for factoring integers that are not of some known special form is perhaps 120 digits, according to Robert D. Silverman of the MITRE Corp.

At the end of 1991, Stuart Haber and Arjen Lenstra of Bell Communications Research (the research institute of the Bell telephone companies) discovered how the person selecting the prime number key in the NIST scheme could arrange for it to contain a secret additional "trapdoor." Consequently, any digital signature based on that prime could be forged.

Turing test. In a famous 1950 paper, computer scientist Alan Turing proposed what has become known as the Turing test for determining whether computers can think. Human judges type conversational questions into computer terminals and try to determine whether the respondent is a human or a computer program. If a computer program fools the judges, Turing said, the computer should be regarded as intelligent.

Recently, philanthropist Hugh Loebner established a $100,000-prize competition to stimulate the development of such programs. In 1991 an initial "tournament" of computer programs was held in a competition in which topics of the "conversations" were limited to subjects chosen by each program's designer (to improve the odds for the programs). The best of the programs was able to fool 5 of 10 judges. But the judges were untrained observers, and computer experts were easily able to distinguish the programs from the human respondents.

Chess and pi. Lewis Stiller, a computer scientist at Johns Hopkins University, Baltimore, Md., used a supercomputer to solve an endgame in chess, producing an unexpected result. Starting from a specified position, a king with a rook (castle) and a bishop can prevail over a king with two knights—in 223 moves. Previously, the situation had been unresolved, experts concluding that neither side could force a win and players consenting to draws in those

circumstances. The rules of chess provide that if 50 moves elapse without a capture (or a pawn move), the game is drawn.

David and Gregory Chudnovsky of Columbia University, New York City, extended the calculation of the digits of pi to 2,160,000,000 in their search for any patterns that may lie in those digits. Their calculation, done on a parallel supercomputer that they assembled from mail-order parts, doubled the previous record. No patterns emerged; according to David Chudnovsky, "We need a trillion digits."

—Paul J. Campbell

See also Feature Article: KNOT THEORY AND SPACE-TIME.

Medical sciences

Physicians and medical researchers made progress during the past year in the understanding and treatment of Alzheimer's disease, cancer, heart disease, and shingles. Smoking was linked with impotence in men and incontinence in women. New methods were being developed to diagnose advanced gum disease—the leading cause of tooth loss—and the world's first veterinary school marked its 200th anniversary.

General medicine

AIDS continued its deadly march, but researchers made great advances in their understanding of how Alzheimer's disease ravages the brain, how genes act when a cell turns cancerous, how the various senses are wired in the brain, and what smoking does to the body.

AIDS. The preeminent AIDS (acquired immune deficiency syndrome) research institution in Africa, Project SIDA, was closed, perhaps permanently, by rioting in its home base of Kinshasa, Zaire. The project, run by U.S., French, Belgian, and Zairian scientists, was the first to determine that AIDS is not related to malaria, that its primary mode of transmission in Africa is heterosexual sex, and that it is not transmitted by mosquitoes.

In a study of blood from 18 hemophiliacs sampled before and after infection with the human immunodeficiency virus (HIV, the virus that causes AIDS), University of Edinburgh scientists may have discovered a way to determine who is likely to develop the disease soon after infection. They found that those who had high levels of certain antibodies in their blood, and who produced more immune system stimulators and certain immune cells and antibodies immediately after infection, were likely to develop the syndrome earlier.

As laboratories around the world continued their developmental work on AIDS vaccines, the World

Health Organization got ready for testing by picking four testing sites—Thailand, Brazil, Rwanda, and Uganda. This was done even before WHO chose the actual vaccines to be tested.

The blood-transfusion program in France was faced with two scandals. The government was charged with stalling on an application for licensure of a U.S.-made HIV blood test so that it could first give approval to a French product. And transfusion officials were put on trial for delaying heat treatment for the blood products used by hemophiliacs for nine months after a French researcher showed that it would be protective.

While a virus similar to HIV is known to exist in nonhuman primates, where HIV itself comes from remained a mystery. During the past year a University of Oxford researcher suggested an answer to the riddle. Through historical research he discovered that from the 1920s to the 1950s a few dozen people received blood from nonhuman primates that carried malaria parasites to see if the humans would develop malaria. The nonhuman primates could also have been carrying an HIV-like virus; researcher Charles Gilks suggested that HIV may be a mutation of one of those viruses that infected one of the people in the experiments and gradually worked its way into an epidemic.

The risk of becoming infected with HIV by means of heterosexual sex received prominent attention in the U.S. media following the announcement by basketball star Earvin ("Magic") Johnson that he was infected. Johnson retired from basketball and was named to the President's Commission on AIDS.

Alzheimer's disease. A brain molecule called the beta-amyloid precursor protein had already been strongly suspected of playing a causative role in Alzheimer's disease. The protein accumulates in the brains of people with the disease, which causes increasing dementia and eventually death. Researchers from St. Mary's Hospital in London announced during the year further incriminating evidence: in two families with hereditary Alzheimer's, the gene that produces that protein was abnormal in family members with the disease, suggesting that the gene—and, in turn, the protein it produces—induces the disease. Later in the year the report was supported by another from the Indiana University School of Medicine describing another defect in the same gene in Alzheimer's patients.

Researchers trying to determine the cause and treatment of Alzheimer's disease have been hampered by the lack of a small-animal model on which to experiment. During the past year, however, several independent research groups reported that mice loaded up with the suspect gene subsequently developed amyloid deposits in their brains similar to those in humans with Alzheimer's disease. Further stud-

AP/Wide World

Earvin ("Magic") Johnson announces his retirement from the Los Angeles Lakers professional basketball team in November 1991 after discovering that he had tested positive for the virus that causes AIDS.

ies failed to confirm these findings, however, greatly disappointing Alzheimer's disease researchers. Several Boston-area researchers implicated the protein when they injected it into rats' brains, where it caused the same sort of damage seen in humans with the disease.

Bacteria, viruses and vaccines. A vaccine effective against chicken pox evidently also prevents shingles. Shingles, a disease marked by a painful rash, is caused by the same virus that causes chicken pox. Not everyone who has had chicken pox will develop shingles, but those who do generally develop the rash decades after the initial infection. Researchers from Columbia University, New York City, and other institutions exploited a medical quirk—that children with leukemia who are infected with the chicken pox virus develop shingles just a few years after infection rather than after the customary gap of several decades. They tested the vaccine in 96 children with leukemia and compared the subsequent development of shingles with that in 96 unvaccinated children with leukemia who had developed chicken pox. While 15% of the unvaccinated children developed shingles, just 2% of the vaccinated group did. As of early 1992, the vaccine was being marketed in Japan and South Korea and was available for limited use in parts of Europe.

Three microbiologists at the State University of New York at Stony Brook created a virus in the laboratory, perhaps the first time this feat had been accomplished. They steeped the genetic material from a poliovirus in a broth containing the protein-manufacturing machinery of human cancers. The genetic material was able to assemble full virus particles that were virtually identical to polioviruses. The researchers hoped to use the process to learn more about the workings of polioviruses and structurally related viruses such as those that cause the common cold.

Debate continued over the existence and the cause of chronic fatigue syndrome, the "yuppie flu" first diagnosed in a U.S. resort community. A University of Southern California researcher reported that he had identified a type of virus called a spuma virus in 10 people with chronic fatigue; spuma viruses are extremely rare in humans and had not been known to cause illness. European researchers linked another virus type, enteroviruses, to the syndrome. In early 1992 researchers from several U.S. institutions reported a connection to human herpesvirus type 6, but it was not clear whether the virus causes the disease or is a result of it.

Cold viruses proved themselves more effective attackers in people who are stressed. A British-U.S. consortium of scientists from the Medical Research Council in England, the University of Wales, and Carnegie Mellon University in Pittsburgh, Pa., deliberately infected 394 volunteers either with one of five different cold viruses or with a harmless saline solution. The subjects who had reported the most stress were more likely to develop an infection, though they were not necessarily more likely to become ill, but the link between stress and cold viruses had not yet been proved. A Massachusetts General Hospital researcher pointed out that there might be hidden reasons for the stress that could explain the difference; for example, living alone and not having been previously exposed to the virus.

The U.S. pharmaceutical manufacturer Merck, Sharp & Dohme, along with researchers from Johns Hopkins University, Baltimore, Md., and Hadassah Hospital in Jerusalem, developed a vaccine against hepatitis A, a virus that can be transmitted by food or unhygienic conditions and that can, on occasion, be lethal. In a field test on more than 1,000 children, all 18 who developed hepatitis A had received a placebo vaccine; there were no occurrences of hepatitis A in those children who had received the active vaccine. The vaccine had already passed safety tests in adults.

Belgian and French researchers field-tested a new rabies vaccine, intended for use in the wild, that represents improvements over a previous version, which can on occasion cause the disease itself. While injected rabies vaccines are widely used in domes-ticated animals, eradicating the disease in wild animals has proved problematic. The Belgian vaccine, inoculated into bait, protected 80% of the foxes in a 2,200-sq km (850-sq mi) district.

Cancer. Physicians from the U.S. National Cancer Institute initiated the first assault on cancer using gene therapy. They removed white blood cells from two patients with malignant melanoma and loaded the cells up with the gene that produces tumor necrosis factor, a chemical that alerts the immune system to attack. (TNF alone causes extreme weight loss.) They reinjected the white blood cells with the extra gene into the patients in the hope that the cells would flock to the cancer and signal the immune system to attack. Later the same team removed cancer cells from several other patients, loaded the cells up with the TNF gene, and injected the cells back into the patients. The theory in that situation is that the TNF will alert the immune system not only to the newly injected cancer cells but also to other cancer cells throughout the body. A team from Johns Hopkins University proved this approach effective in mice with kidney cancer. (*See* Feature Article: GENE THERAPY: A NEW FRONTIER IN MEDICINE.)

It took an international effort—scientists from Johns Hopkins University, the Cancer Institute in Tokyo, and the University of Utah—to find the gene that causes familial colon cancer, which represents at least a fifth of all colon cancers. The normal gene governs slow, steady reproduction of the cell; the mutated, cancerous form allows unfettered division. Discovery of the gene, which sits on chromosome five, was likely to lead to a test to try to determine those who are at risk of the cancer, so that physicians can monitor those people and catch colon cancer in its early, treatable stage.

Scientists from the Massachusetts General Hospital and the U.S. National Cancer Institute found a "hot spot" within a particular gene that is apparently capable of causing liver cancer. Liver cancer is relatively rare in the U.S. and Europe but is prevalent in parts of Asia and Africa and is among the leading causes of death from cancer throughout the world.

Researchers from Stanford University and Kaiser Permanente Medical Center in Oakland, Calif., implicated a bacterium already associated with stomach ulcers as a culprit in the development of stomach cancer. They studied 186 patients with stomach cancer and 186 people free of the disease and discovered that 84% of those with stomach cancer were infected with *Helicobacter pylori* and that only 61% of the cancer-free people were infected. The researchers concluded that the bacteria play a role in three out of five cases of stomach cancer, but since many infected people never go on to develop the disease, their discovery's immediate public health value was minimal.

Proving that cancer preventives can be found in unexpected places, several groups of scientists linked tea with tumor prevention. A researcher at the National Cancer Center in Japan identified an antioxidant in green tea that appeared to protect cancer-prone mice from liver cancer and intestinal cancer. Scientists from Rutgers University, New Brunswick, N.J., reported that mice watered with green tea developed fewer skin tumors after exposure to ultraviolet light and a known carcinogen than did mice that drank regular water.

Cancer cells are basically cells that never grew up and therefore retain their ability to reproduce indefinitely. Columbia University researchers announced that they had developed a series of drugs capable of forcing the cells to mature; the drugs looked promising in preliminary clinical trials.

Diabetes. While some diabetics have benefited from pancreas transplants, the procedure depends on the availability of a matching pancreas and is difficult and costly. A Washington University, St. Louis, Mo., researcher began exploration of an alternate method for getting the benefits of the pancreas cells into diabetics—he implanted porous tubes containing pancreas cells under the skin of diabetic mice. The tubes allow nourishment for the islet cells to flow in and the islet cells' insulin to flow out and into the body, where it is needed. Attacking immune-system cells cannot fit through the holes in the tube, so the problem of rejection is eliminated. The procedure, according to its developers, could be ready for humans in three years.

People with Type 1 diabetes, the kind that usually strikes during childhood, have fewer of the "flags" on the surface of their cells that tell their immune system that these cells are "self" and should not be attacked. That reduction, said the Massachusetts General Hospital researchers who observed it, could explain why the immune system is so willing to attack and destroy the pancreas cells.

Genetics. Scientists discovered the gene that causes Marfan syndrome, a genetic condition that results in such outward signs as tall stature and oversized hands and feet and, internally, in a weakened aorta that can burst without warning. The gene, discovered by researchers from the Shriners Hospital for Crippled Children in Portland, Ore., the University of Connecticut, and Mt. Sinai School of Medicine in New York City, was found on chromosome 15. It codes for fibrillin, a protein found in much of the body's connective tissue. The gene itself is quite large, and the scientists were able to find a number of different anomalies that lead to varying degrees of disease.

While gene therapy has long been pursued by scientists, a proper carrier for the implanted gene has remained elusive. Researchers from Stanford University and the University of Michigan announced a new host candidate—muscle cells. They implanted muscle cells loaded up with the human-growth-hormone gene into the muscles of mice. The genes became active and pumped the hormone out into the bloodstream. Other cell systems had not worked well—the cells died, for example, or lost their blood supply. The scientists were hopeful that this system would work because muscle cells fuse with one another and the fusion may aid in their persistence.

A gene for amyotrophic lateral sclerosis (ALS) was assigned to chromosome 21 in a team effort by U.S., Australian, Belgian, and Canadian researchers. About 5–10% of the cases of the invariably fatal disease are believed to be genetic; the international group of scientists was able to pool results from enough ALS families to determine the approximate location of the faulty gene. By early 1992 the scientists knew the general location of the gene but not its exact address on the chromosome. Once they have pinpointed the gene's location, they can explore ways of treating the disease.

Scientists from France, Switzerland, Norway, Denmark, Australia, and the U.S. identified the gene that causes Fragile-X syndrome, a form of mental retardation caused by a weak spot on the X chromosome. Fragile X was first recognized as a cause of retardation in 1980. Researchers soon realized that it was the major cause of inherited retardation, afflicting one of every 1,000 to 1,500 male infants and one of every 2,000 to 2,500 female infants. With identification of the gene came a test that can be used on fetuses and children. The syndrome ranges in symptoms from an inability to do mathematics to full mental retardation. The new test can determine not only the presence of the weak gene but also, depending on how it is weakened, the degree of retardation.

Heart disease. A discovery by University of Washington scientists could lead to a way to improve coronary angioplasty, a procedure in which a tiny balloon is inflated within severely narrowed coronary arteries to push the inner walls of the artery out and let blood flow through. About 40% of the arteries close up again within months of angioplasty, at least partly because muscle cells within the walls of the artery grow, pushing the artery wall into the space where blood normally flows. The Washington researchers discovered in studies on mice that they could prevent the arteries from reblocking by injecting antibodies that block the activity of a growth factor normally promoting growth of the muscle cells.

When heart attacks occur, they are usually caused by a blood clot lodging in a clogged artery that feeds the heart muscle. During the year several U.S. drug companies were working on monoclonal antibodies that keep platelets from clumping together into a new blood clot following an initial heart attack, and preliminary tests on humans yielded promising results.

Scientists from Brigham and Women's Hospital in Boston had some bad news for short people—in a study of tens of thousands of physicians, those under 1.7 m (5 ft 7 in) were 60% more likely to have a heart attack than were people 1.85 m (6 ft 1 in) or more. Researchers from the same hospital also studied estrogen use in women past the age of menopause; the ability of estrogens to cut heart attack risk in postmenopausal women has been debated for years. Their 10-year study of nearly 50,000 U.S. women suggested that taking estrogen cuts a woman's heart attack risk in half.

Hormones. Men's ability to think may be related to the season of the year. A psychologist at the University of Western Ontario, who caused a stir previously when she linked the stage of women's menstrual cycles with their ability to think, announced a similar relationship for men. However, rather than a monthly cycle, she found that men's cycles are seasonal. Their ability to solve spatial relationship problems, the researcher found, was subtly better in spring than in fall. The link parallels low testosterone levels—spatial relationship ability was higher in the spring when testosterone levels were low.

University of Maryland researchers linked a hormone, ouabain, to blood pressure, finding that the greater the level of ouabain, the higher the blood pressure. They also found that it is secreted by the adrenal gland.

Tufts University (Boston, Mass.) researchers discovered that bacteria co-opt immune system hormones in the body when they invade. They found that disease-causing strains of *Escherichia coli,* a usually benign class of bacteria found in the gut, grab onto the immune system stimulator interleukin 1 and begin dividing. Researchers from Sherbrooke (Que.) University and University Hospitals of Cleveland, Ohio, had previously described immune system stimulators that promote the growth of foreign organisms, but this was so surprising to scientists that few believed it.

Senses. While it was once thought that ultrahigh-pitched sounds were for dogs, not humans, Medical College of Virginia researchers discovered that humans—including deaf humans—can discern ultrasonic speech when it is delivered through the bones of the skull. Their hope is to use the discovery to design a patch to be placed on the skin over bones near the ear, changing normal sound to ultrasound that can be deciphered by the wearer.

Columbia University scientists may have drawn one step closer to an understanding of the molecular biology of smell. They identified a family of genes that evidently produce specific proteins that sit on the surfaces of cells high up in the nasal cavity. These proteins recognize and bind to odorant molecules, cuing the brain to the smell. (*See* Feature Article: THE BIOLOGY AND CULTURE OF HUMAN ODOR.)

In a study, babies demonstrated a pronounced liking for garlic. Researchers from the Monell Chemical Senses Center, Philadelphia, found that nursing babies drank more of their mothers' milk after the mothers had ingested garlic. The same researchers also found that babies drank less after their mothers had ingested alcohol.

Harvard University researchers announced that dyslexia, a condition that affects a person's reading ability but not intellect, is related more to the sense of vision than to language ability. Dyslexics, they said, basically see more slowly.

Smoking. A Boston University study linked smoking with impotence-causing narrowing of the arteries. They found more damage in the penile arteries among a group of 195 impotent men than they had expected. They estimated that men who had smoked a pack of cigarettes a day for five years were 15% more likely to have artery damage than were nonsmokers, and those who had smoked a pack a day for 20 years were 72% more likely to suffer damage.

Researchers from the Medical College of Virginia linked smoking to incontinence in women. They compared smoking habits among 606 women, 322 of whom were incontinent, and found that 35% of the incontinent women smoked. Whereas 68% of the continent women had no history of smoking, only 49% of the incontinent women did.

Treatments. Every year, researchers experiment with therapies. The following are some of the experiments during the past year that offered promising results. In most cases more work needs to be done before these therapies can come into common practice.

A National Cancer Institute study showed that a six-month regimen of chemotherapy and radiation, rather than just radiation alone, was the best after-surgery treatment for colon cancer patients whose disease had spread outside the rectum but not beyond nearby lymph nodes. The combination cut the cancer death rate by 36%.

Researchers from the U.S., Sweden, Denmark, and Switzerland announced that gamma interferon, an immune system stimulator, helps people with a rare immune system condition called chronic granulomatous disease resist the infections that often kill them. In tests on 128 children, half as many of those on the drug were affected with life-threatening infections as were those on placebo.

In a trial at the University of Florence, capsaicin, the active chemical in hot peppers, cut the incidence of cluster headaches. The chemical was squirted in the noses of volunteers with cluster headaches, which cause intense pain around the eye.

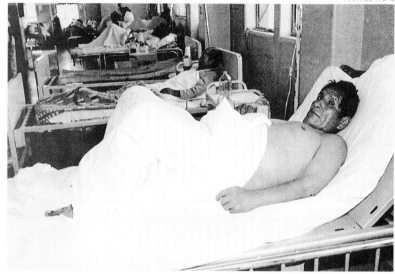

Victims of cholera lie in a hospital in Lima, Peru. An epidemic of the disease spread throughout Peru and neighboring countries, in part because Peru reduced the chlorination of its water on the grounds that chlorine posed a cancer risk.

Aspirin continued to win praise, during the past year for cutting the risk of pregnancy-induced hypertension. Researchers from Case Western Reserve University, Cleveland, Ohio, combined the results of several small studies and concluded that daily doses of aspirin smaller than in conventional tablets could cut the risk of pregnancy-induced hypertension by 65%.

A Mexican surgeon from the Instituto Mexicano del Seguro Social transplanted fetal brain tissue into the brain of a woman with Huntington's disease, a fatal neurological disease with no known treatment. Some of her symptoms subsequently became less severe. The same surgeon had previously used fetal tissue transplants in people with Parkinson's disease. The use of fetal tissue in experimental therapy remained highly controversial.

Tropical diseases. Chagas disease, widespread in South America but previously rare in the U.S., began appearing there during the past year. The disease is carried by a parasite transmitted by the reduviid insect. When the bug bites someone, the parasite gets into the bloodstream and can travel to the heart, where it damages the muscle, sometimes fatally.

Peru was struck by a cholera epidemic, at least partly because it had stopped chlorinating the drinking-water supply. *Nature* magazine reported that because a U.S. Environmental Protection Agency analysis had shown that chlorine poses a small, but real, risk of cancer, Peru began holding back on chlorine use in the 1980s. That allowed the cholera-causing bacteria to thrive. More than 300,000 new cases of cholera were reported in Peru and the nearby countries in South America to which it had

The New World screwworm fly (above) lays eggs in livestock through open wounds (right), and the subsequent larvae often kill the animals. By sterilizing male flies and releasing them to mate with fertile females, the UN Food and Agriculture Organization eradicated the pest from Libya.

spread. Africa also suffered a renewal of its cholera epidemic, and the disease appeared to be more deadly there.

An insect from the Americas that had hitchhiked to Libya was eradicated from that African nation. The New World screwworm infiltrated Libya in 1988 aboard South American sheep. The adult fly lays eggs on open wounds, and the subsequent larvae eat their way into the animal and can kill it in a few days. The eradication was accomplished by the United Nation's Food and Agriculture Organization, using a technique developed years ago by U.S. scientists in which sterilized male screwworm flies are released to mate with fertile females, thus breaking the life cycle.

—Joanne Silberner

Dentistry

Dentistry joined the growing avalanche of opposition to smoking during 1991 by supporting a coalition of 75 organizations urging the U.S. Senate to pass tobacco education legislation. The proposed Tobacco Product Education and Health Protection Act was expected to become law in 1992. It was intended to prevent children from smoking, inform Americans more effectively about the dangers of tobacco use, and strengthen requirements on additives and labeling for tobacco products. The American Dental Association (ADA) in a letter to each Senate member said that the "Association has maintained official policy in opposition to the use of tobacco products for over 20 years. The use of tobacco has been linked to oral cancer, leukoplakia and periodontal (gum) disease. Each year, 30,000 people die from oral cancer, which accounts for 5% of all cancer deaths."

Child abuse was on the rise in the U.S., and dentists could be the first health care professionals to suspect and report such cases to the authorities, according to University of Michigan dental researchers. Untreated rampant cavities and untreated pain, infection, bleeding, or trauma affecting facial regions could indicate dental neglect or worse, Paul J. Loos told the ADA annual session. The American Academy of Pediatric Dentistry defined dental neglect as the willful failure by a parent or guardian to seek dental treatment for a child.

Gum disease. New high-tech methods for diagnosing periodontitis (advanced gum disease) were expected to improve the treatment of this prevalent dental disorder. The ADA estimated that 75% of all adults over the age of 35 would suffer from some form of gum disease during their life. Gum disease, not tooth decay, is a major cause of tooth loss. Roy C. Page of the University of Washington in Seattle listed new diagnostic approaches, including microbiological assessment, biochemical analysis,

and physical measurements. Traditional diagnosis methods include measuring the depth of periodontal pockets and taking conventional X-rays, which indicate only past and not current disease status. (Periodontal pockets are infected pockets that form below the gum line between the teeth and gums when the gums begin to recede.)

Page pointed to new methods of biochemical analysis of enzymes in the fluid of diseased gum tissues. "There is a good association between the presence of these enzymes—including interleukin-1 and prostaglandin E2—and active disease state in the bone that supports the teeth," he explained. "Other enzymes, such as collagenase, are now known to destroy the connective gum tissue. Testing for the presence of still other enzymes, which are released at the time of cell death, also indicate gum disease."

These new diagnostic techniques were also being used in combination with other high-tech tools, such as color-coded digital radiography (a new type of computerized X-ray). Two of these special X-rays would be taken at separate patient visits and then compared with one another. Any difference, even as little as 0.1 mm (1 mm = 0.04 in) of bone change around teeth and dental implants, could be detected, enabling the dentist to identify progressive periodontal disease with over 90% accuracy. Changes were far more difficult to detect with conventional X-ray diagnosis. Another computerized method was electronic probing, which could detect less than 0.4 mm of soft tissue attachment loss and thus reveal the earliest stages of periodontal disease.

A new high-tech option in the treatment of gum disease was the guided regeneration of existing tissues as well as bone replacement, according to Marvin Sugarman in Atlanta, Ga. By means of guided tissue regeneration, periodontal ligament could be reattached to the root surface of the tooth. In some cases, synthetic teflon fibers were placed between the connective tissue and the root surface, thus allowing for the regeneration of ligament and cementum (the soft tissue layer on the surface of teeth roots). In other cases, periodontal disease had caused significant bone loss in the jaw, thus weakening the support for the teeth. Successful treatment could require bone regeneration. This included three options: replacement of lost bone with other bone from the patient (usually from the hip), replacement of lost bone from a cadaver (freeze-dried bone), and bone substitution with synthetic products or a combination of the options, Sugarman said.

A synthetic membrane developed by University of Florida dental researchers could assist in the treatment of periodontal disease. Resembling a thin sheet of opaque white plastic, the membrane was wrapped around the tooth's root to prevent the root from coming into contact with bone and gum tissue

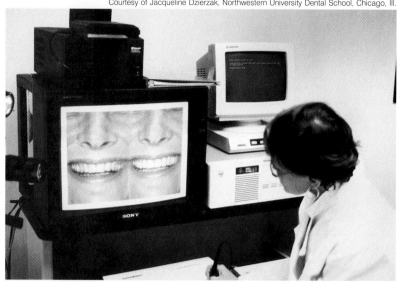

Computer imaging is being used in dentistry to demonstrate to patients the benefits and drawbacks of treatment before it begins.

during healing. Ingvar Magnusson at the University of Florida College of Dentistry explained that the membrane could encourage tissue growth by preventing bone and gum cells from invading the root area. Cells from surrounding tissue, such as the periodontal ligament that runs along the root's side, then would have a chance to repopulate the area and weave connective support tissue as part of the guided tissue-regeneration process.

Swimming pools and tooth enamel. Some swimming pools may be healthier for tooth enamel than others, reported the Academy of General Dentistry. To assess the effects of pH levels on tooth enamel, researchers at the Hebrew University of Jerusalem dunked packets of powdered tooth enamel and sections of human teeth into 14 swimming pools of various pH levels for at least one hour. They found that erosion of tooth enamel is somewhat higher in swimming pools with a pH level lower than 5. Though the effects were not considered significant for occasional swimmers, frequent swimmers would be at some risk.

The pH level shows how acidic or alkaline the water is in a swimming pool. The lower the pH levels, the more acidic the water and thus the greater the erosion of tooth enamel. To safeguard swimmers' health and tooth enamel, a pool pH level of 7 or 8, with the free residual chlorine ranging between 0.4 and 0.7 parts per million, was generally recommended by health authorities. Backyard swimmers could purchase pool-testing kits to check swimming pool water.

Fluoridation and osteosarcoma. A new study found no link between drinking fluoridated water at recommended levels and the formation of malignant bone tumors, a condition known as osteosarcoma. In fact, researchers from three dental schools who conducted the study concluded that fluoridated water may actually provide protection against the disease.

The study matched 22 osteosarcoma patients with people without cancer by age, gender, and county of residence at the time of diagnosis. The three different analytic methods used by the researchers prompted them to conclude that there was no link between fluoridated water and osteosarcoma. Because all three methods showed an odds ratio of less than one, the researchers hypothesized "that fluoridation at recommended levels may provide a protective effect against the formation of osteosarcoma." The researchers planned to test their hypothesis through a nationwide, multicenter analytic study.

Amalgam fillings. While the safety of amalgam tooth fillings was heatedly debated at a meeting in Düsseldorf, Germany, a U.S. National Institutes of Health panel reaffirmed the effectiveness and safety of such fillings. The panel chairman, William D. McHugh, said, "There is no reason for anyone staying away from the dentist and no reason for anyone to avoid having an amalgam filling if the dentist recommends it." McHugh, director of the Eastman Dental Center at the University of Rochester, N.Y., noted that he had recently received two amalgam fillings.

The 14-member panel, while recognizing that virtually all restorative materials had some components with potential health risks, emphasized the safety of amalgam fillings. "Available data do not justify discontinuing the use of any currently available dental restorative materials or recommending their replacement," the panel stated.

Tooth wear. Using a powerful scanning electron microscope, an anatomist apparently discovered how to measure directly the daily or weekly rates of tooth wear. Mark Teaford of Johns Hopkins University, Baltimore, Md., said that it represented "a real breakthrough" that would generate dental research in such areas as age-related changes of teeth, the effects of orthodontics, and tooth attrition linked to diets.

The loss of enamel on molars each year rarely exceeds 50 micrometers (millionths of a meter) in most human groups, largely because modern foods contain few abrasive components. However, changes in the number of microscopic marks dug into human tooth enamel while chewing showed weekly rates of wear at specific locations on teeth. In the Johns Hopkins study, two sets of epoxy casts were made from putty impressions of the lower first and second molars of nine healthy adults, with the second set made no more than seven days after the first. Each volunteer recorded all food eaten between the two sessions. Teaford then placed the epoxy casts under a scanning electron microscope and took pictures of tiny scratches and pits that had been etched into teeth during the study period. Some images focused on the chewing surface nearer the cheek, used in shearing and crushing; others centered on the grinding area nearer the tongue. The number of marks from each tooth region on both sets of casts showed the proportion of new microscopic "wear features" for each volunteer.

The ability to record daily or weekly tooth wear could have many applications, according to Teaford. For example, orthodontists could monitor the changes in tooth use as a result of their procedures, rather than relying on such indirect measures as impressions of bite patterns. The technique might also provide a yardstick for tooth grinding, as well as help dentists assess the benefits of mouthguards worn by people who clench their teeth.

Smoking. Researchers from the University of Minnesota announced that smokers were five times more likely than nonsmokers to have periodontal disease, thus confirming the long-held assumption of a link between smoking and gum disease. The study, which involved 800 healthy adults aged 28–75, showed that smokers were five times more likely than their nonsmoking counterparts to have an average periodontal pocket depth of four millimeters or more.

—Lou Joseph

Veterinary medicine

The establishment in 1791 of what is now called the Royal Veterinary College, London, not only marked the introduction of the first veterinary school into the English-speaking world, it also marked the introduction of the "veterinary art" into the United Kingdom. The first veterinary class began with four students. Britain celebrated this bicentenary in 1991 with a yearlong series of special events that in-

cluded a commemorative ceremony. Princess Anne presided over the commemorative ceremony, which was highlighted by her conferral of the degree doctor of veterinary medicine, *honoris causa*, on Queen Elizabeth, the Queen Mother.

Texas A&M University's College of Veterinary Medicine celebrated its 75th anniversary in 1991 and also announced the establishment of a center for greyhound medicine. More than 40 veterinarians and scientists representing a wide array of disciplines were to participate in the activities of the center with the goal of promoting, developing, and improving specialized medical care for racing greyhounds. To better address the medical and other special needs of all canine athletes, the American Canine Sports Medicine Association was established. The association planned to develop guidelines for safe participation of dogs in sporting events.

The potential for progress in reducing genetic problems in dogs took a major step forward with the establishment of a canine genetics research team consisting of veterinarians and physicians from the University of Michigan and Michigan State University. The team planned to apply new technology currently being used for the identification of human genetic problems to the detection of genetic diseases in dogs. This technology was expected to enable the development of a canine genetics resource library of special probes or markers that would be made available for use in canine genetic research and for the clinical detection of genetic abnormalities.

Avian medicine. The 1991 meeting of the Association of Avian Veterinarians was attended by more than 1,000 veterinarians from about 20 countries. The increase in attendance at the meeting reflected the growth in involvement of veterinary practices with the care of nondomestic or companion species of birds. The association also supported a grant program to promote research on clinical problems of exotic and wild birds. A petition was filed with the American Veterinary Medical Association to establish a specialty board in avian medicine.

The improved health management of pet birds greatly increased the longevity of these animals, which encouraged efforts to gain understanding of the special needs of older birds. In budgerigars, for example, gout is a common problem but is responsive to therapy initiated early in the course of the disease. In cockatiels diabetes is fairly common. Beak problems require special attention, with hereditary or congenital deformities now being corrected with the aid of prosthetic devices. Lead toxicity emerged as a significant problem in pet birds allowed to roam freely in the household. Some birds, particularly cockatiels and Amazon parrots, appear to be attracted to items containing lead, such as lead weights in curtain hems and lead solder in stained-glass art.

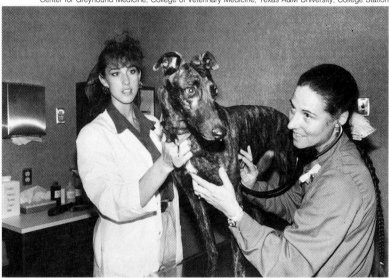

A greyhound is examined at Texas A&M University's newly established center for greyhound medicine. The center sought to promote, develop, and improve medical care for these racing dogs.

Aquatic medicine. Another emerging specialty in which veterinarians were playing a key role was in the medical component of aquaculture. Aquaculture is the raising, under controlled conditions, of freshwater and seawater food fish and ornamental or pet fish. The treatment of diseases in food fish is a major challenge, as the approved drugs include only two antibiotics, one anesthetic, and a few disinfectants in addition to two vaccines. This situation emphasizes the need for research to develop more medicines. With the increasing demand for seafoods and a static or declining natural supply, seafood production can be increased only by means of aquaculture.

Asia and Europe continued to make progress in the production of farmed seafoods. Five veterinarians in Britain were employed full time in the salmon-farming industry, which grew dramatically in Scotland and Ireland during the 1980s. The level of production of meat from farmed fish in the U.K. was approaching that produced from farmed mammals and birds. The establishment of the Society of Aquatic Veterinary Medicine and the International Association for Aquatic Animal Medicine and, recently, in the U.K., the establishment of the Fish Veterinary Society indicated the growing interest and involvement of veterinarians in this field.

Transfusion medicine. The recently formed Association of Veterinary Transfusion Medicine reflected the rapid growth of this new field of veterinary medicine. Improved understanding of the multiple blood types in dogs and cats enhanced transfusion efficacy and safety, particularly when repeated transfusions were needed. Transfusion of a very small quantity of incompatible blood can cause a serious, potentially lethal, reaction. In the absence of such reactions, it is possible that the survival of the infused, incompatible cells will be dramatically shortened,

which results in loss of therapeutic benefit of the transfusion. This situation further emphasized the need for understanding of blood typing in animals.

The importance of blood and blood components in the treatment of animals that are traumatized or anemic or that have a blood disease led to the establishment of animal-blood banks. The largest of these was a nonprofit, full-service blood bank called Hemopet in Irvine, Calif. In addition to whole blood, Hemopet can provide packed red blood cells and fresh-frozen plasma to southern California veterinarians. The founder of Hemopet, W. Jean Dodds, hoped to develop a national blood bank program similar to that provided for humans by the American Red Cross and one that would include safety regulations for animal bloods.

Using a grant from the Bernice Barbour Foundation, the University of Pennsylvania School of Veterinary Medicine purchased, equipped, and staffed a bloodmobile. The vehicle traveled to large breeding kennels and to blood drives organized by kennel clubs. In this way the bloodmobile was helping to alleviate the University of Pennsylvania Veterinary Hospital's frequent need for blood for patient treatment.

The Virginia-Maryland Regional College of Veterinary Medicine, in cooperation with the Virginia Veterinary Medical Association, established a companion-animal blood bank. Initially this blood bank planned to collect only canine blood, but later it was expected to include cat and horse bloods. The blood bank, located at the college, could provide whole blood or blood products such as platelet-rich plasma to veterinary hospitals in its region within 24 hours.

Veterinary researchers at Colorado State University's Feline Bone Marrow Transplant Laboratory performed the laboratory's 100th bone marrow transplantation (replacement). The procedure proved to be of value in treating diseases associated with the feline leukemia virus (FeLV) and feline immuno-deficiency virus (FIV). Both diseases are fatal if untreated.

These viruses, although not infective to people, have similarities to the human HIV virus, which causes AIDS. Destroying a cat's virus-infected marrow cells by radiation is beneficial only if transplanted marrow successfully repopulates the cat with new uninfected blood and immune cells. Efforts were being directed toward refining this procedure so that it could be performed by private practitioners and be more readily available. Infection of a cat with FeLV or FIV may precipitate the onset of feline infectious peritonitis (FIP) because the virus causing the latter disease can be present in a latent state in the absence of stress. As the result of 12 years of research and safety and efficacy studies, the first vaccine to aid in the prevention of FIP was approved for inclusion in the veterinarian's armamentarium for prevention of feline diseases.

Veterinarians in the Persian Gulf war. Veterinary services were utilized by the U.S. Army, Navy, Air Force, and Marine Corps in Operations Desert Shield and Desert Storm. About 50 Veterinary Corps officers, including 37 reservists, were assigned to the Gulf region. About 127 veterinary reservists were involved in food inspection in the U.S. for foods to be shipped in the form of rations to the Gulf.

Veterinary services included food inspection, food safety, and food sanitation; care for military working dogs; and care for native animals such as camels and for zoo animals affected by the conflict. About 95% of the veterinary effort was directed at ensuring a safe supply of food for U.S. military personnel as well as for as many as two million prisoners of war near the end of the conflict. The desert environment, with temperatures of 50°–65° C (120°–150° F), greatly enhanced the rate of food spoilage and made monitoring the processing of foods in the region especially important, particularly when the foods were produced there.

Following the war the American Association of Equine Practitioners (AAEP) responded to a request from one of its members, a U.S. Army veterinarian stationed in Kuwait, for veterinary supplies to treat horses there that were suffering from malnutrition and neglect. With the help of veterinary supply companies, the AAEP was able to provide medicines and surgical support materials. The European Avian Veterinarians association helped recruit a team of wildlife biologists that included one veterinarian to coordinate the rescue and rehabilitation of wildlife, especially birds, adversely affected by the Persian Gulf oil spill. About one-third of the oil-soaked birds taken to the Wildlife Rescue Center in Jubail, Saudi Arabia, were saved.

—John M. Bowen

Optical engineering

During early 1991 optical engineering frequently appeared in newspaper headlines as a result of successes in the Gulf war. Electro-optical systems made the news as a result of their stunning capability to guide missiles and bombs to precise locations during the brief conflict. Decades of development of "smart" electro-optically guided weapons appeared to pay off

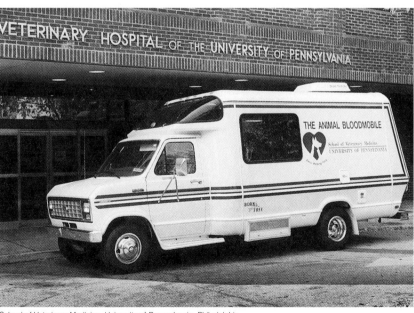

An animal bloodmobile is operated by the University of Pennsylvania School of Veterinary Medicine. Staff from the school take it to blood drives at kennels, where they collect blood that could help save the lives of critically ill dogs.

School of Veterinary Medicine, University of Pennsylvania, Philadelphia as surgically precise destruction of targets in Iraq was carried out. Video replays on the evening news showed optically guided bombs entering buildings through windows with amazing reliability, ensuring that the warheads were delivered with maximum and local effectiveness. In some cases the first of a pair of bombs was guided to a specific location on the side of a building, and a second bomb entered the building through the hole blasted by the first bomb. Infrared and visible detectors acquired the target, correlated the appearance of the target with stored information on the desired location, and placed the warhead precisely on a given position. The Gulf war was the first to demonstrate the importance of optical methods in weaponry.

Less dramatic but equally important were the thousands of night-vision devices used to provide security during the nighttime hours. The ability of troops to continue to advance during night hours by the use of night-vision and infrared viewers permitted a rapid advance into and through Iraq and Kuwait. The accuracy of land-based munitions was further enhanced by the use of laser range finders, with the targeting capabilities expanded by infrared viewers.

Despite this high degree of success, the growth pattern in the defense-oriented optical industry did not survive the economic realities of the reduction in defense spending that followed the breakup of the Soviet Union. A major portion of the optical industry did not escape the reductions in procurement of defense materials and subsequent layoffs that pervaded other high-technology areas. The industry continued to seek new markets for optical products in the commercial sector as international competition became stronger. The commercial sector of the industry, especially smaller optical companies, seemed as busy as ever in early 1992.

The various Strategic Defense Initiative projects that had counted on the use of directed laser energy as a weapon were effectively ended as it became evident that many of the problems associated with the handling of high-intensity laser beams could not be solved easily and economically. The Free Electron Laser program demonstration was reduced in magnitude to a few demonstrations of high-energy oscillators, and the beam-direction part of the program was terminated. The proposed number of orbiting optical detection and warning systems was reduced, primarily for economic reasons. The heavily publicized "Brilliant Pebbles" concept of a multitude of independent space infrared detectors and interceptors was dropped but lived on to a reduced extent as a "Brilliant Eyes" missile-launch-detection system.

On the nonmilitary front considerable progress was made in specialized areas. Applications of lasers as tools in manufacturing, including the sophisti-

cated production of electronic devices, continued to widen. The power available from diode lasers (compact coherent light sources based directly on semiconductor chips) increased, but the market for most other types of lasers appeared to become saturated. The ability to mass-produce lenses directly from the glass melt without grinding and polishing appeared to have reached maturity for some products. Medical applications expanded, with new types of lasers becoming important.

Continuing the development of primary mirrors for new large ground-based telescopes, Schott Glassworks of Germany cast the world's first two 8.6-m (28.2-ft)-diameter mirror blanks. These blanks were to be finished for use in the European Southern Observatory's telescope array project, which comprised four telescopes with apertures of 8 m (26.2 ft) working together as a coherent imaging array. Japanese astronomers announced plans to build a single telescope that would be eight meters in diameter and also placed an order with Corning Glass Works for a low-expansion glass blank.

The Keck I telescope, using a segmented 10-m (32.8-ft) primary mirror, came closer to full operation during the past year with a demonstration of images using a portion of the segments that would eventually populate the aperture of the telescope. Construction of a second, twin, Keck II telescope was begun. These two telescopes were to work together as a coherent array.

The most outstanding demonstration of the viability of ground-based astronomy was the revelation of

The Keck I telescope on Mauna Kea in Hawaii was completed in April 1992. With a segmented primary mirror measuring 10 meters (32.8 feet) in diameter, the telescope was designed to see to the edge of the visible universe.

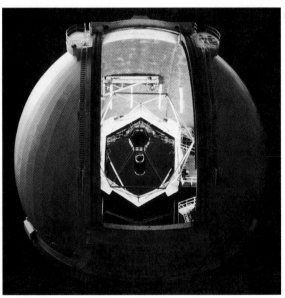

a technique that corrected the effects of blurring by atmospheric turbulence. Carried out by the U.S. Air Force's Phillips Laboratory, the work was originally intended to permit the correction of high-energy laser beams projected through the atmosphere, but as the need for such systems decreased after the reduction of the Soviet threat, the work was declassified and reported in the open literature. In the experiment the laboratory projected a laser beam up into the atmosphere. Scattering of the laser light at the upper levels of the atmosphere served as an artificial star source that was observed by detectors on the telescope. These detectors analyzed the time-dependent scattering of the light from the artificial star that was caused by the constantly changing turbulence in the atmosphere. The spreading of light from the artificial source was corrected by the use of an adaptive optical component—a flexible mirror with many actuators—which compensated for the blurring. The result was to smooth out the errors in the atmosphere such that astronomical objects that are viewed through the same portion of the atmosphere would be compensated by reflection from the flexible mirror and thus could be imaged without distortion.

The Hubble Space Telescope continued to send back blurred images because of the spherical aberration caused by its flawed primary mirror, but the ability to remove the blurring effects by computer processing of the images restored the instrument to almost full capability. The spectrographic instruments on the Hubble were less affected by the spherical aberration and produced significant useful information. The U.S. National Aeronautics and Space Administration instituted programs to replace some key components on a shuttle flight in late 1993 or 1994.

The development of visible and diode lasers continued. Visible red diode lasers with powers of 10–20 mw became generally available. A common product during the past year was the diode laser lecture pointer, which was about the size of a ballpoint pen. Short-wavelength blue-green compact lasers became important for future applications involving storage of optical data, and several devices using frequency doubling (in which the output wavelength is half the input wavelength) of diodes in nonlinear optical crystals, including an announcement of doubling in an organic crystal, were made available. During the year the 3M Corp. announced the experimental pulsed operation of a zinc selenide diode laser that has an intrinsic output (light emitted directly by the semiconductor laser) of a blue-green wavelength.

The Holmium laser, the output of which is at a wavelength that does not deeply penetrate human tissues, became important as a new surgical

The Photo-CD, developed by Eastman Kodak, provides digital storage of photographic negatives. The disc can also be used as a permanent method of ordering additional copies of prints.

laser. The use of near-ultraviolet-wavelength excimer lasers (gas lasers in which high-energy molecular transitions take place) in medicine continued, but the intended mass application for corneal sculpturing for vision correction did not win approval of the U.S. Food and Drug Administration, and the procedure remained an experimental one, although it was available in some other countries.

Optical computing and communications did not show significant change during the past year, although some interesting new components that would have applications in the future were demonstrated. Actual progress included the coupling of arrays of parallel electronic digital computers using optical links. The all-optical digital computer appeared to be no closer to reality.

Electro-optics for the mass market continued to be centered on the ever present video camera. Electronic cameras to replace the 35-mm camera did not make many inroads. However, Eastman Kodak announced a product called a Photo-CD, which would provide a digital electronic method of storing the negatives that normally would be provided by the photo processor. Such a compact disc would be provided to the consumer, who could update the disc with photographic-quality storage of many rolls of film and use the disc as a permanent method of ordering additional copies of prints. Industry observers expected that this Photo-CD eventually would be used with personal computers and television systems for image editing and printing in the home.

—Robert R. Shannon

Physics

During the past year physicists succeeded in their long efforts to make blue-green laser diodes, reported surprising behavior in observations of fast-spinning atomic nuclei, and sought ways to fill a growing need for dedicated supercomputers in theoretical high-energy physics. Researchers also improved their understanding of sonoluminescence, the emission of light from ultrasonically created bubbles in liquid.

General developments

Advances in understanding the interaction of matter and energy on the microscopic and atomic scales featured prominently in physics research during the past year. Scientists studied the focusing of energy in bubbles ultrasonically stimulated into violent oscillation, carried out interference experiments using beams of whole atoms rather than of light or subatomic particles, and manipulated the ability of matter to preferentially pass or inhibit electromagnetic radiation at certain wavelengths.

Sonoluminescence. For many years ultrasonic sound waves have been used in liquids to excite the rapid formation and oscillation of bubbles, a process called acoustic cavitation, sometimes for the purpose of inducing chemical reactions and sometimes for the purpose of cleansing surfaces. In some cases the expansion and collapse of the bubbles are so violent that light is produced. In the past this phenomenon, known as sonoluminescence, had been difficult to study since the light emission is transient.

Recently experimenters at a number of laboratories have been able to control sonoluminescence well enough to conduct observations and measurements. Bradley P. Barber and Seth J. Putterman of the University of California at Los Angeles, for example, studied the sonic behavior of bubbles in pure water. They discovered that sound waves having a frequency of 20 kilohertz (20,000 cycles per second) could reliably cause a single bubble to expand (to a size of about 100 micrometers [μm], or 100 millionths of a meter) and then collapse (to a size of only a few micrometers) in synchrony with the sound wave. The collapse of the bubble succeeds in concentrating a lot of energy into just a few atoms or molecules inside the bubble, which then radiate a short pulse of light lasting only 50 picoseconds (trillionths of a second) or less, far shorter than expected from previous studies. The pulses may well be shorter than this; the best photomultiplier tubes available could not catch the rise and fall of the light pulse. The spectrum of the emitted light extends into the ultraviolet, with wavelengths as short as 250 nanometers (nm; billionths of a meter). The visible light is so intense that the radiating bubble can be seen with the unaided eye. The clocklike nature of the emission is also remarkable; the jitter in the interval of time between pulses is less than 50 picoseconds.

Putterman concluded that this conversion of sound energy into light energy represents a focusing factor of at least 100 billion. The reason for the enormous concentration of energy is still not well understood, but the short pulse duration may involve some laserlike correlation of radiation among the atoms in the bubble.

Kenneth Suslick and his colleagues at the University of Illinois at Urbana-Champaign have studied sonoluminescence from transient (nonstable) cavitation. They measured the temperature of the bubble during cavitation and found it to be at least 5,000 K (8,540° F), as hot as the surface of the Sun and hot enough to trigger interesting reactions—in effect, a sort of "sonochemistry." For example, the Illinois researchers formed amorphous (noncrystalline) iron by sending ultrasound waves into a solution of iron pentacarbonyl, $Fe(CO)_5$. In the bubble-collapse phase of the process, the high pressures and temperatures

Amorphous (noncrystalline) iron produced from the irradiation of iron pentacarbonyl with ultrasonic waves is shown in a high-resolution scanning electron micrograph made by Kenneth S. Suslick and Mark W. Grinstaff of the University of Illinois at Urbana-Champaign.

Micrograph by Kenneth S. Suslick and Mark W. Grinstaff in the Center for Microanalysis of Materials, University of Illinois at Urbana–Champaign

liberated the iron atoms from the CO groups. In the bubble-expansion phase, the consequent cooling was so rapid (as fast as 10 million kelvins per second) that it froze the iron into an amorphous powder before it had a chance to crystallize. The amorphous iron turned out to be purer than amorphous metals (so-called metallic glasses) made by other processes. It may prove to be valuable as a catalyst (because of its large surface area) or as a practical material for magnetic storage of data.

Atom interferometry. In 1802 the British physicist Thomas Young demonstrated that light behaves as if it were a wave phenomenon. In Young's device, the first interferometer, a collimated beam of light was directed at a screen in which two narrow slits had been cut. The slits served to divide the light, which can be considered to be a succession of wave fronts, into two beams. Beyond the screen the waves coming through the slits interfered with each other, sometimes in a constructive manner (crest adding to crest) and sometimes in a destructive manner (crest canceling through). When the light coming through the slits was projected on a second screen, the resultant interference pattern showed as a series of bright and dark fringes.

Almost 200 years later scientists are still doing interferometry, not only with light waves but also with particles. Quantum mechanics holds that particles can be thought of as waves and that in certain experimental situations, such as in interferometers, the wavelike attributes can be quite important. In neutron interferometry, for example, a beam of neutrons from an external source (such as a nuclear reactor) can be sent into a crystal. The neutrons typically have an associated quantum wavelength (called the de Broglie wavelength) of a few angstroms, comparable to the spacing of the atoms in the crystal lattice. (An angstrom, abbreviated Å, is a tenth of a nanometer, or a ten-billionth of a meter.) As the neutrons pass through the crystal, the neutron waves can diffract from the layers of atoms in the lattice and later interfere with each other, setting up a distinctive interference pattern (detected outside the sample) that provides information about the structure of the crystal. Because the wavelength of a matter particle is thousands of times shorter than that of a photon of light, the tolerances in the experimental setup for particle interferometry are much more exacting, but the potential precision of physical measurements is also much higher.

It is for this reason that scientists at several laboratories around the world have attempted to do interferometry with whole atoms, which are heavier still than neutrons and electrons. Jürgen Mlynek and Olivier Carnal of the University of Konstanz in Germany made what was perhaps the simplest atom interferometer, an atom version of Young's double-slit interferometer. Instead of light, the Konstanz scientists used helium atoms having de Broglie wavelengths of either 1.03 or 0.56 Å. These atom waves were sent through a pair of two-micrometer-thick slits set eight micrometers apart in a piece of gold foil and then recombined to form detectable interference patterns.

David E. Pritchard and his colleagues at the Massachusetts Institute of Technology (MIT) used not slits but gratings to first divide and then later recombine atom waves. They employed sodium atoms moving at a velocity of 1,000 meters/second; such atoms have a de Broglie wavelength of only 0.16 Å. The waves were split into separate beams by a grating having spacings of only 0.4 μm. The separated beams than moved on to a second grating where they were diffracted in just such a way as to bring the two beams back together at a third grating, where they recombined and formed an interference pattern, which was sampled by a detector. The precise alignment of this three-grating system was maintained throughout by sending a beam of laser light through the interferometer at the same time. Interferometers such as Pritchard's are extremely sensitive to rotation and acceleration, making them potentially useful for a number of applications, such as for use in guidance systems or for the study of general relativity.

This sensitivity to rotation is an integral part of an interferometer designed by a group of scientists, led by Jürgen Helmcke, from the Physicalische-Technische Bundesanhalt, Braunschweig, Germany, and the University of Paris-North. In their apparatus a beam of calcium atoms was split into four separate atom wave packets by a pair of laser beams. The separated waves were then deflected by another pair of laser beams moving in a direction opposite to the first pair. This reconverged the separated waves in two sets of two overlapping packets, creating interference patterns at two separate detectors. The phase shift, the fraction of a wavelength by which one packet is out of phase with the other packet, depends on the frequency of the laser light and on the rotation of the whole apparatus, which is mounted on a turntable for just that purpose. Like the MIT interferometer, the Braunschweig apparatus may provide an extremely sensitive detector of rotation, perhaps billions of times more sensitive than present light interferometers.

A fourth experiment, operated by Steven Chu and Mark Kasevich of Stanford University, began with sodium atoms contained in an atom trap, an apparatus that uses magnetic fields and laser beams to slow down and confine atoms. The atoms are then gently pushed upward out of the trap by a laser beam, forming what Chu called an "atomic fountain." The Stanford experiment, like the one at

Braunschweig, exploited the fact that atoms (unlike neutrons and electrons) have internal states, that at any moment the atom may exist as a superposition of these states, and that laser light can have different effects on the different states. Thus, in the Stanford setup the rising atoms were struck by a sequence of laser pulses that, first, split the atom waves into two packets (reaching spatial separations as great as 2.4 mm); second, brought them back together; and, finally, measured the interference pattern. The observed phase shift, among other things, can be used to calculate the effect of gravity on the falling sodium atoms to within 3 parts in 100 million. Chu expects to achieve 100 times this precision in the future.

Photonic semiconductors and insulators. A semiconductor for light waves, *i.e.*, a material in which certain photon wavelengths would be excluded—creating, in effect, a photon band gap analogous to the forbidden electron energy bands in semiconductors—was developed by scientists at Bell Communications Research (Bellcore), Red Bank, N.J. Eli Yablonovitch and his colleagues drilled three sets of holes into a slab of dielectric material, creating a crisscross, face-centered cubic structure whose unit cell is a rhombic dodecahedron. Theorists had predicted that such a geometry would result in the exclusion of electromagnetic radiation at certain wavelengths. Indeed, when the Bellcore scientists sent microwaves into one sample (which, because of the holes, was 78% empty), they discovered a forbidden gap, a range of wavelengths that could not pass through the material. (See *1992 Yearbook of Science and the Future* Year in Review: PHYSICS: *Condensed-matter physics*.)

Using beams of ions to etch fine holes, the researchers more recently extended their technique to infrared wavelength bands and expected to achieve the exclusion of visible light as well. They expressed their belief that these "photonic crystals" will be useful in a variety of research areas, such as atomic physics and microelectronics. The hope is that if the band of forbidden photonic energies overlapped with the band of allowed electronic band gap energies in the material, then the spontaneous recombination of electrons and holes (electron vacancies) would be forbidden; the photon arising from such a recombination would not be allowed to exist. According to Yablonovitch, such suppression would lead to much more efficient semiconductor lasers.

Photons can be prohibited in other ways. For years it has been known that the radiating properties of atoms or molecules can be influenced by the surrounding environment. For example, the spontaneous emission of light from molecules in a cavity can be inhibited if the cavity geometry is not suited to light at that wavelength. In recent experiments Nabil M. Lawandy and Jordi Martorell of Brown University, Providence R.I., were able to inhibit the radiation of laser-excited dye molecules distributed among colloidal suspensions of polystyrene spheres in water. The spheres are electrically charged and arrange themselves in a crystalline array. Provided that the mean separation of the spheres is less than the wavelength of the radiation from the dye molecules, the presence of the spheres influences the ability of the vacuum (space) surrounding the dye molecules to accept radiated photons. Like the Bellcore work, the Brown University research in inhibiting radiation at certain wavelengths may be useful in the design of electronic devices.

There are two sides to every coin, and if light can be inhibited in some materials, it can be encouraged to pass through others. Transparency in certain gases, for example, can be induced with lasers. Stephen E. Harris of Stanford University and his co-workers used an effect called population trapping to make strontium gas transparent to light that is normally absorbed. In this process, discussed by theorists for years but not until now applied to gases, the absorption of laser light at a certain frequency—corresponding to energy needed for atoms to make the transition from their low-energy ground state into a more energetic, excited state—is inhibited by means of interference from a second laser beam at a wavelength corresponding to a transition from an intermediate energy state to the upper excited state. Thus, strontium was made transparent to ultraviolet light at a wavelength of 337 μm by imposition of a second, green beam having a wavelength of 570 μm. Harris believed that the technique could be applied to materials other than gases.

—Phillip F. Schewe

High-energy physics

The past year in high-energy physics was marked by the patient accumulation of new data, mostly at the Large Electron-Positron (LEP) collider operating at CERN (European Laboratory for Particle Physics) near Geneva. All of the new information appears to be consistent with what has come to be known as the standard model, the theory of interacting subatomic particles devised in the 1970s. The standard model has several components, including the electroweak theory (unified theory of weak and electromagnetic interactions) of Sheldon Glashow, Abdus Salam, and Steven Weinberg and the theory of interacting quarks and gluons, which was the work of many physicists and which goes under the name of quantum chromodynamics (QCD). According to QCD, the hadrons—familiar particles that undergo strong interactions, such as the neutrons and protons found in atomic nuclei—are composites made out of particles called quarks held together by the exchange of yet other particles called gluons.

The electroweak theory and QCD are similar in their main details. In each one the particles of matter—the quarks and leptons (*e.g.*, electrons or muons), collectively known as fermions—emit and absorb other particles, known as gauge bosons, which can also interact among themselves. The form of the interaction between fermions and gauge bosons, and among gauge bosons, is determined by a principle known as local gauge invariance, and the theories governed by this principle have come to be known as gauge theories. Despite the similarities, an important difference exists between the electroweak theory and QCD, one that affects the ease with which useful information can be extracted from the results of experiments.

For the electroweak theory to describe the implications of the electroweak interactions, it is sufficient to use a mathematical approach called perturbation theory, which physicists have employed for many years. The method, which relies on finding successive, ever more accurate approximations to the answer by using rules for evaluating pictorial representations (Feynman diagrams) of the processes taking place, can be used for the electroweak interaction because the fundamental interaction, the emission of a gauge boson by a fermion, has a small probability of occurring; consequently, the successive approximations converge quickly to an answer.

For QCD the situation is more complex. That theory obeys a property known as asymptotic freedom, first recognized in the 1970s, according to which, at comparatively high particle energies, the probability of interaction is small enough to use perturbation theory. Therefore, the consequences of QCD for processes that occur at high energy are readily evaluated, and the predictions have been found in good agreement with experiment. When the energy of the particles is small, however, the probability of the fundamental QCD interaction becomes large, and perturbation theory is no longer appropriate.

This latter situation applies to some of the more interesting potential consequences of the theory, such as the ratios of the masses of hadrons. An especially important phenomenon that is expected to be a consequence of QCD is the confinement of quarks and gluons. Confinement refers to the fact that, whereas quarks and gluons are thought to be the fundamental constituents of hadrons, it has proved impossible experimentally to produce isolated examples of quarks and gluons. Instead, under the conditions now obtaining in the universe, quarks and gluons exist only in certain combinations and manifest themselves as the observed hadrons. Physicists firmly believe that confinement is no accident but rather a consequence of the strength of the QCD interaction at low energy. Nevertheless, it has not been possible to demonstrate confinement by using perturbation theory, and physicists are convinced that any successful method must take into account the increasing strength of the interactions at low energy.

Lattice gauge theory. The method that has proved the most successful to date makes use of the great progress in computer capability that has taken place in recent years. First suggested by the American theoretical physicist Kenneth Wilson, it has been given the name lattice gauge theory. In order to apply computers to the interactions of particles, it appears necessary to replace the continuous space and time that most physicists believe actually applies to nature by a discrete set of points, the lattice.

Such a substitution allows mathematical functions that are defined at an uncountable infinity of points to be replaced by functions that are defined at a finite set of points. The latter functions are much more readily adapted to computer calculations. For example, integrals over a many-dimensional space, which occur in expressions for physical quantities in QCD, are replaced by sums over the points of the lattice. By varying the spacing of points in the lattice, it is often possible to extrapolate the result to what would be obtained for the original theory, in which the separation between the points is arbitrarily small. The latter result is what presumably represents the actual prediction of QCD.

The introduction of a lattice also serves another purpose. Like most other field theories, QCD is not mathematically well defined when formulated in continuous space and time. Its equations predict infinite values for some physical quantities. These meaningless infinites are replaced by finite values when the theory is formulated on a lattice; thus, the lattice also serves to define precisely the quantities that should be calculated.

When such calculations are done on a lattice, the input parameters include the spacing between the points on the lattice, the total number of points in the lattice, and the masses of the quarks. (The gauge boson masses are taken to be zero.) In addition, the calculation can be carried out as a function of a temperature, which may be considered to represent the energy density of an interacting mixture of quarks and gluons. This temperature dependence is of interest in its own right. It is thought that confinement is a temperature-dependent phenomenon, occurring at the low temperatures that characterize the present universe but not at the high temperatures that prevailed in the first instants of universal history. It is believed that when the early universe was at a particular temperature, corresponding to an average particle energy of a few hundred million electron volts (MeV), a change took place from a situation in which the most stable state was a mixture of quarks and gluons (the so-called quark-gluon plasma; see *Nuclear physics*, below) to the present situation, in which the most stable state consists of quarks and gluons bound into hadrons. This type of changeover is analogous to the change that takes place in a liquid like water, which as it cools past its freezing point converts suddenly into the solid form of ice. Such sudden, dramatic changes in the condition of a system as the temperature varies are known as phase transitions.

Need for faster computers. Early calculations in lattice gauge theory were carried out on the general-purpose supercomputers then available. Such computers are capable of carrying out hundreds of millions of arithmetic operations per second. These early calculations showed some indication that a phase transition from a quark-gluon plasma to bound hadrons is an actual consequence of QCD. Only relatively small lattices could be treated with these computers, however, and it is doubtful that the required extrapolation to an infinite lattice could be done reliably with them. It became clear to a number of physicists that a novel type of computer would be necessary to obtain more reliable results.

General-purpose computers, including the earlier supercomputers, calculate serially; that is, they do the required steps in sequence on a single central processing unit, or processor, with one step not begun until the previous one has finished. During the 1980s another type of computer, using an approach known as parallel processing, became increasingly available to carry out calculations, such as those required in QCD, that would take too much time on even the fastest conventional computers. Parallel processing involves dividing up a calculation into parts that need not be carried out in series but can instead be done simultaneously. The computer consists of a number of processors, suitably connected to one another, each of which may be simpler and operate more slowly than a single-processor supercomputer. Because they operate at the same time, however, they can carry out a task in less time than a single, fast processor. In a newer variant of this approach, called massively parallel processing, a calculation is divided among hundreds to thousands of efficiently interlinked microprocessors, each of which is essentially the same kind of chip used in personal computers.

Parallel processing computers for QCD calculations have been constructed by physicists in a number of places, including the IBM Thomas J. Watson Research Center, Yorktown Heights, N.Y., and at laboratories in Italy and Japan. Perhaps the most successful have been a series built at Columbia University, New York City, by the physicist Norman Christ and co-workers. The latest involves 256 connected microprocessors and can carry out several billion of the computations needed for QCD each second. The first large-scale massively parallel computers were designed for specific kinds of calculations, and the process of programming them tends to be more complicated than for general-purpose computers. However, massively parallel computers that can be used for any of a variety of problems were becoming commercially available in the early 1990s.

Recent results. Computer calculations have achieved significant results concerning a number of questions involving QCD. Convincing demonstrations have been given for a phase transition from the hadron state to the quark-gluon plasma at a temperature corresponding to an energy of about 200 MeV. The details of this transition, such as whether energy is released when it takes place, are being actively investigated. This prediction of QCD may be tested in a few years when the Relativistic Heavy Ion Collider (RHIC) is completed at Brookhaven National Laboratory, Upton, N.Y. At that facility two beams of heavy nuclei will be accelerated to high energies and made to collide. For a short time during the collision, the densities of energy in the region of collision should be high enough to re-create the conditions in the early universe in which the quark-gluon plasma was the most stable state. Researchers can then study this plasma by observing the pattern of subatomic particles that emerges from it as the plasma cools. (See *1991 Yearbook of Science and the Future* Year in Review: *Physics: Nuclear physics*.)

QCD calculations of the ratios of hadron masses have also been done with various computers. One of the important goals of such calculations is to obtain the observed value of 1.22:1 for the ratio of the mass of the proton to the mass of the rho meson. The calculations done to date give somewhat larger numbers, in the neighborhood of 1.5:1. It is thought that this discrepancy is the result of using a lattice spacing that is too large and of doing calculations on lattices having too few total points. Both limitations could be avoided if still faster computers were available.

The Teraflop Project. To improve QCD calculations still further, a consortium of physicists from 23 U.S. universities and physics laboratories was formed to design and use a new massively parallel computer that would operate at a sustained rate of one trillion operations per second, several hundred times faster than existing QCD-oriented computers. Combining the acronym for floating point operation (flop) with the prefix for trillion (tera), the consortium called its proposal the QCD Teraflop Project. The computer itself would cost approximately $40 million and would be built by Thinking Machines Corp., Cambridge, Mass. The design and construction would take about three years to complete.

If the Teraflop Project is carried out, it should allow for the accurate calculation of masses and other properties of hadrons, such as their rates of decay via electroweak interactions. It also will allow for more accurate analysis of the quark-gluon phase transition and indicate which heavy-ion–collider experiments are likely to provide the most information. Furthermore, the physicists involved in the project believe that their computational methods will furnish new insights into the electroweak part of the standard model, of which some aspects, especially those at high energies, cannot reliably be studied by perturbation theory.

It is clear that, in view of a proposal like the Teraflop Project, computational physics is heading down a new road—one previously traveled by experimental

high-energy physics—in terms of both cost and the institutional arrangements through which research is carried out. It will be interesting to see what lies ahead for the development of theoretical physics.

—Gerald Feinberg

Nuclear physics

In the past year rapid progress was made in a number of diverse areas of nuclear physics. New facets of nuclear structure continued to be revealed as more sensitive gamma-ray detectors became available. This richness of structure was exemplified in the recent discovery of so-called identical rotational bands in nuclei that differ by many units of mass. The scattering of low-energy polarized neutrons from nuclei exhibited a striking pattern of violations of mirror symmetry (parity), a finding at odds with theoretical expectations. In collisions of heavy ions at high energies, the production of particles of strange antimatter was observed for the first time. The observation served as a useful probe of the properties of hot, dense nuclear matter. The short-distance structure of the deuteron, the lightest composite nucleus, was explored by electron scattering at high momentum transfer, providing a glimpse of finer mesonic structure beyond the classical picture of the deuteron as a bound state of a neutron and a proton.

Identical rotational bands. For the past two decades one of the most active areas of nuclear physics has been the study of energetically excited nuclei possessing high angular momentum, in which the nucleus rotates at extremely fast rates. Advances in this field have been made possible by successive developments of novel systems for detecting and interpreting the cascade of gamma rays emitted by fast-spinning nuclei as they slow down, passing through sets of discrete energy states, called rotational bands, toward their ground state. By the early 1990s such development efforts had culminated in the construction of multidetector arrays like the Gammasphere in the U.S. and the Eurogam in Europe. In the mid-1980s nuclei in states of so-called superdeformation were discovered by physicists at the Daresbury Laboratory near Liverpool, England; since then, such nuclei have been mapped throughout much of the periodic table. In these states the nuclear shape is that of a deformed ellipsoid undergoing rapid rotation in which competition among centrifugal, Coriolis, and nuclear forces leads to special configurations having a 2:1 ratio of major to minor axes.

In 1990 a startling discovery was announced by a consortium of U.K. and French nuclear physicists, as well as a group from the Lawrence Berkeley and Lawrence Livermore Laboratories in the U.S., concerning some of these superdeformed states: the differences in energy (*i.e.*, the transition energies) between corresponding states in rotational bands of neighboring nuclei (those differing by one proton or neutron) were extraordinarily small. These differences between nuclei were expected to vary by at least as much as $A^{5/3}$, in which A is the mass number, or number of nucleons (*i.e.*, protons and neutrons) in the nucleus. For nuclei having mass numbers near 150, this implied about a 1% difference between transition energies for corresponding states of nucleus A and nucleus $A + 1$. The observed differences, however, were only about 0.1%, an order of magnitude smaller than anticipated. The discrepancy suggests that some subtle cancellation effects occur in energy differences such that changes in nuclear shape and mass tend to offset each other.

When these so-called identical bands were first discovered in superdeformed states, they were thought to be unique. Subsequently, however, a group at Argonne (Ill.) National Laboratory found evidence in 1991 for identical bands in certain "normal" deformed nuclear states, which constitute the vast bulk of nonspherical nuclear excitations. The Argonne work also hinted that identical bands need not be restricted to nearby nuclei. A study in 1992 by a collaboration from Brookhaven National Laboratory, Upton, N.Y.; the University of Cologne, Germany; Clark University, Worcester, Mass.; and the Institute of Atomic Physics, Bucharest, Rom., indeed demonstrated that identical bands are not restricted to adjacent nuclei; in fact, they appear in a series of widely dispersed nuclei as diverse as dysprosium-156 and osmium-180, fully 24 mass units apart. Perhaps even more striking in this latter study is the "context" in which these particular nuclei are situated. All previous examples of identical bands had been found in regions of nuclei that display very stable properties from one element or isotope to the next. In contrast, the identical bands found in widely

dispersed rare earth nuclei from dysprosium (Dy) to osmium (Os) occur in a "transition" region in which neighboring isotopes (*e.g.*, ^{154}Dy, ^{156}Dy, ^{158}Dy) have very different structures, ranging from nearly spherical shapes (with vibrational modes of excitation) to deformed and rotational nuclei.

The scheme that was used to search for identical bands is interesting in itself, as it focuses attention on one of the prime determinants of the evolution of nuclear structure; namely, the interactions between the outermost, or valence, protons and neutrons. The identical bands in the sequence ^{156}Dy, ^{160}Er, ^{164}Yb, ^{168}Hf, ^{172}W, ^{180}Os (Er is erbium, Yb is ytterbium, Hf is hafnium, and W is tungsten) are characterized by nearly equal products of the numbers of the valence protons (N_p) and neutrons (N_n). This "$N_p N_n$ scheme" has the capability of predicting which nuclei will have virtually identical structure, even when they are widely separated in mass number or atomic number. Such predictive power, vividly demonstrated by the identical band phenomenon, has wide implications; for example, in estimates of the properties of unknown, unstable nuclei that are important in the r-process of nucleosynthesis, which is responsible for the creation in supernovas and other violent cosmic events of nearly all of the elements beyond iron.

Parity nonconservation for neutron resonances. The investigation of space-time symmetries in nuclear systems continued. These symmetries include mirror symmetry (parity) and time reversal invariance. Mirror symmetry refers to the behavior of physical observables under reflection in a mirror: directions and momenta of particles are reversed, while their spins remain the same. Parity, a quantity associated with mirror reflections, is thought to be conserved in the strong interactions of particles like neutrons and protons but not in weak interactions, as evidenced by many studies of the decays of nuclei.

Photo shows part of the beam injector that will supply electrons at an energy of 45 million electron volts (MeV) to the main accelerator of the Continuous Electron Beam Accelerator Facility (CEBAF) in Virginia. Scheduled to be operational in 1994, CEBAF will use electrons accelerated to four billion electron volts (GeV) in scattering experiments to explore nuclear structure at short distances.

U.S. Department of Energy; photo, Frank Hoffmann

Parity is not conserved if the interaction contains a component that changes sign under a mirror reflection; for instance, the product of the spin and the momentum of a particle. The influence of such a component can be detected by scattering neutrons from nuclear targets and measuring the fractional difference of the number of collisions for neutrons whose spin is oriented parallel or antiparallel to the direction of momentum. A neutron whose spin is lined up along its momentum is said to be polarized.

Recently the TRIPLE collaboration, whose participants included scientists from North Carolina State University; Los Alamos (N.M.) National Laboratory; the TRIUMF laboratory, Vancouver, B.C.; the University of Technology, Delft, Neth.; and Duke University, Durham, N.C., performed a decisive series of measurements of very low-energy polarized-neutron scattering from uranium-238 and thorium-232 nuclei, taking advantage of the intense flux of neutrons available at the Los Alamos Neutron Scattering Center (LANSCE). The scattering of low-energy neutrons (1–400 electron volts [eV]) exhibits strong and closely spaced resonant structures, called compound nuclear resonances. Near these resonances the violation of mirror symmetry (parity) in the neutron scattering process is as large as 10%.

The remarkable feature of the ^{232}Th data is that all significant parity-violating effects have the same positive sign; that is, the interaction of the neutron with the nucleus is larger when its spin and momentum are parallel. This observation provoked intense theoretical interest since such strong sign correlations had not been predicted by theoretical models. At the fundamental level such violations of reflection symmetry arise from the weak interactions between neutrons and protons. The energy scale for these interactions is of the order of tens of electron volts.

Strange antimatter from heavy-ion collisions. In the experimentally produced encounters of heavy ions (nuclei of heavy elements stripped of their electrons) at high energies, a large number of nucleon-nucleon collisions take place, leading to the production of a multitude of secondary particles, mostly pions. In this collision debris one occasionally finds a particle of so-called strange matter or antimatter, typically in the form of a hyperon (Λ or Ξ^-) or antihyperon ($\bar{\Lambda}$, $\bar{\Xi}^+$). The hyperons are closely related to the familiar proton and neutron constituents of nuclei but contain strange quarks (s) as building blocks as well as the up (u) and down (d) quarks that make up the nucleon. For instance, the quark structure of Λ is sud and that of Ξ^- is ssd, whereas the structures of the proton and neutron are uud and ddu, respectively.

Hyperon or antihyperon production serves as a useful probe of the dynamics of nuclear matter under the extremes of density and temperature realized in high-energy heavy-ion collisions. A prime motivation for heavy-ion research is the search for the quark-gluon–plasma phase of nuclear matter (see *High-energy physics*, above). According to quantum chromodynamics, the underlying theory of strong interactions, nuclear matter should show a sudden change of properties if its energy density is increased 10-fold over that of ordinary nuclei. In the quark-gluon plasma, quarks (and the gluon "force" particles that bind the quarks into nucleons) are no longer localized inside individual nucleons but are free to roam over the entire reaction volume. If the quark-gluon plasma is indeed created in heavy-ion collisions, it is anticipated that strange particle production will be enhanced, in particular, that of antihyperons.

Recently a multinational collaboration at CERN (European Laboratory for Particle Physics) near Geneva observed the production of multiply strange Ξ^- and $\bar{\Xi}^+$ particles (*i.e.*, two of the three quarks of each particle are strange) for the first time in collisions of sulfur-32 ions at an energy of 200 GeV (billion electron volts) per nucleon with a tungsten target. Hyperons having a large transverse momentum (perpendicular to the beam direction) were selected to be observed in order to accentuate the sensitivity to particles that originate in the early stages of quark-gluon–plasma formation, if this indeed occurs. The ratio of $\bar{\Xi}^+$ to Ξ^- production was found to be about 2:5, a remarkably large value compared with that observed in proton-nucleus collisions at similar energies, which was an order of magnitude smaller. The $\bar{\Xi}^+/\Xi^-$ ratio seen in heavy-ion collisions is larger than predicted in theoretical models and may signal the formation of the quark-gluon plasma. At the very least, the observations indicate the formation in the laboratory of hot, dense nuclear matter, in which the strange quarks reach an approximate thermal and chemical equilibrium.

Electron scattering and structure of the deuteron. The deuterium (hydrogen-2) nucleus, called the deuteron, is the simplest composite nucleus, a spin-1 system consisting, according to the standard viewpoint, of a neutron and proton weakly bound via the strong interaction. From many experiments it is known that the deuteron is a slightly nonspherical object, possessing a complicated internal distribution of electric charge.

If one transfers a certain amount of momentum q to the deuteron, for instance, by means of an electron beam, one can investigate the response of the system as a function of momentum. As momentum increases, one is able to probe shorter distances (the distance scale varies inversely with momentum), ultimately revealing the quark structure of the deuteron. Recent experiments on elastic electron-deuteron scattering at momentum values corresponding to a spatial resolution of 0.22–0.26

femtometers (a femtometer is one ten-trillionth of a centimeter), carried out at the MIT-Bates Linear Accelerator Center, Middleton, Mass., provided stringent constraints on the theoretical description of deuteron structure. The relative size of the charge monopole and quadrupole response was determined by the use of a spin-polarized deuteron target and measurement of both the scattered electron and the polarization (spin state) of the recoiling deuteron. In addition to the conventional neutron-proton component, the data required the introduction of pion fields in the deuteron. (The pion is the lightest meson; its exchange mediates the interaction that binds the neutron and proton together in the nucleus.) This cloud of pions interacts directly with the electromagnetic field provided by the electron beam, producing a marked effect on the deuteron polarization. The MIT-Bates data are not consistent with a simple six-quark picture of the deuteron or with a description in which the interactions of quarks and gluons are treated as small perturbations. The use of electron scattering at higher momentum transfer to explore nuclear structure at short distances is one of the most exciting endeavors in nuclear physics and represents the prime focus of future work at the Continuous Electron Beam Accelerator Facility (CEBAF) in Newport News, Va., a 4-GeV electron accelerator to be operational in 1994.

—Carl B. Dover

Condensed-matter physics

During the past year a three-decade effort to make light-emitting laser diodes in the blue region of the spectrum from large-band-gap II-VI semiconductors finally bore fruit, evidence of an impurity-induced change in the atomic structure and electronic properties of a surface was obtained from scanning tunneling microscopy, and a new tubular form of carbon having predicted electronic properties that range from metallic to semiconducting was discovered.

Doping of II-VI semiconductors. It is well known that the electronic properties of most semiconductors can be tailored by the selective addition of impurities, a process known as doping. For example, the compound gallium arsenide (GaAs) can be doped to form an n-type semiconductor through the incorporation of electron-donor impurity atoms like silicon or germanium into the GaAs crystalline lattice. These two impurities preferentially replace gallium atoms. Since silicon and germanium have four outer electrons in their valence shell whereas gallium has only three, the extra electron of the impurity atom is "donated" to the conduction band, thereby making the sample conducting. Similarly GaAs can be doped to make a p-type semiconductor by replacing some gallium atoms with an electron-acceptor impurity such as beryllium (Be), which has only two electrons in its outer valence shell. To remove its deficiency of one electron, the beryllium atom "accepts" an electron from the filled valence band and creates a positively charged "hole" that makes the sample conducting.

In terms of chemical bonding and electronic band structure, the basic idea of doping is quite simple. It is surprising, therefore, to find situations in which the simple picture is inadequate. Physicists have made great efforts to understand, at a microscopic level, the reasons for the failure to dope some semiconductors. The most challenging problems have been encountered in connection with large-band-gap II-VI semiconductors (so named from the column positions of their constituent elements in the periodic table) like zinc selenide (ZnSe), for which repeated attempts over the past 30 years to obtain low-resistivity p-type samples had proved unsuccessful until recently. The fundamental band gap of ZnSe, corresponding to the minimum energy difference between the unoccupied conduction band and the occupied valence band, is 2.67 electron volts (eV) at room temperature (a comparatively large value; hence, the term *large-band-gap*). Recombination of electrons with holes at a p-n junction (an interface of p-type and n-type material) made from ZnSe would create photons of nearly this energy and yield blue-green light. In comparison, the band gap of GaAs is only about 1.4 eV at room temperature; light-emitting diodes made from GaAs give light in the infrared region of the electromagnetic spectrum.

Zinc selenide can be doped n-type relatively easily, for example, by the addition of chlorine impurity atoms, which substitute for selenium atoms, or of gallium atoms, which substitute for zinc atoms. The primary problem encountered was in p-type doping. The periodic table's column-V impurities phosphorus (P) and arsenic (As), with five valence electrons each, were studied extensively. Substitution of these atoms for selenium, a column-VI atom, was expected to lead to the creation of holes. The holes so created, however, seem to have properties very different from those in GaAs and other III-V semiconductors. Compared with the holes in GaAs, they are much more tightly bound to the impurities. Because the tightly bound holes have a much higher resistance to current flow in the presence of an electric field, p-type conductivity is affected. Another deleterious consequence of the large binding energy of the holes is a large downward shift of the electron-hole recombination energy, which shifts the color of the emitted photons from blue-green toward red. Moreover, the doping efficiency, *i.e.,* the density of holes obtained from a given concentration of impurity, is very small.

Such difficulties have led to many speculations on possible mechanisms operating on the microscopic level for the behavior of acceptors in ZnSe. An early

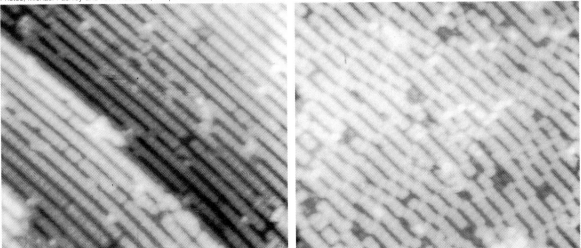

Scanning tunneling micrographs reveal the changes in atomic structure that occur when a clean surface of gallium arsenide (left) is modified (right) by doping with silicon. See discussion on p. 406.

theory postulated that large-band-gap semiconductors were difficult to dope in general because impurities reduce the energy required to form deleterious lattice defects by an amount directly proportional to the band gap. In other words, the larger the band gap, the lower the energy needed to form defects that neutralize the desired effects of doping. For example, in zinc selenide, a defect in the form of a missing atom (vacancy) at a selenium site creates four broken bonds, leaving unbonded electrons on neighboring zinc atoms. The unbonded electrons act as donors and tend to neutralize the holes created by the acceptor impurities. In ZnSe, acceptor impurities would lower the energy for selenium-site vacancy formation by almost twice the band gap of 2.67 eV, significantly reducing the defect creation energy and thus enormously enhancing the probability of defect formation. In practice it is possible to counterbalance the tendency toward vacancy formation by varying the conditions of crystal growth such that excess selenium is incorporated into the lattice. Many different approaches along these lines were tried, but the difficulties with p-type doping remained.

The main problem with the defect formation theory is its prediction that it should be equally difficult to dope n-type zinc selenide. In this case zinc-site vacancies, which behave as acceptors, would be expected to neutralize the presence of impurity donors. This effect, however, is not experimentally observed. Using a first-principles theoretical approach, David Laks, Chris Van de Walle, and Sokrates Pantelides of the IBM Thomas J. Watson Research Center, Yorktown Heights, N.Y., and Gertrude Neumark of Columbia University, New York City, showed conclusively that "native" defects like vacancies and interstitials (extra atoms occupying spaces between normal

sites) resulting from either a deficit or an excess of zinc and selenium atoms occur at concentrations far too low to explain the neutralization of impurities in ZnSe. Further theoretical work by James Chadi and Kee Joo Chang at the Xerox Palo Alto (Calif.) Research Center and subsequently by Chadi at the NEC Research Institute, Princeton, N.J., showed that the large binding energies of holes introduced by arsenic and phosphorus acceptors in ZnSe are an *intrinsic* property and result from unexpectedly large atomic rearrangements, or lattice relaxations, around these impurities. Such relaxations are absent for typical donor or acceptor impurities in GaAs except under high-pressure conditions or alloying. The theory also predicts that nitrogen (N) impurities should be electrically much better behaved than either arsenic or phosphorus and lead to loosely bound holes. (See *1991 Yearbook of Science and the Future* Year in Review: Physics: *Condensed-matter physics*.)

Doping of zinc selenide with nitrogen was tried many times in the 1980s, but the results were not much better than those with phosphorus or arsenic. By 1992 some of the reasons for those failures were becoming clear. Pure nitrogen occurs in the form of the extremely stable and chemically inert N_2 molecule. In order to introduce nitrogen into ZnSe, experimentalists used nitrogen-containing compounds like ammonia (NH_3) or the chemically similar trilithium nitride (Li_3N). The latter choice is particularly interesting since both components—lithium substituting for a zinc atom and nitrogen substituting for a selenium atom—are expected to give holes. A major, unforeseen problem with both choices is that hydrogen and lithium diffuse very easily and combine with nitrogen into stable complexes, in which they go into "bond-centered" sites between zinc-nitrogen bonds. The combinations N + H or N + Li in these complexes are electronically equivalent to a selenium atom, and as a result no holes are introduced into the valence band. The underlying mechanism for hydrogen- and lithium-induced neutralization of acceptors in p-doped silicon and gallium arsenide has been studied and is well understood. The neutralization of acceptors in zinc selenide is expected to follow a very similar mechanism.

Success in doping zinc selenide with nitrogen into a p-type material having hole densities 10 times larger than those obtained previously and the demonstration of the first blue-green diode lasers using ZnSe were major breakthroughs of 1991. They were achieved by the team of Michael A. Haase, Jun Qiu, James M. DePuydt, and Hwa Cheng at the 3M Co., St. Paul, Minn. The new doping process used a novel approach to nitrogen doping developed by Robert M. Park, M.B. Troffer, and C.M. Rouleau of the University of Florida at Gainesville in 1990. Ultrapure molecular nitrogen is split into its atomic components by means of a 13.5-MHz radio-frequency power source, which generates a plasma discharge. The atomic nitrogen is then guided into a molecular-beam-epitaxy system in which ZnSe is grown atomic layer by atomic layer on a GaAs substrate by means of a molecular beam containing zinc and selenium. A blue-green light-emitting laser diode operating at 77 K ($-196°$ C or $-321°$ F) and made from a zinc selenide p-n junction was demonstrated shortly after this achievement. The results show conclusively that the long-sought goal of creating both n- and p-type wide-band-gap semiconductors is realizable. The new diode lasers made from ZnSe should replace bulky, expensive dye lasers currently used to access the short-wavelength blue region of the optical spectrum.

Impurity-induced surface changes. Study of the atomic and electronic structure of the surfaces of semiconductors and metals has been an active field of research for almost 30 years. The development of the scanning tunneling microscope (STM) in the early 1980s by Gerd Binnig and Heinrich Rohrer of the IBM Zürich (Switz.) Research Laboratory has led to a tremendous advance in knowledge of both the atomic and electronic properties of surfaces. In 1991 Michael Pashley and K.W. Haberern of Philips Laboratories, Briarcliff Manor, N.Y., used the STM to identify the microscopic nature of Schottky-barrier formation on a gallium arsenide surface. The term *Schottky barrier* is used primarily in connection with metal-semiconductor interfaces. When metals are deposited on a semiconductor surface, the application of a voltage across the junction generally does not lead to current flow unless the voltage is increased above a certain minimum value. It is as if a barrier for electron motion existed across the metal-semiconductor interface. For most III-V semiconductors the value of the critical voltage needed to overcome the Schottky barrier varies from nearly zero to about one volt. At the critical voltage electrons flow from the highest energy occupied electronic states of the metal into the empty conduction band of the semiconductor.

Many materials including GaAs tend to show a well-defined value for the Schottky barrier voltage, which is for the most part independent of the type of metal in contact with the semiconductor surface. The microscopic origin of this "pinning" of the barrier voltage to a particular value has been a subject of intense investigation since the early 1980s. Many different models for the pinning have been proposed, but experimental verification has been limited. Pashley and Haberern studied the problem via the STM, and their investigation led to the discovery of a new mechanism for pinning on the GaAs surface.

In their experiment Pashley and Haberern deposited silicon atoms onto a GaAs surface. Since silicon, which has four valence electrons, substitutes preferentially for gallium, which has only three, the effect is to introduce free electrons into the conduction band of GaAs. Although one thus would expect the surface layer to become conducting, the experiments clearly showed that the surface responds to the addition of silicon atoms in a way that neutralizes the free electrons. STM images of the surface (*see* photos on p. 405) reveal the distinctive change in atomic structure that occurs with the deposition of silicon. On a clean surface, with no silicon atoms present (left photo), the arsenic atoms on the topmost layer bond together into two-atom units (dimers), which reduces the number of broken bonds and lowers the energy. Each bright spot corresponds to two surface arsenic atoms of a dimer. The dimers fall into straight rows. The dark lines between the dimer rows correspond to missing dimers (two-atom vacancies), which are present in a nearly periodic manner on the surface. The combination of dimers with missing dimers actually leads to a more stable surface than one in which there are no arsenic vacancies. On a GaAs surface that has been doped with silicon (right photo), the dimers appear much more disordered than on the clean surface. Short rows of arsenic dimers are displaced from each other by "kinks." Pashley and Haberern demonstrated a linear relationship between the kink density and the silicon impurity concentration at the surface. On average, the addition of each silicon atom was found to give rise to an extra kink in the surface.

The STM was used not only to image atomic structure changes induced by silicon doping but also to determine the electronic structure at the kink sites. This was done by varying the electrical potential at the atomically sharp, needlelike tip of the

Sumio Iijima, NEC Fundamental Research Laboratories, Tsukuba, Japan

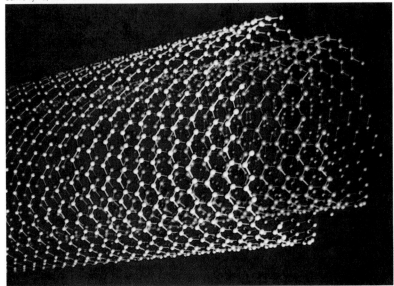

The molecular structure of a pair of concentric "buckytubes" is depicted in a computer simulation. All of the carbon atoms in the tubes are members of hexagonal rings, as in graphite; the tubular structure itself can be considered a one-atom-thick sheet of graphite rolled into a cylinder.

microscope so that electrons are either injected into a surface electronic state or extracted from such a state. In this mode of operation the STM becomes a scanning-tunneling-spectroscopic probe and provides atom-specific information on the electronic states of the surface. It was shown in this way that each kink acts as an acceptor that neutralizes exactly one silicon donor electron. As a result, the doping does not lead to a conducting surface having a zero Schottky-barrier voltage, as might have been expected.

It will be interesting to learn the extent to which additional GaAs layers applied by molecular beam epitaxy on top of the silicon-doped surface is affected by the altered surface structure. Presumably, after a few layers are deposited, the surface returns to its original structure; the atoms below the surface assume their crystalline bulklike positions; and the silicon atoms below the surface, no longer neutralized by kinks, become normal donors, thereby making the bulk of the sample n-type. Scanning tunneling microscopy and its derivatives are ideal tools for answering such questions.

Buckytubes. Fullerenes, the recently discovered family of "molecular crystals" whose archetype, buckminsterfullerene, is made up of 60 carbon atoms arranged in the form of a hollow spherical shell, have received a great deal of attention because of their unusual properties (*see* Year in Review: CHEMISTRY). It also appears that the electric arc discharge between graphite rods that has been used to make fullerenes has another by-product in the form of "buckytubes"; *i.e.*, pure carbon tubes having extremely small diameters. High-resolution transmission-electron-microscopy measurements by Sumio Iijima at NEC Fundamental Research Laboratories, Tsukuba, Japan, led to the discovery of these new carbon fibers, which consist of 2–50 or more coaxial tubes of graphitic-like carbon. All the carbon atoms in the microtubes are members of hexagonal rings of atoms, just as in graphite. The structure resembles what one might obtain from rolling a one-atom-thick sheet of graphite into a cylinder. Mathematically, there is an infinite number of ways of rolling graphite sheets, leading to structures of various helical order and diameter. Helical order arises when a line of atoms on a graphitic plane is matched with a different but parallel line of atoms as the plane is rolled into a cylinder. Iijima found both helical and nonhelical structures in the microtubes.

The electronic properties of such carbon fibers were recently examined theoretically by Noriaki Hamada, Shin-ichi Sawada, and Atsushi Oshiyama at NEC. They predicted a striking range of electronic properties, from those of metals to those of narrow-gap and normal semiconductors, that depend on the tube diameter and on the degree of helical ordering. The band gap between occupied and empty states in the semiconducting regime was calculated to range from 0.2 to 1.2 eV. For purposes of comparison, the room-temperature band gaps of indium antimonide (InSb) and silicon are about 0.23 eV and 1.14 eV, respectively. The theorists showed that the variations in the band gap of the fibers could be understood through a simple mapping of their electronic state wave functions onto those of graphite. Only those microtubes that have electronic states similar to the metallic states of graphite were found to have zero or small band gaps. The unusual structural and predicted electronic properties of buckytubes are certain to make them one of the more exciting areas of future research.

—James D. Chadi

Psychology

The year 1992 was the centennial of the founding of the American Psychological Association (APA). To mark the occasion, year-long celebrations were started at the 1991 annual meetings held in San Francisco. With well over 100,000 members, representing more than half of the world's psychologists, the APA was the world's second largest scientific-professional organization (only the American Chemical Society was larger). The 17,400 registrants at the 1991 San Francisco meetings contrasted sharply with the 18 academic psychologists who had met on July 8, 1892, at the home of the Clark University president, psychologist G. Stanley Hall, to form the new association.

Enhancing human performance. The long-awaited second report of a special U.S. National Research Council committee, *In the Mind's Eye: Enhancing Human Performance,* appeared during the year. Initially formed in 1984 in response to the U.S. Army's request for expert scientific help in evaluating the many special training programs that were being supported within the military community, the committee of 13 psychologists issued its first report in 1988; that report dealt primarily with unconventional techniques that had been developed mainly outside the academic research community. Its findings were largely negative.

The new report completed the second phase of the committee's agenda. It was mainly concerned with the more basic issues of training and performance. Three focal areas were investigated: (1) training intended to improve posttraining, real-life performance; (2) alteration of mental states to enhance performance; and (3) preparation for performance under pressure. Selected samples of conclusions from each of these research areas are described briefly below.

Perhaps the most important conclusions concerned the differences that were found between variables that facilitate training itself and those that improve posttraining performance. For example, conditions that facilitate training—massed rather than spaced practice, regularity of environmental conditions, and increased external feedback—were found to have the opposite effect on posttraining, on-the-job performance. Such performance was found to be markedly enhanced when spaced practice under highly irregular contextual conditions with little external feedback was used in training. These counterintuitive results were especially significant because trainers typically see only the comparatively immediate results of the training program and are not, therefore, in a position to draw appropriate conclusions concerning the efficacy of the variables on posttraining performance.

With respect to alterations of mental states, no theoretical or empirical support was found for the alleged efficacy of subliminal tapes—in spite of their estimated annual sale of more than $50 million. The committee also found no support for any special advantage provided by meditation, beyond effects attributable to rest and relaxation. More positive conclusions were drawn for some of the psychological efforts to control pain; nonpharmacological factors—such as the enhancement of the feeling of control, the use of relaxation to reduce stress, and the provision of information about what to expect—were found to have promise as alleviators of subjective pain experience.

Some promising techniques for preparing to perform under pressure were identified from sports psychology, neuroscience, and motor-behavior research. For example, preparation strategies such as mental rehearsal and automation of preperformance motor routines were found to stabilize cognitive-motor processes that underlie on-the-job performance.

Sexual harassment. The primary issues so dramatically raised during the Anita Hill-Clarence Thomas confrontation in the U.S. Senate hearings on the Thomas nomination as a U.S. Supreme Court justice may have been "news" to many people in the U.S. in October 1991, but they were hardly such to many psychologists, especially to those who were involved in the study of women. Sexual harassment had for more than a decade been a much-studied facet of that study.

A major conclusion of the studies is that sexual harassment has more to do with the dynamics of power in interpersonal relationships than with sex itself. Los Angeles psychologist Nancy Baker found that women in traditionally "masculine" jobs, such as surgeon and machinist, report a much higher rate of harassment than women in traditionally "feminine" jobs, such as stenographer or clerk.

Baker also discovered that it is not the economically most vulnerable women who are most likely to be sexually harassed, as she originally had anticipated. Instead, the professionally more vulnerable women, those concerned with job security, are most likely to suffer from harassment. This vulnerability was identified by several researchers as being responsible for the failure of harassed women to make complaints; another major factor in this regard was the inconsistent and relatively light reprimands generally meted out to male offenders. Baker also identified sexual harassment as a common but generally unreported cause of women's leaving the work force.

Whatever its dynamics, sexual harassment can have devastating effects on women's lives. Clinical studies have shown increases in eating disorders, general anxiety, and depression and the formation of new fears, as of men, after repeated harassments.

In a comprehensive review article on sexual harassment published several months before the Hill-Thomas confrontation, psychologist Stephanie Riger of the University of Illinois at Chicago reported that relatively few complaints were being received by organizations that had set up formal policies and procedures to deal with the issue. The most common explanations of this scarcity, in light of the relatively high percentages of occurrence of such incidents indicated in surveys, were that either there was really not much of a problem or the victims were too timid or fearful to complain. Riger's explanation was that the way the reporting procedures were generally set up was more in accord with the way men view both the harassment and the dispute-resolution process than with the way women do; thus, women were disproportionately less likely to file complaints.

Although the situation is far too complex to permit full discussion here, especially with respect to the more subtle differences in gender bias, Riger's analysis pointed out two major factors. First, women generally tend to feel that sexual overtures are insulting, whereas men tend to see them as complimentary. Second, men are far more likely to be in positions of power in business organizations, so the policies and procedures by means of which sexual harassment is reported are largely determined by them rather than by the women who are the typical victims.

Self-esteem gender gap. Another type of "gender gap" was uncovered by a national survey of 3,000 students in the 4th through the 10th grades, sponsored by the American Association of University Women (AAUW). This new gap was caused by a decline in reported self-esteem during adolescence, which was found to be markedly greater in girls than in boys.

At ages eight and nine, 60% of the girls surveyed and 67% of the boys were found to be confident and assertive and to have positive feelings of self-regard. During the next eight years, however, there was a much sharper drop in self-esteem ratings among the girls—only 29% of high-school girls reported positive self-regard—whereas 46% of the boys reported positive feelings.

The survey found a correspondingly greater decline in girls' interest in mathematics and sciences as compared with boys. In elementary school 81% of the girls and 84% of the boys reported liking math; by high school these scores had dropped to 61% for girls and 72% for boys. Similar scores were found in regard to science.

These data were interpreted by AAUW officers as supporting other research results that have suggested that girls are systematically, if unintentionally, discouraged from entering a wide range of occupations, particularly those involving math and science. Support for these conclusions was available in studies of gender-biased classroom instruction. For exam-

Keith Carter

Harvard University psychology professor Carol Gilligan (right) and colleague Normi Noel (left) exercise with fifth-grade girls as part of a project to help girls develop and maintain positive self-esteem.

ple, gender differences in classroom treatment were reported by Myra and David Sadker, both professors of education at American University, Washington, D.C. Teachers treat boys and girls differently, Myra Sadker reported. She commented that teachers "give boys more attention and better quality of attention. They not only ask them more questions, but they give them more precise feedback. . . . They're usually not aware they're doing it."

Such instructional and attitudinal differences are believed to have significant implications for career choice. Girls were found to feel that they were "not smart enough" to achieve their "dream" careers.

The AAUW survey confirmed, on a national scale, many of the results earlier reported in smaller, long-term studies by Harvard University psychologists Carol Gilligan, Lyn Mikel Brown, and Annie Rogers. They reported finding young girls in conflict between retaining their own initially positive feelings of self-regard and accepting the more negative evaluations of their society. The cumulative effects of negative social pressures can be devastating. For example, Gilligan commented: "We knew girls who at 10 or 11 were just standing adamantly by their own feelings and knowledge, but by 12 or 13 were starting to say, 'I don't know.' Not to know is a way of resolving conflicts."

Resolution of the problems caused by these differences in treatment will require radical educational reform, according to AAUW executive director Anne Bryant. "The education reform movement holds out an empty promise unless we improve education for our girls. Failure to address this challenge short-changes girls and shortchanges America." The problem was seen as a national one because it is expected that by the year 2000 two of every three new entrants to the work force will be women.

A somewhat different attack on the problem was recommended by University of Colorado psychologist Jacqueline Eccles. In two long-term studies she found that girls report less self-confidence in mathematics as early as the first grade even when they are doing just as well as boys in math classes. Eccles concluded that a critical factor in mediating children's self-evaluation is their parents' attitudes. As long as these attitudes reflect the strong cultural stereotype that girls are naturally inferior in math and science, there is little positive influence, but when more realistic and personal evaluations are made by the parents, and particularly perhaps by the mother, maintenance of the girls' early positive self-regard is facilitated.

Reciprocal teaching. Psychologist Ann Brown of the University of California at Berkeley received an award from the American Educational Research Association at its annual convention during the past year. She led a research team that demonstrated the practicality of a new educational procedure, called "reciprocal teaching."

Initially developed as an alternative to traditional classroom methods, reciprocal teaching has been widely adopted by school systems across the United States. The procedure involves having all of the students in a small study group participate by taking turns in leading group discussions. They are trained to use four types of strategy with reference to the text being studied: ask specific questions, clarify ambiguities, summarize content, and predict what comes next. This kind of practice has been found to be effective in developing the cognitive skills of children who have learning problems, especially in groups of children with varying achievement levels, so that the more skilled students can serve as role models.

Another modification of traditional classroom practices entails allocating an unusual amount of control of the learning program to the students themselves. They are allowed to select their own research topics, do their own sorting of students into study groups, write and revise reports, and use a computer to publish the reports. Relinquishing so much control was difficult for many teachers, and implementing this program proved to be difficult.

Children under stress. Another facet of the educational process was the topic of a special forum on "America's Children Under Stress" convened during the past year in Washington, D.C. The theme was the importance of building up children's coping strategies, especially before they are confronted with serious stress.

A number of such intervention programs were described at the conference. For example, J. Anne Pedro-Carroll, a psychologist at the University of Rochester, N.Y., described her program designed to help children cope with parental divorce. She stated that children who receive no special attention after their parents divorce have two to three times as many serious emotional problems as those from intact families. The use of mental health professionals to lead support groups with games and exercises has helped children of divorce to cope better with family changes and to communicate more readily with both parents, as well as to avoid anxiety and withdrawal in the classroom. By 1992 the program was in use in more than 60 school districts and had been positively evaluated over an eight-year period.

Psychological testing. During the past two decades the use of psychological tests for evaluation has suffered from a barrage of criticism from civil rights advocates and activists. The alleged bias of these tests against minorities and ethnic groups has been the major part of this criticism. That such complaints are still effective was demonstrated during the year when the U.S. Social Security Administration announced that it was de-emphasizing the use of psychological tests and planning instead to depend more heavily on applicants' self-reports and a mental health status report in evaluating claims for mental disability. This evaluation was important because there are more than 400,000 such applications each year. The new rules held that "the individual can usually best describe his or her functional limitations." This highly dubious position was the subject of a protest by the APA on the grounds that more objective methods of evaluation are needed before benefits are paid.

A recent development with more positive overtones for psychological testing was the resurgence of personality assessment in the field of industrial and organizational psychology. Lee Etta Hough of Personnel Decisions Research Institutes in Minneapolis, Minn., reported that experts in the field were beginning to reassess the value of personality tests. A new consensus seemed to be forming, and its main thrust was that personality assessment when used with traditional testing makes more successful prediction of job performance possible. It was also believed, at least tentatively, that personality assessment is not vulnerable to complaints of ethnic-minority bias in the way that cognitive assessments are.

—Melvin H. Marx

International developments. Internationally the concerns of psychologists reflected the major world events of the past year. The traumas of the Gulf war were over, but its psychological reverberations remained. Some of the greatest victims of this type of traumatic stress are children living in the war zones of the world. In an effort to discover how to protect the mental and emotional development of children from the most serious effects of war, international scientific efforts were made to study the grave psychological consequences of sustained exposure to violence. Exposure to chronic danger can produce such far-reaching effects on children as posttraumatic stress disorder, alterations of personality, and night terrors, and it also can lead some children to self-destructive acts. However, when given a chance, despite the hurt and long suffering, most children can recover from the experiences if informed help is at hand in the recovery process. Community-based social and psychological intervention programs and family-reunification efforts were found to be effective measures in the recovery process. Attention was drawn especially to the needs of Kuwaiti children, many of whom witnessed such traumatic events as executions, kidnappings, and bombings and may have also lost a family member through death or disappearance.

Despite the dramatic changes in South Africa seen over the past year as the foundations of the apartheid regime were dismantled, psychologists sought to understand the disturbing outbreaks of intercommunity violence in terms of consequences for the young. Many South African black youths grew up in a culture of violence, and they all lived their lives without political rights and institutions of peaceable change. They have never known institutions that could bring a better life to them and their parents by nonviolent means. Add racism and social neglect to this profile, and the potential for violence increases dramatically, as was stressed by Lloyd Volgelman, director of the Project for the Study of Violence at the University of the Witwatersrand, Johannesburg, South Africa. People are, however, less prone to violence when the future has something to offer.

In the recently emerged eastern European democracies, where human rights have been restored, the psychological legacy of former repressive regimes, such as that of Nicolae Ceausescu in Romania, will take time to repeal. In Romania psychology was outlawed in the early 1980s, and psychology departments were closed down. Now that psychology departments have begun to form again, Romanian psychologists are seeking to update their skills in all fields of psychological knowledge and practice. Plans were developed to persuade Western psychologists to visit Romania to teach and train, and psychological associations in the U.S., Britain, and western Europe developed projects for Romanian and other eastern European psychologists to visit and study abroad.

The International Union of Psychological Science arranged a series of advanced training seminars in conjunction with the International Association for Cross-Cultural Psychology for psychologists from less developed countries and those that are economically less privileged. The relevance of existing psychological knowledge to a non-Western context was to be given careful attention. The International Union of Psychological Science also continued to support an initiative directed toward unraveling important psychological dimensions in the dynamics of global environmental change. Concern was focused on the way human attitudes and motives, perception, and assessment of risk are important factors in whether individuals act in a way that will reduce the dangers of global warming by, for instance, avoiding unnecessary automobile use or wasteful use of electricity. Market solutions such as taxing consumption of limited resources can help, but the fundamental problem is that of motivating individuals to change their behavior in a situation where a worldwide cooperative effort is needed.

—Colin V. Newman

Space exploration

The U.S. space probe Magellan continued to make remarkable discoveries about the planet Venus during the past year, and the Voyager probes neared the edge of the solar system on their journeys into interstellar space. Several manned U.S. space shuttle missions were completed successfully, but budget cuts reduced the number of future flights. The breakup of the Soviet Union raised questions about the former nation's space program.

Manned flight

Humans were moderately busy in space during the past year as the United States and the Soviet Union flew several space shuttle and Soyuz missions, but administrators on the ground were kept busy adjusting programs to new economic and political realities—including when to retrieve a cosmonaut "stranded" in space. Economic problems in Europe—including the high price of German reunification—caused the European Space Agency (ESA) to rethink the pace of some of its projects. And the future of the Soviet manned space program was very much in doubt as the year ended with the dissolution of the Soviet Union. Russia was expected to acquire most of the major assets with the exception of the Baikonur launch facility in Kazakhstan, where Soyuz missions were launched. In anticipation of the new age, 10 cosmonauts in October formed Space and We Co., Ltd., the Soviet Union's first space consulting firm. The U.S. and the Soviet Union signed protocols to expand joint missions, including possible flights of each nation's crews on the other's vehicles.

Space shuttle. Flights started late when cracks in critical hinges on the bellies of three space shuttle orbiters delayed launches for two months. The hinges close doors that let propellant lines pass through the heat shield. While *Discovery's* March 9, 1991, launch was delayed for nearly two months, *Atlantis* remained on schedule because it had only a single, less hazardous "hairline crack" (*Columbia* also had to be repaired).

On the first shuttle mission of the year, the second of the U.S. National Aeronautics and Space Administration's (NASA's) "Great Observatories for Space Astrophysics" was launched with an assist from two astronauts who helped unstick a primary antenna. *Atlantis* carried the 17-ton Gamma Ray Observatory (GRO) into orbit on April 5 and released it two days later. The crew comprised commander Steven Nagel, pilot Kenneth Cameron, and mission specialists Jerry Ross, Linda Godwin, and Jerome Apt. As GRO was activated, its high-gain antenna stayed in the stowed position. Ross and Apt made an unscheduled space walk to free the antenna. On a second, scheduled space walk the next day, they rehearsed space station assembly with three space trolleys that were tested along a 14-m (47-ft)-long rail in the payload bay. *At-*

Transfer tunnel for the International Microgravity Laboratory is installed in the cargo bay of the shuttle orbiter Discovery. *The laboratory was designed to study the responses of living organisms to weightlessness.*

lantis landed at Edwards Air Force Base, California, on April 11 after 143 hours 32 minutes in space, a day later than planned because of high winds.

Discovery returned to flight on April 28 with a payload related to the Strategic Defense Initiative. The crew comprised commander Michael Coats, pilot Blaine Hammond, Jr., and mission specialists Guion Bluford, Jr., Gregory Harbaugh, Richard Hieb, Donald McMonagle, and Charles Veach. The payload included an infrared telescope (called CIRRIS), which scanned the aurora and other parts of the upper atmosphere. The SPAS-2 satellite was released (and later recovered) to observe *Discovery* and rocket fuels that it sprayed into space. The objective of the experiments and other observations was to understand what future sensors would see when they searched for missile warheads against the background of space and Earth. *Discovery* landed at the Kennedy Space Center at Cape Canaveral, Fla., on May 6 after 199 hours 22 minutes.

Space shuttle *Columbia* carried the most ambitious life sciences mission put into space by the U.S. since 1974. The Space Life Science-1 used the Spacelab module as an onboard laboratory for mission specialists James Bagian, Margaret Rhea Seddon, and Tamara Jernigan and payload specialists Francis Gaffney and Millie Hughes-Fulford to conduct experiments on themselves, 29 rats, and over 2,400 jellyfish in the larval stage. The mission commander was Bryan O'Connor, and the pilot was Sidney Gutierrez. The experiment regimen included extensive tests on the crew in the months before launch, to establish a "baseline" set of measurements, and corresponding tests after landing. *Columbia* landed on June 14 at Edwards Air Force Base after 218 hours 14 minutes.

The first scheduled landing at the Kennedy Space Center since 1986 was made at the end of *Atlantis'* second 1991 mission (August 2–11), which deployed the fourth Tracking and Data Relay Satellite. Commander John Blaha, pilot Michael Baker, and mission specialists James Adamson, David Low, and Shannon Lucid flew the mission. After deploying the satellite, they spent the remaining time conducting medical and technological experiments. Other work included testing a lower-body negative-pressure device—a can that reduces air pressure around an astronaut's lower body, forcing blood back from the upper body. The landing at Kennedy—which saves time and money in comparison with landing at Edwards—was made possible by improvements to the runway and the shuttle's brakes. Mission time was 213 hours 21 minutes.

A night landing at Kennedy was scrubbed when bad weather forced the next shuttle mission to divert to Edwards. *Discovery* carried the Upper Atmosphere Research Satellite (UARS) into space on September

Artist's concept reveals an HL-20 shuttlecraft docked to the space station Freedom and another HL-20 returning to the Earth. The HL-20, designed to achieve rapid access to space with low maintenance costs, could carry as many as 10 passengers and small amounts of cargo to and from low Earth orbit.

12 in a rare night launch. The crew comprised commander John Creighton, pilot Kenneth Reightler, and mission specialists Charles Gemar, James Buchli, and Mark Brown. Deployment of UARS was slowed by minor radio problems, but the satellite was deployed on September 15. Soon afterward, *Discovery* had to make a slight orbit change to avoid the upper stage of a Soviet rocket that would have passed within 1.7 miles of it. That was too close for mission safety. After 149 hours 27 minutes, *Discovery* landed at Edwards on September 18.

The last mission of 1991, STS-44 (November 24–December 1), also resulted in the most extensive damage yet to *Atlantis'* boosters. As they parachuted into the ocean, the boosters apparently hit rough seas, causing a severe crack in the forward section of the right-hand booster. On an earlier mission three of four motor sections on a left-hand booster had been damaged beyond repair. In both cases the boosters performed as planned during launch and appeared to have normal reentries. No hazard to flight crews was diagnosed, but NASA was looking at ways to prevent any repetition of these events.

During the mission the crew of *Atlantis*—commander Frederick Gregory; pilot Terence Hendricks; mission specialists James Voss, Mario Runco, Jr., and Story Musgrave; and payload specialist Thomas Hennen—deployed a missile early warning satellite called Defense Support Program. Afterward, Runco and Hennen conducted the first acknowledged space spying test as they evaluated the ability of humans in orbit to assess targets and other objects on the ground. The mission was to last 10 days but was cut short when part of the guidance system failed.

NASA's first manned mission of 1992 was the International Microgravity Laboratory (IML-1), flown on *Discovery* January 22–30 by mission commander

Ronald Grabe; pilot Stephen Oswald; mission specialists Norman Thagard, David Hilmers, and William Readdy; and payload specialists Roberta Bondar of Canada and Ulf Merbold of Germany. IML-1 was designed to study the responses of living organisms and growing crystal to the weightless environment of space. (Microgravity describes the extremely low levels of acceleration that can still be measured in space.) Both Merbold and Thagard had performed similar work on Spacelabs 1 and 3, respectively. Several of their earlier experiments—such as growing gamma ray-detector crystals from a vapor or infrared-detector crystals from a solution—were being reflown to take advantage of lessons from their first flights. One group of experiments, provided by the U.S. and Canada, was dedicated to a better understanding of how the human inner ear reacts and adapts to space. More than half of all space travelers become space sick.

U.S. astronauts faulted their training in an "internal audit" leaked to the news media on Jan. 30, 1991. Among their complaints were simulators that often failed and were unrealistic, training materials that were poor or outdated, instructors who lacked experience, and secondary payload training that was late. Shuttle director Robert Crippen (who was later named director of the Kennedy Space Center) responded that only 10% of the astronauts cited those faults and that more than 70% rated the training as good to excellent.

The fourth and last Shuttle orbiter, *Endeavour*, was delivered to NASA at Rockwell's Palmdale, Calif., assembly plant on April 25, 1991. *Endeavour* replaced *Challenger*, which exploded in 1986. Although NASA wanted more orbiters, U.S. Vice Pres. Dan Quayle announced on July 24 that no more would be built. Soon afterward NASA announced

Soviet cosmonaut Sergey Krikalev aboard the space station Mir (above left) and on his return to the Earth (right) was marooned in orbit for 313 days because of the Soviet Union's financial crisis and political breakup.

that shuttle missions probably would not exceed 8–10 per year because of budget cuts, and at the year's end NASA was planning to cut some 5,000 jobs from the shuttle payroll.

Construction proceeded on a new factory in Mississippi to build an advanced solid-rocket motor that would increase shuttle payloads by 5,450 kg (12,000 lb), but NASA's 1993 budget plan proposed canceling the facility because of high costs. Meanwhile, *Columbia,* the first shuttle orbiter, was returned to its builder for six months of repair work and addition of a power module that would allow it to fly two-week missions starting in mid-1992.

A new enhancement for the shuttle neared completion as 1991 ended. Spacehab, a commercial venture involving U.S. and Italian aerospace firms, is a short module designed to provide extra storage and experiment space behind the shuttle cabin. Alenia of Italy delivered the first unit in early 1992, and preparations were under way for a first flight in 1993.

Design work continued on the HL-20, a small shuttlecraft that could carry up to 10 persons into space and back. The vehicle would be launched by a new rocket—the National Launch System—that went into early design work in 1991.

Two astronauts died during the year. Manley ("Sonny") Carter, Jr., was killed in the same plane crash that took the lives of former U.S. senator John Tower and 21 others on April 5. And James Irwin, who walked on the Moon as a member of the Apollo 15 crew in 1971, died of a heart attack (*see* OBITUARIES).

The Soviets retired their first *Buran* shuttle orbiter, which had flown only once, in 1988. A second

orbiter was nearing completion at the end of 1991, but there were doubts as to whether it would ever fly without a well-defined mission or source of funds. French astronaut Jean-Loup Chretien, an air force general and highly respected fighter pilot, started training in July 1992 on *Buran* systems; there was some speculation that he might fly on an early manned *Buran* mission about 1994. Meanwhile, the breakup of the Soviet Union loosened secrecy rules and allowed Western experts to visit a number of restricted facilities. There they learned that the Soviets had been developing a space fighter to shoot down U.S. military shuttle missions. Scale models of the space fighter had been photographed during ocean recovery after test flights in the 1980s, but their attack mission was not publicly known. The program was halted after the U.S. canceled plans to launch shuttle missions from a California site that would have allowed them to cross all of the U.S.S.R.

The first launch of Hermes, a three-person shuttlecraft to be boosted into space by the Ariane 5 rocket, was delayed from 1998 to 2000. In October there was talk of postponing the first launch until 2002 and the first manned flight until 2004. The vehicle would resupply ESA's *Columbus* space station and repair European science satellites in low-Earth orbit.

Space stations. One of the more bizarre aspects of the breakup of the Soviet Union was the apparent marooning of cosmonaut Sergey Krikalev aboard the *Mir* space station. Krikalev was supposed to return, after five months in orbit, on a Soyuz mission in October. As the Soviet Union's financial crisis deepened, it canceled a Soyuz mission to *Mir* and sent a later flight with cosmonauts to make up a combined crew with others already on *Mir*. The net result was that Krikalev lost his seat on the ride home, while crewmate Anatoly Artsebarsky returned to Earth. Krikalev was expected to return in March 1992 aboard a Soyuz mission that would take to *Mir* a German "guest" cosmonaut; another launch was planned in July with a French crew member, and a third was planned for autumn. Rumors that *Mir* might be sold "as is" prompted the crew to ask whether they, too, were up for sale.

During the year Helen Sharman, a British chemist, became the second person to take a paid trip to *Mir* when she flew aboard Soyuz TM-12 on May 18–26. Sharman was selected in the Juno advertising program, which largely failed and had to have its expenses covered by a Soviet-owned bank. The TM-12 mission was crewed by Artsebarsky and Krikalev, who stayed aboard *Mir* after rendezvous. Musa Manarov and Viktor Afanasyev returned to Earth on Soyuz TM-12.

During several summertime space walks, *Mir*'s crew enhanced the station by assembling a large trusslike structure made of advanced "memory" alloys that shrank back to their original shape when heated by sunlight. A thruster, to be attached to the truss later, was designed to improve *Mir*'s attitude control by virtue of its location farther from the center of mass. Other space walks deployed a cosmic-ray detector, fixed a TV camera, and moved solar panels from one module to a better position on another.

In October the Soviets announced that rather than launch the *Mir 2* space station in 1992, they would rearrange the modules on the current *Mir* (launched in 1986) in a pattern similar to the U.S. *Freedom* station. This would allow them to deploy solar panels in a more efficient manner.

The Soviet Union's Salyut 7 space station—one of the most successful in history—reentered the Earth's atmosphere and landed in the Atlantic Ocean on Feb. 6, 1991. Salyut 7, launched in 1982, had been unused (in favor of the more advanced *Mir*) since 1986. Some extended use had been expected, but solar activity expanded the Earth's atmosphere and dragged the station down faster than expected.

The U.S. space station *Freedom* went through a major redesign effort following orders from the U.S. Congress in October 1990 to make it simpler and less expensive. The redesigned *Freedom* would be host to four rather than eight astronauts in its initial operations and would require that a space shuttle remain docked with it for several months. Also reduced was the number of space walks that would be required for assembling the station. Even before the new design was released on March 21, 1991, the National Research Council criticized it as being inadequate to support meaningful studies on the effects of space travel on humans or to conduct advanced materials

science experiments; a centrifuge was later added to meet some of that criticism. Meanwhile, the American Geophysical Union led some 13 professional science organizations in opposing the space station. Hard on the heels of the redesign, station supporters had to fight a tough battle to keep the program alive when the Appropriations Committee of the U.S. House of Representatives voted to divert all but $100 million of its budget to veterans' and other programs. Most of the funding was later restored by the full House.

Budget problems in Europe postponed the first launch of modules for ESA's *Columbus* space station for three years, until 2003 (the delivery of the module for the U.S. station was unaffected). Japan took applications from 370 men and women who wanted to be in that nation's portion of *Freedom*'s crew.

Planetary exploration. During the year the Boeing Co. offered concepts for large surface rovers that would support two astronauts on a 14-day trek across the lunar surface. The rover would ride on wire-mesh wheels and have a large robot arm on the front to reduce the number of Moon walks the crew would have to make.

Using old space technology to reach Mars was advocated by the Synthesis Group, formed in 1990 to develop less expensive methods than other studies had developed and reporting on June 11. The group recommended that the Nuclear Engine for Rocket Vehicle Application (NERVA) be revived as a means of propelling manned missions into deep space. NERVA was nearing a space demonstration when it was canceled in 1972. Elements of the Saturn V moon rocket should also be adapted for the future, the group said, and new technologies for space suits, life support, and robotics should be developed.

Space probes

The year ended with the U.S. initiating plans to send small, unmanned probes back to the surface of the Moon to pave the way for manned missions early in the 21st century. The U.S. dominated the field during the year with Galileo, the most advanced space probe ever launched, encountering serious antenna problems, and Magellan, the Venus radar mapper, completing its primary mission just in time to be turned off.

The problems with Galileo apparently began several years before its launch but did not appear until long after it had departed from the Earth and was far beyond the kinds of rescue missions that had been mounted by space shuttle astronauts in the mid-1980s. Galileo's high-gain antenna had been kept furled—like a compact umbrella—since launch to protect it from intense sunlight as the spacecraft sailed past Venus. (Because its booster stage lacked the energy for a direct flight, Galileo was sent on a billiardlike trajectory that used the gravitational fields of Venus and Earth to boost it into the outer solar system.) The antenna, needed so that data and pictures could be transmitted at high rates after Galileo went into orbit around Jupiter in 1994, was supposed to be opened four months after the December 1990 flyby of the Earth, but it failed to do so.

Engineers concluded that lubricant on three or four of the antenna's rollers may have been lost during the long launch delay caused by the *Challenger* accident in 1986. Several attempts to shake the antenna loose failed, and engineers then started devising complex schemes to "soak" the mechanism with sunlight and in shade in hopes that the rollers would pop loose. That also did not work, and further attempts were postponed until the spring of 1992, when Galileo's trajectory brought it closer to the Sun (during its second flyby of Earth) and warmed the spacecraft even more.

Venus. The Magellan spacecraft, launched May 4, 1989, arrived at Venus on Aug. 10, 1990. The craft experienced few problems after arriving at Venus, but on Jan. 4, 1992, following a routine star calibration, it lost its backup transmitter. The main transmitter

During the past year the Magellan spacecraft, launched from the space shuttle Atlantis in 1989, provided views of the surface of Venus that had a resolution 10 times greater than that achieved by previous probes.

NASA

had failed in March 1991. However, with changes to the computer's software, engineers were able to resume mapping with the backup transmitter in late January although the data rate was reduced by more than half to avoid noise problems.

In October 1991 scientists released their first global maps of the surface. These had a resolution 10 times greater than previous satellite mappers and showed a striking, broken terrain with craggy valleys, mountains, and craters. (For additional information on Venus and Magellan, *see* Feature Article: DEMYSTIFYING THE MISTY PLANET.)

Mars. For the first time since the Viking landers arrived in 1976, Mars was scheduled to be revisited by the United States. NASA's Mars Observer, scheduled for launch in September 1992, was to carry an array of instruments to measure the atmosphere and remotely assay the chemistry of the surface. Late deliveries of instruments and other problems raised some doubts about whether it would be launched on time, though. What had started as a low-cost modification of an "off-the-shelf" satellite had grown into a $500 million project. Meanwhile, Soviet scientists tested a working model of a Mars surface rover on the rough terrain of the Kamchatka Peninsula in September and were invited by the Planetary Society to go to California's Mojave Desert, where U.S. designs were tested. Soviet plans to launch a balloon expedition on Mars were postponed two years, from 1994 to 1996, by budget problems. The balloon was designed to drift with an instrument package when warmed during the day. A mission with one orbiter and surface instruments was still planned for 1994, however.

Asteroids. An asteroid was visited by a man-made probe for the first time when Galileo flew past Gaspra on October 29 and took the first close-up pictures of such a body (although some scientists believe that the moons of Mars are captured asteroids). Because Galileo's main antenna could not be deployed, scientists were less certain of its position and speed relative to the asteroid and had to aim it to miss at a slightly larger distance—1,600 km (1,000 mi)—than originally intended. This reduced the resolution of the television images and delayed the transmission of all but one picture (sent in November) until late 1992 as Galileo neared the Earth. Gaspra is about 13 km (8 mi) in diameter and is believed to be a remnant from the creation of the solar system. It orbits about 485 million km (300 million mi) from the Sun.

More direct exploration of asteroids was proposed with the start of NASA's Discovery program, which would launch small, low-cost spacecraft atop midsize Delta rockets. The first near-Earth asteroid rendezvous mission could take off as early as 1997. But a more ambitious mission—Comet Rendezvous/Asteroid Flyby (CRAF)—was cut out of the 1993

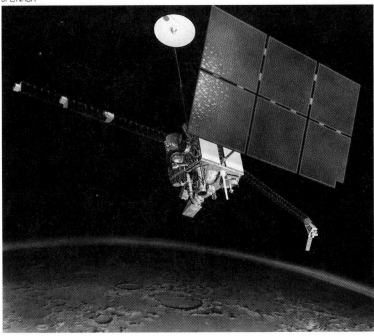

Artist's drawing shows the Mars Observer scanning the surface of Mars from its orbit around the planet. Scheduled for launch in September 1992, the probe was to carry instruments to measure the atmosphere of Mars and remotely assay the chemistry of its surface.

budget plan. CRAF would use a large Mariner Mark II spacecraft that would fire a small probe into a comet's nucleus for direct sampling. In a related area, ESA was hoping to have the Giotto spacecraft, which flew past Comet Halley in 1986, take a close look at Comet Grigg-Skjellerup in 1992.

Jupiter. Jupiter received a brief visit on Feb. 8, 1991, as Europe's Ulysses probe used the planet's intense gravity to make a hairpin turn and become in mid-1994 and mid-1995 the first spacecraft to fly over the polar regions of the Sun. (Virtually all solar missions had been restricted to observations along the same plane as the Earth's orbit.) The unusual route was selected in the 1970s because it takes less energy to go to Jupiter than to the Sun.

As it passed Jupiter, Ulysses measured charged particles, magnetic fields, and other aspects of the near-Jupiter environment. Even though it had been traveling through a "known" region of space—the plane of the ecliptic (the plane of the Earth's or-

Prototype of a Mars surface rover is tested by Soviet scientists on the rough terrain of the Kamchatka Peninsula. Photographing the vehicle is Harris Schurmeier, former associate director of the Jet Propulsion Laboratory, Pasadena, California.

bit extended to meet the celestial sphere)—Ulysses' advanced instruments yielded new data about the speed, composition, and energy of the solar wind. A nutation (wobble) problem in the rotating spacecraft was solved, and the spacecraft continued to perform exceptionally well.

The Voyagers. Deepest space was explored as the Voyager 1 and 2 spacecraft continued to send data from the edge of the solar system. The two explored Jupiter and Saturn in the 1980s, and Voyager 2 went on to fly past Uranus and, in 1990, Neptune. Each encounter accelerated the spacecraft, placing them on interstellar trajectories.

On the Voyager Interstellar Mission (VIM) they would seek the heliopause, the shock wave where the solar wind runs into the gases of intergalactic space. The heliopause in effect is a magnetic bubble that defines the outer limits of the solar system. Scientists anticipated that one of the Voyagers would hit the heliopause by the end of the century at a distance of 11 billion–22 billion km (7 billion–14 billion mi) from the Sun. That crossing would be measured by instruments that measured radiation belts and magnetic fields as the Voyagers flew past the four gas giant planets of the outer solar system.

At the same time, the ultraviolet spectrometers on the Voyagers were collecting data on active galaxies, quasars, and white dwarf stars. Because the spacecraft were so distant from the Sun, they could see the stars more clearly; there was less dust to reflect sunlight back into instruments and less sunlight (including solar ultraviolet) to be reflected. Thus, isolation in deep space increased the sensitivity of the spectrometers. Further, there were rarely other activities that kept the instruments from "staring" at one target for days or weeks, and no other instruments on the scan platform were in use. Astronomers were using the spectrometers through a guest observer program, often in concert with terrestrial observatories. This work was expected to continue through the year 2000, and contact with the Voyagers was expected to last until 2020 or 2030, when their nuclear power supplies would decay too low for signals to be sent to the Earth.

—Dave Dooling

Transportation

One of the major transportation events in the United States during the past year was congressional passage of the Intermodal Surface Transportation Efficiency Act. While the act was designed predominantly as a new six-year highway-funding measure, the $151 billion authorized to be spent during 1992–97—generated mostly from highway-user fees—would provide sizable funding for high-tech transport programs.

One such program was the development of Intelligent Vehicle Highway Systems (IVHS), which called for $660 million in funding (see *Highway transport,* below), and another called for $725 million for developing a prototype maglev passenger train (see *Rail transport,* below). Many other high-tech surface transportation innovations were expected to be funded because the new law provided considerable leeway in how grants to state and local governments could be used.

Air transport. Four new transport planes were being built in competition for a major share of the rapidly growing Pacific Rim market. All would have the capability to operate economically in long-distance, transoceanic service, both passenger and cargo. They included the Boeing 777, a twin-engined transport designed entirely with computers; the McDonnell Douglas MD-11, a trijet; and two now-complete Airbus Industrie transports, the two-engined A330 and four-engined A340. All four planes were to be equipped with the latest technologically advanced airframes, engines, and automated operating features. The most successful of the four, according to an Airbus Industrie official, would depend for the most part on the aircraft's ability to fill the needs of the Pacific Rim. These include the capability to offer high passenger capacity at low seat-kilometer costs and to service a relatively small number of origin–destination points for a region with a huge concentration of people around large hub airports.

Airbus Industrie announced that it had begun production of its all-freighter A300-600F two-engined, widebody jet transport following an order by Federal Express Corp. for 50 of them with an option for an additional 25. Deliveries were scheduled to start early in 1994, at a rate of six per year. These planes would replace Federal Express' 150 B-727 trijets. The new aircraft, according to Federal Express, had 40% greater capacity, required only two instead of three pilots, and should provide operating cost savings of about 20%. It was to be built to handle standardized containers and pallets; on some domestic routes each A300 could replace two B-727s.

Mostly because of the potential market between Asia and the U.S./Europe, with its long distances, interest in developing a new supersonic air transport continued to increase. Using the supersonic Concorde as a yardstick, the new High-Speed Civil Transport would have to carry twice as many passengers, operate at much higher speeds, fly much more quietly, and emit far less pollution before being considered acceptable for widespread use.

Because the technological and sociological challenges were so great and were still far from being solved, the multibillion-dollar costs necessitated a multinational approach. Such joint ventures were being formed, including Boeing and McDonnell Doug-

Airbus Industrie's all-freighter A300-600F, shown here in an artist's drawing, went into production during the past year. The first six of the two-engined, widebody jets were scheduled for delivery in 1994.

las to design an airframe; competing against them was the team of British Aerospace and France's Aérospatiale (the same partnership that built the Concorde). For the engines the two pairs included U.S. firms Pratt & Whitney and General Electric, with Britain's Rolls-Royce joining France's Snecma in a similar project.

The U.S. National Aeronautics and Space Administration (NASA) planned to spend $284 million over five years in order to develop new technologies to help the U.S. companies. Some of these included cutting the aircraft's weight by using composites of silicon and carbon and reducing noise by changes in the aircraft's silhouette and using engine noise suppressors or by using a combination engine able to operate in a quiet, turbofan mode on medium-distance domestic flights. Perhaps most challenging of all, economic feasibility would require a surcharge over regular airfares of more than 10–15%.

Expanded global air transport was not confined to commercial air carriers, as manufacturers of business aircraft began developing such planes capable of flying distances as far as Los Angeles to Moscow nonstop. The Canadian Group of Bombardier, Inc., and the U.S. Gulfstream Aerospace both were planning such an aircraft—with the former to start its program in late 1992 if it received 50 bona fide orders and the latter predicting actual first flights in early 1994. Canadair's Global Express aircraft was to have a range of 9,095 km (1 km = 0.62 mi), carry eight passengers, and cruise at a speed of Mach 0.85 or slightly better.

Because of strong public opposition to the construction of new, large commercial airports close to congested urban areas, few had been built in many years. An exception was one under construction near Denver, Colo. Touting it as the "world's first super-hub airport," supporters of that city's new $2 billion international terminal expressed confidence that it would sharply boost the area's economy and attract both passenger and air cargo carriers. Being built 50 km from downtown Denver, it would cover 137 sq km (1 sq km = 0.39 sq mi) in area.

Two AT&T electrical failures in September and November 1991—the first virtually shutting down the New York City area's three major airports during the evening peak travel period—quickly resulted in actions by AT&T and the U.S. Federal Aviation Administration (FAA) to prevent reoccurrences. AT&T tightened maintenance procedures and began rerouting lines so that such disruptions would occur at sharply reduced levels at any one place. The FAA announced that it would soon approve the Leased Interfacility National Airspace Communications System (Lincs), an advanced backup system that would allow the Air Traffic Control System to continue functioning if a similar failure occurred in the future. On the negative side, Lincs involved about 14,000 circuits in 5,000 locations and was expected to take three years to complete and install.

Highway transport. The Intermodal Surface Transportation Efficiency Act, passed in 1991, authorized $660 million over the period 1992–97 ($23 million in 1992) to promote the use of IVHS technologies, to sponsor operational tests of such systems, and to create an information clearinghouse. A strategic plan had to be submitted by the end of 1992, and a long-range goal was to have a fully automated roadway or test track in operation by the end of 1997. In brief, the IVHS program would adopt computer-control of highway traffic lights to facilitate traffic flow, employ advanced communications to provide drivers with continuous updated traffic conditions and suggested alternate routes, and eventually achieve automatic auto and truck control. Many IVHS projects were being tested in 1992.

Automatic toll-collection systems could reduce motor vehicle travel time, especially for commuters moving daily through high-volume tollgates. During the past year they were being tested for widespread use in New York, New Jersey, and Pennsylvania. Under the system a driver purchased an ID card, which was attached to the windshield of his or her vehicle. When the vehicle moved through the tollgate, a computer-responder would detect a radio signal emitted from the card and automatically deduct the toll charge from the driver's prepaid account. The new system was expected to increase each toll lane's capacity to 1,500 vehicles per hour, compared with the average 250 in manned collection lines and 500 with automatic coin collectors. If a driver passed through without paying, the vehicle's license plate would automatically be photographed for ticketing, or possibly fining, by mail. An unresolved problem was the inability of the computer to read ID cards on vehicles with unusual or dirty windshields. Automatic toll-collection systems were being introduced in Texas, Louisiana, and Oklahoma.

Because of the public's growing concern about truck accidents, a number of safety innovations were announced. An especially touchy area was accidents involving large trucks carrying hazardous materials, and so a new tank truck was designed and built to reduce rollovers. Developed jointly by Rohm & Haas Co., Freightliner Corp., Heil Co., and Shell Oil Corp., the truck had a low center of gravity, a turn-signaling system to sense close proximity of other motor vehicles, and an onboard computer able to monitor the truck's speed and even cut off its engine in an emergency. While the vehicle would cost about $170,000—about 30% more than a conventional truck—the backers believed the added investment to be worthwhile, since about 80% of tanker spills were the result of rollovers.

Truck manufacturers were also seeking ways to get rid of the blind-spot problems long faced by drivers of large vehicles. Tests were carried out with trucks using such innovations as a fiber-optic viewing system in the cab that provided a sharp and detailed picture of the blind spot created by the right front fender of most such trucks; the installation of special mirrors, including full-door ones on the passenger side, that could reflect both large and small motor vehicles; and the use of a closed-circuit television camera mounted on back of the trailer or large single-unit truck, which transmitted a picture of the rear of the vehicle to a screen in the cab.

On the law-enforcement side of truck safety, the U.S. Federal Highway Administration and the Arizona Department of Public Safety started testing a device designed to help identify and pull out of service truck drivers too fatigued to operate their vehicles safely. The device, called the Truck Operator Proficiency System, was developed by Systems Technologies of Hawthorne, Calif. The government sponsors cited statistics showing that driver fatigue was responsible for more than half of all large truck accidents. The device, to be applied where trucks were operating unsafely and thus pulled over by highway police, could measure about 20 areas of driver performance, including speed, response to signals, steering, throttle activity, lane deviation, accelera-

Handheld scanner (below) is used by a Roadway Package System (RPS) driver to scan a bar code on a package to achieve rapid delivery and more effective record keeping. RPS also developed an automated tilt-tray system (right) to sort packages efficiently.

Photos courtesy of Roadway Package System, Inc.

Gas pipeline of the United Texas Transmission Co. undergoes rehabilitation by a HydroKleaner that utilizes high-pressure water jets to strip the old coating material from the base metal and remove most corrosion. On the basis of an average 6.5 hours of running time, the jets cleaned about 1,400 meters (4,600 feet) of the 75-centimeter (30-inch) pipeline per day.

tion, and braking. Despite successful test results, the promoters expected strong opposition from truck-driver groups, especially owner-operators.

The small-package, intercity, for-hire trucking industry continued to be dominated by United Parcel Service (UPS). A major competitor in the business portion of this field was Roadway Package System (RPS) of Pittsburgh, Pa., which claimed that it handled 20% of this portion. Its rapid gain since starting its specialized service in 1985 could be attributed largely to its emphasis on high-tech innovations. It immediately installed bar codes on packages, along with hand scanners, in an effort to facilitate deliveries and record keeping. Its latest innovation, called STAR (for scan to automate receipt), permitted the firm's approximately 3,000 contracted drivers, using special electronic scanners, to record instantly both package deliveries and consignee receipts. At the day's end the scanner data were sent to RPS headquarters for storage on optical discs, thereby allowing rapid response to customer inquiries regarding deliveries.

UPS also announced high-tech innovations. It expected to have all of its 65,000 drivers equipped with a handheld computer as part of a $350 million program, Delivery Information Acquisition Device (DIAD). Designed, as was STAR, to permit quick and easy recording of both pickup and delivery information, the new system programmed a driver's route into the DIAD; on delivery of the package, the customer signed the DIAD with a penlike stylus. The computer data were electronically transferred to the UPS Information Services Data Center in Paramus, N.J., from which customers could obtain quick shipment-delivery information.

Yellow Freight System, one of the largest LTL (less-than-truckload) trucking companies, was given authority by the Interstate Commerce Commission to use laser-imaging technology to store the "millions of pieces of paper" that the ICC required it to retain. The carrier was now allowed to use optical scanners to read each document and convert the visual image to digital form. The image and data were burned by laser beam onto a permanent disk for storage and retrieval. Once on the disk, the data could be read but not altered or erased.

Pipeline. United Texas Transmission Co. of Houston, Texas, rehabilitated 19.2 km of its 75-cm (30-in) pipeline, utilizing a one-pass cleaning and recoating process that some experts believed could be the future of exterior pipeline rehabilitation. The contractor first excavated the pipe, then lifted it out of the ditch and cradled it, utilizing a side boom mounted on a crawler tractor that permitted its continuous movement ahead of the cleaning/coating units. A highly automated machine called the HydroKleaner was then positioned around the pipe, the machine's wraparound design making this possible. Its cleaning head contained high-pressure water jets that stripped the old coating material to a base metal and removed most corrosion. The machine's control panel and 22,750-liter (6,000-gal) water tank were part of the combined unit pulled by a single tractor. The water jets cleaned about 1,400 m (4,600 ft) per day, based on an average 6.5 hours of running time. Following the jet cleaning, the pipe was further cleaned to a near-white finish. This was followed by a coating system that used spray guns that completely circled the pipe to coat it evenly with a hot Protegol mixture. A handheld spray gun then was used for touch-ups.

The quick-drying properties of the Protegol allowed the pipe to be handled almost immediately for repositioning and retrenching.

New U.S. safety standards, as a result of recently passed legislation, affected the shoring of trenches, an activity commonplace in the pipeline field. According to the Occupational Safety and Health Administration, a construction crew was more likely to be killed or seriously injured by a trench cave-in than by any other type of construction accident. Contractors now had to comply with the new standards, and they were subject to a fine of a minimum $5,000 and a maximum $70,000 (multiplied by the number of workers involved) per violation. Furthermore, they had to take into account a wide variation of environmental conditions, such as soil (granular, clay, and firm), that govern the type of shoring (v-type if space permitted, wood if of standardized strength, heavy metallic shielding boxes, and aluminum hydraulic systems). The latter, because of their lightness and their use of ladder-type cylinders hydraulically pressurized to maintain strong and consistent pressure against the aluminum sidings, were believed to be the best choice in most instances.

Rail transport. Supporters of high-speed magnetic-levitation passenger trains (maglevs)—both lifted and propelled by electric magnets—received a major boost when the U.S. Congress authorized $230 million in 1992 and $495 million during 1993–97 toward development of this new form of transportation as a way to help ease the nation's highway- and air-congestion problems. Before Congress passed this legislation, its Office of Technology Assessment, after studying the research-and-development efforts already made to develop this mode of passenger transport, submitted a mixed report. It concluded that maglevs were technically feasible and, from a travel-time standpoint, could be competitive with air transportation. If adopted for U.S. use, they would require considerable government financial support, with $800 million to $1 billion needed just to develop a full-scale prototype. Major offsets to the high cost included energy efficiency and harmless effect on air quality. A possible temporary setback was the accident during a test run of Japan's only working prototype maglev train, which caught fire and was destroyed at 512 km/h. Despite this accident, Japan planned to put maglev trains into regular service early in the next century.

In Florida, with the full support of its High-Speed Rail Transportation Commission, a U.S.-German-Japanese consortium, Maglev Transit Inc. (MTI) of Orlando, was chosen to build the "world's first commercial high-speed maglev line." It was to be a 21.7-km system linking the Orlando International Airport with nearby Disney World and other vacation attractions. Construction was expected to cost about $600 million, with completion scheduled by the spring of 1995. The maximum speed of the train would be 400 km/h, and there would be four cars per train (three for passengers and one for baggage); the train would accommodate 400 people and 1,000 pieces of baggage. The short trip would take only 6½ minutes, at an estimated cost of $11.50 per passenger.

Amtrak, the U.S.-government-owned intercity passenger-train service, announced that in 1992 it would begin operating tests of a high-speed Swedish train capable of speeds up to 240 km/h on standard rail tracks. Under continuous pressure to reduce government subsidies, Amtrak could not expect to get the heavy funding needed to build a line in the congested Washington–New York–Boston corridor for bullet trains such as in France and Japan. Therefore, it chose the Swedish X2000 for cutting travel time—especially along the highly curved New York–Boston segment. This was possible because of the unique automatic tilting feature of this train, using an onboard computer to sense upcoming curves and automatically turn the wheel-and-axle assembly to allow the train to tilt around the curve, thus permitting faster, safer, and more comfortable rides for passengers. Preliminary passenger service was scheduled to be tested in 1993 for evaluation purposes; full regular service was not expected until 1997.

The Community of European Railways (CER) announced plans for a network of 30,000 km of new or modernized track capable of handling high-speed trains at 250 km/h between most cities throughout the 12-nation European Communities (EC), whose full union was scheduled for January 1993. While serious political and geographical problems remained to be solved, the transportation problems were just as serious. While most rail track gauges—other than Britain's—were the same, they took different sizes and weights of rolling stock, used varying signaling systems, and operated electric locomotives with different types of power. Regardless, CER claimed that the rail systems of the 12 EC nations plus those of the linking Austrian and Swiss systems would be able to raise the almost $100 billion investment needed from public and private funds to meet the technological challenges and permit formation of a fully integrated rail network.

GEC Alsthom, the builder of France's high-speed TGV (Train à Grande Vitesse) passenger trains, celebrated a decade of service between Paris and Lyon— a 467-km route. It claimed that its two-hour service, operating at an average speed of 275 km/h with departures every three minutes during rush hours, had taken 80% of the previous air service between the two cities. The company said that average speeds of 305 km/h were being phased into schedules and that further increases to 320 km/h were planned. In 1991 a test run through central France with a full

A high-speed magnetic-levitation passenger train system was being developed to link Orlando (Florida) International Airport with nearby Disney World and other vacation attractions. Completion of the project was expected in 1995.

train at up to 515 km/h was completed without any problems, the company stated.

In an effort to divert a major share of the huge frozen products market from truck to rail transport, General American Transportation Corp. (GATX) announced the development of a new refrigerated car, named Arcticar, that could handle 50% more cubic capacity than a conventional refrigerated car. A key feature of the Arcticar was its refrigeration by carbon dioxide, thus not requiring any moving parts. The car could be charged in one hour with up to 15 liquid tons of carbon dioxide. GATX claimed that savings for shippers could be sizable, especially for those with a large volume of traffic.

As one response to complaints of auto manufacturers about damage to new cars during rail transit, Greenbrier Companies of Lake Oswego, Ore., developed a system that moved new cars in standardized containers. Called Autostack, it allowed cars to be driven onto an open platform for two-level loading and allowed drivers to get out before loading, thus eliminating the banging of doors. Using rollers, the autos were placed on a special steel rack, which then slid into the container as a six-car unit. Tests with Fords and Nissans were said to show an extremely low damage rate and avoidance of paint contaminants (a frequent complaint).

Efforts by large U.S. freight railroads to require a new and successfully tested automatic equipment-identification system (AEI) were again delayed as shipper groups and small railroads opposed the move—mostly on the basis of cost. AEI consisted of attaching transponders (tags) to the side of rolling stock, with the cars' numbers plus other data coded on them. At selected roadside points the tags were read by a radio transmitter/receiver for relaying to a computer center, thus providing car-location data to the carrier on a continuous basis. After successfully operating the system for two years, CN Rail tagged its entire main-line fleet of locomotives with transponders and installed 190 interrogator sites across its system. Major ocean shipping lines also started using the AEI system on containers for rapid tracking. Similar systems in the past were less expensive but were rejected because the ID data on equipment tags often could not be read by roadside receivers because of dirt, ice, etc.

Water transport. U.S. Navy spokesmen cited the major role that roll-on/off cargo ships played in the Gulf war, and they said that 20 to 25 new ones were needed to fill future U.S. security goals. Such ships were of limited use for commercial purposes, but their self-loading/unloading capabilities made them ideal for the military. The Navy specified new design goals for maximum sustained speeds of 24 knots, a range of 12,000 nautical miles, self-contained cranes for handling palletized cargo, and ship lengths of 200–275 m (700–900 ft).

While containerships continued to gain a growing share of transoceanic general freight traffic, many carriers handling break-bulk cargoes (which could be unloaded in a piecemeal manner at various points on the voyage) were holding their own—largely through the use of new ship designs and cargo-handling techniques. Such carriers believed that break-bulk ship design favored vessels having deep, rectangular, and open single decks with huge holds covered by hatches of virtually the same width. This allowed rapid loading and unloading by onboard cranes of both palletized and containerized shipments. Cargo-

423

handling time could be reduced sharply by the use of rotary-type and gantry cranes, which allowed pallet/ container pickups of 20–30 per hour, as compared with only 6 when the kingpost boom was used. Break-bulk carriers also operated specialized ships dedicated to moving only one type of cargo, such as steel, automobiles, and lumber.

As directed by the U.S. Congress, oil tankers entering U.S. ports, starting in the year 2015, would be required to have double hulls or be built to a design equally effective in preventing oil spills. The National Research Council released an analysis of 17 different design concepts and concluded that "on the basis of cost-effectiveness, the double hull is among the best values." Views of other reputable groups were expected in early 1992.

As a possible sign of things to come, the U.S. Coast Guard was expected to put into service in the summer of 1992 "the most advanced vessel traffic system in the world" for safeguarding oil tanker traffic. It was being installed in Prince William Sound, Alaska, the site of the huge *Exxon Valdez* oil spill. The completed system would automatically provide around-the-clock positions, within 10 m (33 ft), of all ships operating in the sound.

Specialization of containers was being tried to generate new ocean cargo. One approach was to use high-tech equipment to control the amounts of nitrogen, oxygen, and carbon dioxide within the container in order to lengthen dramatically the shelf life and freshness of high-value perishables such as asparagus, cut flowers, and delicate fruits. Such a container would be equipped with a computer system that monitored the air and made adjustments throughout the cargo trip, tripling the cargo's life on a normal move. Ocean carriers saw this development as a way to compete with high-cost, low-volume air freight, despite the additional expense per container of about $1,100 for the modified-atmosphere model.

—Frank A. Smith

U.S. science policy

Rep. John Dingell (Dem., Mich.) might seem an unlikely character to play a pivotal role in shaping key aspects of U.S. science policy. Although as chairman of the House Energy and Commerce Committee's Oversight and Investigations Subcommittee he exerted a powerful influence over several large federal agencies, he readily admitted that he was no expert in science, modestly referring to himself as a simple lawyer whose job it was to look out for the taxpayers' interests. Yet during the past year, investigations started by his committee shook the scientific community right down to its roots. The presidents of two of the most prestigious research institutions in the country—Stanford University and Rockefeller University, New York City—announced their resignations in the wake of investigations begun by Dingell. His committee also forced the federal government to reexamine the way it dealt with scientific misconduct, as well as the way it supported university-based research. Not bad for a simple lawyer.

Of course, Dingell was not the only key player in the science policy arena. In 1991 the National Institutes of Health (NIH) got its first woman director, cardiologist Bernadine Healy, and Healy went right to work setting a bold new agenda for her $9 billion agency.

Scientific misconduct. If there was one issue certain to start arguments at all levels of the scientific establishment, it was scientific misconduct. Dingell began the first of his celebrated misconduct investigations in 1989 when two whistle-blowers at the NIH told him about the charges of a postdoctoral fellow at Tufts University, Medford, Mass., against her boss, immunologist Thereza Imanishi-Kari. Imanishi-Kari had been studying the immune responses of mice she had genetically altered. The fellow, Margot O'Toole, claimed that Imanishi-Kari's original laboratory data did not support the results that were published in the journal *Cell* in 1986. Imanishi-Kari insisted that O'Toole's accusations were unfounded, as did Nobel Prize-winning biologist David Baltimore, who was one of Imanishi-Kari's coauthors on the *Cell* paper. Dingell was not satisfied, however. He believed that O'Toole's concerns were not being taken seriously enough. He insisted that the NIH open a formal investigation, and he called on the U.S. Secret Service to check out Imanishi-Kari's laboratory notes.

By the spring of 1991 the NIH had completed its investigation and, in a widely circulated draft document, concluded that Imanishi-Kari had fabricated data and that Baltimore, while not guilty of any personal misconduct, had failed to address O'Toole's concerns in an appropriate way. After years of vigorously defending Imanishi-Kari, Baltimore changed his stance and apologized to O'Toole. Scientists throughout the nation were stunned. If they had had no particular reason to believe Imanishi-Kari, they had certainly believed the word of a Nobel laureate and leading biologist. The uproar prompted Baltimore, who had been appointed president of Rockefeller University in the fall of 1989, to resign.

A second investigation of a prominent scientist begun at Dingell's urging failed to reach a firm conclusion in 1991. In 1989 an investigative reporter for the *Chicago Tribune* raised questions about whether National Cancer Institute scientist Robert Gallo and his colleagues had done the work necessary to claim credit as codiscoverers of the human immunodeficiency virus (HIV) that causes AIDS. Gallo's work was published in a landmark paper in the journal

Science in 1984. At first, the NIH ignored the *Tribune* article, but Dingell insisted that the agency look more closely at the newspaper's accusations. The NIH concluded that there was sufficient doubt about the accuracy of some details in the *Science* paper to begin a full-scale investigation. In a draft report of their conclusions that leaked to the press, NIH investigators concluded that Gallo had been guilty of sloppiness and lack of collegiality but not misconduct. The draft was more critical of Gallo's associate Mikulas Popovic, suggesting that he might have been guilty of misconduct for mislabeling some figures in the paper. Gallo and Popovic's defenders argued that the case against the pair was inconclusive, and by year's end the issue had not been settled.

The investigations of Imanishi-Kari and Gallo prompted the government to consider changing the way it oversaw scientific conduct. For biomedical research, the NIH Office of Scientific Integrity (OSI) handled most investigations, although a preliminary investigation was always carried out by the accused scientist's host institution. But OSI had been slow to close many cases, and by the end of 1991 the federal government was looking into some way of creating government-wide misconduct procedures that would streamline future investigations.

Healy and the NIH. As the new NIH director, Healy took an active role in trying to reform the misconduct-investigation process, but her effectiveness was compromised when she ran afoul of Dingell. Soon after taking office in April, Healy ordered Suzanne Hadley, former deputy director of the OSI, to give up her role directing the Imanishi-Kari and Gallo investigations. Healy said she did this because Hadley had formally left the OSI, and she did not want Hadley running a "satellite investigation office" from her new position in the Science Policy and Legislation Division. Dingell accused Healy of trying to backpedal on the two high-profile investigations, and a public showdown before Dingell's committee left both sides seeing red.

Despite her problems with Dingell, Healy scored well with most of the rest of Congress. She pleased feminist legislators by starting the Women's Health Initiative, a $500 million project billed as the largest clinical trial of all time. She also began planning for a minority health initiative. For the scientific community, she offered a new research award called the Shannon Grants. The new grants, worth up to $100,000 over two years, were designed to help individual scientists who just missed the cutoff for receiving a grant keep their labs going while they reapplied for funding. She promised federal research scientists at the NIH campus in Bethesda, Md., that she would address some of their long-standing concerns about noncompetitive salaries, tedious red tape for purchasing equipment, and restrictions on travel.

Healy's debut was not all smooth sailing. Although she had approved funding for a survey of teenage sexual behavior—deemed crucial by social scientists looking for a way to slow teen pregnancy rates and curb the spread of HIV—she was overruled by an angry Health and Human Services Secretary Louis Sullivan, who felt that she should have consulted him before awarding such a controversial grant. Healy was already unpopular with the more conservative members of Pres. George Bush's administration for her position favoring the use of fetal tissue from induced abortion in transplantation research. The administration said it would not support such research, although in Congress the House passed legislation that would permit funding.

Healy ran into more than a little bit of opposition when she began a strategic planning process for the NIH. Although most observers agreed that some sort of central planning for the agency was appropriate, many feared it would lead to centralized planning of research. Although the planning process continued, the NIH Strategic Plan had become a controversial document.

Government funding for research and development. Healy also caused much consternation among research administrators for her views on indirect costs, the money the federal government pays research institutions to cover their "overhead" related to research. Typically, indirect costs are figured as a percentage of the direct costs of a research grant or contract, but Dingell began in 1990 to ask just what universities were doing with their indirect cost money. What he found shocked the nation. In many instances the cost of flowers for the college president's dinner table, lavish parties for donors to the university, fancy furniture, and even tickets to football games got lumped under "indirect costs." Dingell's investigations uncovered so much dirty linen in the case of Stanford University that its president, Donald Kennedy, announced his resignation.

Both Congress and the White House started looking into ways of curbing indirect-cost abuses. Healy argued in favor of caps on the indirect-cost rates institutions could charge the government. The White House Office of Management and Budget, with the support of Congress, opted for a 26% cap on all administrative indirect costs, but Healy promised to look into ways of achieving additional savings in the payment of those costs.

The political push to reduce indirect-cost payments came at a particularly difficult time for research universities, both public and private. For the first time in more than a decade, the average spending by states to institutions of higher education fell in 1991, putting the squeeze on many public institutions. At the same time, the economic recession was taking its toll on the private universities, lowering

Photos, AP/Wide World

(Right) Rep. John Dingell (Dem., Mich.), as chairman of the House Energy and Commerce Committee's Oversight and Investigations Subcommittee, strongly influenced U.S. science policy during the past year. Among his efforts was an investigation of National Cancer Institute scientist Robert Gallo (far right) to determine the legitimacy of Gallo's claim to have been a codiscoverer of the virus that causes AIDS.

their income from endowments and placing practical restrictions on the tuition increases they might consider to offset other losses.

Ironically, one area in which universities fared well was the receipt of earmarked funds from Congress, so-called pork-barrel politics. Often with the aid of a Washington, D.C., lobbyist, a university would approach a member of Congress representing the university's district or state and ask for a special appropriation to build a building or open a center. If the congressman was a member of one of the appropriations committees, so much the better. According to an investigation by the Congressional Research Service requested by Rep. George Brown (Dem., Calif.), chairman of the House Science, Space and Technology Committee, an astounding $509 million worth of special research and development projects went to academic institutions through the pork-barrel process. Brown and others were trying to find ways of limiting "pork," since it flies in the face of any kind of rational planning for a coherent research policy.

Despite the distress in universities, individual scientists seemed to be doing a bit better financially in 1991 after a dismal showing the year before. The NIH, for example, was able to award nearly 6,000 new research grants, about 1,800 more than two years earlier. Nevertheless, many scientists maintained that support for "small science" was woefully inadequate. A report prepared by Nobel Prize-winning physicist Leon Lederman provided anecdotal evidence that many scientists felt frustrated as they tried to garner research support, although the report itself was admittedly "unscientific" in its sampling. Lederman called for a doubling of the U.S. science budget, but critics thought that that was an unrealistic goal in a climate of constrained fiscal growth. Lederman's concern for the individual scientists was not wholly unfounded. Clearly, declin-

ing budgets at the Department of Defense meant less money for individual researchers, and expanding budgets for Big Science projects were putting a strain on money reserved for the smaller research portfolios at the National Aeronautics and Space Administration (NASA) and the Department of Energy (DOE). Congress did fairly well by the DOE in 1991, however; the fusion energy program was put back on track, with a $337 million budget, and there also was additional money for renewable energy sources and advanced nuclear reactor development. Walter Massey took over from Erich Bloch at the National Science Foundation (NSF), promising to preserve most of Bloch's programs and working effectively behind the scenes to keep the agency on track to receive a promised doubling of its budget. Individual researchers continued to be the funding agency's primary focus, but some of the NSF's other activities tended to steal the spotlight. In February the NSF announced that it would be supporting another 14 Science and Technology Centers. These centers, worth approximately $10 million over five years, were intended to allow scientific projects to proceed on a larger scale than an individual researcher could contemplate but not become so large that they deserved megaproject status. The new crop of centers focused on research topics ranging from Antarctic astronomy to cognitive science to light-microscope imaging. The centers were intended to facilitate the transfer of technology from the research lab to industry and to improve science education.

Although the centers took only a tiny fraction of the NSF's total research budget, critics charged that centers would deprive individual researchers of opportunities to win support for their own ideas and force them to join large teams that would stifle innovation. Massey disagreed, insisting that the centers were an important new direction for the agency. He also indicated that he was happy to see the NSF's spending on science education increase. President Bush made good on his 1988 campaign promise to become the education president, with budget proposals of $390 million for the NSF's education activities. Not to be outdone, Congress tacked on an additional $52 million, bringing the 1992 total to $442 million.

Although federal spending on AIDS research continued to grow, the rate of growth slowed considerably, especially for basic research on the HIV virus. Total spending on AIDS for fiscal 1992 amounted to $4.4 billion. The AIDS epidemic also prompted a rethinking in the way the Food and Drug Administration (FDA) approved new therapies. Activists argued persuasively that AIDS patients could not afford to wait years to gain access to promising new drugs, and the FDA listened. The first drug approved to treat HIV infection—Zidovudine, or AZT—cleared the FDA in 1987 after only 13 months of clinical trials—the fastest approval in FDA history. In 1991 dideoxyinosine (DDI), another drug that apparently slows the devastating course of the disease, also received approval in near-record time. With David Kessler as the new agency head, the FDA seemed poised to begin a major overhaul of its drug-approval practices. An interesting conflict that could have long-term implications for federal researchers arose over the marketing of AZT. Although the Burroughs Wellcome Co. was the exclusive supplier of AZT, a generic drug manufacturer sued the company in a North Carolina court, arguing that Burroughs Wellcome's patents on AZT were not enforceable because government scientists who were not working for Burroughs Wellcome contributed significantly to the drug's development. The government, anxious to see the cost of AZT come down, granted a license to the generic manufacturer for its rights to AZT in the event that the court agreed that Burroughs Wellcome did not deserve an exclusive patent.

Big Science projects. The Human Genome Initiative, a project to create a genetic map and then sequence all three billion base pairs that make up the DNA in the 23 human chromosomes, continued on track during the year, with both the DOE and the NIH receiving the requested budget increases for the program. In the summer the NIH applied for a patent on some 1,000 partial sequences of genes known to be active in human brains. Scientists and even some in government were horrified at this idea. The NIH had no idea what the genes that were being sequenced did, but by the use of modern techniques, determining the sequences was a fairly simple task. If the patent were awarded, however, scientists feared that when the functions of the genes were discovered, researchers would have to pay the NIH royalties in order to study them. Critics worried that this would stifle research, but NIH officials countered that they were merely trying to protect the government's legitimate financial interest in commercial products that might be based on government scientists' research. By the year's end, the government was trying to decide whether to file a patent on an additional 1,800 sequences.

The problems affecting another Big Science project, the Superconducting Super Collider (SSC), were technical as well as political. Any project with a price tag of $8.5 billion was certain to get some political heat, and there were those in Congress and even within the Bush administration who argued that in the current budget climate it would be unwise to undertake such a large project. Despite a government pledge to obtain one-third of the SSC's cost from foreign partners in the project, efforts to attract substantial financial support from other countries did not come to fruition during the past year, although it was still possible that Japan would make a significant contribution to the project. Even without foreign investment, Congress provided the SSC with $434 million for construction costs in its 1992 budget.

The SSC's technical problems were thornier. The super collider was to consist of an 87-km (54-mi)-diameter ring of superconducting magnets that would propel charged particles in opposite directions at high energy and at speeds approaching the speed of light. When the two opposing beams collided, they would give off a spray of daughter particles that would be analyzed for clues about the fundamental nature of matter. Two giant detectors, each based on a different design principle, would be placed in special chambers inside the ring. In the spring of 1991, however, SSC director Roy Schwitters rejected plans for a detector being designed by a team led by Nobel Prize-winning physicist Samuel Ting. Schwitters was not convinced that Ting could complete the project on schedule. That left SSC planners with only one approved detector design and touched off a scramble to design a different detector that could be built in time.

Space programs. Many would argue that the third Big Science project to win congressional support in 1991 was not a science project at all. In July a coalition of 14 scientific societies, led by the American Physical Society (APS), launched a campaign to persuade Congress to kill plans for the space station. The societies were concerned not only that the space station would offer little opportunity for worthwhile science but also that its ever-escalating costs would gobble up scarce discretionary funds that might otherwise go into more meritorious science projects. Robert Park of the APS called the project "orbiting pork barrel" since it offered so many politically attractive investment opportunities without having a good scientific rationale. At one point, when an appropriations committee had eliminated funds for the space station during the budget process, it appeared

RESEARCH HAND SIGNALS

THIS IS GOING TO TAKE ABOUT NINE YEARS

I THINK I'M ON TO SOMETHING

WE NEED ANOTHER $3 MILLION

that the scientists might have their way. But a fight led by Brown, among others, restored the funds in the full House, and NASA received the full $2 billion it requested for the station.

Overall, it was a mixed year for NASA. Recovering from the debacle of the faulty mirror design in the Hubble Space Telescope, astronomers found that there were still valuable investigations that could be carried out with the telescope, and sophisticated image-enhancement techniques were able to overcome some of the telescope's optic problems. In April NASA launched another in its "great observatory" series, the Gamma Ray Observatory; consequently, by summer scientists were poring over data from a new part of the electromagnetic spectrum. The Magellan radar mapper nearly completed its high-resolution surface map of Venus, providing dramatic evidence of volcanic activity. The satellite Ulysses, a joint mission with the European Space Agency, continued its journey to Jupiter, where it would loop out of the plane of the planets and head back toward the Sun to study the solar polar regions. The long-delayed Jupiter probe and orbiter, Galileo, continued its celestial billiard shot as it swung around Venus once and the Earth twice to pick up sufficient velocity to make it to the outer planets. To their horror, however, NASA scientists were unable to deploy Galileo's primary antenna. With the antenna folded up like an umbrella for launch, one of the pins holding it closed apparently got stuck, and the antenna might never be usable. If various maneuvers to shake the pin loose failed, Galileo would be able to provide only a tiny fraction of the data expected from it.

NASA also continued developing a large new Earth-observation system that would play a key role in the future of global-change research. The issue of whether the Earth was heating up as a result of the rise in man-made greenhouse gases continued to be a hot topic in scientific circles. Some scientists, however, worried that climate research was being sold under false pretenses. They worried that if it turned out that the greenhouse effect was not responsible for the rise in temperature, or if the rise was transient, lasting only a few years, scientists would be accused of misleading the public. Whether or not that happened, the global-change bandwagon continued to roll along, with $1.1 billion in the 1992 budget designated specifically for environmental research.

Global change was one of five so-called crosscutting initiatives being developed under the auspices of the Federal Coordinating Council for Science, Engineering and Technology (FCCSET), which was mandated by Congress in the 1970s to provide a mechanism for the various federal agencies involved in scientific research to coordinate their activities. Nevertheless, it was not until President Bush appointed former Yale University physicist D. Allan Bromley as his science adviser that the FCCSET began to function effectively. Bromley inherited one FCCSET initiative—in high-performance computing—and immediately approved two more, one in science education and another in global change. In 1991 two more initiatives were approved: biotechnology research and material science.

Some critics grumbled that the FCCSET was taking individual agencies' budget discretion away from them, and others complained that the coordination process was time consuming and unwieldy. Congress seemed pleased with the process, however, and it was likely to continue, even if Bromley left the White House.

—Joseph Palca

428

Scientists of the Year

Honors and awards

The following article discusses recent awards and prizes in science and technology. In the first section the Nobel Prizes for 1991 are described in detail. The second section is a selective list of other honors.

Nobel Prize for Chemistry

Before Swiss professor Richard Robert Ernst, winner of the 1991 Nobel Prize for Chemistry, began refining the methodology of high-resolution nuclear magnetic resonance (NMR) spectroscopy, the technique was a specialized tool of limited utility for chemical analysis. Ernst's contributions not only made NMR spectroscopy a basic and indispensable tool in chemistry but also extended its usefulness into other scientific fields, including physics, biology, and medicine.

According to the Nobel citation, "NMR spectroscopy has during the last 20 years developed into perhaps the most important instrumental measuring technique within chemistry. This has occurred because of a dramatic increase in both the sensitivity and the resolution of the instruments, two areas in which Ernst has contributed more than anybody else."

The phenomenon of nuclear magnetic resonance was first observed in 1945, independently, by two U.S. scientists, Felix Bloch and Edward M. Purcell, who were awarded the 1952 physics Nobel for their discovery. The term refers to the selective absorption and reemission of very-high-frequency radio waves by certain atomic nuclei when they are subjected to a strong stationary magnetic field. Electrons, protons, and neutrons (the constituents of an atom) all spin somewhat like tops and so have angular momentum, a term used to describe the persistence of rotation of a body. Both the spins and the orbital motions of these atomic components give rise, in turn, to angular momentum in the nuclei of many atoms. This nuclear angular momentum is known as nuclear spin, though it is more complicated than the spinning of a top. The spin is also said to have a certain orientation, meaning that it can spin in one direction or the other about its axis of rotation.

Nuclei in which at least one proton or one neutron is unpaired (that is, nuclei in which the spins of the various components do not completely cancel one another) act like tiny magnets. If such nuclei are placed in a strong magnetic field, they will precess around the direction of the magnetic field, describing a cone just as the axes of spinning tops trace out cone-shaped surfaces while they precess in the

Earth's gravitational field. The possible angles of the cone—or the different orientations that the nuclear spin can take in the field—are quantized, that is, they can have only certain values. Any changes in the orientation of nuclear spin correspond to changes in the nucleus' energy level and are accompanied by energy jumps.

The technique of NMR spectroscopy exploits this fact, forcing a jump between nuclear energy levels by the application of weak radio waves. The frequency of the waves is varied until it matches the angular precession frequency of the nucleus—called the nucleus' resonance frequency. When this condition is met, the precessing nucleus absorbs energy from the radio waves and jumps to a higher energy level. In laboratory practice, the energy change induces an electric signal in a detector. The strength of the signal is then plotted as a function of frequency in a diagram called an NMR spectrum.

Such a diagram is useful because the amount of energy absorbed by the nucleus depends on the identity of the nucleus and on its immediate chemical environment. Consequently, when the phenomenon of nuclear magnetic resonance was discovered, chemists realized that they could use NMR measurements to determine both the nature of a nucleus and the molecular structure of the molecule of which that nucleus was a part. The technique, though successful, was restricted in its applications for more than two decades by a lack of sensitivity: only certain strongly responsive isotopes of a few elements—primarily hydrogen, fluorine, and phosphorus—could be reliably analyzed by means of NMR.

In 1966 Ernst, working with a U.S. colleague, Weston A. Anderson, found that the sensitivity of NMR spectroscopy could be dramatically increased if the slow, sweeping radio waves traditionally applied to a sample to induce energy transitions were replaced by short, intense pulses. Ernst and Anderson measured the signals generated from the nucleus' energy jumps as a function of time elapsed after each pulse rather than as a function of frequency. The NMR signal plotted in this way yields a complex graph that is not easily interpreted. However, it is

Richard R. Ernst
© The Nobel Foundation 1991

possible to analyze the resonance frequencies that are present in the signal and to convert the signal to an NMR spectrum by using a computer to perform a complex series of mathematical operations known as a Fourier transformation.

Using these methods, Ernst and Anderson improved the sensitivity of NMR spectroscopy as much as a hundredfold. Their advance, called Fourier-transform NMR, enabled chemists to study more types of nuclei and smaller amounts of materials and, consequently, to analyze such rare isotopes as carbon-13, which makes up only about 1% of the natural carbon in existence.

Ernst's second major contribution to the field of NMR spectroscopy came in the mid-1970s, when analytic chemists faced a new hurdle: the study of very large molecules. Ernst and his colleagues developed a so-called two-dimensional NMR technique that gave better resolution—that is, allowed finer discrimination of specific details about the identity and positions of atoms in a mass of complex signals—than had been possible with earlier methods.

The new technique involved subjecting nuclei in a magnetic field to sequences of radio pulses, rather than to single pulses, and varying the length of time between pulses and measurement. The Fourier transformation was then performed twice, with respect to two different time parameters, to obtain a two-dimensional frequency spectrum. According to the Nobel committee, the higher resolution attained as a result of introducing the second frequency dimension was "like looking at the skyline of a mountain range and then looking at the whole range from an aircraft above." Ernst's technique gave chemists the ability to resolve complex NMR measurements and to find which atoms in a molecule lie nearest each other.

Ernst was born on Aug. 14, 1933, in Winterthur, Switz. He earned a diploma in chemistry in 1956 from the Eidgenössische Technische Hochschule (ETH; Federal Technical Institute) in Zürich and a Ph.D. in physical chemistry from the same school in 1962. In 1963 he went to the United States, where he was employed as a research scientist at Varian Associates in Palo Alto, Calif. He returned to Switzerland in 1968 to join the faculty at the ETH, where he remained, becoming a full professor in 1976. In 1978 he began serving as a consultant for Spectrospin AG, Fallanden, Switz., and became vice president of its board of directors.

Ernst is credited with numerous inventions and holds several patents in his field. He has received many awards in addition to the Nobel Prize, including the 1991 Wolf Prize in Chemistry, which he shared with Alexander Pines of the U.S., and the Louisa Gross Horwitz Prize of Columbia University, New York City, shared with fellow NMR researcher Kurt Wüthrich. Other awards include a silver medal from ETH, Zürich (1962), the Ruzicka Prize (1969), a gold medal from the Society for Magnetic Resonance in Medicine, San Francisco (1983), the Benoist Prize (1986), the Kirkwood Award from Yale University (1989), and the Prix Ampère (1990).

Nobel Prize for Physics

According to some of his colleagues, French physicist Pierre-Gilles de Gennes was the "Isaac Newton of our time." Winner of the 1991 Nobel Prize for Physics, de Gennes earned the epithet for his ability to perceive common features in widely differing physical systems and to formulate broad, generalized rules and mathematical formulas for the ways in which such systems move from order to disorder. The Nobel committee cited in particular de Gennes's work in furthering the understanding of how complex forms of matter such as liquid crystals (used for displays in calculators, digital watches, and laptop computers) and polymers (long chains of identical molecular units used to make such substances as nylon) behave during the transition from order to disorder.

De Gennes began his career by studying the relatively straightforward phenomenon of phase changes in magnets. In an ordinary permanent magnet, the constituent atoms themselves behave as tiny magnets, and it is their alignment that confers magnetic properties on the bulk material. Heating the magnet disrupts the alignment and creates a disordered state in which the atomic magnets are more randomly oriented. The transition from order to disorder always occurs at a well-defined temperature. Sometimes it takes place by means of sharp jumps rather than through a gradual randomization process. De Gennes's contribution to this picture was a description of these transitions in mathematical terms.

During the 1960s and 1970s de Gennes branched out into the study of other systems, most notably superconducting materials, liquid crystals, and polymers. Some of these systems appeared so complicated and unpredictable that few physicists had thought it possible to incorporate them into any general physical description, but it was his ability to perceive the mechanisms within even the most complex systems that earned de Gennes his reputation.

In the late 1960s de Gennes formed the Orsay Liquid Crystals Group, an interdisciplinary scientific consortium at the University of Paris. Liquid crystals are substances that flow like a liquid but maintain some of the ordered structure characteristic of a crystal. Liquid-crystal structures are easily affected by changes in mechanical stress, electromagnetic fields, temperature, and chemical environment. One category of liquid crystals, called smectic liquid crys-

Pierre-Gilles de Gennes
© The Nobel Foundation 1991

tals, consists of flat layers of cigar-shaped molecules with their long axes oriented perpendicularly to the plane of the layer. Each layer is one or two molecules thick, and the positions of the molecules within each layer can be ordered or random, depending on the substance. Although the layers flow freely over each other, the molecules within each layer remain oriented and do not move between layers.

Nematic liquid crystals, another category, are also oriented with their long axes parallel, but they are not separated into layers. They behave somewhat like toothpicks in a box, maintaining their orientation but free to move in any direction. Two of de Gennes's scientific contributions involved nematic liquid crystals. He explained anomalous light scattering from such crystals, which depends in a complicated way on fluctuations in the orientational order of the molecules. He also described the phenomenon whereby an electric field, by inducing a phase change in a region of the nematic liquid crystal, transforms the region from transparent to opaque. As a result, the region becomes visible—the phenomenon exploited in liquid-crystal digital displays.

De Gennes subsequently turned his attention to polymers, the behavior of which is yet more complicated than that of liquid crystals. Polymers are composed of very large molecules that are themselves formed of long chains of tens of thousands of repeating chemical units. In solution, polymer molecules form complicated loops and tangles. Polymers had long eluded scientific attempts to untangle their structure and behavior, but by applying the principles he had learned from simpler systems, particularly magnets, de Gennes succeeded where others had failed.

His descriptions of order phenomena in polymers were soon extended to polymers in more concentrated solutions, in which the various chains can partly entangle themselves, and in high concentrations in pure melts of polymers. Two of de Gennes's models for polymer-chain motion, which have been experimentally confirmed, are the "blob" model, in which a certain segment of a chain can move as if it were free, and the "reptation" model, which describes the serpentine motion of a polymer chain within a tangle of surrounding polymer chains.

With this work, de Gennes opened the way for new descriptions of complicated order phenomena in polymers and, of equal importance, established guidelines for predicting how polymer chains and their individual parts can move. These achievements made it possible for scientists to determine and control polymer properties and so put the materials to better practical use.

De Gennes was born on Oct. 24, 1932, in Paris. He earned a Ph.D. from the École Normale Supérieure, Paris, in 1955. For the next four years he worked as a research scientist at the Center for Nuclear Studies, Saclay, and then briefly as a postdoctoral fellow at the University of California at Berkeley.

From 1959 to 1961 de Gennes served as an ensign in the French Navy. Thereafter he became a professor of solid-state physics at the University of Paris, where he remained for 10 years. He then joined the faculty of the Collège de France as a professor. In 1976 de Gennes accepted the directorship of the École de Physique et Chimie, Paris, and in 1988 he also became science director for chemistry and physics at Rhône Poulenc SA, Paris.

De Gennes was awarded the Hollweck Prize (1968), the Prix Cognac-Jay (1970), the Prix Ampère (1977), the Gold Medal of the CNRS (1981), the Matteucci Medal of the Science Academy, Rotte (1988), the Harvey Prize, Technion, Israel (1988), and the Wolf Prize in Physics (1990). He held memberships in several science academies and societies around the world.

Nobel Prize for Physiology or Medicine

Two German scientists, Erwin Neher and Bert Sakmann, won the 1991 Nobel Prize for Physiology or Medicine for their research into basic cell function and for their development of the patch-clamp technique—a laboratory method widely used in cell biology and neuroscience to detect electrical currents as small as a trillionth of an ampere through cell membranes. According to the Nobel committee's citation, "This new knowledge and this new analytical tool has during the past ten years revolutionized modern biology, facilitated research, and contributed to the understanding of the cellular mechanisms underlying several diseases, including diabetes and cystic fibrosis."

The membrane of each cell contains numerous porelike channels that control the passage of ions, or charged atoms, into and out of the cell. Regulation of these ion channels, which are actually specialized protein molecules, helps the cell communicate and function. Although scientists had long known that a rapid exchange of ions takes place across the cell

Erwin Neher
© The Nobel Foundation 1991

membrane, no one had been able to demonstrate exactly how this is accomplished. By developing a technique that allows the registration of the "incredibly small electrical currents that pass through a single ion channel," the Nobel committee said, "Neher and Sakmann conclusively established that ion channels do exist and how they function."

The laureates' patch-clamp technique uses a thin glass pipette, a thousandth of a millimeter (about four hundred-thousandths of an inch) in diameter, fitted with a recording electrode. When the tip of the pipette is pressed against the cell membrane, the membrane forms a tight seal around the tip. The effect is to isolate the ion channel in that portion of the membrane. When ions flow through the ion channel, the pipette's electrode registers the flow as an electrical current. "The technique is unique," according to the Nobel committee, "in that it records how a single channel molecule alters its shape and in that way controls the flow of current within a time frame of a few millionths of a second."

All cells have a characteristic set of ion channels, consisting of single molecules or complexes of molecules, that enable them to carry out their specific functions. Some channels permit the flow only of positively charged sodium, potassium, or calcium ions; others allow only negatively charged chloride ions. Neher and Sakmann discovered how ion channels accomplish this degree of specificity. First, they found that the diameter of the passage within an ion channel is matched to the diameter of a particular ion. Second, they determined that certain ion channels contain rings of positively or negatively charged amino acid molecules. These rings form a sort of filter that allows only ions having the opposite charge to pass through. Thus, only ions of a particular size and charge can traverse any given ion channel.

Neher and Sakmann used the patch-clamp technique to study a broad range of cellular function, from the way that different parts of ion-channel molecules operate to open and close the channel to the electrical activity of entire cells. The laureates concentrated particularly on nerve and muscle cells.

Neher was born on March 20, 1944, in Landsberg, Germany. He earned a degree in physics from the Technical University of Munich and then attended the University of Wisconsin at Madison, where he was awarded a master of science degree in 1967. From 1968 to 1972 he did graduate and postdoctoral work at the Max Planck Institute for Psychiatry, Munich. He first developed the idea of the patch-clamp technique in his doctoral thesis. He earned his Ph.D. from the Technical University of Munich in 1970.

In 1972 Neher joined the Max Planck Institute for Biophysical Chemistry, Göttingen, beginning a collaboration there with Sakmann two years later. He moved to the University of Washington to work with Charles F. Stevens and then traveled with Stevens to Yale University, although he continued to collaborate with Sakmann. Neher and Sakmann first presented their patch-clamp findings at a scientific gathering in 1976.

Neher returned to the Max Planck Institute that same year and was made director of the institute's membrane biophysics department in 1983. He was named honorary professor at the University of Göttingen and became a member of the U.S. National Academy of Sciences.

Sakmann was born on June 12, 1942, in Stuttgart, Germany. From 1969 to 1970 he worked as a research assistant in the department of neurophysiology at the Max Planck Institute for Psychiatry and then finished his postdoctoral studies as a British Council fellow in the department of biophysics at University College, London, working under the renowned neurophysiologist Bernard Katz. After receiving his medical degree from the University of Göttingen in 1974, Sakmann joined the department of neurobiology at the Max Planck Institute for Biophysical Chemistry, where he shared laboratory space with Neher. In 1979 Sakmann became a research associate in the institute's membrane biology group. He was made head of the membrane physiology unit in 1983, and he became director of the Max Planck Institute for Medical Research's cell physiology department in Heidelberg two years later.

—Carolyn D. Newton

Bert Sakmann
DPA/Photoreporters

AWARD	WINNER	AFFILIATION
ANTHROPOLOGY		
L.S.B. Leakey Prize	Phillip V. Tobias	University of Witswatersrand, Johannesburg, South Africa
Order of Merit of the Italian Republic	Luigi Cavalli-Sforza	Stanford University, Calif.
ARCHITECTURE AND CIVIL ENGINEERING		
Award of Merit of the American Society of Civil Engineers	U.S. Army Corps of Engineers	Portland, Ore.
Gold Medal of the American Institute of Architects	Benjamin C. Thompson	Benjamin Thompson & Associates, Cambridge, Mass.
Praemium Imperiale	Gae Aulenti	Milan, Italy
Pritzker Architecture Prize	Robert Venturi	Venturi, Rauch and Scott Brown, Philadelphia, Pa.
ASTRONOMY		
Bruno Rossi Prize	John A. Simpson (Emeritus)	University of Chicago, Ill.
Crafoord Prize	Allan R. Sandage	Carnegie Institution of Washington, Washington, D.C.
Dannie Heineman Prize for Astrophysics	Wallace L.W. Sargent	California Institute of Technology, Pasadena
Distinguished Public Service Medal	Harlan Smith	University of Texas, Austin
Heinrich Hertz Medal	John D. Kraus (Emeritus)	Ohio State University, Columbus
Helen B. Warner Prize	Shrinivas Kulkarni	California Institute of Technology, Pasadena
Henry Norris Russell Lectureship	Donald Osterbrock	University of California, Santa Cruz
Newton Lacy Pierce Prize	Kenneth Libbrecht	California Institute of Technology, Pasadena
CHEMISTRY		
Agnes Fay Morgan Research Award	Cynthia Friend	Harvard University, Cambridge, Mass.
Arthur C. Cope Award	K. Barry Sharpless	Scripps Institution of Oceanography, La Jolla, Calif.
Austin M. Patterson-E.J. Crane Award	David R. Lide, Jr.	*Journal of Physical & Chemical Reference Data*
Award for Chemistry in Service to Society	Vladimir Haensel	University of Massachusetts, Amherst
Buerger Award	Jack Dunitz	Swiss Federal Institute of Technology, Zürich
Chemical Sciences Award	Richard N. Zare	Stanford University, Calif.
David C. Grahame Award	Barry Miller	AT&T Bell Laboratories
Distinguished Achievement in Science Award	James R. Griffith	Naval Research Laboratory, Washington, D.C.
Earle K. Plyler Prize	Kenneth M. Evenson	National Institute for Standards and Technology, Gaithersburg, Md.
Edward W. Morley Award	Derek Horton	Ohio State University, Columbus
Ernest Guenther Award	Leo A. Paquette	Ohio State University, Columbus

AWARD	WINNER	AFFILIATION
Frank H. Field and Joe L. Franklin Award	Burnaby Munson	University of Delaware, Newark
Frederic Stanley Kipping Award	Nils Wiberg	University of Munich, Germany
Garvan Medal	Jacqueline K. Barton	California Institute of Technology, Pasadena
Havinga Medal	Marye Anne Fox	University of Texas, Austin
Herty Medal	Ernest L. Eliel	University of North Carolina, Chapel Hill
Inorganic Chemistry Award	Walter G. Klemperer	University of Illinois, Urbana
Ipatieff Prize	Mark E. Davis	California Institute of Technology, Pasadena
Irving Langmuir Prize in Chemical Physics	Richard E. Smalley	Rice University, Houston, Texas
James Flack Norris Award	Joseph F. Bunnett	University of California, Santa Cruz
Joel Henry Hildebrand Award	Benjamin Widom	Cornell University, Ithaca, N.Y.
Kurnakov Medal	George Kauffman	California State University, Fresno
Lawrence K. Cecil Award	Selim Senkan	University of California, Los Angeles
Max Planck Research Prize	Erhard Rothe	Wayne State University, Detroit, Mich.
	Peter Andresen	Institut für Stroemungs-forschung, Germany
Peter Debye Award	Frank H. Stillinger	AT&T Bell Laboratories
Priestley Medal	Carl Djerassi	Stanford University, Calif.
Pure Chemistry Award	Charles M. Lieber	Harvard University, Cambridge, Mass.
Thomas Jefferson Award	Ernest L. Eliel	University of North Carolina, Chapel Hill
Willard Gibbs Medal	Gunther Wilke	Max Planck Institute and University of Bochum, Germany

DEFENSE

Ernest Orlando Lawrence Memorial Award	Wayne J. Shotts	Lawrence Livermore National Laboratory, Calif.

EARTH SCIENCES

Arthur L. Day Medal	Ian S.E. Carmichael	University of California, Berkeley
Award for Outstanding Achievement in Biometeorology	Donald E. Aylor	Connecticut Agricultural Experiment Station, New Haven
Award for Outstanding Contribution to the Advance of Applied Meteorology	Michael R. Smith	WeatherData, Inc., Wichita, Kansas
Bigsby Medal	R.S. White	University of Cambridge, England
Carl-Gustaf Rossby Research Medal	Syukuro Manabe	National Oceanic and Atmospheric Administration and Princeton University, N.J.
Charles L. Mitchell Award	Marvin E. Miller	National Oceanic and Atmospheric Administration
Clarence Leroy Meisinger Award	Roger M. Wakimoto	University of California, Los Angeles
Cleveland Abbe Award	Earl G. Droessler	North Carolina State University, Raleigh
Delmer S. Fahrney Medal	Timothy Coffey	Naval Research Laboratory, Washington, D.C.

AWARD	WINNER	AFFILIATION
Donath Medal	Brian P. Wernicke	Harvard University, Cambridge, Mass.
Henry G. Houghton Award	Judith A. Curry	Pennsylvania State University, University Park
Horton Award	Garrison Sposito	University of California, Berkeley
Ian Campbell Medal	William L. Fisher	Bureau of Economic Geology, Austin, Texas
Jule G. Charney Award	Lance F. Bosart	State University of New York, Albany
Kyoto Prize	Edward N. Lorenz (Emeritus)	Massachusetts Institute of Technology, Cambridge
Lyell Award	F.A. Gibbons	University of Wales, Cardiff
Lyell Medal	John Imbrie	Brown University, Providence, R.I.
Major Edward D. Ewes Fitzgerald Coke Medal	C.H. Holland	Trinity College, Dublin
Marc-Auguste Pictet Medal	Albert V. Carozzi (Retired)	University of Illinois, Urbana
Murchison Award	D.H.W. Hutton	University of Durham, England
Murchison Medal	M.R. House	University of Southampton, England
Outstanding Service to Meteorology Award	WSI Corp.	Billerica, Mass.
Penrose Medal	William R. Dickinson	University of Arizona, Tucson
R.H. Worth Prize	J.E. Robinson	University College, London
Sue Tyler Friedman Medal	H. Torrens	University of Keele, England
Sverdrup Gold Medal	Mark A. Cane	Lamont-Doherty Geological Observatory, Palisades, N.Y.
21st Century Earth Award	Meyer Steinberg	Brookhaven National Laboratory, Upton, N.Y.
William Smith Award	R.A. Chadwick	British Geological Survey, Nottingham, England
William Smith Medal	W.R. Dearman	Plymouth, England
Wollaston Award	P. Turner	University of Birmingham, England
Wollaston Medal	X Le Pichon	École Normale Supérieure, Paris

ELECTRONICS AND INFORMATION SCIENCES

A.M. Turing Award	Robin Milner	University of Edinburgh, Scotland
Karl V. Karlstrom Award	David A. Patterson	University of California, Berkeley
Medal of Honor of the Institute of Electrical and Electronic Engineers	Leo Esaki	IBM Corp.

ENERGY

Henry H. Storch Award	Stephen E. Stein	National Institute of Standards and Technology, Gaithersburg, Md.
Major John Sacheverell A'Deane Coke Medal	D.A.L. Jenkins	BP Exploration, London
Pew Charitable Trusts Award	Ashok Gadgil	Lawrence Berkeley Laboratory, Calif.

ENVIRONMENT

Award for Applied and Environmental Microbiology	Ronald Atlas	University of Louisville, Ky.
Governor's Medal for Science Achievement	Thomas D. Wheelock	Iowa State University, Ames

AWARD	WINNER	AFFILIATION
Pew Charitable Trusts Award	Kamaljit Bawa	University of Massachusetts, Boston
Pew Charitable Trusts Award	Alwyn Gentry	Missouri Botanical Garden, St. Louis, Mo.
Pew Charitable Trusts Award	Calestous Juma	African Centre for Technology Studies
Pew Charitable Trusts Award	Constance Millar	U.S. Forest Service
Pew Charitable Trusts Award	Mark Sagoff	University of Maryland, College Park
Right Livelihood Award	Pastoral Land Commission	Brazil
	Movement of Landless Workers	Brazil
	Save Narmada Movement	India
Sasakawa International Environment Prize	Wolfgang and Francoise Burhenne	Bonn, Germany
Stockholm Water Prize	David W. Schindler	University of Alberta, Edmonton
Veris Award	William A. Pryor	Louisiana State University, Baton Rouge

FOOD AND AGRICULTURE

Distinguished Service Award of the American Institute of Biological Sciences	John S. Niederhauser	University of Arizona, Tucson
Eunice Rockwood Oberly Memorial Award	Michael J. Balick	Institute of Economic Botany, New York, N.Y.
	Hans T. Beck	Institute of Economic Botany, New York, N.Y.
Joseph B. Goldberger Award in Clinical Nutrition	Charles D. Davidson	Truro, Mass.
Kenneth A. Spencer Award	John E. Kinsella	University of California, Davis
Rank Prize	Hans R. Herren	International Institute of Tropical Agriculture, Nigeria
Stephen S. Chang Award	John E. Kinsella	University of California, Davis
Sterling Hendricks Award	Roy L. Whistler (Emeritus)	Purdue University, West Lafayette, Ind.
Tyler Prize for Environmental Achievement	M.S. Swaminathan	Green Revolution Movement, India
World Food Prize	Nevin Scrimshaw	United Nations University, Tokyo

LIFE SCIENCES

Alfred Bader Award	Richard H. Holm	Harvard University, Cambridge, Mass.
Albert Lasker Basic Medical Research Award	Edward B. Lewis (Emeritus)	California Institute of Technology, Pasadena
	Christine Nüsslein-Volhard	Institute for Developmental Biology, Tübingen, Germany
Biological Physics Prize	Watt W. Webb	Cornell University, Ithaca, N.Y.
Claude S. Hudson Award	Akira Kobata	University of Tokyo
David Starr Jordon Prize	Jeffrey Palmer	Indiana University, Bloomington
David and Lucile Packard Award	Martin F. Yanofsky	University of California, San Diego
Eli Lilly and Company Research Award	John Mekalanos	Harvard University, Cambridge, Mass.
Gustavus John Esselen Award	Thomas Eisner	Cornell University, Ithaca, N.Y.
	Jerrold Meinwald	Cornell University, Ithaca, N.Y.

AWARD	WINNER	AFFILIATION
Louisa Gross Horwitz Prize	Richard Ernst	Eidgenössische Technische Hochschule, Zürich, Switz.
	Kurt Wüthrich	Eidgenössische Technische Hochschule, Zürich, Switz.
McKnight Award	Seymour Benzer	California Institute of Technology, Pasadena
Pew Charitable Trusts Award	Russell Greenberg	Smithsonian Environmental Research Center, Washington, D.C.
Pew Charitable Trusts Award	Georgina Mace	Institute of Zoology, London
Pew Charitable Trusts Award	Carl Safina	National Audubon Society
R.H. Wright Award	John Hildebrand	University of Arizona, Tucson
Ralph F. Hirschmann Award	Louis Carpino	University of Massachusetts, Amherst
Repliger Award	William W. Parson	University of Washington, Seattle
Richard Lounsbery Award	Marc W. Kirschner	University of California, San Francisco
	Harold Weintraub	Fred Hutchinson Cancer Research Center, Seattle, Wash.
Robert A. Welch Award	Edwin G. Krebs	University of Washington, Seattle, and Tufts University, Medford, Mass.
	Earl R. Stadtman	National Institutes of Health, Bethesda, Md.
Silver Medal in Speech Communication	Arthur S. House	Institute for Defense Analysis, Princeton, N.J.

MATERIALS SCIENCES

AWARD	WINNER	AFFILIATION
Ernest Orlando Lawrence Memorial Award	S. Thomas Picraux	Sandia National Laboratory, Albuquerque, N.M.

MATHEMATICS

AWARD	WINNER	AFFILIATION
Dannie Heineman Prize for Mathematical Physics	Jürg Fröhlich	Swiss Federal Institute of Technology, Zürich
	Thomas C. Spencer	Institute for Advanced Study, Princeton, N.J.

MEDICAL SCIENCES

AWARD	WINNER	AFFILIATION
Albert Lasker Clinical Medical Research Award	Yuet Wai Kan	University of California, San Francisco
Alfred Burger Award	Everette L. May	Medical College of Virginia, Richmond
Alfred P. Sloan, Jr., Prize	Leland Hartwell	University of Washington, Seattle
Artois-Baillet Latour Health Prize	Thomas Waldmann	National Institutes of Health, Bethesda, Md.
Bower Award	Solomon Snyder	Johns Hopkins University, Baltimore, Md.
Bristol-Myers Squibb Award for Distinguished Achievement in Infectious Disease Treatment	Barry R. Bloom	Albert Einstein College of Medicine, New York, N.Y.
Bristol-Myers Squibb Award for Distinguished Achievement in Neuroscience Research	Eric R. Kandel	Columbia University, New York, N.Y., and Tufts University, Medford, Mass.
	T.V.P. Bliss	National Institute for Medical Research, London

AWARD	WINNER	AFFILIATION
Charles F. Kettering Prize	Victor Ling	University of Toronto and Ontario Cancer Institute
Charles S. Mott Prize	Peter Vogt	University of Southern California, Los Angeles
Distinguished Service Award of the American Medical Association	John W. Eckstein	Iowa City, Iowa
Doctor William Beaumont Award	John C. Morrison	Jackson, Miss.
Ernest Orlando Lawrence Memorial Award	F. Ward Whicker	University of Georgia, Athens
Gairdner Foundation International Award	Sydney Brenner	Medical Research Council, London
	John Sulston	Medical Research Council, London
Gairdner Foundation International Award	M. Judah Folkman	Harvard Medical School, Boston, Mass.
Gairdner Foundation International Award	Robert Furchgott	State University of New York, Brooklyn
Gairdner Foundation International Award	David MacLennan	University of Toronto, Ontario
Gairdner Foundation International Award	Kary Mullis	Nucleic Acid Chemistry Co., La Jolla, Calif.
Georg Charles de Hevesy Award	Alfred Wolf	Brookhaven National Laboratory, Upton, N.Y.
Perkin Medal	Miguel A. Ondetti	Bristol-Myers Squibb Pharmaceutical Research Institute, Princeton, N.J.
Rank Prize	George K. Radda	University of Oxford, England
Sandoz Prize in Gerontology	Leonard Hayflick	University of California, San Francisco
	Hans Thomae	Bonn, Germany
Scientific Achievement Award	Byrl J. Kennedy	Minneapolis, Minn.
Supelco Award	Fred H. Mattson	University of California, San Diego
Tyler Prize for Environmental Achievement	C. Everett Koop	Washington, D.C.

OPTICAL ENGINEERING

AWARD	WINNER	AFFILIATION
Adolph Lomb Medal	David F. Welch	Spectra Diode Laboratories, San Jose, Calif.
Charles Hard Townes Award	Elias Snitzer	Rutgers University, New Brunswick, N.J.
David Richardson Medal	Gary K. Starkweather	Apple Computer Inc.
John Tyndall Award	David N. Payne	University of Southampton, England
Joseph Fraunhofer Award	James G. Baker	Harvard University, Cambridge, Mass.

PHYSICS

AWARD	WINNER	AFFILIATION
Bingham Medal	Louis J. Zapas (Retired)	National Institute of Standards and Technology, Gaithersburg, Md.
C.E.K. Mees Medal	Florin Abeles	University of Paris
Catalonia Prize	Abdus Salam	International Centre for Theoretical Physics, Trieste, Italy
David Adler Lectureship Award	John R. Smith	General Motors Research Laboratories

AWARD	WINNER	AFFILIATION
Davisson-Germer Prize	Neville V. Smith	AT&T Bell Laboratories
Dirac Medal	Jeffrey Goldstone	Massachusetts Institute of Technology, Cambridge
Dirac Medal	Stanley Mandelstam	University of California, Berkeley
Edward Longstreth Medal	R. David Middlebrook	California Institute of Technology, Pasadena
	Slobodan Cuk	California Institute of Technology, Pasadena
Einstein Prize for Laser Science	Lorenzo M. Narducci	Drexel University, Philadelphia, Pa.
	Stephen E. Harris	Stanford University, Calif.
Elliot Cresson Medal	Yakir Aharnov	Tel Aviv University, Israel, and University of South Carolina, Columbia
	David Bohm	University of London
Ernest Orlando Lawrence Memorial Award	John J. Dorning	University of Virginia, Charlottesville
Ernest Orlando Lawrence Memorial Award	Maury Tigner	Cornell University, Ithaca, N.Y.
Frederic Ives Medal	John L. Hall	National Institute of Standards and Technology, Gaithersburg, Md.
Herbert P. Broida Prize	David E. Pritchard	Massachusetts Institute of Technology, Cambridge
High-Polymer Physics Prize	Edwin L. Thomas	Massachusetts Institute of Technology, Cambridge
I.I. Rabi Prize	Chris H. Green	University of Colorado, Boulder
International Commission for Optics Prize	Rosario Martinez-Herrero	University Complutense, Madrid
International Prize for New Materials	Francis J. DiSalvo, Jr.	Cornell University, Ithaca, N.Y.
	Frederic Holtzberg	IBM Corp.
Irving Langmuir Prize	Richard E. Smalley	Rice University, Houston, Texas
J.J. Sakurai Prize	Vladimir N. Gribov	Landau Institute for Theoretical Physics, Moscow
James Clerk Maxwell Prize	William L. Kruer	Lawrence Livermore National Laboratory, Calif.
John H. Dillon Medal	Kenneth S. Schweizer	University of Illinois, Urbana
John Price Wetherill Medal	Peter J. Twin	University of Liverpool, England
Julius Edgar Lilienfeld Prize	Daniel Kleppner	Massachusetts Institute of Technology, Cambridge
Kyoto Prize	Michael Szwarc	University of Southern California, Los Angeles
Lyle Medal	Bruce H. McKellar	University of Melbourne, Australia
Maria Goeppert-Mayer Award	Alice E. White	AT&T Bell Laboratories
Max Born Award	James P. Gordon	AT&T Bell Laboratories
Nishina Memorial Prize	Kaoru Yokoya	KEK Laboratory, Japan
Oersted Medal	Freeman J. Dyson	Institute for Advanced Study, Princeton, N.J.
Oliver E. Buckley Prize	Patrick A. Lee	Massachusetts Institute of Technology, Cambridge
Prix Ricard	Marcel Banner	National Saturne Laboratory, Saclay, France

AWARD	WINNER	AFFILIATION
Prix Scientifique	Sergio Ferrara	CERN (European Laboratory for Particle Physics)
Public Welfare Medal	Victor F. Weisskopf	Massachusetts Institute of Technology, Cambridge
R.W. Wood Prize	Thomas F. Deutsch	Massachusetts General Hospital, Boston
	Daniel J. Ehrlich	Massachusetts Institute of Technology, Cambridge
	Richard M. Osgood	Columbia University, New York, N.Y.
Silver Medal in Physical Acoustics	Allan D. Pierce	Pennsylvania State University, University Park
Tom W. Bonner Prize	Peter J. Twin	University of Liverpool, England
Trent-Crede Medal	Gideon Maidanik	David Taylor Research Center
Von Hippel Award	Theodore H. Geballe	Stanford University, Calif.
W.K.H. Panofsky Prize	Gerson Goldhaber	University of California, Berkeley
	François Pierre	National Saturne Laboratory, Saclay, France
William F. Meggers Award	Daniel Kleppner	Massachusetts Institute of Technology, Cambridge

TRANSPORTATION

Charles Stark Draper Prize	Hans J.P. von Ohain	University of Dayton, Ohio
	Sir Frank Whittle	U.S. Naval Academy, Annapolis, Md.
Daniel Guggenheim Medal	Joseph F. Sutter (Retired)	Boeing Co.
Distinguished Service Award of the Federal Aviation Administration	H. Tom Nunn (Retired)	Northwest Aerospace Training Corp.
Eric Konrad Medal	Frederick J. Kovac	Goodyear Tire & Rubber Co.
Frank G. Brewer Trophy	Lockhart J. Smith (Retired)	Wentworth Institute of Technology, Boston
Prince Philip Prize	John Cundy	Rolls-Royce Ltd., England

SCIENCE WRITING

George and Cynthia Mitchell Prize	Daniel B. Botkin	University of California, Santa Barbara
George and Cynthia Mitchell Prize	José Goldemberg	Secretary of Science and Technology, Brazil
George and Cynthia Mitchell Prize	Diana Liverman	Pennsylvania State University, University Park
James T. Grady-James H. Stack Award	Malcolm W. Browne	The New York Times
Louis J. Battan Author's Award	John W. Firor	National Center for Atmospheric Research, Boulder, Colo.
Pew Charitable Trusts Award	Donella Meadows	Dartmouth College, Hanover, N.H.
Walter Sullivan Award	Eugene Linden	Time

AWARD	WINNER	AFFILIATION
OTHER AWARDS		
Charles Lathrop Parsons Award	Mary Good	Allied-Signal
Earth Prize for Environmental Leadership and Humanitarian Excellence	Ted Turner	Cable News Network
	Dalai Lama	Exiled Leader of Tibetan Buddhists
	Carlos Salinas de Gortari	President of Mexico
	Gro Harlem Brundtland	Prime Minister of Norway
	United Nations Children's Fund	
Edward A. Flinn III Award	Robert Watson	NASA
Ettore Majorana Science for Peace Prize	Edward Teller	
	Viktor Weisskopf	
	P.A.M. Dirac	In Memoriam
	P.L. Kapitza	In Memoriam
	A.D. Sakharov	In Memoriam
George C. Pimentel Award	Fred Basolo (Emeritus)	Northwestern University, Evanston, Ill.
George E. Pake Prize	Albert Narath	Sandia National Laboratories, Albuquerque, N.M.
James Flack Norris Award	John W. Moore	University of Wisconsin, Madison
Meritorious Service Award of the U.S. Department of Energy	James W. Swafford	U.S. Department of Energy
National Medal of Science	Mary Ellen Avery	Harvard Medical School, Boston, Mass.
	Ronald Breslow	Columbia University, New York, N.Y.
	Alberto Calderon (Emeritus)	University of Chicago, Ill.
	Gertrude Elion (Emeritus)	Burroughs Wellcome Co., Research Triangle Park, N.C.
	George Heilmeier	Bellcore, Livingston, N.J.
	Dudley Herschbach	Harvard University, Cambridge, Mass.
	G. Evelyn Hutchinson (Deceased)	Yale University, New Haven, Conn.
	Elvin A. Kabat (Emeritus)	Columbia University, New York, N.Y.
	Robert W. Kates	Brown University, Providence, R.I.
	Luna B. Leopold	University of California, Berkeley
	Salvador Luria (Deceased)	Massachusetts Institute of Technology, Cambridge
	Paul A. Marks	Memorial Sloan-Kettering Cancer Center, New York, N.Y.
	George A. Miller (Emeritus)	Princeton University, N.J.
	Arthur Schawlow (Emeritus)	Stanford University, Calif.
	Glenn T. Seaborg	Lawrence Berkeley Laboratory, Calif.
	Folke Skoog (Emeritus)	University of Wisconsin, Madison
	H. Guyford Stever	Washington, D.C.
	Edward C. Stone	California Institute of Technology, Pasadena

AWARD	WINNER	AFFILIATION
National Medal of Science (continued)	Steven Weinberg	University of Texas, Austin
	Paul C. Zamecnik	Worcester Foundation for Experimental Biology, Shrewsbury, Mass.
National Medal of Technology	Stephen D. Bechtel, Jr.	Bechtel Group, Inc.
	C. Gordon Bell	Stardent Computers
	Geoffrey Boothroyd	University of Rhode Island, Kingston
	John Cocke	International Business Machines, Inc.
	Peter Dewhurst	University of Rhode Island, Kingston
	Carl Djerassi	Stanford University, Calif.
	James J. Duderstadt	University of Michigan, Ann Arbor
	Robert W. Galvin	Motorola, Inc.
	Grace Murray Hopper (Deceased)	Digital Equipment Corp.
	F. Kenneth Iverson	Nucor, Inc.
	Frederick M. Jones	Thermo King
	Joseph A. Numero	Thermo King
	Pegasus Team: David W. Thompson, Antonio L. Elias, David S. Hollingsworth, Robert R. Lovell	Orbital Sciences Corp. & Hercules, Inc.
	Charles E. Reed	General Electric Co.
	John Paul Stapp (Retired)	U.S. Air Force Space Center
Public Welfare Medal	Philip Hauge Abelson	*Science*
Westinghouse Science Talent Search	1. Kurt S. Thorn	Shoreham-Wading River High School, Shoreham, N.Y.
	2. Claudine D. Madras	The Winsor School, Boston, Mass.
	3. Michael S. Agney	Melbourne High School, Melbourne, Fla.
	4. Leonid N. Reyzin	Sinai Academic Center, New York, N.Y.
	5. Patricia R. Bachiller	Scotch Plains-Fanwood High School, Scotch Plains, N.J.
	6. Christopher M. Bouton	St. Ann's School, New York, N.Y.
	7. Erica B. Goldman	Hunter College High School, New York, N.Y.
	8. Peter G. Khalifah	Shawnee Mission South High School, Shawnee Mission, Kan.
	9. Benjamin Che-Ming Jun	Montgomery Blair High School, Silver Spring, Md.
	10. Robin A. Niles	Commack High School, Commack, N.Y.
W.R. Grace Award	Robert D. Kennedy	Union Carbide

Obituaries

Anderson, Thomas Foxen (Feb. 7, 1911—Aug. 11, 1991), U.S. biophysical chemist, used the electron microscope to study the genetics of bacteria and bacterial viruses and conducted pioneering research that furthered an understanding of how viruses infect cells, reproduce, and alter the cells they infect. Anderson, who pioneered a "critical point" method of drying specimens to be viewed under the electron microscope, adjusted pressures and temperatures of specimens that had been immersed in liquid to eliminate the boundary between liquid and gaseous phases. He was then able to discover how certain bacteria enter their host cells. Anderson earned a Ph.D. in chemistry from the California Institute of Technology in 1932 and served as a professor at the University of Pennsylvania from 1942 to 1977. He then served as director of the Institute for Cancer Research in Philadelphia until his retirement in 1983. He was president (1960–64) of the International Federation of Electron Microscope Societies and president of the Electron Microscope Society of America, which awarded him its distinguished service award in 1978.

Barrett, Alan H. (June 7, 1927—July 3, 1991), U.S. physicist, achieved a landmark discovery in radio astronomy in 1963 when, with colleagues at the Massachusetts Institute of Technology (MIT), using a 26-m (84-ft)-diameter instrument at the university's Lincoln Laboratory on Millstone Hill, he detected and measured the presence of hydroxyl in interstellar space. This seminal finding represented the first time that a molecule had been discovered in the Milky Way and ushered in a new field of research: the study of molecules in the distant regions of the universe. Barrett earned a B.S. (1950) from Purdue University, West Lafayette, Ind., and an M.S. (1953) and Ph.D. (1956) from Columbia University, New York City. He joined the faculty of MIT in 1961 as associate professor of electrical engineering and became professor of physics in 1967, a post he held until his retirement in 1987. He was also involved in determining characteristics of the Earth's atmosphere by using high-altitude balloons and radio astronomy techniques. Another field of interest was microwave spectroscopy of planetary atmospheres. He designed the microwave-detection equipment that was carried aboard the Mariner 1 and 2 probes to Venus. The microwave 19-mm and 13.4-mm radio-frequency telescope in Mariner 2 helped Barrett and his co-workers determine that the surface temperatures on the planet are far too extreme to support human life as it is known on Earth. Barrett served as a consultant to the National Aeronautics and Space Administration, the National Science Foundation, and the National Radio Astron-

omy Observatory. He was the recipient of the American Academy of Arts and Sciences' 1971 Rumford Prize, and in 1977 and 1978 he was awarded a Guggenheim fellowship to study the molecular properties of interstellar space.

Birch, (Albert) Francis (Aug. 22, 1903—Jan. 31, 1992), U.S. geophysicist, conducted pioneering studies on the composition of the Earth's interior and published his findings, which were based on geochemical, experimental, and seismological observations, in a 1952 landmark paper. The latter set forth that the Earth consists of two major regions: a central core, which is almost completely molten (the solidity of the inner core was confirmed in 1971 by A.M. Dziewonski and Freeman Gilbert), surrounded by a predominantly solid shell comprising the mantle and crust together. Birch and his colleagues also studied the effects of extremely high pressure on elastic materials. By measuring sound velocities in those materials, scientists could interpret the seismic waves recorded from distant earthquakes. His other areas of study included phase relations and thermal conductivity of rocks. After graduating (1924) magna cum laude from Harvard University with a B.S. in electrical engineering, Birch briefly worked for the New York Telephone Co. before returning (1928) to his alma mater as an assistant in physics. At Harvard he served as research associate in geophysics (1932–49) before being named Sturgis-Hooper professor of geology in 1949. He became professor emeritus in 1974. From 1942 to 1945 he was a staff member of the Radiation Laboratory at the Massachusetts Institute of Technology, served as an officer in the U.S. Naval Reserve in the Bureau of Ships in Washington, D.C., and played a leading role in designing the Little Boy atomic bomb while a member of the team that assembled that device at Los Alamos, N.M. Birch helped load the explosive on the bomber at

(Albert) Francis Birch
Courtesy of the Harvard
University Archives

Tinian Island before it was dropped on Hiroshima at the end of World War II. For his diverse contributions, Birch received many awards, including the Legion of Merit (1945), the Day Medal (1950) and the Penrose Medal (1969) of the Geological Society of America, the William Bowie Medal (1960) of the American Geophysical Union, the National Medal of Science (1968), and the Gold Medal (1973) of the Royal Astronomical Society. He was also the editor of the *Handbook of Physical Constants* (1942), published by the Geological Society of America, of which he served as president in 1946.

Elton, Charles Sutherland (March 29, 1900—May 1, 1991), British zoologist, as a pioneer in the field of animal ecology, studied animal communities in their natural habitats and stressed the need for nature conservation. In his first book, *Animal Ecology* (1927), he introduced the principles of the food cycle, including the idea that each species occupies a niche within the food chain, and discussed the environmental factors that govern population numbers. Elton was educated at Liverpool (England) College and New College, Oxford, from which he graduated (1922) with first-class honors in zoology. He quickly became an authority in the emerging field of ecology, and in 1932 he was chosen to head the new Bureau of Animal Population at the University of Oxford. He remained at Oxford as director of the bureau (1932–67), reader in animal ecology (1936–67), and senior research fellow at Corpus Christi College (1936–67). He was named an honorary fellow of Corpus Christi when he retired in 1967. Elton was also founding editor (1932–51) of the *Journal of Animal Ecology* and a member (1950–67) of the scientific policy committee of the British Nature Conservancy. He was honored as a fellow of the Royal Society in 1953 and won numerous awards, notably the Linnean Society's Gold Medal (1967), the Royal Society's Darwin Medal (1970), and the Tyler Ecology Award (1976). Elton's other books include *Voles, Mice and Lemmings* (1942), *The Ecology of Invasions by Animals and Plants* (1958), and *The Pattern of Animal Communities* (1966).

Fletcher, James Chipman (June 5, 1919–Dec. 22, 1991), U.S. government official, was the administrator of the National Aeronautics and Space Administration (NASA) during two crucial periods (April 1971–May 1977 and May 1986–April 1989); he held that position longer than anyone else in the history of the agency. During his first tenure, Fletcher was instrumental in persuading the U.S. government to fund the Space Transportation System, which included the space shuttle, in an era of shrinking budgets and declining public interest in the manned space-flight program. In his typical low-key yet highly effective style, he argued that the program would pay for itself (it did not). He oversaw or initiated

James Chipman
Fletcher
NASA

such major space projects as the three missions of Skylab (an Earth-orbiting space station visited by astronauts in 1973 and 1974), the two Viking probes that landed on Mars in 1976, the Voyager space probe, the space telescope program, and the 1975 Apollo-Soyuz mission, which linked the spacecraft of U.S. and Soviet astronauts. In the aftermath of the calamitous explosion on Jan. 28, 1986, of the space shuttle *Challenger* with seven crew members aboard, U.S. Pres. Ronald Reagan persuaded a reluctant Fletcher to return to the helm of a devastated NASA. A U.S. Senate committee subjected him to intense scrutiny for his own possible responsibility in the events leading up to the disaster because the flawed booster rockets that caused the shuttle explosion were designed by Morton Thiokol Inc., the company that in 1973 he had favored for providing NASA's booster rockets, and he was also accused of cost cutting at the expense of safety. In 1987 a congressional investigation cleared him of violating conflict-of-interest regulations. In a capable and systematic manner, Fletcher reorganized NASA, supervised the redesign of the flawed booster rockets that had powered *Challenger,* and returned the shuttle program to flight in 1988. He tendered his resignation in 1989 shortly after the third successful post-*Challenger* shuttle mission. Fletcher, who had earned a B.A. from Columbia University, New York City (1940), and a Ph.D. in physics from the California Institute of Technology (1948), taught at the latter (1946–48), as well as at Princeton University (1942–45). While teaching at the University of California at Los Angeles (1948–50), he also served as a laboratory director at Hughes Aircraft Co. From 1954 to 1958 he was a laboratory director at the Ramo-Wooldridge Corp.; he then became founding president of the Space Electronics Corp. in Glendale,

Calif. After the latter company merged with Aerojet General Corp. in 1960, Fletcher became an executive in the new corporation. He served as president of the University of Utah (1964–71) before joining NASA. From 1977 to 1986 he headed a consulting engineering firm in McLean, Va., and taught at the University of Pittsburgh, Pa.

Friedman, Maurice Harold (Oct. 27, 1903—March 8, 1991), U.S. physician, conducted pioneering reproductive physiology research and in the 1930s developed the "rabbit" pregnancy test that bore his name. Friedman's test involved injecting a sample of a woman's urine into a female rabbit. When laboratory clinicians inspected the ovaries of the rabbit (after it was killed and the ovaries were surgically exposed), they were able to determine that a woman was pregnant if certain formations called corpora lutea and corpora hemorrhagica had developed in the rabbit's ovaries as a result of hormones contained in the woman's urine. Friedman's test was later replaced by over-the-counter pregnancy tests that did not require the use of animals. After entering the University of Chicago at the age of 16, Friedman earned a B.A., a Ph.D., and an M.D. degree there before joining (1928) the faculty of the University of Pennsylvania, where he began his studies in reproductive physiology. In 1936 he moved to the Beltsville (Md.) Agricultural Research Center to pursue further research. After serving with the Army Air Force as a medical officer during World War II, he opened (1946) a private medical practice in Washington, D.C., specializing in gastroenterology. He was affiliated with Georgetown University Hospital and was an associate professor of medicine at Georgetown's medical school. Friedman retired from private practice in 1959 but remained active as financial adviser to the Planned Parenthood Association.

Hamburger, Jean (July 15, 1909—Feb. 1, 1992), French physician, was a pioneer in the field of nephrology and founding president (1960–63) of the International Society of Nephrology. On Feb. 12, 1962, Hamburger and his medical team at Necker Hospital in Paris performed the first successful kidney transplant between nonidentical twins (the first successful organ transplant of any kind in France), and the next year they performed one of the first successful cadaver transplants using immunosuppressive therapy. Hamburger was born in Paris and graduated (1928) from the Sorbonne with a degree in the natural sciences before his growing interest in the physiology of fluid and electrolyte balance induced him to switch to medicine. During the 1930s and '40s he did clinical research at the Paris Hospitals, where he developed improved methods of intensive care treatment, studied the connections between electrolyte disturbances and kidney failure, and supervised the creation of an early artificial

kidney. In 1952 Hamburger's team transplanted a woman's kidney to her healthy son, whose only kidney had been damaged in an accident. The recipient's temporary survival was a turning point in the study of histocompatibility, and Hamburger championed the research that led to the human leukocyte antigen (HLA) system of genetic markers used in establishing donor compatibility. He later did extensive research into renal histology and immunology and wrote many papers and books, including *Néphrologie* (1966) and *La Transplantation rénale* (1971). Hamburger was awarded the Legion of Honor and the National Order of Merit. He was president (1968–70) of the International Society of Transplantation, a member of the National Academy of Medicine, and a fellow of the American College of Physicians and the Royal College of Physicians. In 1991 he was named president of the French Academy of Sciences.

Heidelberger, Michael (April 29, 1888—June 15, 1991), U.S. immunochemist, utilized the methods of analytic chemistry to provide a basis for the development of immunology into a precise and rigorous scientific discipline. He also helped synthesize a medicine for African sleeping sickness and invented the refrigerated centrifuge, a machine of great value in biochemistry. At the Rockefeller Institute for Medical Research (now Rockefeller University), New York City, with his colleague Oswald Avery, Heidelberger demonstrated that the immunologically specific substances of the pneumococcus bacterium were pure carbohydrates and that they could be measured by standard methods of organic chemistry. On the basis of this work, he later determined that if he could react pure carbohydrate substances with antibodies to form antigen-antibody complexes, then any protein in such complexes could serve to measure the concentration of antibodies. This quantitative theory allowed him to predict a method for the isolation of pure antibodies and provided the foundation for devising theories as to how and where in the body antibodies are formed. After earning a Ph.D. in chemistry from Columbia University, New York City, Heidelberger was associated with the Rockefeller Institute before returning (1928) to his alma mater's College of Physicians and Surgeons. He taught and conducted research there until his mandatory retirement at age 65. He then served (1955–64) as a visiting professor at Rutgers University, New Brunswick, N.J., and in 1964 he joined New York University as adjunct professor of pathology, a post he retained until his death at age 103. He was twice the recipient of the prestigious Lasker Clinical Medical Research Award, and in 1967 he was awarded the National Medal of Science.

Hopper, Grace Murray (Dec. 9, 1906—Jan. 1, 1992), mathematician and rear admiral (ret.), U.S. Navy, as a pioneer in developing computer tech-

445

nology, helped devise Univac I, the first commercial electronic computer, and used her expertise to develop naval applications for Cobol (computer business oriented language). After earning (1928) a degree in mathematics and physics from Vassar College, Poughkeepsie, N.Y., she received an M.A. (1930) and a Ph.D. (1934) from Yale University. Hopper taught mathematics at Vassar before joining the U.S. Naval Reserve in 1943. She became a lieutenant and was assigned (1944) to the Bureau of Ordnance's Computation Project at Harvard University, where she worked on Mark I, the first large-scale automatic calculator and a precursor of electronic computers. Hopper remained at Harvard as a civilian research fellow while maintaining her naval career as a reservist. It was at Harvard that she coined the term *bug* to refer to unexplained computer failures. The first such mysterious occurrence was actually caused by an insect, a moth that had infiltrated the circuits of the Mark I. In 1949 Hopper joined Eckert-Mauchly Computer Corp., where she designed an improved compiler (a program for translating a programmer's instructions into codes that a computer can read). She remained with the firm when it was taken over by Remington Rand in 1951 and by the Sperry Corp. in 1955. In 1957 her division developed the first English-language data processing compiler, which was known as Flow-Matic. By 1961 Hopper had risen to the position of staff scientist, and in the following year she was elected a fellow of the Institute of Electrical and Electronic Engineers. In 1966 she retired from the Navy as a commander, but she was recalled to active duty the following year to help standardize the Navy's computer languages. She was the oldest officer on active naval duty when she retired in 1986, just months short of her 80th birthday. In 1969 Hopper was named the first com-

Grace Murray Hopper
U.S. Navy

puter science "Man of the Year" by the Data Processing Management Association, and in 1991 she was awarded the National Medal of Technology by Pres. George Bush.

Hutchinson, G(eorge) Evelyn (Jan. 30, 1903—May 17, 1991), British-born U.S. zoologist, conducted important research on the physical, chemical, meteorologic, and biological conditions of freshwater lakes in Transvaal, South Africa, in the Tibetan plateau, and in northeastern North America and was considered one of the founders of the science of ecology. After graduating (1924) from the University of Cambridge, Hutchinson spent two years (1926–28) as a lecturer at the University of the Witwatersrand, Johannesburg, South Africa, before returning to earn a master's degree at Cambridge. In 1928 he joined the faculty of Yale University, and he became a U.S. citizen in 1941. He was professor (1945–71) of zoology at Yale and professor emeritus after 1971. Hutchinson also studied the stratification of lakes and in 1935 showed the importance of the horizontal movements of water in stratified lakes in mixing the uppermost layers of water with the lowest layer. After World War II he proved the circulation of phosphorus in stratified lakes, a discovery that enabled scientists to determine the amount of undesirable agents in the water on the basis of the amount of phosphorus present. Hutchinson's studies also extended to lake sediments and various aspects of evolution. He was the author of such books as *The Clear Mirror* (1936), *The Itinerant Ivory Tower* (1953), *A Treatise on Limnology* (3 vol., 1957, 1967, 1975), *The Enchanted Voyage* (1962), *The Ecological Theater and the Evolutionary Play* (1965), *Introduction to Population Ecology* (1978), and *The Kindly Fruits of the Earth* (1979). Hutchinson maintained a laboratory at Yale until illness forced him to leave in early 1991. He completed the definitive draft of his fourth and final volume on limnology just prior to his death.

Irwin, James Benson (March 17, 1930—Aug. 8, 1991), U.S. astronaut, walked on the Moon during the Apollo 15 mission (July 26–Aug. 7, 1971) and made three separate excursions across the lunar surface in a battery-operated, four-wheeled lunar rover to collect rock and core samples, to photograph the lunar Apennine Mountain range and the rim of Hadley Rille canyon, and to conduct experiments on the lunar surface. Irwin, the first astronaut to pilot the specially designed lunar module, traversed the Moon with mission commander David R. Scott for more than 18 hours while Alfred M. Worden piloted the command module that orbited the Moon. One of their greatest finds was the so-called Genesis Rock, which was estimated to be 4,150,000,000 years old. On August 2 Irwin and Scott blasted off from the Moon and rejoined Worden in lunar orbit. After returning to the Earth, the three were reprimanded by NASA officials for having smuggled 400 specially stamped and canceled envelopes on the mission in a secret arrangement with a West German stamp dealer. Upon graduating (1951) from the U.S. Naval Academy, Annapolis, Md., Irwin transferred to the U.S. Air Force and was assigned to desk duty before being chosen (1966) for the manned spaceflight program. He also earned a master's degree in aeronautical and instrumentation engineering at the University of Michigan. Irwin, who viewed his Moon voyage as a religious experience, left the space program in 1972; he became a minister and started the High Flight Foundation, an interdenominational religious organization. He later led several highly publicized expeditions to Mt. Ararat in search of remnants of Noah's Ark. Irwin was the coauthor of *To Rule the Night* (with William A. Emerson, Jr.; 1973).

Land, Edwin Herbert (May 7, 1909—March 1, 1991), U.S. physicist and inventor, revolutionized photography as the inventor of a one-step process for developing and printing photographs instantaneously; he introduced (1948) the first Polaroid Land Camera, which produced dry photographs in just 60 seconds. A largely self-taught technical wizard, the inquisitive Land dropped out of Harvard University to pursue research on polarized light. He devised the first light-polarizing apparatus in 1932 by aligning and embedding submicroscopic crystals of iodoquinine sulfate in a synthetic sheet. This Polaroid J sheet had wide-ranging applications in the field of optics. Land briefly returned to Harvard before dropping out again to establish (1932) Land-Wheelwright Laboratories in Boston. The name Polaroid was assigned to the plastic light-polarizing material manufactured at the company and was later given to the new corporation founded by Land in 1937. Polaroid material was used in sunglasses, camera filters, and equipment for three-dimensional movies. During World War II Land worked on a guided-missile project and used his polarizing technique for such military equipment as infrared filters, lightweight range finders, sights for antiaircraft guns and other weapons, and night-adaptation goggles. After the war Land began working on his instant photographic process, and he demonstrated the system at a 1947 scientific meeting. At first only sepia images were reproduced, but black-and-white film was made available in 1950 and color film in 1963. Land's fascination with color led him to propose a new theory of color perception. His 1959 "retinex" theory of color vision set forth the idea that at least three independent image-forming mechanisms (retinexes) perceive different colors and work in tandem to indicate the color seen. During the 1970s Land, who had become a multimillionaire, introduced the SX-70 instant camera, which was more compact than the

original Polaroid Land Camera, and the Polavision instant movie system; the latter failed commercially owing to the advent of home video systems. Land, Polaroid's president (1937–75) and chairman (until 1982), held more than 500 patents. From 1980 until his death, he was founder-director of the Rowland Institute for Science in Cambridge, Mass. There he discovered that perception of light and color is regulated primarily by the brain. He was the recipient of numerous awards, notably the Presidential Medal of Freedom (1963) and the National Medal of Science (1967), and in 1977 he was enshrined in the National Inventors Hall of Fame.

Lawrence, John Hundale (Jan. 7, 1904—Sept. 7, 1991), U.S. biomedical researcher, was the founder (1936) and director (1948–72) of the Donner Laboratory at the University of California at Berkeley, the world's first facility devoted to nuclear medicine, and was one of the first to warn of the dangers associated with exposure to nuclear radiation. After earning an M.D. degree (1930) from Harvard Medical School, Lawrence taught at Yale University, where he studied the effects of radiation on the pituitary gland and, with Harvey Cushing, found that estrogen helped protect against radiation. He then joined (1935) his brother, Ernest (winner of the 1939 Nobel Prize for Physics for the invention of the cyclotron), at the Lawrence Berkeley Laboratory at the University of California at Berkeley. There in 1935, in collaboration with Paul Aebersold, Lawrence conducted the first biomedical experiments using energized atomic particles. He found that neutrons had a damaging effect on human tissue that was five times greater than that of X-rays. Lawrence then became interested in exploring the possible medical uses of isotopes and high-energy radiation beams to treat various illnesses. He joined the faculty at the University of California at Berkeley, where he established the Donner Laboratory. Lawrence and his colleagues used neutron beams to treat cancer, acromegaly, Cushing's disease, and several other illnesses. In 1955 he served as a delegate to the Geneva conference on the peaceful uses of atomic energy. In 1983 he was the recipient of the Enrico Fermi Award, given by the U.S. Department of Energy, for his "pioneering work and continuing leadership in nuclear medicine."

Luria, Salvador Edward (Aug. 13, 1912—Feb. 6, 1991), Italian-born U.S. molecular biologist, shared the 1969 Nobel Prize for Physiology or Medicine with Max Delbrück and Alfred D. Hershey for their research into the replication mechanisms and genetic structure of bacteriophages (viruses that infect bacteria). Luria studied medicine at the University of Turin (M.D., 1935) and radiology in Rome before leaving fascist Italy for Paris in 1938. Two years later he immigrated to the U.S., where he contin-

Salvador Edward Luria
The MIT Museum

ued his research at Columbia University, New York City (1940–42) and received a Guggenheim fellowship (1942–43) to Vanderbilt University, Nashville, Tenn., and Princeton University. At Vanderbilt he became involved in bacteriophage research, and in 1943 he and Delbrück devised the Luria-Delbrück fluctuation test, which provided experimental evidence that phage-resistant bacteria were the result of spontaneous mutations rather than a direct response to changes in the environment. Even after he left Vanderbilt to teach at Indiana University (1943–50), the University of Illinois (1950–59), and the University of Notre Dame (1959), he continued to work with Delbrück and Hershey in a transcontinental team known as the "Phage Group." In 1959 he joined the faculty of the Massachusetts Institute of Technology (MIT), where he remained as a professor (1959–91) and as director (1972–85) of the MIT Center for Cancer Research. He also taught a course in world literature to encourage science students not to become isolated from society at large. An outspoken opponent of U.S. involvement in Vietnam, Luria was active in the U.S. peace movement, and in 1969 the National Institutes of Health blacklisted him, thus barring him from government advisory panels. From 1984 he served as senior scientist for a leading biotechnology company in Cambridge, Mass. His only nontechnical book, *Life: The Unfinished Experiment* (1974), won the National Book Award and was translated into Japanese and several European languages.

McMillan, Edwin Mattison (Sept. 18, 1907—Sept. 7, 1991), U.S. physicist, shared the 1951 Nobel Prize for Chemistry with Glenn Seaborg for his discovery of and research on transuranium (heavier than uranium) elements. After earning a B.S. (1928) and an M.S. (1929) in physics from the California Institute of Technology and a Ph.D. (1932) from Princeton University, McMillan did research for two years with Ernest Lawrence at his laboratory (later named the Lawrence Berkeley Laboratory) at the University of California at Berkeley before joining (1934) the faculty. In 1940 McMillan and Philip H. Abelson discovered element 93, neptunium, the first element to be found that was heavier than uranium. McMillan was certain that other such elements were present, but he had to abandon his research on them during World War II. He helped the Navy develop radar and sonar before working on the Manhattan Project at Los Alamos, N.M., which produced the first atomic bomb. During McMillan's absence from Berkeley, Glenn Seaborg discovered plutonium—element 94—and, later, elements 95–102; the two shared the Nobel Prize for their work. After returning to Berkeley, McMillan advanced the technological limits of Lawrence's cyclotron. There he devised a theory of phase stability that enabled the cyclotron to maintain synchronization for indefinite speeds. He coined the term *synchrocyclotron* for particle accelerators using this principle. When Lawrence died in 1958, McMillan became head of the laboratory, a post he held until his retirement in 1973. He also served as chairman (1968–71) of the National Academy of Sciences and was awarded the National Medal of Science in 1990.

Page, Irvine Heinly (Jan. 7, 1901—June 10, 1991), U.S. physician, conducted vital research on hypertension while serving as director of research (1945–66) at the Cleveland (Ohio) Clinic Foundation. As the discoverer of angiotensin and serotonin, two hormones that affect blood pressure, he was able to shed light on the complex causation of hypertension. Page was the first to identify hypertension as a disease and was able to dispel the commonly held belief that high blood pressure was a result of aging and that blood pressure rose to help the heart pump blood through arteries thickened by arteriosclerosis. Instead he promulgated the "mosaic" theory, which held that high blood pressure resulted from intricate interactions of many regulatory systems, including the biochemical and nervous systems and such other components as structural defects in arteries or organs. Page earned both an undergraduate (1921) and medical degree (1926) from Cornell University, Ithaca, N.Y., and conducted research on the chemistry of the brain at the Kaiser Wilhelm Institute, Munich, Germany (1928–31), and at the Rockefeller Institute (now Rockefeller University), New York City (1931–37). While working at Indianapolis (Ind.) City Hospital (1937–44), he helped devise treatments for lowering blood pressure and developed (1937) a therapy for reversing malignant hypertension, the most severe form of high blood pressure. For his pioneering work Page received many prizes, including the prestigious Lasker and Gairdner awards.

Penney of East Hendred, William George Penney, BARON (June 24, 1909—March 3, 1991), British scientist, was a member of the team that developed the atomic bomb at Los Alamos, N.M., in 1944–45 and director of the group that built the first British nuclear weapons in the 1950s. Penney received advanced degrees in physics and mathematics from the University of London's Imperial College of Science and Technology, the University of Wisconsin, and Trinity College, Cambridge. In 1936 he joined the faculty at Imperial College, where he specialized in applied mathematics and theoretical physics. He was sent to Los Alamos in 1944 as Britain's principal scientific officer and the project's chief expert on the properties of blast waves. Penney was an official observer at the dropping of the second atomic bomb on Nagasaki, Japan, in 1945 and at the subsequent U.S. nuclear tests on Bikini atoll; in 1946 he returned to England. As director (1953–59) of the Atomic Weapons Research Establishment at Aldermaston, he supervised the development and testing of British nuclear and thermonuclear weapons. He also served on the U.K. Atomic Energy Authority as a member (1954–61), deputy chairman (1961–64), and chairman (1964–67). Although Penney advocated nuclear deterrence as a military strategy, he worked for the 1963 Nuclear Test Ban Treaty and for the increased peacetime use of nuclear energy. He returned to Imperial College as rector in 1967. Penney was made a fellow of the Royal Society in 1946, knighted in 1952, and created a life peer in 1967.

Revelle, Roger Randall Dougan (March 7, 1909—July 15, 1991), U.S. oceanographer, as head (1951–64) of the Scripps Institution of Oceanography at La Jolla (now part of the University of California at San Diego), spearheaded many scientific endeavors that led to a greater understanding of the Earth and was credited with pioneering research in global warming and plate tectonics. After earning a B.A. (1929) in geology from Pomona College, Claremont, Calif., Revelle received a Ph.D. (1936) from Scripps, where he became an instructor. During World War II he commanded the oceanographic section of the Navy's Bureau of Ships, and he directed (1946–47) the Navy's oceanographic investigation for the 1946 atomic bomb tests at Bikini atoll. Revelle returned to Scripps in 1948 as professor of oceanography, and he became increasingly concerned with the levels of carbon dioxide in the atmosphere, especially after scrutinizing samples of air taken from atop a Hawaiian volcano. He maintained that the high levels of carbon dioxide produced by the burning of fossil fuels and the burning of forests to clear the land for crops could not be absorbed by the oceans but would accumulate in the atmosphere, thereby trapping the Sun's heat and warming the Earth. Revelle was one of the first to warn of the effects of global warming.

By constructing a device that could measure the upward flow of heat through the ocean floors, he was able to ascertain (with Sir Edward Bullard and Arthur E. Maxwell) that hot material was present under the ocean. This discovery helped in the formulation of the theory of plate tectonics, the concept that the Earth's crust consists of discrete plates that move relative to one another. After serving (1961–63) as science adviser to the U.S. secretary of the interior, Stewart Udall, Revelle became interested in helping Third World countries. He founded (1964) the Harvard Center for Population Studies and was its director until he returned (1976) to the University of California at San Diego, where he remained for the rest of his career. Revelle wrote more than 200 scholarly papers and received many awards, including the National Medal of Science in 1990.

Roger Randall Revelle
Scripps Institution of Oceanography/University of California, San Diego

Seibert, Florence (Oct. 6, 1897—Aug. 23, 1991), U.S. biochemist, isolated the active tuberculin protein while working at the University of Pennsylvania and then, after eight years of research, developed the first accurate skin test for tuberculosis while working at the University of Uppsala, Sweden. Though Robert Koch had isolated the causative microorganism of tuberculosis in 1882 and had grown the first nonlethal derivative of the tuberculin germ—which, when injected under the skin, could determine the presence of the disease—he frequently was unable to provide an accurate diagnosis because his tuberculin was extremely impure. Seibert fashioned a special filter to produce a substance that was a purified protein derivative. Her test became the U.S. government's standard in 1941, and it was adopted by the World Health Organization in 1952. After being afflicted with polio at age three, Seibert was left severely lame and as a result was later counseled to change her focus of study from medicine to chemistry. While at Yale University working on

449

her Ph.D., which she received in 1923, she devised a method for cleansing distilled water of contaminants that caused sudden high fevers in surgical patients who were given the water intravenously. Seibert discovered that even though the distilled water had been sterilized as many as three times, traces of toxic chemicals were entering the water from steam droplets produced during sterilization. She designed a still that was equipped with a trap for the steam droplets, an innovation that simplified and shortened the sterilization process. During her professional career she conducted research at the University of Chicago and the Sprague Memorial Institute in Chicago. After her retirement she moved to Florida but continued to pursue cancer research.

Stommel, Henry Melson (Sept. 27, 1920—Jan. 17, 1992), U.S. oceanographer and meteorologist, conducted important field studies on the dynamics of ocean currents and became a respected theoretician in that field of research. In 1977 Stommel and Friedrich Schott developed a method of determining, in principle, the absolute velocity of mean ocean currents from observations of the density alone. After earning a B.S. from Yale University in 1942, he taught there as instructor in mathematics and astronomy (1942–44). He then moved to the Woods Hole (Mass.) Oceanographic Institution, where he was research associate (1944–59) and, from 1978, oceanographer. Stommel was professor of oceanography (1959–60 and 1963–78) at the Massachusetts Institute of Technology and at Harvard University (1960–63). In 1947 he published *The Gulf Stream,* one of the first books to explore that ocean current and other currents in general. He set forth the idea that the Earth's rotation was responsible for pushing the Gulf Stream westward along the coast of North America, and he also theorized that its northward flow must be balanced by a deep, southward flow beneath it. Many of his theories were later proved. Stommel set up observational stations to monitor ocean current, including the PANULIRUS (begun in 1954) in Bermuda and the MEDOC study of deep-water formation in the Mediterranean (1969–72). He was credited with helping to formulate a physical-mathematical treatment of the entrainment of surrounding air into the ascending current of a cumulus cloud. Stommel, who earned honorary Ph.D.'s from Göteborg (Sweden) University in 1964 and Yale University and the University of Chicago in 1970, was elected to the National Academy of Sciences in 1962 and was awarded the National Medal of Science in 1989.

Taylor, Edward Story (Jan. 26, 1903—Feb. 2, 1991), U.S. engineer, served as the founding director (1946–68) of the Gas Turbine Laboratory at the Massachusetts Institute of Technology (MIT) and was instrumental in developing internal combustion, gas turbine, and jet engines. After earning a B.S. from MIT in 1924, Taylor worked for the Public Service Corp. and the Wright Aeronautical Corp. in New Jersey before returning to his alma mater in 1927 as an instructor in aeronautical engineering. He remained there for his entire professional career, becoming professor of aircraft engines in 1942 and professor of flight propulsion in 1962. One of his most successful inventions was a vibration absorber for reciprocating aircraft engines; he was awarded the Sylvanus Albert Reed Medal in 1936 for this innovation, and in 1973 he was honored by the American Institute of Aeronautics and Astronautics, which bestowed on him its Robert F. Goddard Award for 45 years of contributions to aircraft propulsion. Taylor retired from MIT in 1968 but remained active in its Gas Turbine Laboratory. He was the author of such technical volumes as *The Internal Combustion Engine* (with C. Fayette Taylor; 1938, 1948, 1961) and *Dimensional Analysis for Engineers* (1974).

Wilson, Allan Charles (Oct. 18, 1934—July 21, 1991), U.S. biochemist, used innovative molecular techniques to set forth two important evolutionist theories while serving (1964–91) as professor of biochemistry and molecular biology at the University of California at Berkeley. His first work, conducted during the 1960s with Berkeley colleague Vincent Sarich, relied on a "molecular clock" that could be used to trace human origins. The idea of a molecular clock stemmed from the assumption that a given gene (and its protein product) from a species of organism acquires mutations at a reasonably steady rate over time. Consequently, the number of mutations by which the corresponding genes from two species differ can be used to estimate how long ago the species diverged from a common ancestor. The two scientists proposed that humans and apes evolved from different lineages that split off from one another five million years ago. This theory was at first dismissed by paleoanthropologists, who had used fossil bones to study the origins of humans, but later the theory became more widely accepted after anatomists reclassified one of their fossils. For his second theory, which remained controversial, Wilson used mitochondrial DNA comparisons of different living human populations to estimate the source and time of origin of modern humans. He concluded that modern human populations originated in Africa approximately 100,000 to 200,000 years ago and then spread over the Earth, displacing other hominid species in the process. He also hypothesized in 1987 about an "African Eve," a single female who served as the ancestral mother to all existing humans. Wilson earned a B.S. degree in zoology (1955) from the University of Otago, Dunedin, N.Z., and a Ph.D. in biochemistry (1961) from the University of California at Berkeley.

Contributors to the Science Year in Review

D. James Baker *Earth sciences: Oceanography.* President, Joint Oceanographic Institutions Inc., Washington, D.C.

David M. Boore *Earth sciences: Geophysics.* Geophysicist, U.S. Geological Survey, Menlo Park, Calif.

Harold Borko *Electronics and information sciences: Information systems and services.* Professor, Graduate School of Library and Information Science, University of California, Los Angeles.

John M. Bowen *Medical sciences: Veterinary medicine.* Associate Dean for Research and Graduate Affairs and Professor of Pharmacology and Toxicology, College of Veterinary Medicine, University of Georgia, Athens.

Keith J. Bowman *Materials sciences: Metallurgy.* Assistant Professor of Materials Engineering, Purdue University, West Lafayette, Ind.

George G. Brown *Life sciences: Zoology.* Professor of Zoology and Genetics, Iowa State University, Ames.

George R. Brubaker *Chemistry: Inorganic chemistry.* Supervisory Chemist, U.S. Food and Drug Administration, Chicago District Laboratory, Chicago.

Paul J. Campbell *Mathematics.* Professor of Mathematics and Computer Science, Beloit College, Beloit, Wis.

James D. Chadi *Physics: Condensed-matter physics.* Senior Member, Research Staff, NEC Research Institute, Princeton, N.J.

Douglas E. Comer *Electronics and information sciences: Computers and computer science.* Professor of Computer Science, Purdue University, West Lafayette, Ind.

Dave Dooling *Space exploration.* D² Associates, Freelance Science Writing and Aerospace Consulting, Huntsville, Ala.

Carl B. Dover *Physics: Nuclear physics.* Senior Scientist, Brookhaven National Laboratory, Upton, N.Y.

F.C. Durant III *Electronics and information sciences: Satellite systems (in part).* Aerospace Historian and Consultant, Chevy Chase, Md.

Gerald Feinberg *Physics: High-energy physics.* Professor of Physics, Columbia University, New York, N.Y.

Richard L. Gordon *Energy.* Professor of Mineral Economics, MICASU University Endowed Fellow, and Director of the Center for Energy and Mineral Policy Research, Pennsylvania State University, University Park.

David Guise *Architecture and civil engineering.* Professor Emeritus of Architecture, City College of New York, and private practice of architecture, New York, N.Y.

R. Cargill Hall *Electronics and information sciences: Satellite systems (in part).* Aerospace Historian, U.S. Air Force History Office, Arlington, Va.

Robert Haselkorn *Life sciences: Molecular biology.* F.L. Pritzker Distinguished Service Professor, Department of Molecular Genetics and Cell Biology, University of Chicago, Ill.

John Patrick Jordan *Food and agriculture: Agriculture (in part).* Administrator, Cooperative State Research Service, U.S. Department of Agriculture, Washington, D.C.

Lou Joseph *Medical sciences: Dentistry.* Science writer, Chicago.

Allan P. Katz *Materials sciences: Ceramics.* Technical Manager for Structural Ceramics, Wright Laboratory, Wright-Patterson Air Force Base, Ohio.

George B. Kauffman *Chemistry: Applied chemistry.* Professor of Chemistry, California State University, Fresno.

David B. Kitts *Earth sciences: Geology and geochemistry.* Professor Emeritus of the History of Science, University of Oklahoma, Norman.

Mina W. Lamb *Food and agriculture: Nutrition.* Professor Emeritus, Department of Food and Nutrition, Texas Tech University, Lubbock.

Patricia Brazeel Lewis *Food and agriculture: Agriculture (in part).* Public Relations Consultant, New Jersey Agricultural Experiment Station, Rutgers University, New Brunswick, N.J.

Melvin H. Marx *Psychology* (in part). Professor of Psychology, Western Carolina University, Cullowhee, N.C., and Professor Emeritus of Psychology, University of Missouri, Columbia.

John E. McMurry *Chemistry: Organic chemistry.* Professor of Chemistry, Cornell University, Ithaca, N.Y.

Franz J. Monssen *Electronics and information sciences: Electronics.* Instructor, Department of Electronic and Computer Engineering Technology, Queensborough Community College, New York, N.Y.

Larry L. Naylor *Anthropology.* Chair, Anthropology, Institute of Anthropology, University of North Texas, Denton.

Colin V. Newman *Psychology* (in part). Executive Secretary, British Psychological Society, Leicester, England.

Carolyn D. Newton *Scientists of the Year: Nobel prizes.* Free-lance Writer and Editor, Seattle, Wash.

Joseph Palca *U.S. science policy.* Senior Writer, *Science* magazine, Washington, D.C.

Roger A. Pielke *Earth sciences: Atmospheric sciences.* Professor of Atmospheric Science, Colorado State University, Fort Collins.

W.M. Protheroe *Astronomy.* Professor Emeritus of Astronomy, Ohio State University, Columbus.

John Rhea *Defense research.* Free-lance Science Writer, Woodstock, Va.

Phillip F. Schewe *Physics: General developments.* Chief Science Writer, American Institute of Physics, New York, N.Y.

Robert R. Shannon *Optical engineering.* Professor and Director, Optical Sciences Center, University of Arizona, Tucson.

Lawrence J. Shimkets *Life sciences: Microbiology.* Associate Professor of Microbiology, University of Georgia, Athens.

Joanne Silberner *Medical sciences: General medicine.* Senior Editor, Health, *U.S. News and World Report,* Washington, D.C.

Albert J. Smith *Life sciences: Botany.* Professor of Biology, Wheaton College, Wheaton, Ill.

Frank A. Smith *Transportation.* Executive Consultant, Eno Transportation Foundation, Westport, Conn.

Leslie Smith *Earth sciences: Hydrology.* Professor of Geological Sciences, University of British Columbia, Vancouver.

Robert E. Stoffels *Electronics and information sciences: Communications systems.* Editor, *Telephone Engineer & Management* magazine, Chicago, Ill.

Philip R. Watson *Chemistry: Physical chemistry.* Professor of Chemistry, Oregon State University, Corvallis.

Kenneth E.F. Watt *Environment.* Professor of Zoology, University of California, Davis.

James D. Wilde *Archaeology.* Director, Office of Public Archaeology, Brigham Young University, Provo, Utah.

Contributors to the Encyclopædia Britannica Science Update

William S. Fyfe *Minerals and Rocks* (in part). Professor of Geology, University of Western Ontario, London.

Kenneth I. Kellerman *Telescopes* (in part). Senior Scientist, National Radio Astronomy Observatory, Charlottesville, Va.

B.L. Klock *Telescopes* (in part). Physical Scientist, Research and Engineering Directorate, Advanced Weapons Systems Division, Defense Mapping Agency, U.S. Department of Defense, Washington, D.C.

Jane Selverstone *Minerals and Rocks* (in part). Associate Professor of Geology, Harvard University, Cambridge, Mass.

A
Science
Classic

William James

Selections from *The Principles of Psychology*

With the publication of *The Principles of Psychology* in 1890, William James (1842–1910) became the most prominent psychologist in the United States. In this work he strongly supported functionalism, which stressed the importance of empirical, rational thought over an experimental, trial-and-error approach. Reprinted below are two chapters from this book.

Chapter I

The Scope of Psychology

William James
Harvard University News Service

Psychology is the science of mental life, both of its phenomena and of their conditions. The phenomena are such things as we call feelings, desires, cognitions, reasonings, decisions, and the like; and, superficially considered, their variety and complexity is such as to leave a chaotic impression on the observer. The most natural and consequently the earliest way of unifying the material was, first, to classify it as well as might be, and, secondly, to affiliate the diverse mental modes thus found, upon a simple entity, the personal soul, of which they are taken to be so many facultative manifestations. Now, for instance, the soul manifests its faculty of memory, now of reasoning, now of volition, or again its imagination or its appetite. This is the orthodox "spiritualistic" theory of scholasticism and of common-sense. Another and a less obvious way of unifying the chaos is to seek common elements *in* the divers mental facts rather than a common agent behind them, and to explain them constructively by the various forms of arrangement of these elements, as one explains houses by stones and bricks. The "associationist" schools of Herbart in Germany, and of Hume, the Mills and Bain in Britain have thus constructed a *psychology without a soul* by taking discrete "ideas," faint or vivid, and showing how, by their cohesions, repulsions, and forms of succession, such things as reminiscences, perceptions, emotions, volitions, passions, theories, and all the other furnishings of an individual's mind may be engendered. The very self or *ego* of the individual comes in this way to be viewed no longer as the pre-existing source of the representations, but rather as their last and most complicated fruit.

Now, if we strive rigorously to simplify the phenomena in either of these ways, we soon become aware of inadequacies in our method. Any particular cognition, for example, or recollection, is accounted for on the soul-theory by being referred to the spiritual faculties of cognition or of memory. These faculties themselves are thought of as absolute properties of the soul; that is, to take the case of memory, no reason is given why we should remember a fact as it happened, except that so to remember it constitutes the essence of our recollective power. We may, as spiritualists, try to explain our memory's failures and blunders by secondary causes. But its *successes* can invoke no factors save the existence of certain objective things to be remembered on the one hand, and of our faculty of memory on the other. When, for instance, I recall my graduation-day, and drag all its incidents and emotions up from death's dateless night, no mechanical cause can explain this process, nor can any analysis reduce it to lower terms or make its nature seem other than an ultimate *datum*, which, whether we rebel or not at its mysteriousness, must simply be taken for granted if we are to psychologize at all. However the associationist may represent the present ideas as thronging and arranging themselves, still, the spiritualist insists, he has in the end to admit that *something*, be it brain, be it "ideas," be it "association," *knows* past time *as* past, and fills it out with this or that event. And when the spiritualist calls memory an "irreducible faculty," he says no more than this admission of the associationist already grants.

And yet the admission is far from being a satisfactory simplification of the concrete facts. For why should this absolute god-given faculty retain so much better the events of yesterday than those of last year, and, best of all, those of an hour ago? Why, again, in old age should its grasp of childhood's events seem firmest? Why should illness and exhaustion enfeeble it? Why should repeating an experience strengthen our recollection of it? Why should drugs, fevers, asphyxia, and excitement resuscitate things long since forgotten? If we content ourselves with merely affirming that the faculty of memory is so peculiarly constituted by nature as to exhibit just these oddities, we seem little the better for having invoked it, for our explanation becomes as complicated as that of the crude facts with which we started. Moreover there is something grotesque and irrational in the supposition that the soul is equipped with elementary powers of such an ingeniously intricate sort. Why *should* our memory cling more easily to the near than the remote? Why should it lose its grasp of proper sooner than of abstract names? Such peculiarities seem quite fantastic; and might, for aught we can see *a priori*, be the precise opposites of what they are. Evidently, then, *the faculty does not exist absolutely, but works under conditions; and the quest of the conditions* becomes the psychologist's most interesting task.

However firmly he may hold to the soul and her remembering faculty, he must acknowledge that she never exerts the latter without a *cue,* and that something must always precede and *remind* us of whatever we are to recollect. "An *idea!*" says the associationist, "an idea associated with the remembered thing; and this explains also why things repeatedly met with are more easily recollected, for their associates on the various occasions furnish so many distinct avenues of recall." But this does not explain the effects of fever, exhaustion, hypnotism, old age, and the like. And in general, the pure associationist's account of our mental life is almost as bewildering as that of the pure spiritualist. This multitude of ideas, existing absolutely, yet clinging together, and weaving an endless carpet of themselves, like dominoes in ceaseless change, or the bits of glass in a kaleidoscope,— whence do they get their fantastic laws of clinging, and why do they cling in just the shapes they do?

For this the associationist must introduce the order of experience in the outer world. The dance of the ideas is a copy, somewhat mutilated and altered, of the order of phenomena. But the slightest reflection shows that phenomena have absolutely no power to influence our ideas until they have first impressed our senses and our brain. The bare existence of a past fact is no ground for our remembering it. Unless we have seen it, or somehow *undergone* it, we shall never know of its having been. The experiences of the body are thus one of the conditions of the faculty of memory being what it is. And a very small amount of reflection on facts shows that one part of the body, namely, the brain, is the part whose experiences are directly concerned. If the nervous communication be cut off between the brain and other parts, the experiences of those other parts are nonexistent for the mind. The eye is blind, the ear deaf, the hand insensible and motionless. And conversely, if the brain be injured, consciousness is abolished or altered, even although every other organ in the body be ready to play its normal part. A blow on the head, a sudden subtraction of blood, the pressure of an apoplectic hemorrhage, may have the first effect; whilst a very few ounces of alcohol or grains of opium or hasheesh, or a whiff of chloroform or nitrous oxide gas, are sure to have the second. The delirium of fever, the altered self of insanity, are all due to foreign matters circulating through the brain, or to pathological changes in that organ's substance. The fact that the brain is the one immediate bodily condition of the mental operations is indeed so universally admitted nowadays that I need spend no more time in illustrating it, but will simply postulate it and pass on. The whole remainder of the book will be more or less of a proof that the postulate was correct.

Bodily experiences, therefore, and more particularly brain-experiences, must take a place amongst those conditions of the mental life of which psychology need take account. *The spiritualist and the associationist must both be "cerebralists,"* to the extent at least of admitting that certain peculiarities in the way of working of their own favorite principles are explicable only by the fact that the brain laws are a codeterminant of the result.

Our first conclusion, then, is that a certain amount of brain-physiology must be presupposed or included in psychology.[1]

In still another way the psychologist is forced to be something of a nerve-physiologist. Mental phenomena are not only conditioned *a parte ante* by bodily processes; but they lead to them *a parte post*. That they lead to *acts* is of course the most familiar of truths, but I do not merely mean acts in the sense of voluntary and deliberate muscular performances. Mental states occasion also changes in the calibre of blood-vessels, or alteration in the heart-beats, or processes more subtle still, in glands and viscera. If these are taken into account, as well as acts which follow at some *remote period* because the mental state was once there, it will be safe to lay down the general law that *no mental modification ever occurs which is not accompanied or followed by a bodily change*. The ideas and feelings, *e.g.,* which these present printed characters excite in the reader's mind not only occasion movements of his eyes and nascent movements of articulation in him, but will some day make him speak, or take sides in a discussion, or give advice, or choose a book to read, differently from what would have been the case had they never impressed his retina. Our psychology must therefore take account not only of the conditions antecedent to mental states, but of their resultant consequences as well.

But actions originally prompted by conscious intelligence may grow so automatic by dint of habit as to be apparently unconsciously performed. Standing, walking, buttoning and unbuttoning, piano-playing, talking, even saying one's prayers, may be done when the mind is absorbed in other things. The performances of animal *instinct* seem semi-automatic, and the *reflex acts* of self-preservation certainly are so. Yet they resemble intelligent acts in bringing about the *same ends* at which the animal's consciousness, on other occasions, deliberately aims. Shall the study of such machine-like yet purposive acts as these be included in psychology?

The boundary line of the mental is certainly vague. It is better not to be pedantic, but to let the science be as vague as its subject, and include such phenomena as these if by so doing we can throw any light on the main business in hand. It will ere long be seen, I trust, that we can; and that we gain much more by a broad than by a narrow conception of our subject. At a certain stage in the development of every science a degree of vagueness is what best consists with fertility. On the whole, few recent formulas have done more real service of a rough sort in psychology than the Spencerian one that the essence of mental life and of bodily life are one, namely, "the adjustment of inner to outer relations." Such a formula is vagueness incarnate; but because it takes into account the fact that minds inhabit environments which act on them and on which they in turn react; because, in short, it takes mind in the midst of all its concrete relations, it is immensely more fertile than the old-fashioned "rational psychology," which treated the soul as a detached existent, sufficient unto itself, and assumed to consider only its nature and properties. I shall therefore feel free to make any sallies into zoology or into pure nerve-physiology which may seem instructive for our purposes, but otherwise shall leave those sciences to the physiologists.

Can we state more distinctly still the manner in which the mental life seems to intervene between impressions made from without upon the body, and reactions of the body upon the outer world again? Let us look at a few facts.

If some iron filings be sprinkled on a table and a magnet brought near them, they will fly through the air for a certain distance and stick to its surface. A savage seeing the phenomenon explains it as the result of an attraction or love between the magnet and the filings. But let a card cover the poles of the magnet, and the filings will press forever against its surface without its ever occurring to them to pass around its sides and thus come into more direct contact with the object of their love. Blow bubbles through a tube into the bottom of a pail of water, they will rise to the surface and mingle with the air. Their action may again be poetically interpreted as due to a longing to recombine with the mother-atmosphere above the surface. But if you invert a jar full of water over the pail, they will rise and remain lodged beneath its bottom, shut in from the outer air, although a slight deflection from their course at the outset, or a re-descent towards the rim of the jar when they found their upward course impeded, would easily have set them free.

If now we pass from such actions as these to those of living things, we notice a striking difference. Romeo wants Juliet as the filings want the magnet; and if no obstacles intervene he moves towards her by as straight a line as they. But Romeo and Juliet, if a wall be built between them, do not remain idiotically pressing their faces against its opposite sides like the magnet and the filings with the card. Romeo soon finds a circuitous way, by scaling the wall or otherwise, of touching Juliet's lips directly. With the filings the path is fixed; whether it reaches the end depends on accidents. With the lover it is the end which is fixed; the path may be modified indefinitely.

Suppose a living frog in the position in which we placed our bubbles of air, namely, at the bottom of a jar of water. The want of breath will soon make him also long to rejoin the mother-atmosphere, and he will take the shortest path to his end by swimming straight upwards. But if a jar full of water be inverted over him, he will not, like the bubbles, perpetually press his nose against its unyielding roof, but will restlessly explore the neighborhood until by re-descending again he has discovered a path around its brim to the goal of his desires. Again the fixed end, the varying means!

Such contrasts between living and inanimate performances end by leading men to deny that in the physical world final purposes exist at all. Loves and desires are to-day no longer imputed to particles of iron or of air. No one supposes now that the end of any activity which they may display is an ideal purpose presiding over the activity from its outset and soliciting or drawing it into being by a sort of *vis a fronte*. The end, on the contrary, is deemed a mere passive result, pushed into being *a tergo,* having had, so to speak, no voice in its own production. Alter the pre-existing conditions, and with inorganic materials you bring forth each time a different apparent end. But with intelligent agents, altering the conditions changes the activity displayed, but not the end reached; for here the idea of the yet unrealized end co-operates with the conditions to determine what the activities shall be.

The pursuance of future ends and the choice of means for their attainment are thus the mark and criterion of the presence of mentality in a phenomenon. We all use this test to discriminate between an intelligent and a mechanical performance. We impute no mentality to sticks and stones, because they never seem to move for *the sake of* anything, but always when pushed, and then indifferently and with no sign of choice. So we unhesitatingly call them senseless.

Just so we form our decision upon the deepest of all philosophic problems: Is the Kosmos an expression of intelligence rational in its inward nature, or a brute external fact pure and simple? If we find ourselves, in contemplating it, unable to banish the impression that it is a realm of final purposes, that it exists for the sake of something, we place intelligence at the heart of it and have a religion. If, on the contrary, in surveying its irremediable flux, we can think of the present only as so much mere mechanical sprouting from the past, occurring with no reference to the future, we are atheists and materialists.

In the lengthy discussions which psychologists have carried on about the amount of intelligence displayed by lower mammals, or the amount of consciousness involved in the functions of the nerve-centres of reptiles, the same test has always been applied: Is the character of the actions such that we must believe them to be performed *for the sake* of their result? The result in question, as we shall hereafter abundantly see, is as a rule a useful one,—the animal is, on the whole, safer under the circumstances for bringing it forth. So far the action has a teleological character; but such mere outward teleology as this might still be the blind result of *vis a tergo*. The growth and movements of plants, the processes of development, digestion, secretion, etc., in animals, supply innumerable instances of performances useful to the individual which may nevertheless be, and by most of us are supposed to be, produced by automatic mechanism. The physiologist does not confidently assert conscious intelligence in the frog's spinal cord until he has shown that the useful result which the nervous machinery brings forth under a given irritation *remains the same when the machinery is altered*. If, to take the stock instance, the right knee of a headless frog be irritated with acid, the right foot will wipe it off. When, however, this foot is amputated, the animal will often raise the *left* foot to the spot and wipe the offending material away.

Pflüger and Lewes reason from such facts in the following way: If the first reaction were the result of mere machinery, they say; if that irritated portion of the skin discharged the right leg as a trigger discharges its own barrel of a shotgun; then amputating the right foot would indeed frustrate the wiping, but would not make the *left* leg move. It would simply result in the right stump moving through the empty air (which is in fact the phenomenon sometimes observed). The right trigger makes no effort to discharge the left barrel if the right one be unloaded; nor does an electrical machine ever get restless because it can only emit sparks, and not hem pillow-cases like a sewing-machine.

If, on the contrary, the right leg originally moved for the *purpose* of wiping the acid, then nothing is more natural than that, when the easiest means of effecting that purpose prove fruitless, other means should be tried. Every failure must keep the animal in a state of disappointment which will lead to all sorts of new trials and devices; and tranquillity will not ensue till one of these, by a happy stroke, achieves the wished-for end.

In a similar way Goltz ascribes intelligence to the frog's optic lobes and cerebellum. We alluded above to the manner in which a sound frog imprisoned in water will discover an outlet to the atmosphere. Goltz found that frogs deprived of their cerebral hemispheres would often exhibit a like ingenuity. Such a frog, after rising from the bottom and finding his farther upward progress checked by the glass bell which has been inverted over him, will not persist in butting his nose against the obstacle until dead of suffocation, but will often redescend and emerge from under its rim as if, not a definite mechanical propulsion upwards, but rather a conscious desire to reach the air by hook or crook were the mainspring of his activity. Goltz concluded from this that the hemispheres are not the sole seat of intellect in frogs. He made the same inference from observing that a brainless frog will turn over from his back to his belly when one of his legs is sewed up, although the movements required are then very different from those excited under normal circumstances by the same annoying position. They seem determined, consequently, not merely by the antecedent irritant, but by the final end,—though the irritant of course is what makes the end desired.

Another brilliant German author, Liebmann,[2] argues against the brain's mechanism accounting for mental action, by very similar considerations. A machine as such, he says, will bring forth right results when it is in good order, and wrong results if out of repair. But both kinds of result flow with equally fatal necessity from their conditions. We cannot suppose the clock-work whose structure fatally determines it to a certain rate of speed, noticing that this speed is too slow or too fast and vainly trying to correct it. Its conscience, if it have any, should be as good as that of the best chronometer, for both alike obey equally well the same eternal mechanical laws—laws from behind. But if the *brain* be out of order and the man says "Twice four are two," instead of "Twice four are eight," or else "I must go to the coal to buy the wharf," instead of "I must go to the wharf to buy the coal," instantly there arises a consciousness of error. The wrong performance, though it obey the same mechanical law as the right, is nevertheless condemned,—condemned as contradicting the inner law—the law from in front, the purpose or ideal for which the brain *should* act, whether it do so or not.

We need not discuss here whether these writers in drawing their conclusion have done justice to all the premises involved in the cases they treat of. We quote their arguments only to show how they appeal to the principle that *no actions but such as are done for an end, and show a choice of means, can be called indubitable expressions of mind.*

I shall then adopt this as the criterion by which to circumscribe the subject-matter of this work so far as action enters into it. Many nervous performances will therefore be unmentioned, as being purely physiological. Nor will the anatomy of the nervous system and organs of sense be described anew. The reader will find in H.N. Martin's *Human Body,* in G.T.

Ladd's *Physiological Psychology,* and in all the other standard Anatomies and Physiologies, a mass of information which we must regard as preliminary and take for granted in the present work.[3] Of the functions of the cerebral hemispheres, however, since they directly subserve consciousness, it will be well to give some little account.

Chapter VII

The Methods and Snares of Psychology

We have now finished the physiological preliminaries of our subject and must in the remaining chapters study the mental states themselves whose cerebral conditions and concomitants we have been considering hitherto. Beyond the brain, however, there is an outer world to which the brain-states themselves "correspond." And it will be well, ere we advance farther, to say a word about the relation of the mind to this larger sphere of physical fact.

Psychology Is a Natural Science

That is, the mind which the psychologist studies is the mind of distinct individuals inhabiting definite portions of a real space and of a real time. With any other sort of mind, absolute intelligence, mind unattached to a particular body, or mind not subject to the course of time, the psychologist as such has nothing to do. "Mind," in his mouth, is only a class name for *minds.* Fortunate will it be if his more modest inquiry result in any generalizations which the philosopher devoted to absolute Intelligence as such can use.

To the psychologist, then, the minds he studies are *objects,* in a world of other objects. Even when he introspectively analyzes his own mind, and tells what he finds there, he talks about it in an objective way. He says, for instance, that under certain circumstances the color gray appears to him green, and calls the appearance an illusion. This implies that he compares two objects, a real color seen under certain conditions, and a mental perception which he believes to represent it, and that he declares the relation between them to be of a certain kind. In making this critical judgment, the psychologist stands as much outside of the perception which he criticises as he does of the color. Both are his objects. And if this is true of him when he reflects on his own conscious states, how much truer is it when he treats of those of others! In German philosophy since Kant the word *Erkenntnisstheorie,* criticism of the faculty of knowledge, plays a great part. Now the psychologist necessarily becomes such an *Erkenntnisstheoretiker.* But the knowledge he theorizes about is not the bare function of knowledge which Kant criticises—he does not inquire into the possibility of knowledge *überhaupt*. He assumes it to be possible, he does not doubt its presence in himself at the moment he speaks. The knowledge he criticizes is the knowledge of particular men about the particular things that surround them. This he may, upon occasion, in the light of his *own* unquestioned knowledge, pronounce true or false, and trace the reasons by which it has become one or the other.

It is highly important that this natural-science point of view should be understood at the outset. Otherwise more may be demanded of the psychologist than he ought to be expected to perform.

A diagram will exhibit more emphatically what the assumptions of Psychology must be:

1 The Psychol- ogist	2 The Thought Studied	3 The Thought's Object	4 The Psychol- ogist's Reality

These four squares contain the irreducible data of psychology. No. 1, the psychologist, believes Nos. 2, 3, and 4, which together form *his* total object, to be realities, and reports them and their mutual relations as truly as he can without troubling himself with the puzzle of how he can report them at all. About such *ultimate* puzzles he in the main need trouble himself no more than the geometer, the chemist, or the botanist do, who make precisely the same assumptions as he.[4]

Of certain fallacies to which the psychologist is exposed by reason of his peculiar point of view—that of being a reporter of subjective as well as of objective facts, we must presently speak. But not until we have considered the methods he uses for ascertaining what the facts in question are.

The Methods of Investigation

Introspective Observation is what we have to rely on first and foremost and always. The word introspection need hardly be defined—it means, of course, the looking into our own minds and reporting what we there discover. *Everyone agrees that we there discover states of consciousness.* So far as I know, the existence of such states has never been doubted by any critic, however, sceptical in other respects he may have been. That we have *cogitations* of some sort is the *inconcussum* in a world most of whose other facts have at some time tottered in the breath of philosophic doubt. All people unhesitatingly believe that they feel themselves thinking, and that they distinguish the mental state as an inward ac-

tivity or passion, from all the objects with which it may cognitively deal. *I regard this belief as the most fundamental of all the postulates of Psychology,* and shall discard all curious inquiries about its certainty as too metaphysical for the scope of this book.

A Question of Nomenclature. We ought to have some general term by which to designate all states of consciousness merely as such, and apart from their particular quality or cognitive function. Unfortunately most of the terms in use have grave objections. "Mental state," "state of consciousness," "conscious modification," are cumbrous and have no kindred verbs. The same is true of "subjective condition." "Feeling" has the verb "to feel," both active and neuter, and such derivatives as "feelingly," "felt," "feltness," etc., which make it extremely convenient. But on the other hand it has specific meanings as well as its generic one, sometimes standing for pleasure and pain, and being sometimes a synonym of "*sensation*" as opposed to *thought;* whereas we wish a term to cover sensation and thought indifferently. Moreover, "feeling" has acquired in the hearts of platonizing thinkers a very opprobrious set of implications; and since one of the great obstacles to mutual understanding in philosophy is the use of words eulogistically and disparagingly, impartial terms ought always, if possible, to be preferred. The word *psychosis* has been proposed by Mr. Huxley. It has the advantage of being correlative to *neurosis* (the name applied by the same author to the corresponding nerve-process), and is moreover technical and devoid of partial implications. But it has no verb or other grammatical form allied to it. The expressions "affection of the soul," "modification of the ego," are clumsy, like "state of consciousness," and they implicitly assert theories which it is not well to embody in terminology before they have been openly discussed and approved. "Idea" is a good vague neutral word, and was by Locke employed in the broadest generic way; but notwithstanding his authority it has not domesticated itself in the language so as to cover bodily sensations, and it moreover has no verb. "Thought" would be by far the best word to use if it could be made to cover sensations. It has no opprobrious connotation such as "feeling" has, and it immediately suggests the omnipresence of cognition (or reference to an object other than the mental state itself), which we shall soon see to be of the mental life's essence. But can the expression "thought of a toothache" ever suggest to the reader the actual present pain itself? It is hardly possible; and we thus seem about to be forced back on some *pair* of terms like Hume's "impression and idea," or Hamilton's "presentation and representation," or the ordinary "feeling and thought," if we wish to cover the whole ground.

In this quandary we can make no definitive

choice, but must, according to the convenience of the context, use sometimes one, sometimes another of the synonyms that have been mentioned. *My own partiality is for either* FEELING *or* THOUGHT. I shall probably often use both words in a wider sense than usual, and alternately startle two classes of readers by their unusual sound; but if the connection makes it clear that mental states at large, irrespective of their kind, are meant, this will do no harm, and may even do some good.[5]

The inaccuracy of introspective observation has been made a subject of debate. It is important to gain some fixed ideas on this point before we proceed.

The commonest spiritualistic opinion is that the soul or *subject* of the mental life is a metaphysical entity, inaccessible to direct knowledge, and that the various mental states and operations of which we reflectively become aware are objects of an inner sense which does not lay hold of the real agent in itself, any more than sight or hearing gives us direct knowledge of matter in itself. From this point of view introspection is, of course, incompetent to lay hold of anything more than the soul's *phenomena.* But even then the question remains, How well can it know the phenomena themselves?

Some authors take high ground here and claim for it a sort of infallibility. Thus Ueberweg:

When a mental image, as such, is the object of my apprehension, there is no meaning in seeking to distinguish its existence in my consciousness (in me) from its existence out of my consciousness (in itself); for the object apprehended is, in this case, one which does not even exist, as the objects of external perception do, in itself outside of my consciousness. It exists only within me.[6]

And Brentano:

The phenomena inwardly apprehended are true in themselves. As they appear—of this the evidence with which they are apprehended is a warrant—so they are in reality. Who, then, can deny that in this a great superiority of Psychology over the physical sciences comes to light?

And again:

No one can doubt whether the psychic condition he apprehends in himself *be,* and be *so,* as he apprehends it. Whoever should doubt this would have reached that *finished* doubt which destroys itself in destroying every fixed point from which to make an attack upon knowledge.[7]

Others have gone to the opposite extreme, and maintained that we can have no introspective cognition of our own minds at all. A deliverance of Auguste Comte to this effect has been so often quoted as to be almost classical; and some reference to it seems therefore indispensable here.

Philosophers, says Comte,[8] have

in these latter days imagined themselves able to distinguish, by a very singular subtlety, two sorts of observation of equal importance, one external, the other internal, the latter being solely destined for the study of intellectual phenomena. . . . I limit myself to pointing out the princi-

pal consideration which proves clearly that this pretended direct contemplation of the mind by itself is a pure illusion. . . . It is in fact evident that, by an invincible necessity, the human mind can observe directly all phenomena except its own proper states. For by whom shall the observation of these be made? It is conceivable that a man might observe himself with respect to the *passions* that animate him, for the anatomical organs of passion are distinct from those whose function is observation. Though we have all made such observations on ourselves, they can never have much scientific value, and the best mode of knowing the passions will always be that of observing them from without; for every strong state of passion . . . is necessarily incompatible with the state of observation. But, as for observing in the same way *intellectual* phenomena at the time of their actual presence, that is a manifest impossibility. The thinker cannot divide himself into two, of whom one reasons whilst the other observes him reason. The organ observed and the organ observing being, in this case, identical, how could observation take place? This pretended psychological method is then radically null and void. On the one hand, they advise you to isolate yourself, as far as possible, from every external sensation, especially every intellectual work,—for if you were to busy yourself even with the simplest calculation, what would become of *internal* observation?—on the other hand, after having with the utmost care attained this state of intellectual slumber, you must begin to contemplate the operations going on in your mind, when nothing there takes place! Our descendants will doubtless see such pretensions some day ridiculed upon the stage. The results of so strange a procedure harmonize entirely with its principle. For all the two thousand years during which metaphysicians have thus cultivated psychology, they are not agreed about one intelligible and established proposition. "*Internal observation*" gives almost as many divergent results as there are individuals who think they practise it.

Comte hardly could have known anything of the English, and nothing of the German, empirical psychology. The "results" which he had in mind when writing were probably scholastic ones, such as principles of internal activity, the faculties, the ego, the *liberum arbitrium indifferentiæ,* etc. John Mill, in replying to him,[9] says:

It might have occurred to M. Comte that a fact may be studied through the medium of memory, not at the very moment of our perceiving it, but the moment after: and this is really the mode in which our best knowledge of our intellectual acts is generally acquired. We reflect on what we have been doing when the act is past, but when its impression in the memory is still fresh. Unless in one of these ways, we could not have acquired the knowledge which nobody denies us to have, of what passes in our minds. M. Comte would scarcely have affirmed that we are not aware of our own intellectual operations. We know of our observings and our reasonings, either at the very time, or by memory the moment after; in either case, by direct knowledge, and not (like things done by us in a state of somnambulism) merely by their results. This simple fact destroys the whole of M. Comte's argument. Whatever we are directly aware of, we can directly observe.

Where now does the truth lie? Our quotation from Mill is obviously the one which expresses the most of *practical* truth about the matter. Even the writers who insist upon the absolute veracity of our immediate inner apprehension of a conscious state have to contrast with this the fallibility of our *memory* or *observation* of it, a moment later. No one has emphasized more sharply than Brentano himself the difference between the immediate *feltness* of a feeling, and its perception by a subsequent reflective act. But which mode of consciousness of it is that which the psychologist must depend on? If to *have* feelings or thoughts in their immediacy were enough, babies in the cradle would be psychologists, and infallible ones. But the psychologist must not only *have* his mental states in their absolute veritableness, he must report them and write about them, name them, classify and compare them and trace their relations to other things. Whilst alive they are their own property; it is only *post-mortem* that they become his prey.[10] And as in the naming, classing, and knowing of things in general we are notoriously fallible, why not also here? Comte is quite right in laying stress on the fact that a feeling, to be named, judged, or perceived, must be already past. No subjective state, whilst present, is its own object; its object is always something else. There are, it is true, cases in which we appear to be naming our present feeling, and so to be experiencing and observing the same inner fact at a single stroke, as when we say "I feel tired," "I am angry," etc. But these are illusory, and a little attention unmasks the illusion. The present conscious state, when I say "I feel tired," is not the direct state of tire; when I say "I feel angry," it is not the direct state of anger. It is the state of *saying-I-feel-tired*, of *saying-I-feel-angry,*—entirely different matters, so different that the fatigue and anger apparently included in them are considerable modifications of the fatigue and anger directly felt the previous instant. The act of naming them has momentarily detracted from their force.[11]

The only sound grounds on which the infallible veracity of the introspective judgment might be maintained are empirical. If we had reason to think it has never yet deceived us, we might continue to trust it. This is the ground actually maintained by Herr Mohr.

The illusions of our senses [says this author] have undermined our belief in the reality of the outer world; but in the sphere of inner observation our confidence is intact, for we have never found ourselves to be in error about the reality of an act of thought or feeling. We have never been misled into thinking we were *not* in doubt or in anger when these conditions were really states of our consciousness.[12]

But sound as the reasoning here would be, were the premises correct, I fear the latter cannot pass. However it may be with such strong feelings as doubt or anger, about weaker feelings, and about the *relations to each other* of all feelings we find ourselves in continual error and uncertainty so soon as we are called on to name and class, and not merely to feel.

Who can be sure of the exact *order* of his feelings when they are excessively rapid? Who can be sure, in his sensible perception of a chair, how much comes from the eye and how much is supplied out of the previous knowledge of the mind? Who can compare with precision the *quantities* of disparate feelings even where the feelings are very much alike? For instance, where an object is felt now against the back and now against the cheek, which feeling is most extensive? Who can be sure that two given feelings are or are not exactly the same? Who can tell which is briefer or longer than the other when both occupy but an instant of time? Who knows, of many actions, for what motive they were done, or if for any motive at all? Who can enumerate all the distinct ingredients of such a complicated feeling as *anger*? and who can tell offhand whether or no a perception of *distance* be a compound or a simple state of mind? The whole mind-stuff controversy would stop if we could decide conclusively by introspection that what seem to us elementary feelings are really elementary and not compound.

Mr. Sully, in his work on Illusions, has a chapter on those of Introspection from which we might now quote. But, since the rest of this volume will be little more than a collection of illustrations of the difficulty of discovering by direct introspection exactly what our feelings and their relations are, we need not anticipate our own future details, but just state our general conclusion that *introspection is difficult and fallible; and that the difficulty is simply that of all observation of whatever kind*. Something is before us; we do our best to tell what it is, but in spite of our good will we may go astray, and give a description more applicable to some other sort of thing. The only safeguard is in the final *consensus* of our farther knowledge about the thing in question, later views correcting earlier ones, until at last the harmony of a consistent system is reached. Such a system, gradually worked out, is the best guarantee the psychologist can give for the soundness of any particular psychologic observation which he may report. Such a system we ourselves must strive, as far as may be, to attain.

The English writers on psychology, and the school of Herbart in Germany, have in the main contented themselves with such results as the immediate introspection of single individuals gave, and shown what a body of doctrine they may make. The works of Locke, Hume, Reid, Hartley, Stewart, Brown, the Mills, will always be classics in this line; and in Professor Bain's *Treatises* we have probably the last word of what this method taken mainly by itself can do—the last monument of the youth of our science, still untechnical and generally intelligible, like the chemistry of Lavoisier, or anatomy before the microscope was used.

The Experimental Method. But psychology is passing into a less simple phase. Within a few years what one may call a microscopic psychology has arisen in Germany, carried on by experimental methods, asking of course every moment for introspective data, but eliminating their uncertainty by operating on a large scale and taking statistical means. This method taxes patience to the utmost, and could hardly have arisen in a country whose natives could be *bored.* Such Germans as Weber, Fechner, Vierordt, and Wundt obviously cannot; and their success has brought into the field an array of younger experimental psychologists, bent on studying the *elements* of the mental life, dissecting them out from the gross results in which they are embedded, and as far as possible reducing them to quantitative scales. The simple and open method of attack having done what it can, the method of patience, starving out, and harassing to death is tried; the mind must submit to a regular *siege,* in which minute advantages gained night and day by the forces that hem her in must sum themselves up at last into her overthrow. There is little of the grand style about these new prism, pendulum, and chronograph-philosophers. They mean business, not chivalry. What generous divination, and that superiority in virtue which was thought by Cicero to give a man the best insight into nature, have failed to do, their spying and scraping, their deadly tenacity and almost diabolic cunning, will doubtless some day bring about.

No general description of the methods of experimental psychology would be instructive to one unfamiliar with the instances of their application, so we will waste no words upon the attempt. *The principal fields of experimentation* so far have been: 1) the connection of conscious states with their physical conditions, including the whole of brain-physiology, and the recent minutely cultivated physiology of the sense-organs, together with what is technically known as "psycho-physics," or the laws of correlation between sensations and the outward stimuli by which they are aroused; 2) the analysis of space-perception into its sensational elements; 3) the measurement of the *duration* of the simplest mental processes; 4) that of the *accuracy of reproduction* in the memory of sensible experiences and of intervals of space and time; 5) that of the manner in which simple mental states *influence each other,* call each other up, or inhibit each other's reproduction; 6) that of the *number of facts* which consciousness can simultaneously discern; finally, 7) that of the elementary laws of oblivescence and retention. It must be said that in some of these fields the results have as yet borne little theoretic fruit commensurate with the great labor expended in their acquisition. But facts are facts, and if we only get enough of them they are sure to combine. New ground will from year to year be broken, and theoretic results will grow. Meanwhile the experimental method has quite changed the face of the science so far as the latter is a record of mere work done.

The comparative method, finally, supplements the introspective and experimental methods. This method pre-supposes a normal psychology of introspection to be established in its main features. But where the origin of these features, or their dependence upon one another, is in question, it is of the utmost importance to trace the phenomenon considered through all its possible variations of type and combination. So it has come to pass that instincts of animals are ransacked to throw light on our own; and that the reasoning faculties of bees and ants, the minds of savages, infants, madmen, idiots, the deaf and blind, criminals, and eccentrics, are all invoked in support of this or that special theory about some part of our own mental life. The history of sciences, moral and political institutions, and languages, as types of mental product, are pressed into the same service. Messrs. Darwin and Galton have set the example of circulars of questions sent out by the hundred to those supposed able to reply. The custom has spread, and it will be well for us in the next generation if such circulars be not ranked among the common pests of life. Meanwhile information grows, and results emerge. There are great sources of error in the comparative method. The interpretation of the "psychoses" of animals, savages, and infants is necessarily wild work, in which the personal equation of the investigator has things very much its own way. A savage will be reported to have no moral or religious feeling if his actions shock the observer unduly. A child will be assumed without self-consciousness because he talks of himself in the third person, etc., etc. No rules can be laid down in advance. Comparative observations, to be definite, must usually be made to test some pre-existing hypothesis; and the only thing then is to use as much sagacity as you possess, and to be as candid as you can.

The Sources of Error in Psychology

The first of them arises from the misleading influence of speech. Language was originally made by men who were not psychologists, and most men to-day employ almost exclusively the vocabulary of outward things. The cardinal passions of our life, anger, love, fear, hate, hope, and the most comprehensive divisions of our intellectual activity, to remember, expect, think, know, dream, with the broadest genera of æsthetic feeling, joy, sorrow, pleasure, pain, are the only facts of a subjective order which this vocabulary designs to note by special words. The elementary qualities of sensation, bright, loud, red, blue, hot, cold, are, it is true, susceptible of being used in both an objective and a subjective sense. They stand for outer qualities and for the feelings which these arouse. But the objective sense is the original sense; and still to-day we have to describe a large number of sensations by the name of the object from which they have most frequently been got. An orange color, an odor of violets, a cheesy taste, a thunderous sound, a fiery smart, etc., will recall what I mean. This absence of a special vocabulary for subjective facts hinders the study of all but the very coarsest of them. Empiricist writers are very fond of emphasizing one great set of delusions which language inflicts on the mind. Whenever we have made a word, they say, to denote a certain group of phenomena, we are prone to suppose a substantive entity existing beyond the phenomena, of which the word shall be the name. But the *lack* of a word quite as often leads to the directly opposite error. We are then prone to suppose that no entity can be there; and so we come to overlook phenomena whose existence would be patent to us all, had we only grown up to hear it familiarly recognized in speech.[13] It is hard to focus our attention on the nameless, and so there results a certain vacuousness in the descriptive parts of most psychologies.

But a worse defect than vacuousness comes from the dependence of psychology on common speech. Naming our thought by its own objects, we almost all of us assume that as the objects are, so the thought must be. The thought of several distinct things can only consist of several distinct bits of thought, or "ideas"; that of an abstract or universal object can only be an abstract or universal idea. As each object may come and go, be forgotten and then thought of again, it is held that the thought of it has a precisely similar independence, self-identity, and mobility. The thought of the object's recurrent identity is regarded as the identity of its recurrent thought; and the perceptions of multiplicity, of coexistence, of succession, are severally conceived to be brought about only through a multiplicity, a coexistence, a succession, of perceptions. The continuous flow of the mental stream is sacrificed, and in its place an atomism, a brickbat plan of construction, is preached for the existence of which no good introspective grounds can be brought forward, and out of which presently grow all sorts of paradoxes and contradictions, the heritage of woe of students of the mind.

These words are meant to impeach the entire English psychology derived from Locke and Hume, and the entire German psychology derived from Herbart, so far as they both treat "ideas" as separate subjective entities that come and go. Examples will soon make the matter clearer. Meanwhile our psychologic insight is vitiated by still other snares.

The "Psychologist's Fallacy." The *great* snare of the psychologist is the *confusion of his own standpoint with that of the mental fact* about which he is making his report. I shall hereafter call this the "psychologist's fallacy" *par excellence.* For some of the mischief, here too, language is to blame. The psychologist, as we remarked above, stands outside of the mental state he speaks of. Both itself and its object are objects for him. Now when it is a *cognitive* state (percept, thought, concept, etc.), he ordinarily has no other way of naming it than as the thought, percept, etc., *of that object.* He himself, meanwhile, knowing the self-same object in *his* way, gets easily led to suppose that the thought, which is *of* it, knows it in the same way in which he knows it, although this is often very far from being the case.[14] The most fictitious puzzles have been introduced into our science by this means. The so-called question of presentative or representative perception, of whether an object is present to the thought that thinks it by a counterfeit image of itself, or directly and without any intervening image at all; the question of nominalism and conceptualism, of the shape in which things are present when only a general notion of them is before the mind; are comparatively easy questions when once the psychologist's fallacy is eliminated from their treatment, . . .

Another variety of the psychologist's fallacy is the assumption that the mental state studied must be conscious of itself as the psychologist is conscious of it. The mental state is aware of itself only from within; it grasps what we call its own content, and nothing more. The psychologist, on the contrary is aware of it from without, and knows its relations with all sorts of other things. What the thought sees is only its own object; what the psychologist sees is the thought's object, plus the thought itself, plus possibly all the rest of the world. We must be very careful therefore, in discussing a state of mind from the psychologist's point of view, to avoid foisting into its own ken matters that are only there for ours. We must avoid substituting what we know the consciousness *is,* for what it is a consciousness *of,* and counting its outward, and so to speak physical, relations with other facts of the world, in among the objects of which we set it down as aware. Crude as such a confusion of standpoints seems to be when abstractly stated, it is nevertheless a snare into which no psychologist has kept himself at all times from falling, and which forms almost the entire stock-in-trade of certain schools. We cannot be too watchful against its subtly corrupting influence.

Summary. To sum up the chapter, psychology assumes that thoughts successively occur, and that they know objects in a world which the psychologist also knows. *These thoughts are the subjective data of which he treats, and their relations to their objects, to the brain, and to the rest of the world constitute the subject-matter of psychologic science.*

Its methods are introspection, experimentation, and comparison. But introspection is no sure guide to truths *about* our mental states; and in particular the poverty of the psychological vocabulary leads us to drop out certain states from our consideration, and to treat others as if they knew themselves and their objects as the psychologist knows both, which is a disastrous fallacy in the science.

---

[1] *Cf.* George T. Ladd: *Elements of Physiological Psychology* (1887), pt. III, chap. III, §§ 9, 12.

[2] *Zur Analysis der Wirklichkeit*, p. 489.

[3] Nothing is easier than to familiarize oneself with the mammalian brain. Get a sheep's head, a small saw, chisel, scalpel and forceps (all three can best be had from a surgical-instrument maker), and unravel its parts either by the aid of a human dissecting book, such as Holden's *Manual of Anatomy*, or by the specific directions *ad hoc* given in such books as Foster and Langley's *Practical Physiology* (Macmillan) or Morrell's *Comparative Anatomy and Dissection of Mammalia* (Longmans).

[4] On the relation between Psychology and General Philosophy, see G. C. Robertson, in *Mind*, vol. VIII, p. I; J. Ward, *ibid.*, p. 153; J. Dewey, *ibid.*, vol. IX, p. I.

[5] Compare some remarks in Mill's *Logic*, bk. I, chap. III, §§ 2, 3.

[6] *Logic*, § 40.

[7] *Psychologie*, bk. II, chap. III, §§ 1, 2.

[8] *Cours de philosophie positive*, I, pp. 34–38.

[9] *Auguste Comte and Positivism*, 3d ed. (1882), p. 64.

[10] Wundt says: "The first rule for utilizing inward observation consists in taking, as far as possible, experiences that are accidental, unexpected, and not intentionally brought about.... *First* it is best as far as possible to rely on *Memory* and not on immediate Apprehension.... *Second*, internal observation is better fitted to grasp clearly conscious states, especially voluntary mental acts: such inner processes as are obscurely conscious and involuntary will almost entirely elude it, because the effort to observe interferes with them, and because they seldom abide in memory." (*Logik*, II, p. 432.)

[11] In cases like this, where the state outlasts the act of naming it, exists before it, and recurs when it is past, we probably run little practical risk of error when we talk as if the state knew itself. The state of feeling and the state of naming the feeling are continuous, and the infallibility of such prompt introspective judgments is probably great. But even here the certainty of our knowledge ought not to be argued on the *a priori* ground that *percipi* and *esse* are in psychology the same. The states are really two; the naming state and the named state are apart; "*percipi* is *esse*" is not the principle that applies.

[12] J. Mohr: *Grundlage der Empirischen Psychologie* (Leipzig, 1882), p. 47.

[13] In English we have not even the generic distinction between the-thing-thought-of and the-thought-thinking-it, which in German is expressed by the opposition between *Gedachtes* and *Gedanke*, in Latin by that between *cogitatum* and *cogitatio*.

[14] Compare B. P. Bowne: *Metaphysics* (1882), p. 408.

Institutions

of

Science

JPL

and the Exploration of Space

by Katherine A. Dumas

From humble beginnings comprising little more than a handful of college students fascinated with rocketry, the Jet Propulsion Laboratory has grown to become the premier institution for investigating the solar system.

The launch of the first U.S. satellite, Explorer 1, on Jan. 31, 1958, ushered America into the age of space exploration. The mission was designed and managed by the Jet Propulsion Laboratory (JPL) and resulted in the discovery of the famed Van Allen radiation belts. In the more than 30 years hence, JPL has become known worldwide as the preeminent center for solar system exploration. Under its auspices every planet except Pluto has been explored. In addition, JPL is one of the leading institutes that have begun the search for planets circling other stars in hopes of gaining insight into the possibilities of life beyond Earth.

Located in the foothills of Pasadena, California, JPL is an operating division of the California Institute of Technology (Caltech) that serves as a lead center for robotic exploration of the solar system for the U.S. National Aeronautics and Space Administration (NASA). Two months after the formation of NASA on Dec. 3, 1958, JPL sponsorship was transferred from the Army to NASA. The laboratory remains the center for all of NASA's deep-space exploration. In support of its science missions, JPL maintains state-of-the-art research and development activities in such areas of advanced technology as microelectronics, robotics, structures, communications, optics, advanced computing, and information systems, to name a few.

To understand JPL's current objectives in space exploration, it is helpful to have a knowledge of the history and evolution of the laboratory, which had its origins prior to World War II and more than 20 years before the launch of Explorer 1.

Founding years

In the late 1920s, when scientist Robert H. Goddard's pioneering liquid-propellant rocket experiments were banned as a public nuisance in Massachusetts, general attitudes in the West toward rockets were not much

KATHERINE A. DUMAS is Technical Assistant to the Director, Jet Propulsion Laboratory, Pasadena, California.

(Opposite page) Images of eight of the nine planets of the solar system, plus Earth's Moon—all made by JPL spacecraft—surround a 1936 photo of some of the members of the GALCIT research group, JPL's "founding fathers." All photographs courtesy of the Jet Propulsion Laboratory

JPL's main site, located in the foothills of the San Gabriel Mountains near Pasadena, California, comprises some 155 buildings spread across 72 hectares (177 acres) and employs more than 7,500 people.

different. In the mid-1930s, however, a number of interested students under the encouragement and guidance of Theodore von Karman, then director of the Guggenheim Aeronautical Laboratory at Caltech (GAL-CIT), began studying rocket aerodynamics and rocket propulsion. They and von Karman brought to this work a combination of rigorous theoretical calculations and trial-and-error experiments. Their experiments with rocket engines were carried out in a remote dry streambed area adjacent to the current site of JPL.

GALCIT group members (clockwise from top) John W. Parson, Frank J. Malina (later to become the first director of JPL), and Edward S. Forman prepare to test a liquid-propellant rocket engine in a dry creek bed near the current location of JPL. Connected to the engine, which is positioned in front of Parson, are two thick hoses for propellant and oxygen. A thinner hose leads to a can of water used to cool the engine.

An aircraft lifts off from March Field, California, in August 1941 during the first field test of jet-assisted takeoff (JATO) rockets developed by the GALCIT group. In the early 1940s GALCIT's major developmental work centered on JATO units, which cut the time and distance needed for aircraft takeoff by as much as 50%.

Initially, funding for the GALCIT group came from the students' personal resources. In 1938 the commanding general of the U.S. Army Air Corps paid a surprise visit to the GALCIT laboratories and was impressed by what he saw. Always looking for ways to incorporate new science and technology into the military, he asked for and received a grant for the GALCIT group from the National Academy of Sciences to support, among other things, research on rocket-assisted takeoff of aircraft. This funding started research activities in both solid- and liquid-fueled rocket engine designs and became the basis of the relationship between the GALCIT group and the Army Air Corps that would continue throughout World War II. The principal developmental activities during that time centered on jet-assisted takeoff (JATO) units, which shortened the time and distance required for aircraft takeoff by as much as 50%. (In the World War II era the term *jet propulsion* had a broader meaning than it commonly does today and was applied to rocket engines as well as air-breathing jet engines. Further, the word *rocket* had a derogatory connotation in those days, referring more to science fiction than to serious efforts in technology development.)

Driven by intelligence reports that the Germans were developing long-range missiles, the GALCIT group submitted a proposal to the Army that would expand their rocket-engine research and development program. On July 1, 1944, under the new name Jet Propulsion Laboratory, work on a guided-missile program officially started. Although this date marks the origin of JPL, the role of the laboratory in space exploration would not begin for more than a decade.

Frank Malina poses with an early model of the Wac Corporal rocket, one of JPL's principal programs in the years following World War II. The Corporal project was responsible for early advances in rocket guidance and communications techniques.

JPL Director William H. Pickering (left), physicist James Van Allen (center), and rocket pioneer Wernher von Braun raise a model of Explorer 1, the first U.S. orbiting satellite, at a press conference. Working with the Army Ballistic Missile Agency, JPL planned and executed the Explorer mission in less than 90 days after the launch of Sputnik 1. Data from Explorer 1 led Van Allen to the discovery of the high-altitude radiation belts later named for him.

Beginning of the space race

JPL continued its affiliation with the Army for some years after the war. During that time its work centered on developing the propulsion and engines for rocket-powered long-range missiles as well as the electronics for missile telemetry. The most notable programs were the Corporal and the Sergeant, which resulted in America's first- and second-generation surface-to-surface guided missiles. These weapons became integral parts of the U.S. defense system.

During the 1950s a number of individuals at JPL and Caltech, including JPL's director and Caltech's president, became dissatisfied with the possibility that the laboratory could turn into a center for weapons research and wanted a change in direction. The opportunity for such a change came as a result of the political rivalry between the Soviet Union and the United States.

In October 1957 the Soviets launched Sputnik 1, the world's first orbiting satellite, and began a race for technological supremacy. JPL was able to take advantage of this Soviet challenge by proposing the launch of a U.S satellite ahead of the country's dedicated Vanguard satellite program. Approximately three months after Sputnik, the U.S. launched Explorer 1. JPL successfully planned and executed this mission in conjunction with the Army Ballistic Missile Agency, using a ballistic missile as a booster, only 83 days after receiving approval from the Army. The accomplishment established the U.S. presence, and more specifically JPL's presence, in the race for space.

Pres. Dwight D. Eisenhower signed a bill July 29, 1958, creating a new civilian space agency, NASA. JPL was transferred to NASA jurisdiction two months after the agency became operational. Realizing the need to focus the activities of the laboratory, JPL's director at that time, William H. Pickering, decided to concentrate JPL's resources on the science and engineering aspects of interplanetary space exploration. This far-reaching vision set the goal for JPL and is the origin of the laboratory's preeminence in this field.

The '60s and '70s

Following the successful launch of Explorer 1, JPL became involved with three other Explorer-class Earth satellites and with two Pioneer missions. The Pioneer spacecraft represented the first U.S. attempts to escape Earth's orbit and head to the vicinity of the Moon.

Aside from the mission planning and vehicle design necessary for space exploration, new, innovative solutions had to be developed in parallel to support the programs. Ground communication and a navigation network were essential to this activity and required that JPL pioneer its own communications network. At a site in the Mojave Desert about 160 kilometers from Pasadena, JPL built a steerable antenna 26 meters across that was capable of handling the Pioneer lunar missions and a number of planetary exploratory programs planned for the future. (A meter is about 3.3 feet; a kilometer is about 0.62 mile.) This site, currently known as the Goldstone Deep Space Communications Complex,

Mosaic of the Moon's surface is assembled from photos taken by Surveyor 7 after its soft landing in January 1968. Between 1966 and 1968 the Surveyor series produced tens of thousands of lunar surface images and analyzed soil samples in preparation for the U.S. manned landings that followed.

is one of three sites worldwide that make up the Deep Space Network. Each new and ever more ambitious project required that JPL maintain an active and extensive research and development activity in the fields of communications and tracking.

Pres. John F. Kennedy in the early 1960s committed the United States to landing a man on the Moon by the end of the decade and returning him safely. In support of this endeavor, JPL initiated the Ranger series of spacecraft, which were designed to provide photo reconnaissance of the Moon. Over 17,000 lunar images were transmitted to scientists on Earth

Mosaic of photos of Mercury taken by Mariner 10, the only spacecraft to visit that planet, reveals a surface resembling the heavily cratered landscape of the Moon.

before the end of the program. Following on the heels of the Ranger program was a series of soft-landing vehicles known as Surveyor. These missions not only provided lunar surface images but also analyzed soil samples in preparation for a site selection for the first manned landings of the Apollo program.

Paralleling the lunar programs of Ranger and Surveyor, JPL initiated the first exploratory missions to other planets. Beginning in the early 1960s the Mariner series sent spacecraft to Mercury, Venus, and Mars for close-up images and measurements of the surfaces and atmospheres of the planets.

Mariner 10 was the first and only spacecraft to investigate Mercury. The encounter was achieved by use of what was at the time an un-tried technique of a planetary gravity assist, in this case from Venus. This "slingshot" method saved the high energy cost of a direct flight to Mercury and has been used since by many interplanetary spacecraft. The images of Mercury indicated that the planet, like Earth's Moon, is covered with impact craters. Unlike the Moon, however, Mercury has a number of long cliffs three kilometers high that extend across the surface for hundreds of kilometers. Mariner also acquired data on the topography, temperature, and magnetism of the planet.

472

Venus, frequently referred to as Earth's twin owing to its similar size and density, is surrounded by a thick, opaque atmosphere of carbon dioxide and sulfuric acid clouds. The pressure on the surface of the planet is 90 times that of Earth, and the temperature is about 500° C (900° F). Most of what is known about Venus came from later missions, in particular the Magellan spacecraft, which was launched in 1989 and which used synthetic aperture radar mapping to penetrate the thick cloud layer.

Inspired by the works of American astronomer Percival Lowell in the 1890s, who interpreted the dark features on Mars as being the constructed canals of an advanced society, many people hoped to find life on the planet. Dreams of civilization on Mars faded when Mariner 4 flew by in 1965 and sent back images of a landscape that looked similar to the Moon's. The Viking 1 and 2 missions, in which two orbiters and two landers visited the planet in 1976, found no indications of any kind of life, dashing hopes of a nearby intelligent life-form.

The Viking spacecraft had a planned life span of 90 days after reaching Mars. In fact, one orbiter functioned over four years, while one of the landers transmitted its last data six years after landing. The wealth of information collected about Mars as a result of the extended mission has been invaluable. Biological and chemical analyses indicated that no micro-organisms or organic material were present in the soil at the spacecraft landing sites. Soil analysis revealed the dominant elements to be silicon and iron. The iron, in the form of iron oxide (rust), appeared to be mixed throughout the soil, giving Mars its "red planet" nickname. Measurements indicated that the atmosphere is composed of 95% carbon dioxide, 1.6% argon, and as much as 2.7% nitrogen. Water was present as a vapor and a solid. Although no liquid water was found, the large channels on the surface indicated that water did flow during the early history of Mars. High winds and dust storms were known from Earth observations. However, the average wind speeds that were measured were much lower than anticipated, with peaks at 118 kilometers per hour. Temperatures on Mars are cold, with predawn values of $-70°$ C ($-94°$ F), rising to about $-25°$ C ($-13°$ F) by the afternoon.

The Grand Tour

Once every 176 years the outer planets Jupiter, Saturn, Uranus, and Neptune align in such a way that a spacecraft could take advantage of a gravity assist from each planet in succession and visit them all. Such a technique would reduce the flight time of a spacecraft from 30 years for a direct flight to Neptune to 12 years with use of the assist. The journey was proposed by engineers at JPL in the 1960s. The mission, which became known as the Grand Tour, would result in a space odyssey unequaled in history.

The mission requirements of a Grand Tour imposed enormous technical challenges. A spacecraft was needed that could withstand the intense radiation environment of Jupiter and still function for more than a decade. Advanced, high-precision navigation methods and new long-distance communication abilities had to be developed for the 4.5

Photo taken by the Viking 2 lander in 1976 (opposite page, top) shows part of the lander itself as well as Mars's rocky surface and pink-hued sky. A Viking orbiter image (opposite page, bottom) reveals the thin carbon dioxide atmosphere that envelops Mars. Argyre Planitia, the large basin in the foreground, was created by an asteroid impact. Whereas the Viking spacecraft had a planned life span of three months after reaching Mars, one orbiter functioned more than four years and one lander for six years.

473

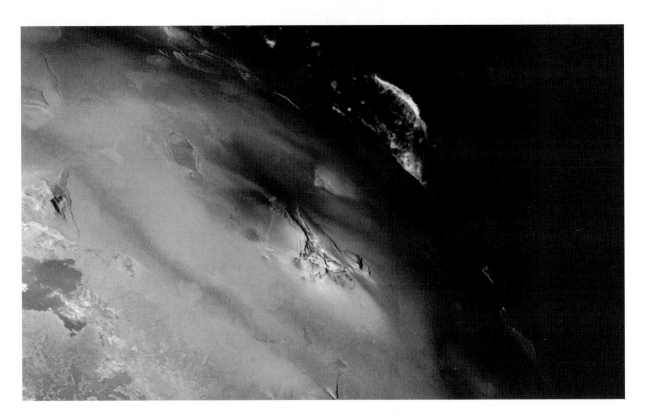

Photomosaic of Jupiter's satellite Io, which was made from images taken by Voyager 2 in 1979, catches the volcano Pele in the act of hurling sulfurous material hundreds of kilometers above the surface. During their visits to the Jovian system, the first stop in the long, spectacularly successful Grand Tour mission to the gas-giant planets, Voyagers 1 and 2 revealed Io to be the most volcanically active body known in the solar system.

billion-kilometer trip to Neptune. Decision-making capability to detect and react to internal problems had to be installed aboard the spacecraft, since communication times between it and Earth would extend to hours later in the flight. Cameras had to work at light levels 1,000 times less than at Earth.

When the initial proposal was submitted to the U.S. Congress, the projected cost of the mission was considered too high. Consequently, in 1972 Congress approved only a mini-Grand Tour that would journey to Jupiter and Saturn. The mission was called MJS77 (for Mariner Jupiter-Saturn for launch in 1977) and was later renamed Voyager. Two highly sophisticated and "intelligent" spacecraft, Voyager 1 and Voyager 2, were developed for the project. The redundant components and computers with which they were equipped allowed them to operate autonomously for long periods of time in the event of a subsystem malfunction. The built-in versatility allowed the Voyagers to be reprogrammed during the mission, a design feature that played a decisive role later in the mission.

While the Viking orbiters and landers were actively returning data from Mars, the Voyager spacecraft were launched from Cape Canaveral, Florida, in August and September 1977. Voyager 1 flew by Jupiter in March 1979, with Voyager 2 following in July. More than 16,500 images of Jupiter and its satellites were taken by Voyager 1 alone, changing scientific knowledge of the planet as profoundly as Galileo's first telescopic view of it had almost four centuries earlier.

The two encounters with Jupiter were just the beginning of the many discoveries made throughout the mission. Active volcanoes were once

thought to be found exclusively on Earth. The Voyager mission dispelled that premise by its images of several active volcanoes ejecting sulfurous material on the moon Io. Io is approximately the size of the Earth's Moon, and its volcanic activity is driven by tidal forces arising from the gravitational interaction with Jupiter. The Great Red Spot on Jupiter has been observed for at least 300 years. Close-up views of the spot indicate a turbulent storm more than 25,000 kilometers (three Earth diameters) across, with wind speeds of 300 kilometers per hour, rotating in a counterclockwise direction once every six days. Other discoveries made by the Voyager spacecraft include a ring around Jupiter similar to Saturn's rings, lightning in the planet's atmosphere, and four new Jovian moons.

Saturn was visited by Voyager 1 in November 1980, followed by Voyager 2 in August 1981. The visible features of Saturn's atmosphere turned out to be far more subdued than those of Jupiter, although both planets are composed primarily of hydrogen and helium. One of the most striking discoveries at Saturn was the complexity of the rings. Identified as rings by Christiaan Huygens in the mid-1600s, they have an outer diameter that spans a region equal to 70% of the distance between the Earth and the Moon but have a thickness of only 10 meters. The smallest of Saturn's satellites are irregularly shaped, suggesting that they are fragments of larger bodies. The larger ones consist mainly of ice and indicate an early geologic history. Titan, the largest of Saturn's 18 confirmed moons (several other moons may exist but have not been verified), is larger than the planet Mercury and has its own atmosphere, which is composed mainly of nitrogen (similar to that of the Earth).

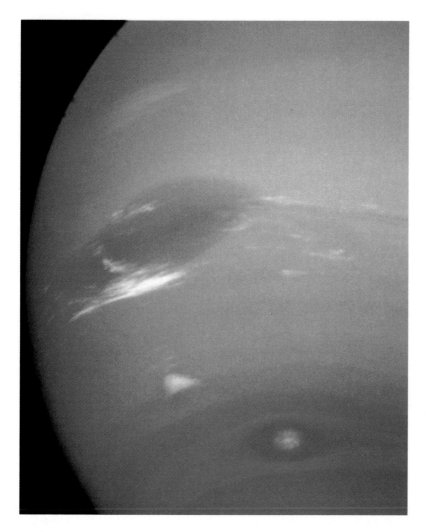

Methane in Titan's atmosphere reacts with ultraviolet radiation from the Sun to create a complex set of hydrocarbons that gives rise to the haze obscuring the satellite's surface. The organic material precipitates to the surface, where it may form lakes of liquid hydrocarbons.

Approval was given for Voyager 2 to continue the Grand Tour after Voyager 1 was deflected out of the plane of the solar system by the Titan encounter to continue its journey to interstellar space. In preparation for the Uranus visit, JPL needed to make improvements in ground-based tracking and communications. A new tracking station equipped with a high-efficiency antenna 34 meters across was completed at the Goldstone site in California. Combining several 64-meter and 34-meter antenna tracking stations, which included an Australian government-owned station, allowed JPL to limit the natural fall of the signal strength at Uranus to only two-thirds of the value that it had at Saturn, rather than to one-fourth, as would otherwise have been the case over the three billion-kilometer distance to Uranus. In addition to improving the communications network, JPL engineers extensively reprogrammed the spacecraft's onboard computers to allow new imaging capabilities. Without these

As Voyager 2 departed the Neptunian system for interstellar space, it took a dramatic photo of the crescents of Neptune and its largest moon, Triton. Both Voyagers have enough fuel and electrical power to return data to Earth until 2015.

changes, the amount of information transmitted by the spacecraft would have been severely reduced.

Voyager 2 made its closest approach to Uranus in January 1986, finding a planet virtually devoid of atmospheric features. Two additional dark rings and an extensive set of dust bands were discovered around Uranus by the forward scattering of sunlight as the spacecraft left the planet. For the first time, a magnetic field was detected at Uranus. The magnetic axis was found to be tilted 59° from the planet's rotation axis (itself tilted on its side) and offset from the center of the planet by 30% of the planet's radius. Ten new moons were discovered, bringing the total to 15. One of the previously known moons, Miranda, has been dubbed "the most bizarre body in the universe" on the basis of Voyager images of its diverse terrain, which includes canyons over 19 kilometers deep.

Because one-way communication to Neptune requires four hours, it was necessary that a number of technology developments unique to the mission requirements be implemented and substantial facility upgrades be completed before Voyager 2 made its final planetary encounter. First, all three 64-meter-diameter antenna stations of the Deep Space Network that had been constructed for the Mariner Mars missions were upgraded to 70-meter-diameter antennas, and antenna arraying (linking two or more antennas in a way that allows them to operate as a single, larger antenna) was used to speed the amount of data transmitted over the long distances. New data-encoding and data-compression methods were developed and transmitted to the spacecraft. Because long exposure times were needed to compensate for the very low light level at Neptune, new techniques were implemented in order to avoid blurred images. Each improvement required major technological advances that pushed the resources and creativity of everyone involved.

Three and a half years after the Uranus flyby, Voyager 2 made its closest approach to Neptune in August 1989. At a distance of 4.5 billion kilometers from the Sun, the low sunlight levels and cold temperatures were expected to minimize the atmospheric activity of the planet. To the surprise of all, Neptune was found to have wind speeds of more than 2,000 kilometers per hour. A storm similar to Jupiter's Great Red Spot and dubbed the Great Dark Spot moves around the planet at a speed of 1,200 kilometers per hour. Cirruslike clouds were observed for the first time in an atmosphere other than that of Earth. Like Uranus, Neptune has an off-center magnetic field, tilted 47° from the direction of rotation, and, like the other giant planets, it has rings. Six new moons were discovered in addition to the two already known. The largest, Triton, has its own atmosphere and is the coldest known object in the solar system at −235° C (−391° F), comparable, it is estimated, to the planet Pluto. Triton orbits Neptune in a retrograde motion (opposite to Neptune's spin), which indicates that the object was captured by Neptune rather than formed in orbit with the planet. Triton has a tenuous nitrogen atmosphere and, despite the moon's extremely cold temperatures, Voyager observed geyserlike eruptions spewing out fine, dark particles.

After the Triton encounter Voyager 2 was deflected out of the plane of the solar system for its continued mission into interstellar space. The two Voyager spacecraft have enough electrical power and fuel to send back data until the year 2015, at which time Voyager 1 will be approximately 20 billion kilometers from the Sun and Voyager 2 will be 17 billion kilometers away.

Computer-generated view of the surface of Venus was made with radar-mapping data collected by the spacecraft Magellan, which went into orbit around the planet in August 1990. The simulated viewpoint, at a height of 1.2 kilometers (0.75 mile), shows two volcanoes on the horizon, Sif Mons on the left and Gula Mons on the right. Added color, which is based on color images obtained from Soviet Venera landers, helps discern small-scale structure.

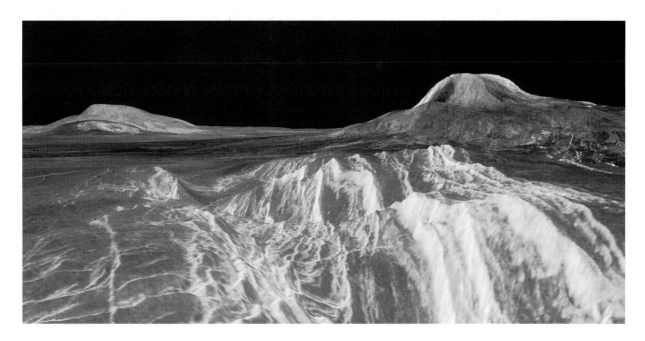

Unusual perspective of the Moon, which includes part of the lunar far side never visible from Earth, was achieved by the spacecraft Galileo in December 1990 as it swung past the Earth for a gravity assist toward its ultimate goal, Jupiter. The large central feature is the Orientale Basin, formed about 3.8 billion years ago by the impact of an asteroid-sized body.

Magellan and Galileo

The Voyager project was the most successful mission of any unmanned exploratory program up to that time. It gave the world the first views of the giant planetary systems and whetted our appetites to return.

Even as the Voyagers were making history, JPL was planning the next phase in the planetary-exploration program. Since every planet except Pluto had been or was being visited during the reconnaissance phase of exploration, the next step was to return to the planets and their satellites for more detailed investigations. Toward this end two missions, Magellan and Galileo, were initiated. The goal of Magellan was to return to Venus, go into orbit around the planet, and map almost all of its surface by using a synthetic aperture radar system to penetrate the thick atmospheric cloud layer. High-resolution images would reveal features nearly as small as a football field on Earth, 10 times better than previously possible. Galileo's mission was to return to the Jovian system and study the planet and its satellites for about two years.

In May 1989, three months prior to Voyager's Neptune encounter, the U.S. space shuttle *Atlantis* launched the Magellan spacecraft on its 15-month journey to Venus. Images returned from the planet allowed scientists to estimate that the surface is approximately 400 million years old, an age between those of the surfaces of the Earth and Mars. Surface features that have been unveiled by the spacecraft range from volcanic domes and impact craters to fractured plains and channels. One channel measures 6,720 kilometers, making it the longest such feature known in the solar system.

Galileo was carried into space by *Atlantis* in October 1989, with an arrival at Jupiter scheduled for December 1995. This planetary spacecraft was the most complex yet launched. Although a direct flight to the planet was the most desirable route, no available launch vehicle was capable of bringing the heavy payload to the required speed and trajectory. Consequently, the trajectory of the spacecraft was designed to include one gravity assist from Venus and two from the Earth. When Galileo nears Jupiter, it will insert a probe into the planet's atmosphere to obtain information on the temperature, pressure, density, and chemical composition of the gases composing the planet. The main craft will orbit Jupiter, continuing to study the planet and its moons in depth for about two years.

JPL today

In the more than half century between the rocket experiments of GALCIT and the launch of Galileo, JPL's physical facilities have undergone an enormous transformation and expansion. Now spread across 72 hectares (177 acres), the laboratory's main Pasadena site comprises some 155 buildings and employs over 7,500 people, of whom more than 60% are scientists and engineers. A number of major technical facilities at the Pasadena location support research and development activities. Among them are environmental test laboratories and two space simulators to check over subsystem and complete spacecraft hardware; a high-bay, controlled-environment Spacecraft Assembly Facility; an Isotope Thermoelectric Systems Application Laboratory; and a Microdevices Laboratory.

At the heart of each space mission lie the two-way communications between Earth and the spacecraft. To maintain this link, JPL manages its worldwide Deep Space Network to transmit to and receive data from spacecraft beyond Earth orbit. There are three network sites: Goldstone Dry Lake in the Mojave Desert; Madrid; and Canberra, Australia. The stations are separated by approximately 120° of longitude so that distant spacecraft are always in sight of one of them. Four large antennas ranging from 26 to 70 meters in diameter serve each station. A Network Operations Control Center located at JPL's main facility oversees and monitors operations at all the sites.

Approximately 96 kilometers northeast of Pasadena in the Angeles National Forest is JPL's Table Mountain Observatory. This 14-hectare (35-acre), 11-building facility conducts experiments in astronomy, solar monitoring, and atmospheric studies such as remote sensing of changes in the ozone layer. A larger facility 112 kilometers north of the main laboratory on the north side of Edwards Air Force Base is the Edwards Facility. On this 245-hectare (600-acre) site, JPL concentrates its hazardous testing experiments. All JPL spacecraft launched prior to 1987 had their propulsion systems qualified at the Edwards Facility.

In addition to the California sites, JPL has facilities on the East Coast. The Washington (D.C.) Business Office supports the visiting scientists

At JPL's main Pasadena location, image analysts (left) study data returned by the Venus-orbiting Magellan spacecraft. On their screens is an image of a group of dome-shaped features found south of the Venusian equator, believed to have been formed by eruptions of viscous lavas. In the Microdevices Laboratory, researchers (below) use an electron cyclotron resonance system to grow silicon and diamond films for semiconductor devices.

program, and the East Coast Technology and Applications Program Office, Vienna, Virginia, provides support to programs and projects. An Eastern Launch Site Office located at the Kennedy Space Center in Florida supports JPL spacecraft launches.

New missions and plans for deep space

Scientific investigations of the Sun have always been restricted to information gathered from a position within the plane of the solar system. A new spacecraft called Ulysses, a joint project between the European

Technicians complete final work on the Galileo spacecraft in the high-bay, controlled-environment Spacecraft Assembly Facility at JPL's main site. Galileo was lifted into space in October 1989 by space shuttle and is scheduled to reach Jupiter in December 1995.

(Right) At the tracking station in Goldstone, California, a 70-meter antenna, the largest of four deep-space antennas at the site, points into the sky. To maintain the vital two-way communications link with spacecraft beyond Earth orbit, JPL manages a worldwide Deep Space Network comprising the California site, another station in Spain, and a third in Australia. Each station is separated by approximately 120° of longitude so that distant spacecraft are always in sight of one of them.

The Ulysses spacecraft passes the Sun in an artist's conception. A joint project of the European Space Agency and the National Aeronautics and Space Administration, Ulysses carries nine instruments to conduct experiments over the Sun's polar regions and in parts of space never before explored. In February 1992 the spacecraft completed a 16-month trip to Jupiter, where a gravity assist from the massive planet flung it out of the plane of the solar system and toward the Sun's southern pole.

Space Agency and NASA/JPL, was launched in October 1990 to gather data outside the plane. Starting in August 1994, Ulysses will study the polar regions of space surrounding the Sun for more than a year.

Returning to the planet Mars has become an American objective. In addition to the manned missions being planned is a series of robotic exploratory missions whose goal is to study the Martian environment. Toward this end the Mars Observer spacecraft is currently scheduled for a September 1992 launch. Once in Mars orbit, the craft will provide a detailed map of the planet's surface along with measurements of the magnetic field and chemical analysis and elemental distribution of the surface and atmosphere. Since Mars Observer will be taking data continuously for one full Martian year (687 Earth days), information on seasonal changes will also be collected.

Also under way is the Mars Environmental Survey (MESUR) program, which will comprise a global network of small landers distributed in geologically diverse locations on the surface of Mars. Further into the future, plans call for a robotic Mars rover and sample-return mission. In support of these plans, JPL will use its extensive in-house research and development activities to address questions of telerobotic manipulations (robotic activity that mimics the motions of a distant human operator and is controlled through a long-distance communications link) and autonomous rover designs.

As Galileo is scheduled to revisit the Jovian system, the Cassini

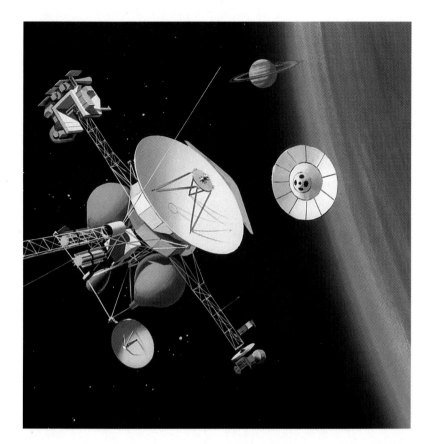

Artist's conception depicts Cassini above Saturn's moon Titan, while a probe launched from the spacecraft begins its descent into Titan's atmosphere. In early 1992 the Cassini mission to the Saturnian system was in the final planning stages, with a launch expected in the mid-1990s.

spacecraft is in the final planning stages for a return to Saturn and its satellites. The European Space Agency will provide Cassini with a probe that will enter the atmosphere of Titan; if it survives the descent, it will relay information about the surface of the moon. Much interest exists in investigating Titan's atmosphere because the organic molecules there now may be similar to those that existed in Earth's atmosphere before life was formed and therefore may provide a clue to the Earth's early chemistry. The orbiter itself will spend four years returning data on Saturn's atmosphere, rings, and magnetosphere and detailed information on its moons. Launch of Cassini is expected in the mid-1990s.

Other activities

Concurrent with its planetary spacecraft programs, JPL is involved in developing space-based instruments. For the Hubble Space Telescope now in operation in Earth orbit, JPL contributed one of the telescope's major instruments, the wide-field-planetary camera. To adjust for the flaw discovered in the Hubble's primary mirror after the telescope was put into space, the laboratory is currently building a replacement camera with corrective optics. Shuttle astronauts may be able to install the replacement as early as December 1993.

In studies of Earth itself, two shuttle imaging radar instruments (SIR-A and SIR-B) developed by JPL were carried on space shuttle flights in the early 1980s. Using sophisticated radar techniques to image the Earth,

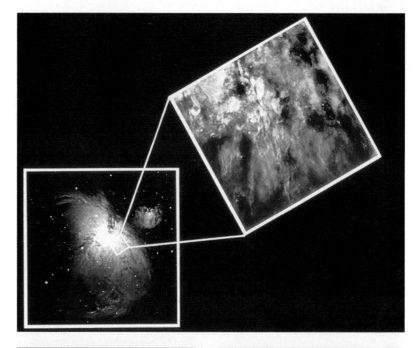

The many unique, detailed images gathered by the Hubble Space Telescope (HST) to date include a huge stellar nursery in the Orion Nebula, taken with the telescope's wide-field-planetary camera contributed by JPL. In the left part of the photo, the position of the HST image is located within a ground-based image of the whole nebula.

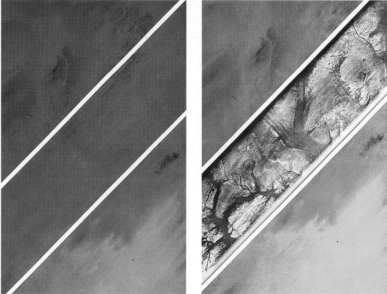

Conventional satellite image of part of the Sahara Desert in The Sudan (left) is compared with a SIR-A radar image of the same area (right, diagonal inset) that was made during a space shuttle flight in the early 1980s. SIR-A imagery revealed the existence of ancient streambeds beneath the dry Sahara sands, prompting archaeological exploration of the area and providing insight into the evolution of Earth's climate.

they revealed ancient streambeds buried beneath the dry sands of the Sahara Desert. Such information has provided insight into the evolution of Earth's climate. A third radar instrument, SIR-C, is planned for a shuttle flight in late 1993.

The Upper Atmosphere Research Satellite that was put in orbit in September 1991 carried two JPL instruments. The first, a microwave limb sounder, will improve scientific understanding of the critical chemical processes that affect the creation and destruction of ozone in the upper atmosphere. The second, an active cavity radiometer irradiance monitor, will measure the variability of solar irradiance over a long period of time.

The Topex/Poseidon mission is a joint venture between NASA/JPL and the French space agency, Centre National d'Études Spatiales, to perform a global study of the Earth's oceans. The spacecraft, scheduled for launch in July 1992, is expected to function in its primary mission for three years.

A number of Earth-observation instruments in support of NASA's Earth Observing System project are under development at JPL. These scientific platforms will continuously monitor the Earth's atmosphere and oceans from space. The information will be used to model the long-term changes to the climate and will provide a deeper understanding of the effects of human life on the Earth's environment and ecology.

The existence of advanced civilizations beyond the Earth has been a favorite subject for science-fiction writers. The search for extraterrestrial life has been one of JPL's objectives in the planetary program. Having found no intelligent life forms thus far in our solar system, the laboratory has now extended the search to other solar systems.

Scientific investigation has centered on two different approaches. First, an effort is being made to develop ways to indirectly detect, and directly image, planets around other stars. Indirect detection involves observing some property of a star (*e.g.,* its position relative to other stars, its line-of-sight motion, or its apparent magnitude) in order to determine any anomalies that may indicate the presence of an unseen object like a planet. Much more difficult, but on the edge of being technologically

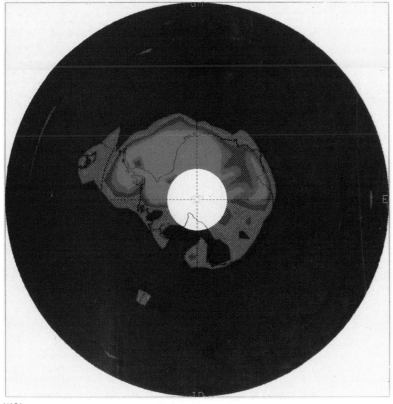

Image of the Antarctic region from Earth orbit was made in late September 1991 from data collected by the microwave limb sounder, one of two instruments supplied by JPL for the Upper Atmosphere Research Satellite. The image delineates chlorine monoxide concentrations—believed to be a major chemical participant in the depletion of Earth's protective ozone layer—at an altitude of 20 kilometers (12 miles) over the Southern Hemisphere. Red areas show high concentrations; blue areas, low concentrations. Such measurements will improve scientific understanding of the critical chemical processes in the upper atmosphere that affect the creation and destruction of ozone.

feasible, is the ability to capture an image of another planet directly. JPL is pursuing development of ground-based and space-based instruments to search for extrasolar planets both indirectly and directly.

Second, communication with extraterrestrial life forms is the objective of NASA's search for extraterrestrial intelligence (SETI) program. In support of this activity, JPL's Deep Space Network will manage a wide-band search for radio signals from extraterrestrial civilizations, if any exist.

In addition to its space science and engineering projects, the laboratory is involved with a number of research and development activities for other U.S. sponsors, such as the Departments of Defense and Energy. Some of these goals include a data processing system that will collect, integrate, and analyze intelligence information for battlefield commanders; an infrared fire-mapping system for the U.S. Forest Service; a real-time weather processor to integrate and distribute weather information to air-traffic controllers nationwide; and a monitoring system to help the National Archives better safeguard the U.S. Constitution, the Declaration of Independence, the Bill of Rights, and other documents. These projects are just a few of those that use JPL's active in-house research and development facilities.

To be first

A dynamic institution, the Jet Propulsion Laboratory is ever improving its technological expertise in order to support its current space science missions and to accommodate the flights of the future. Throughout the laboratory, the emphasis is on increasing humankind's understanding and knowledge of the universe, an emphasis that continuously creates new challenges. The technical staff have an inherent need to be the first at discovery, a need that keeps them no farther behind than the state of the art and, more often than not, the pioneers of new fields.

See also Feature Article: DEMYSTIFYING THE MISTY PLANET; *1991 Yearbook of Science and the Future* Feature Article: THE JOURNEYS OF THE VOYAGERS; *1990 Yearbook of Science and the Future* Feature Article: IN QUEST OF MARS.

FOR ADDITIONAL READING

William E. Burrows, *Exploring Space: Voyages in the Solar System and Beyond* (Random House, 1990).

Bevan M. French and Stephen P. Maran (eds.), *A Meeting with the Universe* (National Aeronautics and Space Administration, 1981, NASA EP-177).

Judith R. Goodstein, *Millikan's School* (W.W. Norton, 1991).

Theodore von Karman with Lee Edson, *The Wind and Beyond* (Little, Brown and Co., 1967).

Clayton R. Koppes, *JPL and the American Space Program* (Yale University Press, 1982).

Index

This is a three-year cumulative index. Index entries for review articles in this and previous editions of the *Yearbook of Science and the Future* are set in boldface type, *e.g.,* **Archaeology.** Feature articles appear under the article title and are identified as such. Entries to other subjects are set in lightface type, *e.g.,* radiation. Additional information on any of these subjects is identified with a subheading and indented under the entry heading. Subheadings in quotes refer to feature articles on that topic. The numbers following headings and subheadings indicate the year (boldface) of the edition and the page number (lightface) on which the information appears. The abbreviation "*il.*" indicates an illustration.

Archaeology 93–281; **92**–279; **91**–281
"In Search of the First Americans" **93**–10
"Lessons from the Master Builders" **91**–56
"Remote Sensing and Archaeology" **91**–144

All entry headings are alphabetized word by word. Hyphenated words and words separated by dashes or slashes are treated as two words. When one word differs from another only by the presence of additional characters at the end, the shorter precedes the longer. In inverted names, the words following the comma are considered only after the preceding part of the name has been alphabetized. Names beginning with "Mc" and "Mac" are alphabetized as "Mac"; "St." is alphabetized as "Saint." Examples:

Lake
Lake, Simon
Lake Placid
Lakeland

a

a-life: *see* artificial life
A0620-00 (star system) **92**–290
A300-600F (air freighter)
air transport **93**–418, *il.* 419
AAAS: *see* American Association for the Advancement of Science
AAEP: *see* American Association of Equine Practitioners
AAPG: *see* American Association of Petroleum Geologists
AAUW: *see* American Association of University Women
ab initio pseudopotential **92**–399
Abbs, James **92**–419
Abegg, Martin, Jr.
Dead Sea Scrolls **93**–276
Abell 2029 **92**–291
Abies lasiocarpa: *see* subalpine fir
Aborigine, Australian: *see* Australian Aborigine
abortion **91**–424
absconding **92**–104
abzyme **92**–116
Acanthaster planci: *see* crown-of-thorns starfish
Acanthostega **92**–367
tetrapod origin **93**–369
acceleration
"The Physics of Thrill Rides" **91**–186
accelerator, particle: *see* particle accelerator
accelerator mass spectrometry, *or* AMS
earliest Americans **93**–22
radiocarbon dating **93**–21
accident and safety
environmental disasters **93**–349
truck accidents **93**–420
see also disaster
accretion disk **92**–290
ACE: *see* Advanced Computing Environment
Acerete, Rafael **92**–295
acid anhydride **92**–294
acid rain
energy consumption **91**–340
environment **92**–344
hydrolic research **91**–320
Persian Gulf oil fires **93**–54
Acinetobacter **92**–357
Acosta, José de
New World peoples **93**–10
acoustic cavitation
bubble formation and oscillation **93**–396
acquired immune deficiency syndrome: *see* AIDS
active-matrix liquid crystal display
high-resolution displays **93**–197, *il.* 198
actuator **91**–165
ADA: *see* American Dental Association
ADA deficiency: *see* adenosine deaminase deficiency
adagen, *or* PEG-ADA
ADA deficiency **93**–128

Adam
human origin **93**–280
Adams, Fred **92**–290
adatoms, *or* adsorbed atoms **91**–405
add-with-carry (math.)
random-number generator **93**–381, *il.* 382
additive **93**–307
Adelman, M.A. **92**–338
adenosine deaminase deficiency, *or* ADA deficiency
gene therapy **93**–126, *il.* 130; **92**–125
adenosine diphosphate: *see* ADP
adenosine triphosphate: *see* ATP
adhesive **91**–387
Adler, Isidore **92**–438
Adler, Stephen **92**–485, *il.*
ADP, *or* adenosine diphosphate
molecular chaperones **93**–368
Adrastea **91**–33
adsorbed atoms: *see* adatoms
adsorption, chemical: *see* chemical adsorption
Advanced Computing Environment, *or* ACE
computer standards **93**–330
Advanced Mobile Phone Service
radio **93**–326
Advanced Neutron Source facility *il.* **92**–275
Advanced Research Projects Agency: *see* ARPA
Advanced X-ray Astrophysics Facility, *or* AXAF (U.S.) **92**–51, *il.*
advertising **91**–16
Advisory Committee on the Future of the U.S. Space Program
manned space flight **92**–405
AEA: *see* American Electronics Association
AEI: *see* Automatic Equipment-Identification System
Aerial Walk *il.* **91**–194
aerogel
1990 Molecule of the Year **92**–305
aerosol
Mount Pinatubo eruption **93**–313
Aérospatiale **92**–413
Afanasyev, Viktor **92**–408
aflatoxin **92**–349
AFP-731 (mil. satellite) **92**–405
Africa
AIDS epidemiology **93**–347, 363
human origin **93**–284
Project SIDA **93**–383
African elephant **91**–368, *il.* 369
African hammer-headed bat **92**–183
African sleeping sickness
parasitism **93**–373
Africanized honeybee **92**–98
Agena Target Docking Vehicle **91**–46, *il.* 45
aging
free radical chemistry **91**–184
medical research **92**–387
agriculture: *see* Food and agriculture
Agriculture, U.S. Department of, *or* USDA
Farm Bill **93**–348
nutrition research grant program **91**–354
"Agroecology" (sci. pub.) **91**–349

AGS: *see* Alternating Gradient Synchrotron
AIDS, *or* acquired immune deficiency syndrome
epidemiology **93**–347; **92**–463
gene therapy **93**–134
global population influence **92**–342; **91**–348
health workers *il.* **92**–465
information services **91**–333
medical research **93**–383; **92**–379; **91**–379
U.S. government spending **93**–427; **91**–429
AIDS in Focus (data base) **91**–333
AIDS Research Laboratory (Bethesda, Md., U.S.) *il.* **91**–349
air plant: *see* epiphyte
air pollution: *see* pollution
air-traffic control: *see* aviation
air transport: *see* aviation
airborne oceanographic lidar **91**–154
Airbus Industrie of France
air transport **93**–418
safeguard features **92**–412
aircraft: *see* aviation
airport
architecture **93**–285
AIX operating system
computers **92**–327
Akers, Thomas **92**–406
Akiyama, Toyohiro **92**–408
ALA: *see* American Library Association
ALACE: *see* Autonomous Lagrangian Circulation Explorer
Alamillo Bridge
civil engineering **93**–287, *il.*
Alar, *or* daminozide **91**–352
Alaska
earliest Americans **93**–17
oil and gas drilling **93**–343
alcohol
genetics **92**–378
mother's milk **92**–387
toxic effects **91**–184
Alexander, James Waddell
knot theory **93**–80
Alexander polynomial
knot theory **93**–80
Alexandria (Egy.)
information services **93**–335
algal bloom, *or* water bloom
environmental damage **93**–323
algebraic number **91**–377
algorithm
mathematics **92**–373
alkali metal **92**–136
all-carbon molecule **91**–299
all-trans-1,4-diphenyl-1,3-butadiene: *see* 1,4-diphenyl-1,3-butadiene
Allen, Leland C. **91**–301
Allied-Signal Inc. (U.S.) **91**–374
Allocebus trichotis: *see* hairy-eared dwarf lemur
Allosaurus atrox *il.* **93**–33
Allosaurus fragilis *ils.* **93**–33, 36
alloy
doped semiconductors **91**–403
metallurgy **93**–377
Almaz
oceanographic studies **93**–325
Soviet satellite program **93**–339
alpha aminoisobutyric acid **91**–298, 367
alpha interferon **91**–383
alpha tocopherol: *see* vitamin E
ALS: *see* amyotrophic lateral sclerosis
Alternating Gradient Synchrotron, *or* AGS **91**–400
Altman, Sidney **91**–428
catalytic RNA **92**–119
altruism
bats **92**–184
alumina
nanocomposites **93**–375
aluminophosphate
zeolite **92**–296
aluminum **91**–293, 375
aluminum arsenide **91**–403
Alvarez, Luis Walter **92**–312
geological sciences **93**–314
"The Search for the KT Crater" **93**–90
Alzheimer's disease **93**–384; **91**–380
amalgam tooth filling **93**–390
Amazon River region (S.Am.)
archaeological investigations **91**–151, *il.* 161
deforestation **92**–279; **91**–369
American Anthropological Association **93**–279; **92**–278; **91**–280
American Association for the Advancement of Science, *or* AAAS
cold fusion **92**–302
history of science **93**–240
American Association of Casualty and Surety Companies
driver responsibility **93**–212, 217
American Association of Equine Practitioners, *or* AAEP
Persian Gulf war **93**–393

American Association of Petroleum Geologists, *or* AAPG **91**–315
American Association of University Women, *or* AAUW
self-esteem gender gap **93**–409
American Canine Sports Medicine Association **93**–391
American Center (Fr.)
architecture **92**–285, *il.* 286
American Commercial Barge Line Co.
water transport **92**–417
American Dental Association, *or* ADA
tobacco legislation **93**–389
American Dietetic Association
dietary supplements **93**–356
American Electronics Association, *or* AEA
defense research report **92**–308
American Forestry Association
reforestation **92**–356
American Indian, *or* Native American
anthropology **93**–279; **91**–279
archaeology **91**–284
earliest Americans **93**–10
Knife River magnetic surveys **91**–147
skeletal remains reburial **91**–280
American Institute of Nutrition **91**–354
American Library Association, *or* ALA
Romanian libraries **93**–335
American Physical Society, *or* APS
space station **93**–427
American President Companies
transportation **92**–417
American Psychological Association, *or* APA **93**–408; **92**–403
American Telephone & Telegraph Company, *or* AT&T **93**–419
Americas, the
European exploration **93**–10
KT crater **93**–91
AMIGOS Bibliographic Council (U.S.)
information-system grants **93**–337
amino acid
mass extinction evidence **91**–298
molecular biology **93**–364
Neanderthal diet study **93**–283
protein engineering **92**–114
ammonia
doped semiconductors **93**–405
ammonium cyanate **91**–229
amnesia
memory **92**–403
amorphous metal
sonoluminescence applications **93**–396, *il.*
amphibian
decline **92**–365
amphipod
animal behavior **92**–367
amphoteronolide B
organic chemistry **92**–297
amplifier **91**–204
AMS: *see* accelerator mass spectrometry
Amskan Ltd. (Austr.)
electronic tracking systems **91**–416
Amtrak
high-speed train **93**–422
amusement park
"The Physics of Thrill Rides" **91**–186
amylin
medical research **92**–381
amyloplast
microgravity research **92**–80
amyotrophic lateral sclerosis, *or* ALS
gene discovery **93**–386
Anacampseros buderiana
mimicry *il.* **92**–93
analog optical device **91**–308
analog system **91**–309
analog transmission
communications **93**–326
anchovy
El Niño **93**–324
Anderson, Carl David **92**–438
Anderson, Michael **91**–295
Anderson, Thomas Foxen **93**–443
Anderson, W. French **92**–419
"Gene Therapy: A New Frontier in Medicine" **93**–126
androgen
hypothalamus **93**–143
Andromeda Galaxy
IRAS infrared astronomy *il.* **92**–35
anemia **91**–384
anesthesia **91**–385
Angell, James K. **92**–309
angonoka (tortoise)
endangered species **92**–203
angular velocity **91**–188
anhydrobiosis
"Life Without Water" **91**–114
aniline purple: *see* mauve
animal: *see* zoology
animal behavior **91**–88, 370
annihilation radiation **91**–394
anomalies
field theory **92**–485
anomalous heat: *see* cold fusion
ant, *or* Formicidae **91**–357

d

g

Acknowledgments

13   (Top left) Detail of Dr. Dickeson excavating a mound from "Panorama of the Monumental Grandeur of the Mississippi Valley," thin flexible paint resembling tempera on muslin sheeting by John J. Egan, 1850, The Saint Louis Art Museum, Eliza McMillan Fund Purchase; (bottom) National Museum of American Art and National Portrait Gallery Library, Smithsonian Institution, Washington, D.C.

17, 19   Illustrations by Steven N. Kapusta

48   Illustration by John L. Draves

96, 100   Illustrations by John L. Draves

112   Courtesy of the U.S. Geological Survey, Flagstaff, Ariz.

130   Illustration by John L. Draves

143   (Main illustration) Adapted from *Hearing, Taste and Smell: Pathways of Perception* by Philip Whitfield and D. Michael Stoddart, © Torstar Books Inc. 1984; all rights reserved

145, 146   Illustrations by Kathryn Diffley

214, 215   Illustrations by Ron Villani

221   (Clockwise from top left) The Bettmann Archive; Hulton–Deutsch Collection Ltd.; The Bettmann Archive; BBC Hulton Picture Library; engraving by Sebastian Le Clerc was published in *Memoirs on the History of Plants,* 1676, by permission of the Houghton Library, Harvard University

224   Frontispiece from *The Life of Sir Isaac Newton,* by David Brewster, John Murray, London, 1831

228   From *Recueil de planches, sur les sciences, les arts libéraux, et les arts méchaniques* by Denis Diderot, quatrième livraison, Paris, 1767

288   (Top) Courtesy of Georgia Dome, Atlanta, Ga.

321   Adapted from "Trends in Stream Quality in the Continental United States, 1978–1987," D.P. Lettenmaier, E.R. Hooper, C. Wagoner, and K.B. Faris, *Water Resources Research,* vol. 27, no. 3, March 1991, pp. 327–339, copyright 1991 by the American Geophysical Union

322   Adapted from "Large-Scale Natural Gradient Tracer Test in Sand and Gravel, Cape Cod, Massachusetts: 1. Experimental Design and Observed Tracer Movement," D.R. LeBlanc, *et al., Water Resources Research,* vol. 27, no. 5, May 1991, pp. 895–910, copyright 1991 by the American Geophysical Union